ISLAND

of

GLASS

NORA ROBERTS

Hot Ice	The Villa
Sacred Sins	Midnight Bayou
Brazen Virtue	Three Fates
Sweet Revenge	Birthright
Public Secrets	Northern Lights
Genuine Lies	Blue Smoke
Carnal Innocence	Angels Fall
Divine Evil	High Noon
Honest Illusions	Tribute
Private Scandals	Black Hills
Hidden Riches	The Search
True Betrayals	Chasing Fire
Montana Sky	The Witness
Sanctuary	Whiskey Beach
Homeport	The Collector
The Reef	Tonight And Always
River's End	The Liar
Carolina Moon	The Obsession

SERIES

Gallaghers of Ardmore Trilogy
Jewels Of The Sun
Tears Of The Moon
Heart Of The Sea

Chesapeake Bay Saga
Sea Swept
Rising Tides
Inner Harbor
Chesapeake Blue

Irish Born Trilogy
Born In Fire
Born In Ice
Born In Shame

Dream Trilogy
Daring To Dream
Holding The Dream
Finding The Dream

Three Sisters Island Trilogy
Dance Upon The Air
Heaven And Earth
Face The Fire

Key Trilogy
Key Of Light
Key Of Knowledge
Key Of Valor

In The Garden Trilogy
Blue Dahlia
Black Rose
Red Lily

Circle Trilogy
Morrigan's Cross
Dance Of The Gods
Valley Of Silence

Sign Of Seven Trilogy
Blood Brothers
The Hollow
The Pagan Stone

Bride Quartet
Vision In White
Bed Of Roses Savor
The Moment Happy
Ever After

The Inn Boonsboro Trilogy
The Next Always
The Last Boyfriend
The Perfect Hope

The Cousins O'Dwyer Trilogy
Dark Witch
Shadow Spell
Blood Magick

The Guardians Trilogy
Stars Of Fortune
Bay of Sighs
Island of Glass

E-BOOKS BY NORA ROBERTS

Cordina's Royal Family
Affaire Royale
Command Performance
The Playboy Prince
Cordina's Crown Jewel

The Donovan Legacy
Captivated
Entranced
Charmed
Enchanted

The O'Hurleys
The Last Honest Woman
Dance To The Piper
Skin Deep
Without A Trace

Night Tales
Night Shift
Night Shadow
Nightshade
Night Smoke
Night Shield

The MacGregors
The Winning Hand
The Perfect Neighbor
All The Possibilities
One Man's Art
Tempting Fate
Playing The Odds
The MacGregor Brides
The MacGregor Grooms
Rebellion/ In From The Cold
For Now, Forever

The Calhouns
Suzanna's Surrender
Megan's Mate
Courting Catherine
A Man For Amanda
For The Love Of Lilah

Irish Legacy
Irish Rose
Irish Rebel
Irish Thoroughbred

Best Laid Plans
Loving Jack
Lawless
Summer Love
Boundary Lines
Dual Image
First Impressions
The Law Is A Lady
Local Hero
This Magic Moment
The Name Of The Game
Partners Temptation
The Welcoming
Opposites Attract
Time Was
Times Change
Gabriel's Angel
Holiday Wishes
The Heart's Victory

The Right Path
Rules Of The Game
Search For Love
Blithe Images
From This Day
Song Of The West
Island Of Flowers
Her Mother's Keeper
Untamed
Sullivan's Woman
Less Of A Stranger
Reflections
Dance Of Dreams
Storm Warning
Once More With Feeling
Endings And Beginnings
A Matter Of Choice

NORA ROBERTS & J. D. ROBB
Remember When

J. D. ROBB

Naked In Death
Glory In Death
Immortal In Death
Rapture In Death
Ceremony In Death
Vengeance In Death
Holiday In Death
Conspiracy In Death
Loyalty In Death
Witness In Death
Judgment In Death
Betrayal In Death
Seduction In Death
Reunion In Death
Purity In Death
Portrait In Death
Imitation In Death
Divided In Death
Visions In Death
Survivor In Death
Origin In Death

Memory In Death
Born In Death
Innocent In Death
Creation In Death
Strangers In Death
Salvation In Death
Promises In Death
Kindred In Death
Fantasy In Death
Indulgence In Death
Treachery In Death
New York To Dallas
Celebrity In Death
Delusion In Death
Calculated In Death
Thankless In Death
Concealed In Death
Festive In Death
Obsession In Death
Devoted In Death
Brotherhood In Death

ANTHOLOGIES

From The Heart • A Little Magic • A Little Fate

Moon Shadows
(with Jill Gregory, Ruth Ryan Langan,
& Marianne Willman)

The Once Upon Series
(with Jill Gregory, Ruth Ryan Langan,
& Marianne Willman)
Once Upon A Castle • Once Upon A Star
Once Upon A Dream • Once Upon A Rose
Once Upon A Kiss • Once Upon A Midnight

Silent Night
(with Susan Plunkett, Dee Holmes,
& Claire Cross)

Out Of This World
(with Laurell K. Hamilton, Susan Krinard,
& Maggie Shayne)

Three In Death

Bump In The Night
(with Mary Blayney, Ruth Ryan Langan,
& Mary Kay McComas)

Dead Of Night
(with Mary Blayney, Ruth Ryan Langan,
& Mary Kay McComas)

Suite 606
(with Mary Blayney, Ruth Ryan Langan,
& Mary Kay McComas)

In Death

The Lost
(with Patricia Gaffney, Mary Blayney,
& Ruth Ryan Langan)

The Other Side
(with Mary Blayney, Patricia Gaffney,
Ruth Ryan Langan, & Mary Kay McComas)

Time Of Death

The Unquiet
(with Mary Blayney, Patricia Gaffney,
Ruth Ryan Langan, & Mary Kay McComas)

Mirror, Mirror
(with Mary Blayney, Elaine Fox,
Mary Kay McComas, and R. C. Ryan)

Down The Rabbit Hole
(with Mary Blayney, Elaine Fox,
Mary Kay McComas, and R. C. Ryan)

ALSO AVAILABLE...

The Official Nora Roberts Companion
(Edited By Denise Little and Laura Hayden)

ISLAND
of
GLASS

Nora Roberts

BERKLEY BOOKS
NEW YORK

Doubleday Large Print Home Library Edition

This Large Print Edition, prepared especially for
Doubleday Large Print Home Library, contains the complete,
unabridged text of the original Publisher's Edition.

An imprint of Penguin Random House LLC
375 Hudson Street, New York, New York 10014

ISBN 978-1-68331-061-7

Printed in The United States Of America

Cover photograph: "Cliffs of Moher" by Kwiatek7/Shutterstock
Cover design by Rita Frangie

This is a work of fiction. Names, characters, places, and
incidents either are the product of the author's imagination
or are used fictitiously, and any resemblance to actual persons,
living or dead, business establishments, events, or locales
is entirely coincidental.

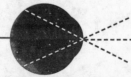

**This Large Print Book carries the
Seal of Approval of N.A.V.H**

For my grandchildren.
They are the magic, and the future.

He lives, he wakes—
'tis Death is dead,
not he.
PERCY BYSSHE SHELLEY

All for one; one for all.
ALEXANDRE DUMAS

Prologue

They met on the high hill, far above the world, beneath a sky struck with the dazzle of stars and a white, waiting moon.

Together the goddesses looked out beyond the castle shining on its own fair hill, to the dark glass of the sea.

"Two stars found, and held safe." Luna lifted her face to the sky in joy, in thanks. "The fates that be chose well with the six. The guardians' own hearts are strong and true."

"Their test is not finished," Celene reminded her. "And what they come to face will need more than true hearts."

"They will fight. Have they not proven themselves warriors, sister?" Arianrhod demanded. "They have risked. They have bled."

"And will risk more. I see battles to come, blood to spill. Nerezza and the evil she created want more than the stars, more than the blood of the guardians. They want annihilation."

"It has always been so," Luna murmured. "In her heart, it has always been so."

"They have weakened her." Arianrhod put a hand on the jeweled hilt of the sword at her side. "All but destroyed her. Without the human she turned, they would have destroyed her."

"Did we not think the same," Celene reminded her sisters, "on the night of the queen's rise, on the night we created the stars?"

Celene stretched out her arms, and below, on the edge of the great sea, the images of what had been shimmered.

"A night of joy," she continued, "of hope and celebration. And we three conjured three stars. For wisdom, forged in fire."

"For compassion," Luna added, "fluid as water."

"For strength," Arianrhod finished, "cold as ice."

"Our powers, and our hopes, in a gift to the new queen. A gift Nerezza coveted."

On the beach, white under a white moon, the three goddesses faced the dark one. As they sent their stars flying toward the moon, Nerezza lashed out, black lightning, to strike them, to curse them.

"And so we cursed her," Celene continued, "cast her into a pit. But we did not, could not destroy her. It was not for us, this duty, this task, this war."

"We protected the stars," Luna reminded her. "They would fall, as Nerezza had cursed them, but we protected them. When they fell, they would fall in secret, and remain hidden."

"Until those who came from us bound together, joined in the quest to find them, to protect them." Now Arianrhod's hand tightened on the hilt of her knife. "To fight, each and all, against the dark. To risk all to save the worlds."

"Their time has come," Celene agreed. "They pulled the Fire Star from its stone, gathered the Water Star from the sea. But the final tests of the quest wait. As will Nerezza and her army profane."

"Whatever their powers, whatever their gifts, the six face a god." Luna pressed a hand to her heart. "And we can only watch."

"It is their fate," Celene said, "and in their fates live the fate of all the worlds."

"Their time has come." Arianrhod reached out, took her sisters' hands. "And with it, if they are strong and wise, if their hearts remain true, may ours."

"The moon runs full, and so the wolf howls." Celene gestured up to the comet streak arching through the sky. "So they fly."

"And courage flies with them," Arianrhod said.

"And there!" Luna pointed across the wide, dark sea where light bloomed, then fired, then quieted. "They are safe."

"For now." With a wave of her hand, Celene dismissed the wavery images on the beach. "Now begins the future."

Chapter One

A man who couldn't die had little to fear. An immortal who'd lived most of his long life as a soldier, waging battle, didn't turn from a fight with a god. A soldier, though a loner by nature, understood the duty, and loyalty, to those who battled with him.

The man, the soldier, the loner who'd seen his young brother destroyed by black magick, who'd had his own life upended by it, who fought a god's crazed greed, knew the difference between the dark and the light.

Being propelled through space by a fellow soldier, a shifter, while they were all still bloody from the battle didn't frighten him—but he'd have preferred any other mode of transportation.

Through the whirl of wind, the blare of light, the breathless speed (and all right then, there was a bit of a thrill in the speed), he felt his companions. The sorcerer who held more power than any Doyle had known in all his years. The woman who was as much the glue who bound them together as a seer. The mermaid who was all charm and courage and heart—and a pure pleasure for the eyes. The shifter, loyal and brave, and a dead shot as well. And the female—well, wolf now, as the moon had risen just as they'd prepared to shift from the beauty and battles of Capri.

She howled—no other term for it—and in the sound of it he heard not fear, no, but the same atavistic thrill that beat in his own blood.

If a man had to align himself with others, had to throw his fate in with others, he could do a hell of a lot worse than these.

Then he smelled Ireland—the damp air, the green—and the thrill died in him. The fates, canny and cold, would drive him back here where his heart and his life had been broken.

Even as he geared himself up to deal

with it, to do what must be done, they dropped like stones.

A man who couldn't die could still feel the jolt and insult of hitting the ground hard enough to rattle bones and steal the breath.

"Bloody hell, Sawyer."

"Sorry." Sawyer's voice came from his left, and in a kind of gasping wheeze. "It's a lot to navigate. Anybody hurt? Annika?"

"I'm not hurt. But you." Her voice was a musical croon. "You're hurt. You're weak."

"Not too bad. You're bleeding."

Bright as sunlight, she smiled. "Not too bad."

"Maybe we should try parachutes next time." Sasha let out a quick moan.

"There now, I've got you."

As his eyes adjusted, Doyle saw Bran shift, gather Sasha close.

"You're hurt?"

"No, no." Sasha shook her head. "Cuts and bumps. And the landing knocked the wind out of me. I should be used to it. Riley? Where's Riley?"

Doyle rolled, started to push himself up— and pressed a hand into fur. It growled.

"She's here." He shifted his gaze, met

those tawny eyes. Dr. Riley Gwin, renowned archaeologist—and lycan. "Don't so much as think of biting me," he muttered. "She's fine. Like she tells us, she heals fast in wolf form."

He got to his feet, noted that however rough the landing, Sawyer had come through. Weapons cases, luggage, sealed boxes of research books, maps, and other essentials lay in a somewhat orderly pile a few feet away on the cool, damp grass.

And of great personal importance to him, his motorcycle stood, upright and undamaged.

Satisfied, he stretched out a hand to Sawyer, pulled the man to his feet.

"Not altogether bad."

"Yeah." Sawyer combed his fingers through his mane of wind-swept, sun-streaked hair. Then grinned when Annika did a series of cartwheels. "Somebody enjoyed the ride anyway."

"You did well." Bran dropped a hand on Sawyer's shoulder. "It's a feat, isn't it, juggling six people and all the rest across the sea and sky in, well, a matter of minutes."

"Got one bitch of a headache out of it."

"And more."

Bran lifted Sawyer's hand—the one that had gripped Nerezza's flying hair while he'd shifted her away. "We'll fix that, and anything else needs fixing. We should get Sasha inside. She's a bit shaky."

"I'm all right." But she remained sitting on the ground. "Just a little dizzy. Please don't," she said quickly, and pushed to her knees toward Riley. "Not yet. Let's just get oriented first. She wants to run," she told the others.

"She'll be fine. There's no harm here." Bran helped Sasha up. "The woods are mine," he said to Riley. "And now they're yours."

The wolf turned, bounded away, vanished into the thick trees.

"She could get lost," Sasha began.

"She's a wolf," Doyle pointed out. "And likely to find her way around better than the rest of us. She changed, but as we were leaving, and needs her moment. Wolf or woman, she can handle herself."

He turned his back on the woods where he'd run tame as a child, where he'd hunted, where he'd gone for solitude. This had been his land once, his home—and now it was Bran's.

Yes, the fates were canny and cold.

In the house Bran had built on the wild coast of Clare, Doyle could see the memory of his own. Where his family had lived for generations.

Gone, he reminded himself, centuries ago. The house and the family, gone to dust.

In its place was the grand, and he'd have expected no less from Bran Killian.

A fine manor, Doyle mused, with the fanciful touches one might expect from a wizard. Stone—perhaps some of it from the walls of that long-ago home—rising a full three stories, with those fanciful touches in two round towers on either side, and a kind of central parapet that would offer mad views of the cliffs, of the sea, of the land.

All softened, Doyle supposed would be the word, with gardens fit for the faeries, blooming wild and free, with the mixed perfumes blown about on the windy air.

Doyle indulged himself for one moment,

allowed himself to think of his own mother and how she'd have loved every bit of it.

Then he put it away.

"It's a fine house."

"It's good land. And as I said to Riley, it's yours as much as mine. Well, that's my feeling on it," Bran added when Doyle shook his head.

"We've come together," Bran continued as the wind tossed his hair, black as the night, around his sharp-boned face. "Were thrown together for a purpose. We've fought and bled together, and no doubt will again. And here we are, standing on where you sprang from, and where I was compelled to build. There's purpose in that as well, and we'll use it."

In comfort, Annika ran her hand down Doyle's arm. Her long black hair was a sexy tangle from the shift. She had bruises on her remarkable face. "It's beautiful. I can smell the sea. I can hear it."

"It's a ways down." Bran smiled at her. "But you'll make your way to it easy enough, I wager. In the morning, you'll see more of what it offers. For now, we'd best haul all of our things inside, and settle in a bit."

"I hear that." Sawyer reached down, hefted some boxes. "And, God, I could eat."

"I'll make food!" Annika threw her arms around him, kissed him enthusiastically, then picked up her bag. "Is there food to make, Bran? Food I can make while you tend the wounds?"

"I had the kitchen well stocked." He flicked his fingers at the big, arched double doors. "The house is unlocked."

"As long as there's beer." Doyle grabbed two weapon cases—his own priority—and started in behind Annika and Sawyer.

"It hurts him," Sasha quietly told Bran. "I can feel the ache in him, the ache of memories and loss."

"And I'm sorry for it, truly. But we all know there's a reason for it, why it's here that we've been led to find the last star and end this."

"Because there's always a price." On a sigh, she leaned against him, closed eyes blue as summer and still hollow from the battle and the shift. "But Annika's right. It's a beautiful house. It's stunning, Bran. I'll want to paint it a dozen times."

"You'll have time for dozens of dozens." He turned her to him. "I said it was Doyle's and Riley's as it's mine. It's Annika's and Sawyer's as well. But, **fáidh**, it's yours as my heart is yours. Will you live with me here, at least some of the time in our lives together?"

"I'll live with you here, and anywhere. But now? I should take a look inside and see if it's as wonderful as the outside."

"It's a true home now that you're here." To dazzle her, he waved a hand. All the windows illuminated. Glowing lights shimmered along garden paths.

"You take my breath." She sighed it, then picked up the case holding most of her art supplies—her priority.

They went inside, into a wide entryway with towering ceilings where wide-planked floors gleamed. A heavy table with curled dragons for its legs held crystal balls and a tall vase bursting with white roses.

It opened to a living area with jewel-tone sofas, more heavy tables, sparkling lamps. And with another wave of the hand, Bran had red-gold flames erupting in a stone fireplace so large the muscular Doyle could have stood upright, arms stretched to either side.

As he walked in from the back, Doyle raised an eyebrow, toasted with the beer in his hand. "You went for posh, brother."

"I suppose I did."

"I'll get more if you'll see to Sawyer. His headache's real enough. I can see it on him. And he's carrying some ugly burns. Annika's hurt more than she lets on."

"Help Sawyer and Annika," Sasha said. "I'll help Doyle."

"He's in the kitchen with Annika." Doyle glanced at Sasha. "I can handle bringing in the rest. You've got your own battle scars, Blondie."

"Nothing major. I'm fine," she told Bran. "The dizziness only lasted a couple minutes this time, and the rest can wait. I could use a glass of wine if you have it."

"I do, of course. Let me see to him, then I'll help you with the rest."

She walked outside with Doyle, started to pick up more bags, then just stared out into the woods.

"She'll be back once she's run it off." Doyle took a pull on his beer. "But you'd be happier with all your chicks in the roost."

Sasha lifted her shoulders, let them fall. "I would. It's been...a day."

"Finding the second star should put a smile in your eyes instead of sorrow."

"A year ago I was still denying what I was. I knew nothing of any of you, of gods— dark or bright. I'd never harmed anyone, much less..."

"What you fought and killed wasn't **anyone**. They were **things** created by Nerezza to destroy."

"There were people, too, Doyle. Humans."

"Mercenaries, paid by Malmon to kill us, or worse. Have you forgotten what they did to Sawyer and Annika in the cave?"

"No." Sasha hugged her arms tight against the quick chill. "I'll never forget. And I'll never understand how human beings could torture and try to kill for money. Why they'd kill or die for profit. But she does, Nerezza does. She knows that kind of greed, that blind lust for power. And I understand that's what we're fighting. Malmon, he traded everything for it. She took his soul, his humanity, and now he's a thing. Her creature. She'd do the same to all of us."

"But she won't. She won't because we won't give her anything. We hurt her today. She's the one wounded and bleeding tonight. I've searched for the stars, hunted her for more years than you can know. I got close, or thought I did. But close means nothing."

He took another long pull from his beer. "I don't like using fate or destiny as reasons or excuses, but the hard fact is we six are together, are meant to be. Are meant to find the Stars of Fortune and end Nerezza. You feel more than others. That's your gift, and your curse, to see and to feel. And without that gift we wouldn't be standing here. It doesn't hurt that you can shoot a crossbow as if born with the bow in one hand and a bolt in the other."

"Who'd have thought?" She sighed, a pretty woman with long, sun-washed hair and deep blue eyes. One who'd gained muscle and strength, inside and out, over the last weeks. "I feel your heartache. I'm sorry."

"I'll deal with it."

"I know you were meant to be here, to

walk this land again, to look out at this sea. And not just for the quest for the stars, not just for the fight against Nerezza. Maybe— I'm not sure—but maybe it's for solace."

Doyle shut down—that was survival. "What was here for me was long ago."

"And still," she murmured, "the coming here tonight is harder on you, and the getting here tonight was hardest on Riley."

"Considering we'd just fought off a god and her murderous minions, it wasn't a ride on a carousel for any of us. All right," he said at Sasha's quiet look, "rough on her."

He put the empty beer bottle in the pocket of his scarred leather coat, hauled up suitcases. "She'll run it off, and be back by morning. Grab what you can, and I'll get the rest. We both know you'd be more help to Bran with the injuries."

She didn't argue, and he noted that she limped a bit. To settle it, he set the bags down inside, plucked her up.

"Hey."

"Easier than arguing. Is the house big enough for you?"

They passed wide archways and the rooms beyond them. Deep, rich colors, simmering fires in hearths, glinting lights, gleaming wood.

"It's magnificent. It's huge."

"I'd say the two of you will have to make a lot of babies to fill it."

"I—"

"That got you thinking."

She'd yet to regain speech when he carried her into the kitchen. There, Sawyer, looking a little less pale, sat on a stool at a long slate-gray counter while Bran treated the burns on his hands.

Annika, who managed to look gorgeous despite the cuts, the bruises, earnestly sautéed chicken in an enormous frying pan at what Sasha recognized as a professional-grade six-burner range.

"Okay, now you want to—" Sawyer broke off, hissed as Bran hit a fresh point of pain.

"I take the chicken out, and put the vegetables in. I can do it," Annika insisted. "Let Bran work."

"I'll help." Sasha poked Doyle in the shoulder. "Put me down."

The order had Bran turning, and moving quickly toward her. "What is it? Where is she hurt?"

"I'm not—"

"She's limping some. Right leg."

"It's just—"

"Put her down there, beside Sawyer."

"It's just sore. Finish with Sawyer. I'll help Annika, and—"

"I can do it!" Clearly frustrated, Annika dumped chicken on a platter. "I like to learn. I learned. I cook the chicken in the garlic and the oil, with the herbs. I cook the vegetables. I make the rice."

"You're pissing off the mermaid," Doyle said, and dumped Sasha on a stool. "Smells good, Gorgeous."

"Thank you. Sasha, you could tend to Bran's wounds while he tends to yours and Sawyer's. Then he can tend to mine. And we can eat because Sawyer needs to eat. He's hurt, and he's weak from..."

Her eyes filled, glistening green pools, before she turned quickly back to the range.

"Anni, don't. I'm okay."

When she only shook her head at Sawyer's words, he started to rise. Doyle simply shoved him back onto the stool.

"I've got this."

Doyle crossed the rugged wood floor, gave Annika's tumbled hair a tug.

She turned, went straight into his arms. "I believed. I believed, but I was so afraid. Afraid she'd take him."

"She didn't. Dead-Eye's smarter than that. He took her for a ride, and we're all here now."

"I have such love." Sighing now, she rested her head on Doyle's chest, looked into Sawyer's eyes. "I have such love."

"It's why we're here," Sawyer said. "I believe that, too."

"He'll need some time to heal," Bran said. "Some food, some sleep."

"And a beer," Sawyer added.

"That goes without saying. And now you." Bran turned to Sasha.

"I don't see that glass of wine."

"I'm on it." Doyle pressed a kiss to Annika's forehead, turned her back to the range. "Cook."

"I will. It will be very good."

While Doyle poured wine, Bran rolled up Sasha's pants leg. Let out a string of oaths at the raw-edged claw marks scoring down her calf. "Bumps and scrapes, is it?"

"I didn't realize, honestly." She took the wine Doyle offered, took a quick gulp. "And now that I do, it hurts a lot more."

Bran took the glass from her, added a few drops from a bottle from his medicine case.

"Drink slow, and breathe slow," Bran told her. "The cleaning of it's going to sting."

Sasha drank slowly, breathed slowly, and when the sting—a dozen angry wasps—struck, grabbed Doyle's hand.

"I'm sorry. **A ghrá.** I'm sorry. Only a minute more. There's infection."

"She's okay. You're okay." Doyle lured her gaze to his as Sawyer stroked her back. "Hell of a kitchen you've got now, Blondie. Somebody who can cook like you ought to do handsprings."

"Yes. I like it—oh, God, okay—I like the cabinets. Not only the fact that there's about an acre of them, but all those leaded-glass fronts. And the windows. It must get wonderful light."

"She needs to drink more," Bran said through gritted teeth. "Sawyer."

"Drink it down." Sawyer held the glass to her lips. "We'll have a cook-off, you and me—and Anni," he added.

"Challenge accepted." Then she let out a long, shaky breath. "Thank God," she said when Bran coated the wound with cool, soothing balm.

"You held up." Doyle gave her a pat on the shoulder.

"Your turn," Sasha told Bran.

"Give yourself a minute—and me as well." Bran sat beside her. "And we'll deal with each other. And when we're done, and while we eat, I imagine Sawyer has a story to tell."

"Believe me," Sawyer replied. "It's a winner."

The kitchen held a long table, backed with benches, fronted with chairs in a wide curve of glass. They sat together, with Annika's meal, with a loaf of brown bread and fresh butter, with beer and wine. And Sawyer's tale.

"When I went up—hell of a boost, by the way," Sawyer said to Bran, "she was fighting to control that three-headed dog she was on."

"The one you shot in all three heads," Sasha pointed out.

"Three for three." Sawyer made a gun with his fingers, said, "Bang. And she was focused on Bran."

"Knock out the sorcerer, knock out our magicks." Doyle shoveled in chicken. "It's not good, Annika."

"Oh!"

"It's damn good."

She laughed, wiggled happily in her seat on the bench as Doyle scooped up more. Then she leaned her head to Sawyer's shoulder. "You were so brave."

"Didn't think about it—that's the trick. She's got the eyeball on y'all, trying to get that beast under control. She didn't see me coming."

Looking down, he flexed his hand, all but healed now. "I grabbed the bitch by the hair—it was flying around, and handy. And then she saw me coming, baby, and it scared her. I could see that—we need to know that. I took her by surprise, and I saw fear. Didn't last long, but it was there."

"We hurt her before, in Corfu." Bran nodded, dark eyes intense. "We beat her back, got the Fire Star, and hurt her. She should be afraid."

"She had armor this time, so she's no idiot. And she's got a hell of a punch. You've got your lightning," he said to Bran, "and she's got hers." He rubbed his chest, easily reliving the burning punch. "Nothing to do but hold on. She thought she had me, and I've got to say, maybe for a minute, I figured she was right. But she'd have me where we weren't because I'd already started the shift. It got wild, really wild, but it was my thing, right? Shifting's my thing. I know how to deal with the force of that, and she didn't. Not so fast, so hard. She started changing."

"Changing?" Sasha prompted.

"I had her by the hair, right? All that flying black hair. And during the shift, the color started leeching out of it. And her face did a Dorian Gray."

"She aged."

He nodded at Sasha. "Put on the years. For a second I thought it was my imagination, and the fact that the wind, the lights were burning the crap out of my eyes, but her face started to sag, and she's aging right in front of me. She's aging, and her lightning strikes barely buzz me. She's weakening, man, and I let go. She nearly pulled me with her—she had that much left. But I pulled away, and she fell. I don't know where the hell, but she dropped. I couldn't get a bead because I'd about used it up by then. And I really needed to get back."

He turned his head, kissed Annika. "I really needed to get back."

Sasha gripped his arm. "Could it have destroyed her?"

"I don't know, but I put a hurting on her, and that fall's going to leave a mark."

"According to legend, it's a sword that brings her end." Still, Bran shrugged. "And legends have been known to be wrong. In either case, despite cuts and bruises"—he paused to give Sasha a telling look—"we hurt her more than she hurt us. If she exists, it will take time for her to recover, and that's advantage us."

"We know she fears," Doyle put in, "and her fear is another weapon against her. With all that, this doesn't end until we have the last star."

"So we'll look, and we'll find." Bran settled back, confident and at home. "As here's where the quest led us."

"I believe we'll find it—the Ice Star," Annika said. "We found the others. But now that we're so close, I don't understand what we do once we have them."

"Go where we're led." Bran looked at Sasha, who immediately poured more wine.

"But no pressure," she murmured.

"Faith," Bran corrected. "All faith. But for tonight, we're all here, we're safe, and we've had a lovely meal."

Pleased, Annika smiled. "I made enough for Riley if she's too hungry to wait for breakfast. I wish she'd come back."

"She will, and soon enough."

"I can feel her," Sasha announced. "I can feel her now. She's not far, but not ready to come in. She's not far though."

"Then we're all safe, as I said. And though Sawyer looks better, it's rest he needs now. I'll show you the bedrooms, and you can choose what suits you."

It didn't matter to Doyle where he slept, so he chose a room at random, one facing the sea rather than the woods. The bed might have been fit for a king with its tall turned posts, but he wasn't ready to use it.

He opened the doors leading to the wide stone terrace that wrapped the sea-front of the house, let the moist air whip through the room, let the rumble and crash of the sea drown out his thoughts.

Restless, anticipating the memories that might flood back in dreams, he strapped on his sword and went out into the night.

However safe they were—and he believed they were for now—it didn't pay to forgo patrol, to ignore the need for vigilance.

Bran had built his home on the same spot where Doyle's had stood—though Bran's was surely five times the size. Doyle couldn't ignore the fact—couldn't pretend there were no reasons for it.

The house stood on the cliff, with a seawall built dry-stone style rambling at its edge. Gardens here as well, Doyle noted, and the scents of rosemary, lavender, sage lifted into the air from their place near the kitchen wall.

He walked out toward the cliff, let the wind stream through his hair, cool his face while his eyes, sharp and green, scanned the turbulent sea, the misty sky, the full white moon that shifted and sailed behind gray fingers of cloud.

Nothing would come tonight, from sea or sky, he thought. But if Sasha's visions held true—and they had till now—they'd find the last star here, in the land of his blood. They'd find it, and they'd find the way to end Nerezza.

His quest, one of centuries, would be done.

Then what?

Then what? he thought again as the soldier in him began to patrol.

Join another army? Fight another war? No, no more wars, he mused as he walked. He was sick down to bone and balls of blood and death. However weary he might be of life after three centuries of it, he was more weary of witnessing death.

He could do whatever he wanted—if he had any idea what he wanted. Find a place to settle awhile? Build his own? He had money set aside for it. A man didn't live as long as he'd lived and not have money, if he had a brain in his head.

But settling? For what? He'd been on the move so long, he could barely conceive the notion of rooting anywhere. Travel, he supposed, though God knew he'd done more than any man's share of that already.

And why think of it now? His duty, his mission, his quest wasn't done. Better to think of the next step, and leave the rest.

He came around the front of the house, looked up. He could see the good, sturdy manor his blood had built. See how Bran had used it, respected it when adding to it, making it his own.

For a moment he heard the voices, long stilled. His mother, his father, his sisters, brothers. They'd worked this land, built their lives, given their hearts.

Grown old, grown ill, died. And he was all that was left of them.

That, just that, was beyond sorrow.

"Bollocks," he murmured, and turned away.

The wolf watched him, eyes gleaming in the filtered light of the moon.

She stood very still at the edge of the wood—beautiful and fierce.

He lowered the hand that had reached instinctively for the sword sheathed on his back. Stood, watching the watcher while the wind billowed his coat.

"So you're back. You worried Sasha and Annika. You understand me perfectly well," he added when the wolf made no move. "If you're interested, Sawyer's healing up, and resting. Sasha was hurt more seriously than we knew. Ah, that got your attention," he said, when the wolf trotted forward. "She's resting, too, and Bran took care of them. She's fine," he added. "One of the bastards gouged her leg, and some infection set in before Bran got to it. But she's fine now."

He watched the wolf angle up, scan the house with those canny golden-brown eyes. "The place is full of rooms, enough beds if we were twice as many. I suppose you want to go in now, see for yourself."

The wolf simply walked to the big front doors, waited.

"Fine then." Doyle strode over, opened the door.

Inside, Riley's things sat in a neat pile.

"We didn't take them up as no one wanted to choose for you. You've plenty to choose from."

The wolf walked—pausing to study the

living area, the fire simmering—then moved to the stairs, looked back.

"I suppose you want me to haul your bloody things up the bloody stairs now?"

The wolf held Doyle's gaze, unblinking.

"Now I'm a porter," he muttered, and picked up her duffle. "You can get the rest tomorrow." He started up, and the wolf kept pace. "Bran and Sasha are down at the end there, in the round tower. Sawyer and Annika, first door there, facing the sea."

He gestured the other way on the landing. "I'm down here, again the sea."

The wolf went down, in the direction of Doyle's room, stood in a doorway, moved on, another, and another, then doubled back and walked into a room facing the forest with an open-canopy bed, a long desk, a fireplace framed in malachite.

Doyle dumped her duffle, prepared to step out again and leave her to it.

But she walked to the fire, looked at him, looked back.

"What? I'm supposed to light a fire for you now? Christ."

Muttering all the way, he took bricks of

peat from a copper bucket, arranged them on the grate as he had as a boy.

It was simple enough, took only moments, and if the scent squeezed his heart, he ignored it.

"Now, if there'll be nothing else—"

She walked to the door, one leading to a little balcony.

"You want out again? For Christ's sake. It doesn't have stairs." He walked over, wrenched it open. "So if you want down, you'll have to jump."

But she only scented the air, walked back in, sat by the fire.

"Doors open then." Since he'd done the same in his own room, he could hardly fault her. "Anything else, you'll need to wait till morning and deal with it yourself."

He started out, paused. "Annika made enough of a meal for you, if you want it in the morning."

Unsure, he left her door open, started toward his own room. He heard the sound of her door closing as he reached his own.

So for what it was worth, he thought, Sasha had all her chicks in the roost.

Chapter Two

Gnawing hunger and shivering chill woke Riley at first light. The fire had burned to embers; rain pattered on the terrace outside the open door.

She lay on the floor in front of the dying fire, naked, disoriented. She rarely slept through the change—it was far too intense. In the rare times she had, it was due to utter exhaustion.

Obviously, a vicious battle followed by a shift via Sawyer's magic compass equaled exhaustion.

Stiff, shivering, she pushed to her feet, shoved at her short, shaggy brown hair, and looked around. Her mind, her reason, her instincts worked perfectly well in wolf form, so she'd selected the room the night before due to not only its big, excellent bed, but also the desk.

She'd need a good work space for research.

But that was for later. Now she needed clothes, and God, she needed to eat. It wasn't just the fasting from sundown to sunrise—a hard and fast rule of her pack— but the massive amount of energy the change burned. From woman to wolf, from wolf to woman.

Now she felt weak, shaky, and grateful Doyle had, however reluctantly, carried up her duffle. She pawed through it, grabbing the first pants that came to hand, and dragged on ancient brown cargoes, then a faded Oxford sweatshirt and warm, thick socks an aunt had knitted her for her birthday one year.

She wanted a shower, a hot, endless shower, but needed fuel more.

Moving quietly, she stepped out of the room, scanned the hallway, thought back. She'd yet to see the kitchen, didn't know exactly where to find it, but went down the stairs.

She thought Bran had done damn well

for himself with the big house on the Irish coast. Not just the size—though **wowzer**—but the style, the craftsmanship. And the clever, mystical touches here and there as a testament to his heritage.

Celtic knots worked into the decor—and dragons, sexy faeries. Good, strong colors; thick, rich woodwork. Compelling art—which reminded her she needed to see two pieces in particular.

Two of Sasha's paintings—two in which Bran had magickally hidden the stars. She trusted, absolutely, they were safe, but she wanted to see them for herself.

Meanwhile, with a hand pressed to her empty belly, she wandered. It seemed most likely the kitchen would be toward the rear of the house, so she headed that way in the gloomy half light of a rainy dawn.

She passed a manly sort of office—lots of leather in chocolate tones, dark green walls, big gorgeous desk. Another that surprised her with its old grand piano, a cello—she'd always wanted to learn how to play the cello—a collection of bodhran drums, flutes, and fiddles. A spacious sitting room that managed to look cozy, a gorgeous library that nearly had her putting aside hunger.

All with wide archways, with gleaming floors, with hearths ready to offer warmth and light.

How many rooms did the man need? she wondered. And finally found the kitchen.

Not just a kitchen, for all its spiffy style, but a big-ass lounge with more leather in big-ass sofas and chairs, a ridiculously sized wall screen. Flanking the kitchen's other side? A game area—snooker table, a full bar that had certainly come out of some wonderful old pub, a couple of old-style pinball tables that again nearly had hunger taking a backseat.

She could have lived in this one huge room for the rest of her life. Especially with the wide glass doors bringing in that bad-tempered sky and gloomy sea.

"You've got class, Irish," she murmured, and all but fell on the fruit piled artistically in a wide, polished wood bowl. Biting into a peach, nearly moaning at the first taste of food, she yanked open both doors of a refrigerator.

Pounced again.

Prying open the container of leftovers, she hunted up a fork, ate Annika's chicken and rice dish cold, washing it down with a Coke—nearly giddy as her system celebrated the protein and caffeine connection.

Steadier, she studied the coffeemaker on the counter, decided, yes, she could work that. As she did, she heard footsteps. She tried not to resent them, but God, she could have used another hour of silence and solitude.

But when Sasha came in, when Riley saw the relief in her friend's eyes, she felt small about that resentment.

"Need coffee," she said.

"Me, too. How are you?"

Riley shrugged, grabbed mugs out of the glass-fronted cabinet. "Good. I inhaled the leftovers Annika left, so I'm good."

And when Sasha's arms wrapped around her from behind, Riley felt even smaller. "I had to run it off."

"I know, I know. I felt you come back, so it's all good. Are you still hungry?"

"Topped off for right now, thanks. How are you? You took some hits."

"Bran took care of it. Sawyer got the brunt."

"Yeah. Yeah, I know. But he's okay?"

"We all are. I hope he sleeps a few hours more—I thought you would."

"Later, most likely. Had to fuel." And fueled, Riley leaned back on the counter, smiled. "Some house."

"It's amazing, isn't it?" With her coffee, Sasha wandered the kitchen. "I haven't seen half of it yet—and I want to get outside, even in the rain, and just **see**. But it's amazing. And I slept in a tower room with a magician. What could be more amazing than that?"

"Slept or had sex?"

Sasha's eyes gleamed at Riley over the rim of her mug. "We did both."

"I just knew you'd end up bragging." Riley wandered over to the glass doors, looked out at the slow, thin rain and the gray sea. "It could be out there. In or under the water, like the other two. Another island, so there's a reason there. I'll have to see about getting us a boat."

Sasha stepped up, looked out with her. "I appreciate you not asking, but I'll answer anyway. I don't know. I haven't felt anything, not yet."

"We just got here. We should have a little time to set things up before she comes at us again."

"Sawyer said she kicked back at him hard during the shift—and you could see how hard. But he also said she weakened, and aged, before he let go."

Riley nodded, sipped coffee. "That follows. We put that gray streak in her hair, those lines on her face after we busted her ass in Corfu. Maybe we'll be dealing with an old crone who can barely work up a bitch slap this round. And no," she added, "I don't really believe that."

"We have two of the stars, and we beat her twice. We'll find the third."

"Optimistic's good."

Sasha looked over at Riley. "Aren't you?"

"I won't diss positive thinking. It's a good tool—as long as you're willing to back it up." Riley gestured. "We've got some room out there to train. More in the front, the forest side, but either way. We could set up a decent target range out there. Then there's the woods. Gotta be at least five, six acres of them from what I ran through last night. Quiet, private. It's Ireland, so we're probably going to do a good chunk of training in the rain."

When Sasha said nothing, Riley shot her a glance. "And we just got here. We all need to take a breath. I'm revved up," she admitted. "Big, bloody battle, the moon, the shift."

"Was it different, traveling in wolf form?"

"Exciting in its way, and weird, at least at first because I was healing as we flew, and I couldn't really focus. The landing was fast and hard, and knocked me back."

"I hear you."

"Then I had to run it off. Mostly I like knowing my ground before the moon, so I can judge where's safe for a run. But I had to work it off. Lucky, like I said, there are acres of private woods. You hooked a big magick fish, Sash."

"You helped."

"Me? I don't remember casting out any lures for you."

"You were my friend. The first friend I ever had who knew what I was, what I had, and accepted me for me. You gave me advice, you listened, you cared. And all that helped me be smart and strong enough to, well, cast those lures myself."

"Boy, you owe me."

Sasha laughed, gave Riley a one-armed hug. "I do. I'll pay you back, in part, by making breakfast. Since we're in Ireland, I'll go with Bran's specialty of a full Irish."

"I'll take it. I want to shower first. Didn't have a chance after the war."

"No rush. I want to walk and wander around the house first. I barely took anything in last night."

"Does Bran play the piano?"

"I don't know. Why?"

"He's got a beaut. Viennese parlor grand, mid-nineteenth century."

"Do you know everything?"

"Pretty much. He's also got a cello, violins, violas, flutes, and an exceptional collection of bodhran drums. He must play some of it."

"It's never come up, so I'll have to ask. Do you play anything?"

"Piano, sure, though it's been a while. And he's got a game room area over there that kicks major ass. And one small cathedral of a library."

"I think you've seen more of the house than I have."

"I didn't have sex."

"There is that."

Sasha turned as Annika—flowing hair, flowy dress, bare feet—came in.

"Riley!" As if it had been years, Annika dashed over, threw her arms around Riley.

"Yeah, good morning to you, too."

"We were worried. Doyle said not to, because you'd come back. But we worried. Now you're here! Good morning."

"How can you look like that first thing? Without coffee?"

"I don't like the coffee. But I like the mornings. Sawyer will rest a little longer, but he feels much better. He felt rested enough to mate, and I was very gentle."

"Sex." Riley shook her head. "It's always about sex. Tell me more—no, tell me more after I get that shower."

"I like sometimes to be above—on top," she corrected. "On top when it should be gentle and slow. Then I can have many orgasms."

"Right." Riley let out a breath. "This may

be a longer shower than initially planned."

When Sasha laughed and Riley hurried out, Annika offered a puzzled smile. "I don't understand. Does she need to get more clean?"

"No, she meant...I'll explain, but I'm going to need more coffee."

The next best thing to a hot shower was a hot meal. By the time Sasha—with an assist from Annika—put the meal together, the team had gathered in the kitchen.

Riley caught the scent—bacon!—heard the mix of voices as she wound her way back down.

"I keep a car here," Bran said. "It'll take all of us, but not comfortably."

"I've got my bike," Doyle put in. "And I can take one pillion."

"True enough. I can arrange for a van, a kind of backup, in the event we want or need to go any distance in one vehicle. And there she is," Bran added when Riley stepped in. "Sasha tells us you've healed and rested. And you found a room that suits you?"

"Yeah, thanks. I took one with a good-sized desk, facing the woods. It's a lot of house, Irish," she said as she snagged more coffee.

"It is. I thought, why go small? And when I have my family here, it fills up quick enough. We should eat, then I'll show everyone around the place."

"I hear the eating part." Sawyer pulled a platter of eggs and fried potatoes out of the warming oven, left someone else to grab the platter of meat and stack of toasted bread.

The table snugged in the rainy window showed Annika's handiwork with napkins shaped into hearts, wooden skewers arranged in a tepee with tiny flowers draping down and a single white rose-bud spearing out of the top. Tea lights formed another heart, its center filled with rose petals.

Bran lit them with a flick of a finger, and made her clap.

"Your gardens are so pretty in the rain," she told Bran. "I think if I lived in this castle by the sea, I would never want to leave."

"I like knowing I can come back to it."

"She likes the rain, too." Sawyer heaped

food on his plate. "I've gotta say, I'm going to miss the island sunshine."

"I'm ready for the rain." Sasha passed a platter to Doyle. "It'll give us a day to regroup."

"It's Ireland," Riley reminded her. "We're likely to get more than a day of wet. But yeah, a little regrouping's earned, considering. Any clue where you dumped her, Sawyer?"

"Not one. But she was hurting when I did."

As he ate, he filled her in as he had the others.

"It fits. We hit her where it hurts, she loses ground, her grip gets slippery. It should give us some time. What about Malmon? Or the thing Malmon's become?"

"Slipped through," Doyle said. "He's stronger, faster than he was."

"Can he stay that way without her?" Riley wondered. "That's a question. I'm going to assume you've got this place locked down, Bran."

"You assume correctly."

"So the stars are here, and safe."

"They are. I'll show you, as you'll want to

see for yourself. I'm thinking you chose your room for the work space, and will likely use it. But there's another area you might find useful as well."

"Oh, yeah?"

"The north tower. We'll have a look at it after breakfast."

"Can you dig we've got a north tower?" Grinning, Sawyer ate more bacon. "A south one, too. And check it." He jerked a thumb at the pinball machines in the lounge area.

"Caught that. I'll kick your ass on them later."

"You will try," Sawyer told Riley. "You will fail. We need a new assignment chart."

Sasha nodded. "I'll take care of that this morning, but since Annika and I handled breakfast, I hereby assign Riley and Doyle to KP. I've had a look at the food and cleaning supplies, and we're more than set there for now, so that puts off shopping for a while, on the domestic front."

"I would like to shop in Ireland."

Riley arched her eyebrows at Annika. "If shopping was an Olympic sport, you'd have all the medals. But at some point, she's going to need some rain gear."

"Some extras there in the mudroom," Bran said, "but we'll want to get out and about. I know the land here, and villages, but I've never looked at either with the quest in mind."

"We'll need more ammo," Doyle pointed out.

"Something else I haven't had in mind while here."

"I've got some contacts." Riley shrugged. "I'll make some calls."

"And that's as big a surprise as Annika shopping. We lost some bolts in the last battle," Doyle continued. "And plenty of bullets."

"I'll take care of it, and once I unpack my books and maps, I'll start working on—"

"Can we take a moment?" Sasha interrupted. "I know we can't let up. I know we need to take advantage of the time we might have before Nerezza comes at us again. But can we take a moment to just be? We're all here, around this table, in this place, after facing what seemed like almost impossible odds against survival, much less success. But we're here, and so are two of the stars. That's a miracle, I think. It was hard won, but still a miracle."

"You're right." Bran met her eyes, then scanned the table. "We'll take our moment, and be stronger for it."

"Works for me." Doyle spoke casually, then glanced at Sasha. "When you're doing that assignment chart, just make time and room for daily training. Including calisthenics."

Sasha heaved a sigh. "That's cruel, Doyle."

"Hey, I need my moment, too. You've toughened up, Blondie, but that was in Sawyer's island sunshine. Let's see how you handle fifty squats and push-ups in the rain."

"I may have an alternative to that. If we're finished here," Bran continued, "I can show you all. And the stars as well. KP can wait a bit, I'd think."

"It can wait for eternity in my world."

"Your world **is** eternity," Sawyer reminded Doyle, but took Annika's hand and rose. "I vote for full house tour."

"Let's start at the top then." When Bran rose, he held out a hand for Sasha's. "I've a lot to show you."

They trooped up the back stairs, followed Bran's lead as he made a turn on the second-floor landing and veered up to the right.

"Access to the roof area," he explained. "The views are spectacular from there, even on a wet day."

He wasn't wrong, Riley thought once Bran opened a thick arched door, and she stepped out into the rain.

The wide, flat area of the roof afforded a three-sixty view.

The angry chop of the steel-gray sea and its violent slap on rock and cliff. The thunder of it boomed and crashed below dense layers of clouds, sluggishly sailing in a brooding wind.

As she turned, she could see the faint shadows of hills curtained behind the gray mist of sky, and around to the forest, deep and shadowed and green. Beyond where she'd run the night before, she saw now a cottage or two, and fields dotted with sheep, the thin plumes of smoke from chimneys where hearths burned on a wet summer day.

"It's a good situation." Doyle spoke from behind her. "Even on a day like this, we could spot an attack from a half mile or more. And it's high ground, with cover close."

He moved over, looked down from the crenelated wall. "It'll be useful."

"I can smell the sea," Annika murmured.

"And hear it," Sawyer put in. "Taking a boat out on that's going to be tricky."

"I'll score us a dive boat and the equipment," Riley said absently. "We'll handle it. Is that a graveyard? At about ten o'clock? How old do you figure..."

She remembered, belatedly. This had been Doyle's family's land. Cursing herself, she turned to him. "I'm sorry. I wasn't thinking."

"The first would have been my great-grandmother, who died in 1582, in child-birth with her sixth child. So old enough. Though archaeologists usually want to dig deeper than that, don't they?"

"Depends."

"In any case," he continued as if she hadn't spoken, "it's a good, strategic situation."

"And before we all drown in the rain, let me show you what else should be useful."

As Bran led the way back in, Sasha rubbed a hand down Riley's arm. When Riley mimed pointing a gun at her head, firing, Sasha shook her head, gave that arm a squeeze.

Then they both moved more quickly when they heard Annika's shout of delight.

They followed the sound, made a turn, and came into a third-floor area spread under a half dozen skylights.

"Hot damn!" Riley didn't do handsprings— as Annika did in front of the wall of mirrors that obviously delighted her—but she did rub her hands together.

The excellent home gym had bamboo floors the color of raw honey, a full circuit of machines. Two treadmills and a pair of elliptical machines faced the rain-splattered wall of windows, as did a recumbent bike. A TRX dominated one corner; a full-sized, glass-fronted refrigerator—already stocked with water and energy drinks— another.

It boasted weight benches, free weights, a rolled stack of yoga mats, kettlebells, medicine balls, balance balls.

"Oh, how I've missed you," Riley said, and immediately plucked a ten-pound weight from the rack.

"Good enough, I'd think, for those calisthenics if the weather doesn't cooperate."

Doyle shrugged at Bran's comment. "Battles happen in foul weather as much as fair. But...It'll be useful. Hmm. Chin-up bar."

"Oh, hell," Sasha muttered, and made him smile.

"Why don't you try it out, Blondie? Show us what you've got."

"I'm still having my moment."

"Tomorrow then. First light. I can work some circuits into the training, and the weights are welcome. But we run outside, rain or shine. A machine doesn't give you the feel of the ground under your feet."

"The walls are so shiny!" Annika executed a graceful and perfect handstand in front of the mirror. "I like to see how it looks."

"So would I, if I looked like you." After a few biceps curls, Riley replaced the weight.

"Free to use anytime, Irish?"

"It's yours as it's mine."

"Solid. I'm going to grab some gym time later. That'll be my moment," she told Sasha.

"It takes all kinds. I intend to set up my easel."

"Speaking of easels, and paintings..." Riley turned to Bran.

"That's next. I should tell you there's a wet area through those doors."

"Wet?" Annika said, coming neatly to her feet.

"A steam room, a Jacuzzi, a shower, and a changing area. I regret the lack of a pool."

"Oh, it's all right. The sea's so close."

Smiling, he gestured toward the door. "There's some storage on this level," he began as he led them out. "More bedrooms, a sitting area."

"How big is this family of yours?" Sawyer asked.

"Including cousins?" With a laugh, Bran paused at a door in a rounded wall—a door of dark wood that looked ancient and had no knob, no hinges. "Well over a hundred, I'd think."

"A...**hundred**?"

He laughed again at Sasha's reaction. "Too late for you to back out now, **mo chroí**."

Bran held his hand to the door, palm out. He spoke in Irish, had Doyle shooting him a look.

For me and mine only, open.

At the words, the gesture, a bolt of lightning scored down the wood, glowed and pulsed blue.

And the door opened.

"Better than a police lock, riot bar, and guard dog," Riley said.

"It will only open for one of us. As will the doors on the second and the first level to this tower. What's held inside is safe from any who try to take."

Bran gestured them in.

Riley didn't gasp, but it was close.

His workshop, she thought, or magick shop. Sorcerer's den. Whatever the term, like the rest of the house, it rang all the bells.

It towered inside the tower—which shouldn't have been physically or structurally possible.

Then again, magick.

Floating shelves held bottles, jars, boxes. She recognized some plants—under eerily glowing lights—the chalices, the ritual knives, the cauldrons and bowls.

Balls and spears of crystal. Books with leather covers, some probably centuries old. Mirrors, candles, charms, statues.

Brooms, she noted, and bones, runes, and tarot cards.

And above a stone hearth, Sasha's paintings.

Here, of course, Riley thought. Magicks within magicks within magicks. Safe from evil, within the light.

"I told you I bought the first of your paintings before I met you, before I knew you." Bran put an arm over Sasha's shoulders as they studied them. "I saw it in a gallery in New York and wanted it. Needed it," he corrected.

"My path through the woods, one I knew so well, leading here. Though only I knew it led here. I often walked that path, toward that light you painted so beautifully, and I thought to hang the painting at my flat in New York to remind me of this. But I brought it here, even then. I placed it here, in my most precious place."

"I dreamed it." Alone, and so long before she'd ever met him. "I dreamed the path and the trees and the light, but I couldn't see the end of the path. Not until now."

"And the second, its companion, you painted from visions as well, visions that guided us here. Not just to home, but to the third star. We'll find it here."

The end of the path, Riley thought, the magnificent house where they now stood, glowing under soft light, festooned with gardens, rising over a turbulent sea.

Things came in threes, she thought—not only the stars, but other things. Would Sasha paint a third?

"Inside your visions, inside your art, the stars shine safe."

Bran lifted both hands. The paintings shimmered, an overlay of color. Red on the path, blue on the house. And they slid out of that world into his hands, closed in clear glass, bright and bold as truth.

"Ours to guard," Bran said. "And the third, the Ice Star, to find."

"And when there are three—fire, water, ice—in the hands of the guardians, the battles will not end." As she spoke, Sasha's eyes went dark, went deep. "When there are three, as three were made, as three were given to the worlds, the dark will seek more blood, more death. Defeat her in unity. Fall to her in chaos. Choices to make, paths to take. Hold true, hold three, one by two, and then, only then, will the Island of Glass appear. Only then will it open to the valiant and the brave heart.

"Will you travel the storm?" With the vision on her like a thousand suns, she whirled to the others. "Will you leap into faith? Will you see what lives inside the stone and sorrow? Will you hear what calls your name? And find the last, and finding, hold strong, hold true?"

On a long breath, Sasha closed her eyes.

"It's cold."

Immediately Bran shot a look at the hearth, had flames leaping to life.

"No, I meant—Sorry. Where it is, the star. Wherever it is, it's cold. I can't see it, but I can feel it. And I don't guess any of that was much help."

"Beg to differ." Riley gave her a rub on the shoulder. "You let us know part three's not the finish. No point looking at it as done when it won't be. We find it, we fight the bitch, and we find the Island of Glass. And get there, with the three stars. Piece of cake, right? If you like rock-hard cake with dirt icing."

"I'm up for it," Sawyer said. "Cake's cake."

"I like cake," Annika said.

"Wouldn't be the first dirt I've eaten." Doyle looked at the stars. "We find the star, we find the island. Whatever it takes."

"I'd say unity's been met, and we've already chosen the path." Bran lifted the stars toward the paintings. They rose to them, slid inside.

To wait for the third.

Chapter Three

With the stars again secured by magick, Bran led them to the central spiral stairs.

The guy had class, start to finish, Riley thought while she scanned the second-floor lounge area. And with its addition of a big, burly desk, it could serve as yet another office or work area.

She approved its mix of old and new— the big flat-screen, an old burl wood bar, plenty of seating in those deep, rich colors he seemed to favor for hanging out, a fireplace framed in granite the color of the forest.

Niches in the rounded walls held statuary, alabaster, bronze, polished wood. Intrigued, Riley stepped over, ran a finger down the fluid lines of three goddesses, carved together in alabaster.

"Fódla, Banba, Ériu." She glanced back at Bran. "Eyeballing it, I'd say circa AD 800."

"So I'm told. It's a favorite of mine, as are the goddesses, so it's come down to me through the family."

"Who are they?" Sasha asked.

"Daughters of Ermnas," Riley told her, "of the Tuatha Dé Danann. They asked the bard Amergin to name the land—this land—for them, and he did. A triumvirate—not our three goddesses, but a triumvirate all the same. Queens and goddesses of an island. It's interesting."

She turned, gestured. "And that bronze. The Morrígan, caught in the change from female form to crow form. Another of Ermnas's daughters, another great queen and goddess. War goddess."

Riley moved to another niche. "Here we have the Lady of the Lake, sometimes known as Niniane. Goddess of water. And here in her chariot, Fedelm, the prophet, who foretold great battles."

"Representing us?" Sasha moved closer to the polished wood carved into the prophet goddess.

"It's interesting, I think. Irish here has plenty of most exceptional art throughout, but it's interesting these particular pieces are in this particular tower."

"Together," Annika said. "As we are. I like it."

"I'm pretty fond of it myself. It's strength," Riley decided. "And it feels like good luck. I wouldn't," she added as Sawyer reached for the statue of the goddess rising from the water. "That's probably worth five, six mil on the market."

"Say what?" Sawyer snatched his hand back.

"The legend of that piece goes that one of my ancestors was enamored of the lady, and conjured the statue." Bran smiled. "However it came to be, it's another that's come through the family for generations. But your sensibilities on the grouping's intriguing, Riley. I put these here with my own hands. I chose their places here before I knew any of you. Yet they fit well, don't they?"

"They're so pretty." But following Sawyer's lead, Annika kept her hands to herself.

"Interesting, too, is I've placed in the other tower a bronze of Merlin the sorcerer, and one of the Dagda."

"Merlin's obvious. The Dagda, again of the Tuatha Dé Danann," Riley put in, "who among other things is known as a god of time." She shot a finger at Sawyer.

"And with him I have Caturix."

"King of the battle," Riley murmured, arching eyebrows at Doyle. "Fits pretty well."

"I have the mate to the triumvirate of goddesses in the first tower as well. The Morrígan, Badb, Macha."

"The second set of daughters of Ernmas. I'd like a look sometime."

"Anytime at all," Bran told Riley.

"As interesting as it may be, they're just symbols." Doyle stood, hands in his pockets. "Statues don't fight. They don't bleed."

"Says the guy cursed by a witch three centuries ago. I don't expect the statues to leap up and join in," Riley continued. "But symbolism matters, and right now it feels like it's weighing on our side."

"I absolutely agree. And that doesn't mean I won't groan my way through pull-ups tomorrow."

Sasha got a half smile from Doyle. "Fair enough."

"The main level may give us more, tangibly, to work with."

"You wouldn't happen to have Excalibur down there?" Sawyer asked Bran.

"Sorry, no. My cousin in Kerry has it. Joking," he said when Riley's eyes popped under her shaggy fringe of bangs.

"Never joke about Excalibur to an archaeologist. What's downstairs?" Without waiting, she started down the spiral.

Doyle heard her reaction before she was halfway down. In his experience the sound she made was one usually made by a woman at the hard crest of an orgasm.

He heard Bran laugh and say, "I thought you'd approve," as he circled down at the rear of the group.

Books, Doyle noted. Hundreds of them. Old, old books on rounded, towering shelves. The air smelled of their leather bindings, and quietly of paper.

One massive book sat on a stand, its carved leather cover locked. But others circled the room with its wide stone hearth. Windows, narrow and tall, offered soft light and recessed seats between the shelves.

A long library table stood gleaming in the center of the room.

His own interest piqued when he noticed the maps.

"Books, collected over generations," Bran began. "On magicks, lore, legend, mythology, history. On healing, on spell casting, on herbs, crystals, alchemy. Journals, memoirs, family lore as well. Maps, as Doyle has discovered, some ancient. You'll find some duplicates to what you already have," he said to Riley.

She just shook her head. "It makes what I already have look like a toddler's bookcase. I could live here." She let out a long breath. "If I can't find answers here, there aren't answers. And there are always answers."

"I've looked, of course, but I don't have your comprehensions all the same. And at this point, the search is more narrow and focused." He crossed over, pulled a thin volume from a shelf. "This is said to have been written by one of my ancestors—on my mother's side. It tells of his visit to the Island of Glass to celebrate the rising of a new queen. It's written in old Irish."

Taking it, Riley opened it carefully. Reverently. "I can work on translating. Doyle's better there, being as he is old Irish."

"I can't speak to its veracity," Bran continued. "But the family lore generally holds it up."

"I can dig through lore and myth." Riley spoke absently as she scanned the book. "I'm assuming what's in here stays in here."

"This chamber is magickally controlled to preserve the books—paper, bindings. Some are so old they'd crumble outside this air, and with handling outside this spell."

"Got it. It's a kick-ass place to work anyway." She laid the book on the long table, gestured to the one on the stand. "What's that one?"

"The Book of Spells, again from my family, from the first set down to the latest. I've added what I created on Corfu, and on

Capri. Only one of my blood can open it." As he spoke, Bran walked to it. "It came to me when I reached my twenty-first birthday. I will pass it to the one who comes after me. It holds knowledge, and legacy, and power."

He laid his hand on the book, spoke in Irish. And as he spoke, the book began to glow. It began to sing.

"Oh!" Annika grabbed Sawyer's hand. "It's beautiful. Can you hear it?"

"Yeah. And feel it."

The air moved; the light changed.

"I am of the blood," Doyle translated Bran's words for the others. "I am of the craft. I am all who came before, all who come after. This is my pledge, this is my duty, this is my joy."

When Bran lifted his hand, the thick lock was gone. He opened the carved cover— a flash, a snap of sound. Then silence.

"Here, all who held the book mark their name."

"So many," Sasha murmured as he turned the page. "Yours is the last."

"So far."

"Would...our child?"

"If the child is willing. If the child accepts."

"A choice?"

"Always a choice. The spells are catalogued. For healing, for knowing, for protection, for deflection, for worship, and so on. If any of you have the need to find a spell, you've only to ask and I'll open it."

"The illustrations," Sasha said as he turned a few pages. "They're wonderful, so vibrant."

"The book creates them. You'll see each page bears a name. If a spell is found useful, we write it out, offer it. If the book accepts, it's added."

"The book accepts?"

"It has power," he said again. "If you have need, ask."

He closed the book, held his hand over it. The lock materialized, snapped shut.

"One day, when we've got plenty of time to spare, I'd like to look through it. But for now..." Riley turned a circle. "I think I have enough to keep me occupied."

"For a couple of decades," Sawyer put in.

"It's okay if I dig in, get started?"

"Of course." As a welcome, Bran gestured

toward the fire, so flames leaped into life. "I'll be on the third level later. There are drinks on the second level, and the makings for tea or coffee."

"Like I said, I could live in here. I'll get some things from my room, then start that digging. My cell phone will work in here, right?"

"Here and anywhere else."

"Can I help you with anything here?" Sasha asked.

"Maybe, but the fact is, Doyle would be more useful."

He didn't look very pleased about it, but shrugged. "I've got some things to see to, then I can give you some time."

"Good enough. I'll make some calls, haul some things down here, get going. Bran?" Hands on hips, Riley turned a circle. "This rocks it."

Before she started, Riley contacted family. She should actually call, actually speak to her family, but...email was quicker, simpler, and she could blast one out to everyone at once.

She'd call her parents after the moon,

but she could give them and her pack details about where she was on the quest—and where she was literally—via email.

Then she scrolled through her contacts list. She needed to line up a dive boat, scuba equipment. Since both the other stars had required diving, she'd assume they'd need it.

She found an archaeologist she'd worked with on a dig in County Cork years before, gave that a try.

It meant some conversation, some catching up—which was exactly why she'd chosen email for the family connection—but she scored a local name.

Within twenty minutes, a lot of phone flirting and negotiation, she had what she needed on tap.

She boxed up the books she wanted, along with her laptop and tablet, a couple of legal pads, and carted everything to the tower.

Wouldn't she have loved working in here alone? she thought as she walked back in. Just her and hundreds of old books—and her own electronics. A big fire, a big table. Rain spitting outside, a little music from her playlist.

But she needed Doyle.

The man spoke and read as many languages as she did—and some of them better than she did. Which was annoying, she admitted as she set up her laptop.

Then again, he'd had a few centuries to learn linguistics. And everything else.

He had a good mind for strategy and tactics—she didn't always agree, but he had a good mind for them. As a drill sergeant he was brutal—but she respected that. This was war, and war on an impossible level, so you trained brutally or you died.

And in battle, he was fierce, fast, and fearless. Of course, being immortal, why fear?

Not fair, she reminded herself. The man felt pain, just like anybody.

Anyway, it wasn't a competition. Which was bullshit, she admitted as she arranged her things. For her, most everything was some sort of competition. She knew how to work on a team—pack animal, after all. But she preferred being an alpha.

Considering the night she'd put in, and what she hoped to accomplish now, she went up the circling stairs, made a pot of strong coffee. After a brief hesitation, she grabbed two thick white mugs.

If Doyle showed, having the second would save time.

Then she settled down at the table, fire roaring, rain pattering, and began to read—as best she could—the book written by Bran's ancestor.

She made notes on the legal pad as she went, stopped when she needed to in order to check a word or phrasing with her laptop.

She barely glanced up when the door opened.

She wondered if the faded Grateful Dead T-shirt he wore was a snarky private joke about his immortality, or if he was—as any sensible rock lover should be—a fan.

Either way, it showed admirable pecs to advantage.

"Bran's many-times-great-grandfather was full of himself," she began. "Or maybe it just comes across that way. His writing's pretty florid, and he's pretty damn smug about getting invited to the rising. It's what he calls the birth of this new queen."

"Okay." Doyle dumped coffee in the second mug.

"You could read this faster."

"You seem to be getting through it. Besides, some guy's trip to the Island of Glass hundreds of years ago doesn't do much for us in the here and now. It's wherever it chooses to be—that's the legend, isn't it?"

"'It comes and goes as it wills,'" Riley quoted, "'sailing the mists of time and place. Many have sought its shores, but the glass parts rarely. Only those chosen by the fates, those whose feats and deeds and powers merit, are gifted to pass through.'" She tapped the book. "Or words to that effect. This guy—Bohannon—is pretty pumped up about his personal merit. He's taking the queen two jeweled birds—a lark and a nightingale—as his gift. One to sing her to sleep, one to sing her awake. There's a whole passage about how he conjured them."

"And that helps us how?"

"It's information, Sparky. He's definitely talking about an infant—so this verifies a birth. Most of the info we've dug up does, though there are theories about a young girl, à la Arthur, being chosen through a task or deed. But he writes about the infant queen, Aegle, and her guardians: Celene, Luna, Arianrhod."

"We've had that much before."

"More confirmation," Riley insisted. "And his invite came through Arianrhod—Celtic to Celtic, I'm thinking. And he traveled from Sligo, to the coast of Clare—that's here and now for us. He had to sail from here, which was rough on him—again thoroughly recounted. Dark sea under the full moon, blah, blah, but then it gets interesting."

Riley flipped back in the book, pushed it to him.

"Read that. Out loud," she said, impatient, when he started to skim the words. "It helps me to hear it."

"Bloody hell. Fine then. 'Though the sea rolled beneath me, and the moon danced behind clouds to blur the light, I did not fear. I drew my power around me like my cloak, and sailed on my own enchantment as the mists swirled and thickened. For a moment, even the moon was lost, and the sea shuddered as if in fear. Some might have cried out, or turned the boat around, but I sailed on, blood cool as I—' For Christ's sake."

"Yeah, yeah, but keep going."

"'As I stayed my course, though the water demon roared.'" Doyle paused, gave her a cool look. "Water demon."

Riley shrugged. "Could be a Wahwee, though that's Aborigine, maybe a Munuane—maybe a whale, a waterspout. Or just hyperbole. Keep going."

"Water demon," he muttered, but continued. "'Through the mists, lights, torches burning bright, and the moon slipped her clouds to shine a beacon to light the way. For me the glass parted, and the sea calmed, and the Island of Glass shimmered like a jewel before me.

"'Sand, white as the moon, with those tall torches blazing. Forests, thick and green, alight with drops of dancing colors. On a hill the palace shined in silver. The music of pipes and flutes and harps enchanted the air. I saw jugglers and dancers, and could smell meat on the fire, mead in the cup as young boys raced into the shallows to pull my boat to shore.'"

When Doyle paused again, Riley just circled her finger in the air.

He cursed under his breath, but continued.

"'And while the night had been chill and damp when I left the shore of my world, here it was warm and dry. I stepped from the boat onto the white sand of the Island of Glass where Arianrhod waited with her sisters to greet me. As my foot touched the ground, I knew I had been granted what few had before, and few would after me. For here is the beating heart of the power of all worlds.'"

Doyle looked up. "You buy that one?"

"Not enough information, but it's interesting, isn't it? Magick is—we can't deny that one. What if there is a core to it, a heart, a world where it generates? It sure makes sense that Nerezza wants the stars—created there, by the three goddesses. It makes sense if she got them in her evil little hands she'd have all the power, and the ability to destroy, well, everything. So it's interesting."

She sat back. "Keep going."

"If I'd known I'd be reading you a story,

I'd've gotten a beer."

"I'll get you a beer if it saves me from translating."

"Deal."

She went up the stairs. "Something else to think about," she called down.

"I have plenty to think about. What's your something else?"

"I'd need to run tests to get a better estimate of the age of this journal, but I'm going with ninth century."

"Okay."

With a roll of her eyes, she looked down over the rail. "Have some intellectual curiosity, Doyle, and ask why."

"You're going to tell me anyway."

"I am." She started down with his beer. "They had a mathematical layout for manuscripts in the ninth century, and the scribes ruled the parchment in hardpoint by scoring it with a stylus on the back. Sometimes they cut too hard. You can see the scoring on the parchment in the book. Bo here's inflated, pretty pleased with his station in life. He'd have some lackey do the scoring. And if it was more like twelfth century—which, by the ink, I don't think so anyway—they started using a kind of pencil to rule the page."

"So it's old, which we knew. What's a couple hundred years matter?"

"Easy for you to say, old man. It matters, in this case?" She handed him the beer, sat. "Because while I've found snippets of the legend of the island that appear to date further back, this is the oldest serious account, and a first-person account. An account of traveling there for the celebration of the rising. When the stars were created, Doyle. It tells us when the stars were born. It's what we call, in my circles, a discovery."

"Dating the stars isn't finding the third one."

"Sometimes knowledge is its own reward." She said it dryly, believed it absolutely. "But if I can date this, and somehow authenticate it, we'd know when the queen was born, the stars created. We know this enchanter dude sailed from the coast of Clare—alone. Odds are slim he had to sail far, as he left at night, arrived the same night. Putting magicks aside a minute, we assume the island was here, off the coast of Clare, which I like because so are we."

Frowning over that, Doyle picked up the beer. "That would make us pretty damn lucky."

"Considering the last couple months, luck be damned. We're where we're meant to be. I don't know if we're going to sail out one night and hit that portal, but using this account, putting it together with other sightings, doing the math, calculating currents, maybe we'd have ourselves a location, or an area anyway. There's always a pattern, Doyle."

He took a slug of beer. "Now you're interesting me."

"Good. This has to be more secondary after today. Logically, we can't take the star back until we find it. But it'd be to our advantage to have a direction, to give Sawyer some possible coordinates when we do find the third star.

"She's going to be even more pissed."

"She's hurt. Maybe we find it before she's back in action. And no," he said when Riley just raised her eyebrows. "I don't believe that for a minute."

"Okay then. To round it up. Find the star, find the island, get the job done. Hope getting the job done includes destroying Nerezza."

"A sword does her, according to our seer."

"And it would be extra nice if it was yours, but neither of us thinks it's going to be that clean and done."

"Bran enchants it with that in mind. It may be time to start working on that part of the deal."

"It couldn't hurt." She'd thought of it herself. "Could be with the spell Bran's already put on the weapons, we're already covered there. But...Let's lay it out while we're here and the others aren't."

She could talk straight to him, she thought. Say things to him she'd hesitate to say to the others. Things that weighed against hope.

"If we don't finish her before we get the stars back to the island, we've still saved the worlds. Yay, us. But she's going to come for us when we've done our job. She can afford to wait."

Her eyes held his, cool and steady as she

continued. "Bran and Sasha go off and get married, have a couple kids. Annika and Sawyer are living on some island— on land for him, in the sea for her. They'll probably even make that work. Me, I'll find a dig or write a book. Likely both. You'll do what you do. And she'll come for us, one or two at a time, and pick us off like flies. She can't kill you, but she can probably come up with something worse."

The image didn't sit well, so she reached over, took his beer, had a sip. "We've been set on this course, every one of us. We've been brought together for one purpose, all of us. To find the stars, return them, save the worlds. We're getting there. I believe we can do it. I think we can complete the quest. But after that, Doyle, nobody says we all live happily ever after. Nobody says we're fated to kill the dark god and do a victory dance."

"Then we'd better say it, and do it." He took the beer back, sipped. "Because no way I'm being the sex slave of some psycho god for eternity."

"I was thinking she'd more likely keep you slow roasting over an open fire pit for eternity."

"I like the heat, but the point remains. We'd better do it, Gwin. All the way. Or nobody rides off into the sunset until we do. We're stuck together until she's blown out of existence."

She'd thought of that, too, but... "Annika's only got a couple months before she's mermaid all the time."

"We do it before. We'll put Bran on the sword. We'll be ready for her when she comes back."

"Okay. One god-destroying sword goes on the list." Riley gestured. "Read."

In her chamber, in her cave, deep underground, Nerezza stirred. The pain! The pain scored like claws, bit like teeth under her skin, burned like jagged tongues of fire and ice over it.

In all of her existence, she had never known such pain.

Her scream of rage sounded as a gasping whimper.

The thing that had once been Andre Malmon—human, wealthy, savage in his way—held a chalice to her lips in his clawed hand. "Drink, my queen. It is life. It is strength."

The blood he fed her trickled down her scorched throat. But the pain, the pain. "How long? How long now?"

"Only a day."

No, no, surely it had been years, decades. She had suffered so much. What had they done to her?

She remembered whirling wind, a terrible fall, scorching heat, blazing cold. Fear. She remembered fear.

And the faces, yes, she remembered the faces of those who'd struck out at her.

Tears burned down her cheeks as she drank, as Malmon's lizard eyes stared into hers with a mixture of adoration and madness.

This, this is what they'd brought her to.

"My mirror. Get my mirror."

"You must rest."

"I am your **god**. Do as I command."

When he scurried away, she fell back, limp, each breath a torture. He came back, clawed feet clicking on stone, held the mirror up.

Her hair, her beautiful hair, now gray as

fetid smoke. Her face yellowed and scored with lines and grooves, her dark eyes clouded with age. All her beauty gone, her youth destroyed.

She would get it back, all of it. And the six who'd caused this would pay beyond measure.

As rage fed her, she grabbed the chalice, drank deep. "Get me more. Get me more, then you will do what I tell you."

"I will make you well."

"Yes." She stared at his eyes, mad into mad. "You will make me well."

Chapter Four

As Doyle read, translating smoothly, Riley took notes. It helped her form a picture of the island—a sketch really, but something more tangible. And one of the three goddesses. Dressed in white robes, belts of silver or gold or jewels. And Arianrhod—Bo definitely had a crush going there—stood out in the description. The slender beauty with hair like a flaming sunset, eyes bright as a summer sky. Yadda, yadda, Riley thought as she wrote **blue eyes, redhead**. He praised her alabaster skin, her voice—like harp song.

Wants to bang her.

"What?"

"Huh?" She glanced up from her notes, met Doyle's eyes. "Didn't realize I said it out loud. I said—wrote down—he wants to bang her. Bo's hot for Arianrhod."

"And that's relevant how?"

"It's called an observation, Lord Oblivious. I also observe we're talking about a forested island, one with tall hills—and a castle, palace, fortress built on one of the tallest. That's strategy. You want high ground. We know there was a civil war, and the rebels lost, ended up being banished, stuck in the Bay of Sighs. Where we found the Water Star. Something else we pull out of this journal may be a step toward the Ice Star."

After considering it, Doyle summed it up. "I don't think Bo getting a woody over Arianrhod tells us anything more than he's got a dick and she's hot."

"Maybe not, but odds are the other two also rate hotness, and he's all about the one. Plus, he writes Arianrhod invited him. Maybe they've got something going. We come from them, that's the story. You gotta bang to beget. It might not make any difference which of us come from which of them, but it's relevant if Bran's ancestor and the goddess—the one with a

Celtic name—did the tango, and Bran's a direct descendant."

After a moment, Doyle gave her an eyebrow jerk she took as acknowledgment of her point. And went back to reading.

He had a good voice, she thought. Not what you'd call harp song, but a good, strong voice. He read well, and not everybody read well out loud.

She wondered how many books he'd read. Thousands maybe—imagine that. Here was a man who'd gone from tallow candles to laser technology, from horse and cart to space travel.

She could spend a decade picking his brain on what he'd seen, how he'd lived, what he'd felt.

For the moment she continued to take notes, following Bohannon's observations and descriptions as he continued on horseback from the beach, through groves of orange and lemon trees—the blossoms perfuming the sweet night air.

"We can surmise spring—orange blossoms."

"That's considering the island runs on

the same rules of seasons as this world," Doyle pointed out. "And on this side of the equator."

"Point." And a damn good one, she had to admit. "But we stick with the physical location, at Bo's time and place, and we get spring. Surmising. A well-kept island, too. He talks of the groves, the wide, dry road—lit with torches. A full moon, which also helps estimating a time. The silver palace—you have to wonder if that's literal or just prose."

She filled in details as he read. Expansive gardens, women in flowing gowns, music piping through open doors and windows, out onto wide terraces. The new queen's standard—a white dove soaring over a blue sea—flew atop every tower.

Doyle got as far as the entrance hall—brilliant tapestries, gilded trees flowering in silver urns—when he put the book down.

"If I have to read interior design, I'm going to need more than a beer."

"And when I can describe the island, the palace—in detail—to Sasha, she can draw it. And drawing it might trigger a vision. The vision might get us closer."

He finished off his beer, set it down. "That's a good idea."

"I have lots of them."

"You have lots of ideas. Some of them are good."

"If you want another beer, bring me down some water. I went up last time. And I need ten."

"Ten what?"

"Ten minutes." She pushed away from the table, went to the sofa by the fire, stretched out. And was asleep in a finger snap.

Doyle appreciated the skill, one a soldier developed. Sleep on command, sleep anywhere.

He left her to it, wandered upstairs and decided water was likely the better choice for now. Opening a bottle, he drank while walking to one of the windows.

A fist closed around his heart, twisted viciously. From here he could see the well, one he'd fetched water from countless times in his youth. Bran had kept it, made it part of a garden area. A garden Doyle knew his mother would have found charming.

Flowers, shrubs, small trees, winding paths ran over what had once been a plot for crops, and the stables were long gone. Likely gone to rubble before Bran had bought the land.

He made himself look out, look over to the gravestones, and felt a new jolt when he saw Annika kneeling beside his mother's grave, arranging...flowers and little stones, he noted.

She had the sweetest heart, he thought, the kindest he'd ever known. And he'd known kindness in his time, as well as brutality. She shifted, took more flowers from her basket, arranged these on his father's grave, along with her pebbles.

She would do this, show these people she'd never known this respect.

And he'd yet to walk out to them.

Nothing there but dust, he told himself, but in his own heart he knew better. Riley had the right of it. Symbols did matter, and respect should be paid.

But for now, he turned away, went back down the stairs.

He took a good long look at Riley. She slept flat on her back, her head on one of the fancy pillows, her arms crossed over her belly at the wrist. A sheathed knife on her belt.

He imagined if she'd had her hat, she'd have tipped it over her face.

It wasn't bad as faces went. It was no Annika, but few were. But she had good bones that would likely serve her well into old age—if she lived that long. A strong jaw that could take a punch, a wide mouth that always had something to say.

He supposed the short hair suited the face, even though he suspected she hacked at it with her own knife when needed.

He'd been known to do the same.

He remembered the first time he'd seen her in wolf form—that night on Corfu, in the midst of battle. The shock of it, the absolute magnificence of her as she'd stared him down with those gilded eyes.

Eyes that had wept for him when she'd thought him dead.

He'd forgotten what it was to have a woman weep for him.

He hadn't allowed himself to have a woman for anything other than the most basic release in a lifetime or two. Looking at Riley now, reminding himself she wasn't remotely the type of woman he'd ever been attracted to, he wondered why she should make him think of that release, and more.

Likely because they were the only two of the six who weren't getting that release. Probably just that simple.

Then she opened her eyes, looked directly into his, and he knew it was far from simple.

"Problem?" she demanded.

"Your ten minutes are up."

"Right."

She sat up, stretched, and he swore he saw the wolf in the gesture.

When she stood, he remained where he was, blocking her.

"Repeat. Problem?"

"No. I forget you're short."

"I'm not short. I'm average. You're taller than average."

"You're short," he said flatly, and moved aside. "I'll give this another hour, then I have to move, get some air."

"I hear that. I wonder who's in charge of

lunch."

"You're hungry again?"

"It's the cycle. It keeps the metabolism on a slow burn. Anyway, another hour or so and we should be able to finish the journal. Did you read any more while I took ten?"

"No."

"So, I'll bet you twenty he bangs the goddess. Or she bangs him. I've got a feeling she'll take the lead there."

Doyle thought of the prissy purple prose. "I'll wager that. She can do better."

He picked up the book; she went back to taking notes.

At the end of the hour, Riley held out her hand, palm up. "Pay me."

"He could've been lying. I nailed the moon goddess in the castle on the hill."

"Pay up."

Resigned, Doyle dug twenty out of his pocket.

"If we had more journals, I'd go double or nothing the sister goddesses did their own bouncing during the celebration." Riley stuffed the bill in her pocket. "It follows. We started there, too, on the island. Our bloodlines. It all started there. And more than a millennium later—by my surmise—we're working our way back there. We're able to do that because of that bloodline, because each of us has something more, a kind of gift."

"I was cursed. It wasn't a gift."

"I'm sorry." Sympathy and briskness mixed in her tone. "I'm sorry for what happened to your brother, and to you. But putting the emotion of it aside, that aspect of you, the curse of immortality is part of the whole. Every one of us brings something special to the table, and together it makes the meal."

His face, his eyes hardened and chilled. His voice flashed, iced fire. "You're saying that my brother was meant to die so I could be cursed?"

She might have answered temper with temper if she hadn't clearly heard the guilt and grief tangled in it. "I'm not, and there's no point getting pissed. I'm saying that even if you'd saved him, you'd have been cursed. If the witch had never lured him, there would have been some other connection, altercation. You said yourself you'd searched for Nerezza, for the stars, for hundreds of years. No luck. But you hook up with us, and in a couple months we have two of the stars, and we've kicked her ass twice. It was always going to be up to us."

"And what was he then, my brother, in your surmising? No more than a pawn to lure the knight?"

"He was your brother." Her tone rolled over the keen edge of his. She didn't flinch from it. "Why something evil chose him is impossible to say. I'm saying something else chose you, and the rest of us. The journal, for me, adds more weight to that."

Though she kept her eyes level with the barely banked fury in his, she paused a moment. Now her tone gentled a little. "I'm the last one who'd ever devalue the bond of family. It's everything. I'm just trying to get a sense of the really big picture, and logic the crap out of it to try to move us forward."

"Logic's the least of it though, isn't it?" He rose again. "I need the air."

After he strode out, she hissed out a breath. "I'm a freaking scientist," she uttered in frustration, then picked up her notes and went out to find Sasha—and lunch.

Since everyone appeared to have scattered, she made her way to the kitchen, hunted up the makings for a sandwich.

As she layered turkey with ham, considered her choice of cheeses, Sasha came in with a new task chart.

"I figured lunch as a free-for-all today," Sasha began, "as everyone's settling in. I've got you down for it tomorrow, unless we head out somewhere."

"Works. You want one of these?"

Sasha glanced at the enormous sandwich in the making. "I think much less. Bran spent some time talking to his family in Sligo, and he's going to work in the tower. Annika wanted to help him, and Sawyer went out to start scouting the best place to set up target practice."

Sasha set the canvas chart, suitably artistic as well as practical, on a ledge.

"So you've got some time?" Riley asked her.

"I can, if you need something."

"Doyle and I worked our way through

that journal. I've got notes. Bran's ancestor—kind of a pompous boor—did it with Arianrhod."

"Did what with—Oh. Ooooh," Sasha repeated, lengthening the word.

"Exactly. You get the implication."

"That it's possible Bran's descended from her? That would make sense, wouldn't it?"

"Logic." Vindicated, Riley poked a finger in the air. "What I didn't add, logically speaking, to Doyle, as he was getting pissy, is we've got two Irishmen who live in the same place—a few hundred years apart, but the same place."

"Doyle could be from the same line." Nodding, Sasha put the kettle on for tea. "It follows, doesn't it?"

"Down the line for me. Let me give you some highlights from the journal."

While she did, Sasha sliced an apple, some cheese, added some crackers, and settled down with tea.

"It may have been right off this coast," Sasha stated. "It may be again."

"I've got some details on what it looks like—sketchy, ha-ha. And what the palace looks like, what the goddesses—Arianrhod in particular—look like. If you were to draw them from my notes..."

"Maybe I'd see more. I can try. And the queen was a baby, so the birth was literal."

"He presented his gift—the songbirds—to the goddesses, and was himself presented to the infant queen." Riley flipped through her notes. "'A fair bairn with golden hair and eyes of blue, deep lakes, already wise. And on her shoulder, bared for all to see, the royal mark. The star of destiny.'"

"Another star. Did he write about her parents?"

"He was more about the food and wine, a lot more about the goddess, the clothes, the queen. He was a little bit of a jerk, at least in his own telling. And by his account the palace comes off as fairytale sparkle. Big and silver and full of art and elaborate rooms. But he also talks about the thick forests, and a stone circle on another hill where he walked to pay respects to the ancients. A waterfall and a troubling path, the Tree of All Life."

"And Nerezza?"

"Gossip. Pretty juicy." Riley took a swig of beer, wiggled closer in her chair. "First, no invite for her. She lives on the far side of the island, semi-banished to that area when she tried stirring up trouble for the former queen. Not much hard data there, but she's feared and disliked. Everybody gives her a wide berth. On the night of his arrival, our narrator hears what he thinks is a storm. He ignores it at first, but it sounds like a big one. He gets out of bed—lots of description of his chamber—and looks out. He sees this scorched gulf cutting across the beach. Deep and black, he says, and the three goddesses on one side of it. He claims he felt the power shake the world, and the white sand flows over the split. As things settle, he looks up, as the goddesses are, and sees three new stars under the moon. More brilliant and beautiful than any star in any heaven and so on. Before dawn, Arianrhod appears in his chamber, they get it on. He's there three days and nights, and she comes to him every night."

"To conceive a child, part god, part sorcerer," Sasha concluded as Riley took a huge bite of sandwich.

Riley nodded, circled a finger in the air. "I figure maybe he comes off smug and pompous in his journal, but he had to have some qualities she valued and wanted. When he left, she gave him a ring with a brilliant white stone. The Stone of Glass, she called it, and told him she would send into his world a greater gift, one that would one day return to her."

"The child. Its descendants."

"Same page, Sash."

"It's sort of lovely. I'll get my sketchbook. It's stopped raining, so I'd like a walk, I'd like to get a sense of where we are, where Bran's home is, then I'll see if I can use your notes to sketch anything."

"I need to unpack and organize a little more."

"I've got dinner tonight, with Bran assisting. I thought I'd try my hand at Guinness stew. I'll make sure it's done before moonrise so you can eat before the fast."

"Appreciate it. Take the path you painted," Riley advised. "In the moonlight it was pretty fantastic. Going out from here's a winner, but coming back? Absolute champ."

Sasha rose, then stopped. "Bran wants me to meet his family."

"Well, sure."

"There are so many of them. And I'm— I'm this American woman they've never met, and who's only known Bran for—"

"Cut it out." Still eating, Riley sliced a finger through the air. "Stop putting up problems. Meeting the parents, et cetera? You can be a little anxious, sure, but, Jesus, Sasha, you're a freaking warrior. You're fighting gods here. This'll be a snap."

"I know I have to meet them—want to meet them," she corrected. "Eventually. I just don't want to mess anything up."

"Look at the man. He's pretty great, right?"

"Beyond that."

"And it's a pretty sure bet his parents had something to do with that. They're probably great, too. Relax."

"It's silly to worry about something like this when there's so much else to worry about."

"It's human," Riley corrected. "Can't get

around being human. Except for me, three nights a month."

Sasha smiled. "And even then. You're right. I'm putting this aside and away. Leave your notes there, and I'll see what I can do with them after I take a walk."

"Will do. And I'll be around if you have any questions."

Doyle walked to the cliffs, and as he had as a boy, climbed down the treacherous rocks, down the unstable hunks of turf. The boy had believed, absolutely, he'd never fall. The man knew he'd survive if he did.

He told himself he risked the fall—the pain of dying and resurrection—in order to survey the caves pocked in the cliff wall. However unlikely the star lay so close to hand, you didn't find until you looked.

But under the excuse, he knew full well he climbed, without rope or harness, simply because he'd done the same as a boy. He did so then, did so now, as the whip of the wind, the throaty roar of the sea, the slick and chilly face of the cliff exhilarated. To cling like a lizard high above the wave-tossed rock, defying death, gulping life like the salt-flavored air.

Oh, how he'd longed for adventure as a lad. To fight brigands, or to be one, to ride off to swing a sword against tyranny, to set sail on a journey to some undiscovered land.

Mind what you wish for, he thought as he paused on a narrow ledge to watch the lash and swirl of sea and rock below.

He'd had adventures, fought brigands—been one from time to time. Lived a soldier's life in war by war by war until he'd lost all stomach for it. He'd sailed, and he'd flown, to lands ordinary and exotic.

And Christ knew he'd grown weary of it all.

But he'd set himself on this quest, and set that course centuries before any of the other six had been born. He'd see it through.

And then...he had no notion whatsoever.

A quiet life for a time—but then he wasn't built for the quiet life. Traveling? But there wasn't a place in the world he had a burning desire to see again. He could entertain himself bedding women, as that desire always burned—though tedium could creep in when the spark guttered.

Whatever he did, however he did it, wherever he did it, he could never stay above a decade or so. Could never create bonds, even loose ones, as after a time people noticed a man who never aged a day.

And to those who wished for immortality, he'd again advise: Be careful what you wish for.

No point brooding over it, he reminded himself. His lot was his lot. But the trouble was once this quest was done, so was the companionship he'd, however reluctantly, come to prize.

Being part of an army equaled comrades, true enough. But being part of this? Part of six who lived and slept and ate and fought and bled together against such odds?

It made family.

Each of them, despite their talents and powers, would go through the natural cycle. They would age, they would die.

He would not.

And no point brooding over it, he thought again as he picked his way over the ledge to the narrow mouth of the cave he'd sought.

Once it had been his secret place—one where he could sit on this same ledge and dream his dreams with no one knowing where he was. He'd snuck tinder and tallow into it, honeycakes and mead. He'd dreamed, and he'd whittled, made wishes, had his sulks, watched the seabirds wing.

The mouth was smaller than he remembered, but wasn't everything? The boy had slipped easily inside, and the man had to work at it a bit.

It smelled the same—dank and delicious—and inside, the roar of the sea echoed so the air seemed to tremble with the sound. For a moment he crouched, shut his eyes, and smiled as in that moment he was transported back to simple, innocent boyhood, where the future lay ahead, all full of color and courage and chivalry.

Rather than the stub of a candle, he took out a flashlight, let the beam play.

Not so much smaller than memory, he

noted as he crab-walked back until he could stand—just barely stand. And there, the little jut where he'd kept a candle. Bending, he rubbed his fingers over the hardened pool of wax. And there, the tattered remains of the old blanket he'd stolen from the stables. It had smelled of the horses, and that had been fine with him.

The cave curved into a little chamber, what he'd designated as his treasure room, as the wall nearer the mouth angled to hide it.

There still lay the bounty of his childhood, like artifacts. The broken cup he'd pretended into a grail—perhaps one of Arthur's. Pebbles and shells hoarded in a chipped bowl, some copper coins, an old arrowhead—ancient even then—bits of rope, the knife he'd used for whittling—and had used to carve his name in the rock.

Again he used his fingers, tracing the name the boy had so painstakingly carved.

Doyle Mac Cleirich

Beneath it he'd done his best to carve a

dragon, as he'd designated the dragon as his symbol.

"Ah, well," he murmured, and turned away.

The beam of his light struck the shallow depression in the facing wall, and the tiny bundle of oilcloth.

"After all this time?"

He stepped over, drew it out, unrolled it. Inside lay the pipe he'd carefully made from a small branch of a chestnut tree. He'd imagined it magic, made for him— and only him—to call up the dragon. The one he, naturally, saved from certain death. The one who became his friend and companion.

Oh, to be a boy again, he thought, with such faith and so many dreams.

He brought it to his lips, placed his fingers over the holes, tested it. To his pleasure and surprise it carried a tune true enough. Mournful perhaps in the echoing cave, but true.

He allowed himself the sentiment, rolled it back in the cloth, and slipped it into his pocket.

The rest could stay, he thought. One day

another adventurous boy might find the treasures and wonder.

He climbed back up, leaving the cave, the memories, the sea.

When he swung over the wall, Sawyer hailed him.

"Hey! Did you climb down?"

"Having a look around."

Shoving up his cap, Sawyer leaned over, looked down. "Tricky. I've been having a look around myself—on more even ground. What do you think about setting up the targets over there?"

Doyle followed the direction. "In front of those gardens?"

"Yeah, well, you can't get away from the gardens, not really, unless we set up in the woods. We could do that, but this is more private. We've got a lot of land, but from what I gather, people can just sort of wander around, and some do. Back here, the noise from the water will mask gunshots."

"The private suits me, though I suspect Bran's well enough known around the area, and no one would make trouble."

Though he knew the ground well, Doyle

considered it.

"More room to spread out on the other side of the house, and we can use that for other training. But this would do well enough for weapons training."

"Good enough. Word is Riley's scored us the boat and gear."

"Has she?"

"She's got some network. I want to take a look at the maps, but I've scouted out the general area, gotten the lay of it."

"So you can get us back here from wherever we might go."

Sawyer jerked a thumbs-up. "No sweat. More word is Sasha's sketching from the notes you and Riley put together out of the journal, hoping for..." He circled his fingers in the air. "Don't know how that's going. And apparently you and I are on weapons detail, so since we've got the target area picked, we can set that up."

"After a beer."

"Can't argue with it."

The fact was Doyle found it hard to argue with Sawyer about anything. The man was affable, canny as a fox, unbreakably loyal, and could shoot the eye out of a gnat at twenty yards.

They went in through the mudroom, into the kitchen that smelled temptingly of whatever Sasha stirred in the pot on the stove as Riley looked on.

"Wow." As he had an interest in cooking as well as eating, Sawyer went over to her. "What is it?"

"Guinness stew. I found a couple recipes online, and I've been playing with them. I think it's going to work."

"Looks awesome. We're after a beer. Want some wine?"

"I think it's just about that time, thanks. I've been dealing with this, sketching. I think the cooking's more successful than..."

She turned, saw Doyle had picked up her sketch pad.

"It's hard to be sure I'm even close, considering I'm going on more or less general descriptions."

When he said nothing, she moved to him, studied, as he did, one of her sketches of Arianrhod. "I can't know if I made her beautiful because the journalist found her beautiful. I don't know the shape of her face, or the length and style of her hair, shape of her eyes. I just went on instinct, I guess."

"This is your instinct?"

The rawness in his voice had her looking up at him in alarm. She saw that same rawness in his eyes.

"Yes. What is it? What's wrong?"

"Dude." Sawyer stepped over, put a hand on Doyle's arm. "You all right?"

"I read the way she was described myself. It's from my reading Riley took the notes for you. And this is how you've drawn the goddess?"

"Arianrhod, yes. It's as close as I can imagine. It's—it's just how I saw her from the notes. Why?"

"Because...you've drawn my mother. This is my mother's face you've drawn in your book."

Chapter Five

Bittersweet. That was the term used, wasn't it? Doyle thought as he stared at the sketch. Those opposing sensations twisting and twining together until they merged into one shaky emotion.

He'd never understood it quite so well until now.

When he forced himself to look away, look up, he saw they'd surrounded him. Sawyer at his back, the women on both sides.

He had to fight the instinct to pull away.

"I won't ask if you're sure," Riley said carefully, "because it's clear you are. Sasha's sketched your mother from the description of Arianrhod."

Another internal battle—to hold Riley's

gaze, to keep everything steady. "My mother might have sat for this."

"There are others." Reaching down, Sasha turned pages in her sketchbook. Profiles, full face, full body.

He made himself take the book, flip through as if it meant nothing...personal. But Jesus, even the half smile in this sketch here, the one that said: I know you've been up to something.

His mother to the life.

"She never dressed so...elaborately, and would usually have her hair braided back or put up, but these might have been drawn of her when she was young."

"Could Sasha have, you know, picked up on Doyle's memories? Not on purpose," Sawyer said quickly. "But just felt them?"

"I don't think so. I really don't. Doyle wasn't around when I worked on these, and I used Riley's notes."

"I've got a theory."

Doyle glanced over at Riley. "Naturally."

Before she could speak, Annika came in with Bran, leading with her laugh.

"I like helping make magick. I'd like to— Oh, hello." Her quick smile faded when she focused in on the faces of her friends. "Something's wrong. Do we have to fight?"

"No, not now, but it's good we're all here. We can go over all this at once." Sasha held out a hand to Bran. "Let's sit over in the lounge by the fire."

"If there's a pint involved, I'm ready for that." As he took her hand, Bran glanced down at her sketches. "What's this now? Did you dig out some old photos?"

"What? No, I—"

"This is my grandmother—my mother's mother—to the life. Well, when she was twenty or so." As he reached for the sketchbook, he caught Doyle's hard stare. "What is it?"

"It's the sound of my theory ringing the damn bell," Riley said. "Your grandmother, Doyle's mother." Riley slapped a finger on the sketch. "Arianrhod."

"I see." Nodding slowly, Bran looked back at the sketch. "I feel I've missed a great deal."

"She's so beautiful." Annika angled around for a better look. "Is Doyle's mother Bran's grandmother, and also a goddess? I don't understand how this could be."

"I don't think so." Sawyer slid an arm around Annika's waist. "Let's get you some wine, and catch everybody up."

When they settled in the lounge, the fire snapping, drinks at hand, Riley remained standing. She rarely taught, and more rarely lectured—formally in any case—but when she did, she knew how to punch her points.

"I'm going to sum up, but first, Bran, you've read your ancestor's journal, the one you gave me."

"Of course. While it may have been written in purple, it gives a good first-hand accounting of the rising of the new queen, his time on the island. Some salt may be doused over the purple."

"I don't understand."

"Expressions," Sawyer told Annika. "I'll explain later."

"So you know he claims to have slept with Arianrhod—on all three of the nights he stayed on the island."

"Well, even gods and sorcerers have needs, and it was quite the party. I don't... Ah, I see. Of course." Leaning back, lifting his beer, Bran nodded to Doyle. "She wanted a child—a magickal child."

"Bloodline," Riley said. "A child she could one day send to Ireland, to continue the bloodline. Descendants of that child settled right here, others migrated. Your family's in Sligo."

"They are, most of them," Bran agreed. "And my grandmother's grandmother was a Clare woman, a witch from Quilty. Not far from here, as the crow flies. So it fits, very well, wouldn't you say? Brother?"

Doyle brooded into his beer. "I don't know of any witches in my family history. And I wasn't born immortal."

As, to her, his grief bled through the iron shield he'd erected, Riley might have felt for him. But she had to press. "No talk around the fire of a relation with the sight or the power to heal, to commune with animals?"

He shifted, shot her an annoyed look. "There's always talk. And it's Ireland, so..."

"Talk has roots somewhere. Regardless, you're not going to argue the facts. Sasha drew Arianrhod, and the resemblance to your mother, to Bran's grandmother is unarguable. We're connected, the six of us. Sasha connected us, every one, when she was still in the States, drawing and painting visions she didn't want to have. We all came to Corfu, at the same time. We all came together. You and Bran, you come from the same root, planted the night of the stars on the Island of Glass. And so do we all."

"We're all from her?" Annika asked.

"There are three goddesses. I doubt they'd have put all their eggs—pun intended—in one basket. Big celebration, lots of magickal people. Plenty, I imagine, of men who suited their needs. Shapeshifters, travelers, merpeople.

"Arianrhod came to Bran's ancestor on the night of the stars, the same night Nerezza cursed them," Riley continued. "The night the goddesses understood the seeds of—let's say misfortune—had been sown. So they took steps to conceive and create guardians. The six. Us."

"Six who carry their blood," Bran stated.

"Plenty diluted," Sawyer observed, "but you have to call it cool. We've got the blood of gods, man."

"They used us even then?" Doyle

demanded as insult—pure and hot—burned through the grief. "Sealed our fates? Determined my brother would die an agonizing death before he was really a man so I would be cursed with immortality?"

"I don't think so." To offset the rise of his anger, Riley spoke briskly. "I'm not claiming the gods can't be cruel, but I also don't believe they refine the details. You'd have had a run-in, somehow or other, with a force that turned you. Sasha might have embraced her gift all her life, but she'd still have ended up in Corfu. Me, too, even if I'd opted to write and teach rather than going for fieldwork.

"But yeah," she said after a moment, "they used us. They gave us some of themselves, and that part of the blood may have influenced us all to come together, to stay together, to risk what we're risking."

"And don't you think it's helped us beat Nerezza?" Sasha met Riley's eyes. "You think that, and so do I now. I'm so sorry, Doyle, and I wish I'd known or felt before you looked at the sketch. I wish there'd been a way to prepare you."

"It's not on you. I read the damn description, and didn't put it together." He could wonder now why it hadn't struck him, but there was no going back. "I don't like the idea that a trio of gods started my bloodline for their own purposes."

"You can take that up with them when we find the island." Riley shrugged. "Odds are they're still around, being gods. And I think odds are we're going to find the island from here, that it's going to be off this coast, just as it was for Bran and Doyle's mutual ancestor."

"I can swim out and look." Annika snuggled next to Sawyer. "Sawyer said he'd take me down tonight so I can swim. I can look, too."

"You can, but I don't think it'll be that easy."

"And it's not time," Sasha added. "No, not a vision, just logic. There's no reason for the island to reveal itself until we have the last star."

"Agreed." Now Riley dropped into a chair, slouched, and stretched. "We probably have some time before Nerezza comes after us, so we shouldn't waste it."

"Training starts tomorrow, dawn," Doyle said.

"Check. And I've lined up the boat and equipment. Do you know these waters, Anni?"

"Not very well, but I'll swim, and look. For caves."

"You got it." Riley toasted her. "So Annika's scouting, I'm on equipment, Bran's already working on more magickal supplies."

"Doyle and I are going to set up the target area," Sawyer put in.

"And I'll finish making dinner, try more sketching."

"I'll grab a bowl of that soup early," Riley told her. "I'd rather not cut it so close to the change again. Bran, any way you can do something on one of the doors so I can get back in on my own?"

"I can, and should have thought of it. I'll charm the door leading into the kitchen so you've only to step up to it."

"Thanks. Unless anybody has more to say, or needs me, I'm going to go use the gym for a while."

"You did hear training at dawn?"

Riley grinned at Sasha. "Entirely different. Hey, come up with me. We'll do some lifting."

"I'm going to lift a wooden spoon to stir the soup."

"I would go with you." Annika popped up. "I like the gym with the mirrors."

"Yes, I know. Come on."

"What will we lift?" Annika asked as she followed Riley out.

"I bet she finds a way to make pumping iron a game." Sawyer smiled after her, started to sip some beer, caught Sasha's glance.

"I've got something," he decided. "Be back in a couple minutes to set up, Doyle."

"I want a fresh pad." Sasha stood, moved out of the room with him. And left Doyle and Bran alone.

"My grandmother lives," Bran began. "She walks five miles daily, rain or shine, has a cat named Morgana, pesters my grandfather over his cigars, and enjoys a whiskey every evening. It will be a hard day for me when her time comes."

He paused, considered. "My family comes here from time to time, and came during the time I was having this house built. My grandmother walked the bones of the house with me in the early stages. She said to me: **'Boy, you've chosen well. This place has known love and grief, laughter and tears, as most have. But this place more than most. You'll honor that even as you make it your own.'**"

"She's a seer?"

"She's not, no. A witch, of course, but not a seer with it. She felt it, I think, felt what was here, as I felt it. Something that called to the blood. Yours calling to mine." Bran leaned forward toward friend, toward brother. "You lost your family, Doyle, some through cruelty, some through the natural order of things. I want to say you have family still."

"Whether I want it or not?"

Bran merely smiled. "Well now, we never can choose that, can we?"

He'd clicked with Bran, he had to admit it, quicker and easier than he'd clicked with anyone in recent, even distant memory. Something there, Doyle thought now, that had simply spoken to him.

In the blood.

"I'd stopped wanting it. Wanting family," Doyle said. "That's survival. For all your power, you don't know what it is to see centuries of sunrises, to know at each dawn there'll be no end for you, but there will for everyone who matters to you. If you let them matter."

"I can't know," Bran agreed. "But I know what's now matters, too. We're blood, and before we knew that, we were comrades and friends. I've trusted you with my life, and the life of the woman I love. I would trust you again. There's no closer bond than that."

The bitter in the bittersweet still sat hard in his belly. "They brought me back here, the gods, the fates."

"But not alone."

Nodding slowly, Doyle met Bran's dark eyes. "No, brother, not alone. So, here it started for me. It may be here we'll finish it."

As the day faded, Riley took a bowl of soup

up to her room. She ate while doing more research. Over the years she'd been to Ireland, and this part of Ireland many times on digs. With her parents as a child on studies.

There would be caves—on land, under the sea—and ruins and stone circles. Until she'd read the journal she'd leaned toward the star being in or around Clare— but had opened to the possibility it fell in another part of Ireland.

But now she was certain Clare held the star.

The Fire Star had been in a cave under the water. Part of a rock in an underground cavern. It had called to Sasha.

The Water Star, again in the water, but this time part of the water, waiting for Annika to find the statue of the goddess and form it back into its brilliant blue.

Pattern would suggest the water again. A cave or cavern in the cold Atlantic waters off the coast. Ice, cold. That fit, too.

Would it sing or call as the other stars had? Who would hear it? Her money, for now, was on Doyle. Possibly Bran, but Doyle had the deepest roots here.

She'd be keeping an eye on him, just in case.

Annika would scout—as only a mermaid could—in the sea itself. And while she did, Riley determined she would dig in her own way, through books, the Internet, maps.

If nothing else, they could start eliminating. If Sasha had a vision or two to give them some direction, some bread crumbs, so much the better, but to Riley's mind nothing replaced research and action based on it.

She lost herself in it, but this time—considering the race to strip down before the change—she'd set the alarm on her phone to go off ten minutes before sunset.

At its warning, she turned off her laptop, closed her books, opened the balcony doors.

No one and nothing stirred in her view. Under the best of circumstances, she much preferred to go through the change in private. Not just for modesty—though, hey, that counted—but because it was personal.

Her birthright, her gift. One she now believed had a connection to the three goddesses. Maybe she'd write a paper on it, she thought as she undressed, send it to the council. It could be someone had more information there. Information that might add to the whole.

Naked, she sat down on the floor in front of the fire as the sun sank in the west, over that cold Atlantic sea.

She felt it building, that rush, the breathless inevitability. Snaps of power, the first hints of pain. Alone, secure, she flowed into it, absorbed it, accepted.

Bones shifted, stretched. Pain, pressure, and a kind of joy.

Her spine arched as she rolled to all fours, as the dark pelt sprang up along her flesh.

She smelled the night, the fire, the smoke, her own sweat.

And with the night came the fierce triumph.

I am.

The wolf became, and inside it the woman rejoiced.

Fierce and free, she raced through the open doors, leaped over the rail into the cool night air, into the shimmering dark.

And landed on the ground, body quivering with impossible energy. Throwing her head back, she howled at the sky, then all but flew into the thick shadows of the woods.

She could run for miles, and often did in the first hour. She smelled deer, rabbit, squirrel, each scent as distinct and vivid as a photograph.

Even had she been starved, she would neither hunt nor feed. The wolf fasted.

She kept to the trees, instinctively veering away whenever she caught the scent of man or exhaust, heard the rumble of a car on a road. Though they would see only a wolf—what many would take for a large dog.

Lycans weren't the stuff of horror movies, shambling around on furry legs with nightmare faces and crazed eyes, desperate to rip the throats out of wayward humans.

As much as she loved popular culture, most werewolf movies and books bugged the crap out of her.

Whatever the roots of that lore, they'd been dug up long ago, when lycans had civilized, when rules were set. And any who broke those sacred rules were hunted in turn and punished.

At last she slowed, the manic energy burned off by speed so she could walk and enjoy the night. She explored as she went. Perhaps the forest held secrets or clues.

An owl called, low and long, a nocturnal companion. As she looked up, she saw its eyes gleam back at her. Above the trees, the moon sailed full and white. She let go her own call, just once, honoring it, then turned to take the journey back to Bran's house on the cliff.

She could have run and explored for hours yet, but dawn came early, and she'd need rest before it did. She thought of her family, her pack, so far away, and missed them like a chamber of her heart. Their scents, their sounds, that elemental bond.

Through the trees she saw the glimmer of lights, caught the scent of peat smoke, of roses. Everyone would be asleep by now, she thought, but they'd left lights on for her. Unnecessary, of course, but considerate.

She cast a glance back, tempted to get

in one more run, watched the owl swoop over the path, its wings spread wide in the moonlight. It pulled at her, as did the night. She nearly turned, raced back, but she caught another scent.

It, too, pulled.

So she moved to the edge of the woods, looked through the shadows to where Doyle stood in his family's graveyard.

The wind kicked just enough to billow his long coat while he stood, still as a statue in the drenching blue moonlight. His hair, dark as the night, tumbled around a face roughened by a few days' growth of beard.

In wolf form, where everything was heightened, she felt the lust she managed to tamp down otherwise. She could imagine his hands on her, hers on him, a tangle of hot bodies giving in to the animal and taking, just taking in a frenzy until needs were met.

And imagining, those needs clawed and bit inside her.

She quivered with it, shocked, angry at the intensity, at her inability to shove it down again.

She'd run after all, she thought, but before she could move, he whirled, the sword on his back out of the sheath and into his hand with a bright shiver of metal.

His eyes met hers. Hers, keen, caught the embarrassment, then the annoyance in his before he controlled it.

"You're lucky I didn't have the bow. I might've shot a bolt." He lowered the sword but didn't sheathe it. "I thought you'd be inside by now. It's past one in the morning."

As if she had a curfew.

"Bran dealt with the door, so you can get in on your own. And as you didn't think of it yourself, Sasha opened your bedroom door, shut the ones to your balcony."

He wanted her to go—she could plainly see—and her preference was to give him what he wanted, as she wanted the same. But he looked unbearably lonely standing there, the sword shining in his hand, with his family buried under his feet.

She moved toward him, through the headstones, over the uneven grass.

"I'm not after company," he began, but she simply stood, as he did, looking down at

the grave. Lichen had grown on the headstone, pretty as the flowers beneath it.

Aoife Mac Cleirich

"My mother," Doyle said when she sat
beside him. "I came back and stayed until
she died. My father, there beside her,
died two years before her. I wasn't here
for her when she lost him."

He fell into silence again, finally slid his
sword back in its scabbard. "At least you
can't talk me blind or argue." Doyle lifted
his brows when she turned her head, stared
coolly. "You do just that, at every possible
opportunity. You see there she was
sixty-three when she died. A good long
age for the times she lived in, for a woman
who'd birthed seven children. She out-
lived three of them, and each who left
the world before she did left a hole in her
heart. But she was strong, my mother. A
strong woman.

"Beautiful," he added. "You saw that
yourself from Sasha's drawing. But that
wasn't the image of her I've been carrying
with me all this time. That one was of age

and illness, of a woman ready to move on. I don't know if it's good or not to have the image replace that of her young and vibrant and beautiful. Does it matter at all?"

She leaned against him a little, a kind of comfort. Without thinking, he laid a hand on her head. And she let him.

"I believe there's an after. With all I've seen there's no choice but to believe it. And that's a hell for me knowing I can't reach it. But it's helpful to know they have. Or sometimes it's helpful. It's easier not to think of it at all. But today..."

He broke off a moment, took a breath. "You see there, how Annika laid the flowers and the stones on every grave here. On my mother's she put them down in the shape of a heart. Christ but Sawyer's a lucky man. He'll have a lifetime of sweetness. So Annika came out and gave them this respect, this sweetness, this remembrance. How could I not come and stand here, even knowing they're not here?"

He looked down, stared at his own hand a moment, then quickly lifted it off her head, stuck it in his pocket. "We need sleep. I'm going to work your asses off come morning." At her snort he gave her a thin smile. "I'll take that as a challenge."

He turned with her, walked back to the house and inside, switching off the kitchen light as they walked through.

Up the back steps, he as quiet as the wolf.

She veered off to her room, gave him one last look before nudging the door closed.

He walked to his own, wondering why he'd said so much, why he'd felt compelled to say so much. And why now he felt lighter of heart for having done so.

In his room he opened his doors to the night, lit the fire more for the pleasure of having one than for warmth. As a matter of habit, he propped his sword beside the bed, within reach, with his crossbow and a quiver of bolts beside it.

He expected no trouble that night, but believed, absolutely, in always being prepared for the unexpected.

He stripped down, switched off the lights. By moon and firelight he lay in bed, let his thoughts circle for a moment. But since they circled to the wolf, and the woman inside it, he shut them off as routinely as he had the lights. With a soldier's skill, he willed himself to sleep.

He often dreamed. Sometimes his dreams took him back to childhood, sometimes back to wars, sometimes more pleasantly back to women. But the dreams that chased through sleep flashed and burned. The witch's lair, his brother's blood, the shocking pain of the curse hurled at him that for one agonizing moment had seemed to boil him from the inside out.

Battlefields littered with the dead, more than a few by his own hand. The stench of war, so much the same whatever the century, the weaponry, the field. That was blood, death, fear.

The first woman he'd allowed himself to love, a little, dying in his arms, and the child she'd died for stillborn. The second woman he'd risked, a century later, growing old and bitter with it.

Dying, the pain of it. Resurrection, the pain of it.

Nerezza, the hunt, around the world, across time. Battling with five he'd come to trust. More blood, more fear. Such courage.

The slice of sword, the death song of a bolt, the snap of bullets. The scream of creatures unearthed from a dark god's hell.

The wolf, impossibly beautiful, with eyes like hot whiskey.

The woman, brilliant and bold, sharp and quick.

Those eyes—they compelled him to wonder.

Beside him the wolf curled, a companion in the night. Warm, soft, and bringing him an odd sort of peace. Dawn broke in bleeding reds and golds, striking the moon away with color and light. The wolf howled once.

Bittersweet.

And changed. Flesh and limbs, breasts and lips. A woman now, the tight, disciplined body naked against his. The scent of the forest on her skin, a beckoning in her eyes.

When he rolled to cover her, she laughed. When he crushed his mouth to hers, she growled, nails biting into his back. He took her breasts, firm and perfect in his hands, smooth as silk against his rough palms. Tasting of the green and the wild under his mouth.

Strong legs wrapped around him as she arched in demand. So he plundered, thrusting, thrusting, hard, fast, deep into the tight, the wet, while those eyes—wolf, woman—watched him.

He drove her, himself, next to madness. Drove mercilessly until…

He woke in the dark, hard as iron and alone.

He cursed, as for an instant the dream scent of her, forest wild, followed him.

The last thing he needed were sex dreams starring a woman who deviled him half the time. Until this quest was done, he needed to keep his mind, his body, his focus on the stars, on defeating Nerezza, on making sure the five who fought with him survived.

When that was done, he'd find a willing woman for a night of uncomplicated, impersonal sex. And then…

That was as far forward as he needed to think.

Restless, annoyed—he wouldn't have

dreamed of her if she hadn't come to stand with him in the graveyard—he rolled out of bed.

He could smell dawn, see its approach in the slight lessening of the dark. Naked, he strode to the open doors and through for air, for the fresh and the damp of it.

The faintest sound had him whirling, braced and ready to spring back for his sword. Down the terrace, facing the sea, Sasha stood at her easel, one of Bran's shirts over her own thin nightshirt. Bran, wearing only jeans, stood behind her while the light from their suite washed out and over them.

In it, Doyle could see the intensity on Sasha's face as she swept charcoal over the sketchbook.

Bran glanced down, angled his head. "You'll want some pants," he called out. "It appears we'll start the day with visions."

"I'll wake the others."

He dressed quickly and, considering the start of the day, grabbed his sword before going on. He knocked briskly on Riley's door, remembered the sun had yet to rise— any moment now—and just shoved the door open.

The wolf stood in front of a fire gone to embers, quivering. And let out a low, warning growl.

"Save it," Doyle snapped. "It's Sasha. No, she's fine," he added as the wolf poised to spring out of the room. "She's painting. Bran's with her. She—"

He broke off as the wolf threw back her head, let out a long moan. The eyes stayed fierce, locked on his, anger striking out. But under it was a helplessness that had him stepping back. Though he considered witnessing the transformation fascinating, he closed the door, gave her privacy.

He heard the howl, pain and triumph, as he hurried away to wake the others.

Chapter Six

As he saw no point in waiting for the others, Doyle went straight into the master suite in the tower. It opened into a gracious sitting room where the doors stood open to the sea terrace.

Bran glanced back at him.

"She woke—or came out of sleep—only a few minutes before you stepped outside. She said she needed her easel. I barely managed to get the shirt on her—it's so cool—before she was coming down here and starting."

He gestured Doyle closer, then to a table on the terrace. "She's done those already."

Doyle studied the charcoal sketches in the backwash of light. Another of Arianrhod, this in warrior garb, a sword at her side.

The others would be Celene and Luna. One a dark beauty, also dressed for battle, holding a bow, the other lovely as sunrise, a dove on her shoulder, a sword in her hand.

He saw something of his sisters—the oldest and the baby—in the dark one, felt that old, hard twist. And his lost brother in the other, so sweet of face, kind of eye.

Projecting, he told himself. Projecting as his family's stones projected from the ground. He stepped back as he heard Sawyer and Annika come in.

"Has she said anything?" Sawyer, his hair still tousled from sleep, moved in to look over Sasha's shoulder.

"She's deep in the drawing," Bran told him, "as you can see."

With Annika, Sawyer turned to the table.

"Oh!" Annika clasped her hands together. "It's my mother. I mean, it's my mother as this is Doyle's. This is how my mother looks."

"Some mother," Sawyer noted. "You look like the other one."

"I do?"

"The eyes. You have the same eyes as

the blond one. And, I've got to say, the blonde looks a lot like my grandmother— or photos I've seen of her when she was young. She was hot."

"Then your granny and my mother are twins," Riley said from behind Sawyer. "I'd say my theory's been as confirmed as it can be. Each one of us—because when Sasha's finished, one of these will ring for her—came from one of them."

"I think it's more."

Riley glanced at Doyle. "More what?"

"This could be a drawing of two of my sisters—not as exact as the Arianrhod to my mother, to Bran's grandmother, but it's striking. And this? The one who rings, as you call it, for you and Sawyer? My brother Feilim."

"Interesting. I say we take a close look, in better light, when Sasha's done." So saying, Riley picked up one of the sketches. "And see if there's more crossover."

"What?" Sawyer scratched his head. "We're all cousins?"

"Considering it's been maybe a millennium since this family tree took root? Yeah, I'm going with the crossover."

"This is so nice." Annika hugged Riley, then Doyle. "We're even more family now."

"We are of the blood." Sasha spoke as in the east the sky bloomed with light. "Conceived and born on the Island of Glass, suckled and nurtured by the mothers, by the gods, and sent from one world to another. Conceived with the stars, born with the moon, gifted and given. Wherever taken by the winds of fate, brought together, blood of the blood, a millennium plus two since the fall.

"The star waits, the Ice Star, frozen in time and place. Its day comes when the worlds still for five beats of a heart. Fire to see, water to feel, ice to fight, to take their place when the Tree of All Life blooms once more."

Drenched in visions, Sasha lifted her hand to the eastern sky. "And she waits, weak and cold, tended by her creature. She waits and gathers powers dark to strike at the heart, the mind, the body. This world will quake from her wrath. Seek the past, open the heart."

Now she lowered that hand, pressed it to her own heart. "Follow its path. Its light is your light. It waits. Worlds wait. She waits. Reach into yesterday, and bring them home."

Sasha lowered her arms, swayed. "I'm okay," she said when Bran put his arms around her. "But I could sit down for a minute."

"You're cold. Damn it. Inside with you. Annika, there's water in the wet bar over there."

"Wet bar?"

"I've got it." Riley dashed inside, pulled open the small cooler in back of the angled bar while Bran half carried Sasha to a chair in front of the fire he set blazing.

Annika pulled a deep green throw off a sofa, tucked it around Sasha's legs.

"Thanks. I'm really okay. It just kept going, stronger and stronger, then dropped away so fast." She took the water with another thanks, sipped. "Honestly, I'd kill for coffee. Why don't we go—Oh." When a thick mug appeared in Bran's hand, she smiled, her voice melting with love as she touched his cheek. "Bran. Don't look so worried. I'm fine."

"Your hands are cold," he told her, and

wrapped them around the mug.

"It all felt so urgent. I **had** to get the images down. I swear I heard their voices in my head, telling me to show them to you, to all of you. I saw them as clearly as I see all of you. And...I felt, I almost felt I could reach out and touch them."

She sipped coffee, sighed deep. "Your mother, you said, Anni, the brunette with the bow."

"It's so like her. She's very beautiful."

"And my grandmother—like Bran and Doyle's connection. I didn't know her—my mother's mother—when she was young. I barely know her at all, really. But I know it. The goddess is Celene, the seer, who created the Fire Star, to gift the new queen with sight and wisdom. Riley and Sawyer's closest connection is Luna—dove and sword—the Water Star, who gifted the queen with heart and compassion. And the last is Arianrhod, the warrior, for courage."

"And we six have some of all of them," Riley said.

"Yes. They chose a mate, conceived a child, guided, loved, nurtured, and sent the child, on their sixteenth birthday, from their world to ours. I felt their grief."

Annika knelt down, laid her head in Sasha's lap. "My mother wept when I left to come to you. She was proud, but she cried. It would be hard to send a son or daughter away."

"It was, and from that time, they could only watch. And to this time, they can only watch, and hope. It's hard to explain, but we're their children. They feel we are. We're their hope, what they began that night."

"The last drawing?"

Sasha looked up at Doyle. "A nightmare."

Riley stepped out, lifted the sketch pad, brought it back. "Looks like things are going to get hot."

With a weak laugh, Sasha looked at the sketch. They stood between house and cliff, armed in the dark night while Nerezza rode the firestorm. Flames rained from the sky, singeing the ground, the trees, opening fissures in the earth that yawned wide, vomited up more fire. It burned even her winged creatures that dived and slashed at the six.

On her beast, Nerezza hurled down spears of flame while her hair, black-streaked white, flew behind her. Her beauty calcified, like a sharp gem crusted with mold.

And the mold was madness.

"I can't say when she'll come like this, but she'll come. She wants the stars, craves them, but she'd destroy us even if that destroys her chances of getting them. When she comes, as she comes here, it's only to burn us to ash."

"I can work with that."

All eyes shifted to Bran, who stroked a hand over Sasha's hair. "I can certainly begin to. The firestorm here is more powerful, more vicious than what we dealt with in Capri. But foretold is forewarned, after all. And we'll be forearmed."

"I appreciate your optimism," Riley said. "But, you know, even witches burn. Historically anyway."

"That simple fact means we like to conjure protections and shields and spells against just that. And as this will be no ordinary fire, it'll take an extraordinary spell. I'll work on it."

He leaned down, kissed the top of Sasha's head. "For now, I believe it's Sawyer's round in the kitchen."

"After training," Doyle said flatly. "Train, then eat. With the exception," he said before Riley could speak. "As Riley needs fuel. Grab it quick," he told her, and looked down at the sketch again. "We've a lot of work to do."

To make it quick, Riley blended an energy smoothie—added in a couple of raw eggs. Not the tastiest, and certainly not what her appetite yearned for—but it would do the job.

He'd already started them on warm-ups—stretching, light jogging—by the time she stepped outside. Standing back for a moment gave her a different perspective of her team. Sasha looked a little washed out—small wonder—but game. Annika—well, Annika was Annika, laughing her way through squats and lunges. Bran and Sawyer? They'd both been in excellent shape when this whole deal started, but now? Ripped City. You had to admire it.

Doyle? The man had started out the sheriff of Ripped City. Though he looked a little rough around the edges to her eye, as promised, he began to work everybody's ass off.

She joined in, determined to work her own ass off. Fiery fissures in the ground, flames raining from the sky, and a very pissed-off god with psychotic tendencies served as one hell of a motivation.

Calisthenics followed by a five-mile run, and Riley broke a good sweat. She didn't complain when Doyle ordered them up to the gym. Hell, she was just getting started.

He split them into groups. Free weights, bench presses, pull-ups, switched them off, switched them again.

"How much can you handle?" he asked Riley when she lay on the bench.

"One thirty-five."

He gave her a dubious stare. "That's more than you weigh."

"I can press one-three-five. Five sets of ten."

He set the weights. "Show me."

She set, regulated her breathing, began.

By the last set her muscles burned like acid, and the sweat ran like a river. But she did her fifty.

"Not bad. Towel off, hydrate. You're up, Blondie."

"You're actually going to make me do that?"

"You're stronger than you think." But he adjusted the weights, dropped them down to ninety pounds. "Try that. Three reps to start. Rest, three more."

Guzzling water, Riley watched Sasha struggle through—grit and guts, and yeah, more muscle than she'd had a couple months before.

"Three more."

"You're a bastard, Doyle."

"You've got three more."

She had three more, then let her arms fall. "Can it be over?"

"Good work. Stretch it out. Hit the showers."

"Thank God." Sasha crawled off the bench, sat on the floor.

Riley took her a bottle of water, sat beside her. "You couldn't have done one rep of ninety the day you walked out on the terrace of the hotel in Corfu."

"I never dreamed of doing one rep of ninety. Ever. I like yoga, maybe some Pilates."

"Both excellent, in most circumstances. We're going to need to get in some tumbling practice with Annika later."

"Yeah, yeah. Let me wallow in this pool of my own sweat for a minute."

Riley poked a finger at Sasha's biceps. "You got guns."

Lips pursed, Sasha flexed. "I kind of do."

"Not kind of do. Girl, you are cut."

Sasha tipped her head to Riley's shoulder. "Thanks. I'd trade all of it for a two-hour nap followed by a gallon of coffee. But thanks."

"Come up." Rising, Riley held out a hand. "We'll hit those showers, get that coffee. I could chew the beans by this time."

By the time she'd showered off the night, the workout, dug out a sweatshirt, cargoes, pulled on her beloved Chucks, the smoothie was a distant memory. She needed food, and plenty of it. Coffee—enough to swim in.

She smelled the coffee as she jogged down the back stairs, followed that siren's song. Sawyer stirred something in an enormous bowl while Annika stirred something else in a smaller one.

Riley scowled at Sawyer. "I figured you'd have it fried up by now."

"Needed to shower."

"Sex in the shower is so nice," Annika said with an easy smile. "But it takes a little time."

"Great. A woman could starve to death while you're doing the slippery slide."

She dumped coffee in a mug.

"Pancakes, bacon, sausage, yogurt-and-berry parfait." Sawyer turned to the stove. "Set the table and you'll eat faster."

Riley grabbed plates, knowing if Annika could manage it, she'd add plenty of flourishes to the traditional setting. For herself, she was a lot more interested in bacon.

The minute Sawyer transferred some from pan to platter, she grabbed a slice, tossed it from hand to hand to cool it. The first bite burned her tongue, but it was worth it.

And when he flipped a pancake off the griddle, she rolled it like a burrito, chomped in. By the time the others wandered in, her pre-breakfast had cut her hunger down to tolerable.

Bran studied the table and the three bud vases Annika had added to it. She'd put a rose in each one—white, red, yellow, draped the vases in white napkins, tied at the "waist" with ribbon, added a wooden skewer for a sword.

"The three goddesses."

"I thought they should join us."

Bran gave Annika a grin. "The food looks fit for gods."

As she considered it more than fit for her, Riley sat, loaded her plate. "I'm going to dig back into the tower library. Anything specific in there on the stars, or the island?"

"The fact is I haven't read a fraction of what's in there, but I do know of a few. Various languages," Bran added. "I'll show you after breakfast."

"Weapons training at noon." Sawyer sampled his pancakes, approved.

"I'll be ready for the break. I'm on lunch today. It's going to be sandwiches."

"Hand-to-hand follows that." Doyle studied the pretty parfait suspiciously.

"It's good," Annika told him, scooping out a spoonful. "Sawyer says healthy, too. I made it."

His soft spot for her left him no choice but to try it. "It's good," he told her, though personally he could live his immortal life without ever consuming yogurt.

"I'll be working on defense and offense— magickally—in the tower, so I'm close if needed."

"I'm on maps," Sawyer said, "so me and my handy compass can get us wherever we need to go."

"Annika and I can help Bran, or Riley, or Sawyer—depending on what's needed." Sasha glanced over at her chart. "Annika's in charge of laundry."

"I like laundry. It's fun to fold, and it smells good."

"It's all yours," Sasha told her. "Since the place is so big, I assigned everyone to different sections for basic cleaning." She lifted her eyebrows at Doyle. "Team morale stays higher if we live and work in a clean house."

"I didn't say anything."

"Out loud," she qualified. "And you're on dinner tonight."

He grunted, glanced at Bran. "Where do I get pizza around here these days?"

"Well now, I'm thinking you'd likely have to go clear into Ennis for it, unless you're meaning frozen. It may be there's closer, but none I know of offhand."

"Ennis then. I'm past ready to get the bike on the road anyway."

"It's a village? With shopping?" Annika all but bounced in her chair. "I can go with you. I like the bike."

Riley didn't trouble to hide her smirk, and inspired Doyle for his out. "I'll take you out for a ride after breakfast." He liked her company, and enjoyed her pure delight in riding pillion. "But if I'm heading all the way to Ennis, Sawyer should go along. We need ammo."

"Then you need Riley." Reaching for the coffeepot, Sawyer missed the looks of annoyance from both Doyle and Riley. "She's the one with the connections. I did inventory there," he continued. "Got a list for you. I don't know if your connections go this far, but I was thinking. The way this place is set up, we've got some excellent vantage points from inside. If we had a couple of long guns with scopes."

"The towers." Thinking it through, Riley nodded. A good long-range weapon, a good shooter—yeah, it could be an advantage. "You any good with a rifle, Dead-Eye?"

"I hold my own. You?"

"Yeah, I hold my own, too. I'll make some calls."

After breakfast, she flipped through a couple of the books Bran pulled for her. She decided she'd work through the ones written in English first, then tackle the one handwritten in Latin—could be fun. And finish with the two in Gaelic, as she wasn't as fluent there.

She set up her laptop, her tablets, pulled out her phone. Started making calls.

Forty minutes in, Doyle surprised her. She'd figured he'd find almost anything to do but join her in the library venture. With the phone at her ear, she pulled one of the books out of her stack, shoved it across the table, circled her finger.

"No problem at all," she said into the phone. "But I'd want to look them over, test them out." She rose, wandered to the window and back as she listened. "Fair enough. I've got a list of ammo. If you can supply us there, it may be we can work out what you'd call a volume discount." Now she laughed. "Don't ask, don't tell, Liam. Sure, hang on."

She dug Sawyer's list out of her pocket, began to read it off. She rolled her eyes to the ceiling, picked up her water, drank. "Like I said, we're a kind of club, having what you could call a tournament of sorts. Reach out to Sean. He'll vouch for me. No question about that, but he's no more full of shit than the next guy. Like I said, I worked with him in Meath on the Black Friary, and again about three years ago on Caherconnell in the Burren. Check with him and let me know. Yeah, this number. Later."

She hung up, blew out a breath. "We're going to score there, but it's going to take another hour or two to confirm."

"Another gunrunner connection?"

"Not exactly, but this Liam's got

connections to certain people who'd supply certain products."

"But he doesn't know you."

"Not directly. He's the cousin of the ex-girlfriend of an associate of mine. My associate, the ex, and the cousin remain friendly, seeing as my associate intro-duced the ex to her husband, with whom she has two kids, and the cousin is godfather to the oldest. My associate and the cousin hunt together once or twice a year. The cousin also runs a kind of side business, cash only, out of his barn, which is, handily, only about twenty kilometers east of Ennis. This works out, we get pizza, guns, and ammo in one trip."

Not on his bike, Doyle thought with disappointment. So it would mean taking Bran's car. "I'm driving."

"Why is that? I know the roads better."

"And how is that?"

"Because I've been here in the past decade and, in fact, consulted for a time on the Craggaunowen Project, which we'll pass on the way to this barn."

"Then you can navigate, but I'm driving."

"We'll flip for the wheel."

"No."

"You prefer rock, paper, scissors?"

He didn't dignify that with an answer, and just continued to read. "This accounting is worthless. It talks of four sisters—in Ireland—charged with guarding an infant queen. Three were pure, and one was lured by a dark faerie, who with promises of power and eternal beauty, turned her against the other three."

"Not worthless," Riley disagreed. "Just the Telephone Game of Time. The root's there."

"Well tangled. It says the three good sisters hid the infant in a castle of glass on an invisible island, and flew to the moon, becoming stars. And in her rage, the fourth sister struck them down from the heavens, blah, blah. One fell as lightning, striking the earth with fire, another into the sea in a swirling tempest, the last into the north where it covered the land with ice."

"Not that far off."

He spared her a single look that mixed equal parts annoyance and frustration. "Far enough when you've got the queen—

apparently growing up fast—flying from the invisible island on a winged horse to do battle with the evil sister, vanquishing her and turning her to stone."

"Shake out the probable hyperbole, and you find roots. Nerezza materialized out of a stone column in a cave on Corfu."

Doyle put the book aside. "I've lived a long time without seeing a winged horse."

"I'll bet you lived a long time without seeing a Cerberus until recently."

He couldn't argue that. And still. "It's a Brothers Grimm version, and bastardized at that."

"Retellings get bastardized and elaborated," Riley pointed out. "That's why you dig out the root. Four sisters." She held up four fingers. "Four goddesses. It's not the first time I've heard or read of them being sisters. It may be they are. Invisible island, Island of Glass, appears and vanishes as it wills. Three stars—fire, water, ice."

"It doesn't add anything."

Civilians, she thought, with some pity. "Not yet. Being thorough may be tedious, Doyle, but being thorough's how you find what's been overlooked or discounted. There are worse things than sitting in a comfortable chair in a library reading a book."

"A little sex and violence in it would keep it from being so tedious."

"Read on. You could get lucky." Her phone signaled, and she smiled at the readout. "I'm betting we just did. Hello, Liam," she said, and wandered back to the window as she brokered the deal.

Since she clearly had it handled, Doyle went back to the book. He could be grateful, at least, that the particular story in it was fairly short. Though the queen defeated the evil sister, the loss of the others, the stars, grieved her. She returned to her island, exiling herself until prophet, siren, and warrior lifted the stars from their graves so they shined again.

He pulled over Riley's pad, scribbled a note.

He started to flip through, see if another story in the book of folklore addressed the stars, then set the book down when Sawyer came in.

"Okay if I use the other half of the table?

I want to try out the maps in here."

"No problem. In fact, I'll work with you, leave the books to Gwin."

"That's not all you can leave to Gwin." Riley smiled, smug, as she pocketed her phone. "I just scored us all the ammo on your list, Dead-Eye."

"The underwater rounds, too?"

"Yeah, them, too. And I got us a pair of Ruger AR-556, along with two dozen thirty-round mags."

"Never shot that model," Sawyer said.

"Me either. The deal's contingent on me looking them over, testing them out. But I googled it while he was talking, and they should be more than fine. Doyle and I can pick them up, along with the ammo, swing back, get the pizza, and we're set."

"Unless you want to go along," Doyle put in. Send the two of them, he thought, and spare him the drive with Riley.

"Wouldn't mind, but no way I'd talk Anni out of coming if I did." Sawyer's eyes, gray as fog, showed both fear and humor. "Then she's loose in Ennis. Shopping."

"Forget it. There and back. Good thing I hit an ATM in Capri or I'd be light on my share." Riley checked the time. "I'm going to dive in here until noon."

"I'll be working with Sawyer on the maps," Doyle told her.

"Fine." She sat, frowned at his scribbled note. "What's this about prophet, siren, and warrior?"

"According to the fairy tale you had me slog through, the queen's exiled herself on her island until they find the stars and let them shine again."

"Always a root," Riley muttered, picked up the book herself.

And happily gave herself over to digging.

Chapter Seven

Sporting a few bruises from hand-to-hand—Sasha was becoming fierce—Riley tossed a small pack over her shoulder, headed out to Bran's car.

She preferred to drive rather than ride, honestly didn't understand anyone who didn't. But Doyle had called it first, and as one who respected dibs, she climbed in the shotgun seat, prepared to relax.

Ireland had excellent scenery, and when you drove—at least the way she did—you didn't have a chance to enjoy it.

When Doyle got behind the wheel, she decided she'd be friendly.

"Too bad we can't take the bike. How was the ride with Anni?"

He backed up, swung around, headed

down the bumpy drive toward the road. "There's a village about eight kilometers off the route I took. It has a couple shops. I'm still wondering how she talked me into turning off and stopping."

"She has breasts."

"She's another man's woman."

"Who still has breasts. And a whole truckload of charm." She shifted to take the weight off her left hip.

"You took a good spill toward the end of hand-to-hand."

"Sasha's craftier than she used to be. My mistake for holding back."

"Bran could have taken care of any bruises."

"You don't have a few bruises, it wasn't a good fight."

The world was beautiful here, she thought. Untamed and rugged even with the rolls of green, the bundles of cropping sheep. It had a wild, timeless feel that had always spoken to her.

The farmer in the field with his tractor— hadn't his ancestors cultivated that same field with plow and horse? And the simple art of those stone walls. Hadn't those stones been dug and pulled out of those same fields by hands now buried in graveyards?

Take away the paved road, the cars, the scatter of modern houses, and it wouldn't look so very different from when Doyle had lived here. Which was something, she thought, he was bound to feel.

Above, the sky had gone from soft blue to sulky with clouds. They drove into rain, then out again.

"Biggest invention or discovery."

He spared her a frown. "What?"

"What's your pick for most important invention or discovery—since you've seen a bunch of them in three centuries—to date."

"I'm not looking to take a quiz."

"It's not a quiz, it's a question. I'm interested in your opinion on it."

He might have preferred silence, but knew her well enough now to know she'd keep at him. "Electricity, as it opened the door to other advances that needed it."

"Yeah, a big leap. I go with fire—the discovery. But for technology, can't argue with electricity."

"If you're going back to the dawn of time—which is well before mine—you'd have the invention of common tools, the wheel."

"Discovering salt and its uses," she added. "Herbal medicines, learning how to make brick, cut stone, build wells and aqueducts. Did you go to school? You're going to want to take a left on the road coming up."

He made the turn, said nothing.

"It's tough for someone in my line of work not to have some curiosity about a man who's lived through eras I've studied. That's all."

"I had schooling."

"I wondered if, given the amount of time and opportunities, you'd gone for more education."

"I learned when something interested me."

"Uh-huh." The road narrowed, wound, and snaked. She loved these kinds of roads, the quick turns, the hedgerows, the blurry flash of a dooryard garden. "Languages. You've got a good head for languages."

"I've been looking for the stars longer than you've been alive. Longer than your grandmother's been alive. So I've traveled. Traveling's more productive if you speak the language."

"No argument. Next road, right. Why a sword? You're a solid shot with a gun."

"If I'm going to kill a man, I'd rather look him in the eye. And," he said after a long beat of silence, "it helps me remember who I am. It's easy to forget."

"I don't think so. I don't think you ever forget."

He didn't want to ask, had deliberately **not** asked. But now couldn't stop himself. "Why did you come to the graves last night?"

"I was heading back and I saw you. I respect the dead, who and what they were, what they did, how they lived, what they left behind. You said they weren't there. You're right, and you're wrong."

"How can I be both?"

"They've moved on, recycled, which is how I think of reincarnation. That's how the system works for me. But they're still there, because you are. Because the land they lived on, they worked on, where they built a home and a life, it's there."

Riley kept her eyes on the scenery as she spoke because she felt it would be easier for him. "There are trees in the forest that lived when they lived, and they're still there.

"The Craggaunowen Project, where I consulted? It's not far from here. Neither is Dysert O'Dea, both amazing places. There are countless places absolutely amazing in Ireland, because it respects its history—its long and layered history—and those who came before, what they did, how they lived and died. That's why you can feel them here, if you let yourself, and other places in the world are voids because in those places everything's about what's next, and nobody much cares about what was."

She gestured. "That's the place. Big white barn, old yellow house—and okay, really big brown dog."

"You should be able to handle a dog."

"Never met one I couldn't. And I'll handle Liam and the deal."

Doyle pulled into the long gravel drive where the house was set well back, and the barn farther back still. The dog let out a series of deep, throaty warning barks, but Riley climbed out, gave the dog a long look as it stiff-legged toward her.

"Knock it off, big boy."

"Sure he only takes small bites." The man who stepped out of the barn wore a tweed cap over tufts of steel-gray hair, and a baggy cardigan and jeans over a bone-thin frame. He grinned, hands on his narrow hips, obviously amused.

Riley opted to set the tone, grinned back, then gestured to the dog. "Come on and have a sniff, pal."

The dog's tail wagged, two slow tick-tocks. He stepped to her, sniffed her legs, her orange Chucks, then licked the hand she held at her side.

"Well now." Liam strolled forward. "That's a new one altogether. While it's true enough he won't take those bites unless I tell him, he isn't one to make friends with strangers."

"Dogs like me." Now that they'd settled the matter, Riley leaned over, gave the dog a quick, rough stroking. "What's his name?"

"He's our Rory. And who's your guard dog this fine afternoon?"

"This is Doyle, part of my team." She

offered Liam a hand.

"It's good to meet you, Dr. Riley Gwin, who our friend Sean says is as smart and quick as they come. And you, Doyle..." He let it hang as he offered Doyle his hand.

"McCleary."

"McCleary, is it? My mother, she married a James McCleary, and lost him in the Second Great War. He left her a widow and a babe in her belly—and that would be me brother Jimmy. She married my own father some three years later, but we've McCleary relations. Do you have people here, Doyle McCleary?"

"Possibly."

He pointed a long, bony finger. "I can hear some of the Clare under the Yank. And you, the famous Dr. Gwin."

"A mongrel, like Rory, but with some of the roots in Galway and Kerry."

"Mongrels, I find, are the smartest and most adaptable. And how long do you plan to be staying in Ireland?"

As she knew the country need for conversation, Riley stood hip-shot and relaxed with the dog leaning companionably against her leg. "Hard to say, but we're enjoying the time. We're on the coast, staying with a friend. Bran Killian."

Liam's eyebrows shot up. "Friends with the Killian, are you? An interesting lad—a magician, it seems. Rumors abound."

"I'm sure he enjoys that."

"Quite the place he has on the cliff, I'm told, and built on what was, long ago, McCleary land. Are you connected there, Doyle?"

"Possibly."

"Doyle's not as keen on digging up the origins as I am," Riley said easily. "You're an O'Dea, an old name, and a prominent one. It's likely your father's people lived in Clare, maybe in the villages that carried your name. Dysert O'Dea, Tully O'Dea. The old name was O'Deaghaidh, and means searcher, likely a nod to your clan's holy men. You lost a lot of land in the rebellions of the seventeenth century."

"Sure Sean said you were quite the scholar." Liam's faded blue eyes danced with amusement. "My mother was born Agnes Kennedy."

Okay, she thought, I'll play. "Kennedy's Anglicized from the nickname Cinnéide or

Cinneidigh. **Cinn**, meaning head, **eide** translates to grim or to helmeted. Cinnéide was nephew to the High-King Brian Boru. There's a record of O Cinnéide, Lord of Tipperary, in the **Annals of the Four Masters**, twelfth century."

She smiled. "You come from prominent stock, Liam."

He laughed. "And you've an impressive brain in your head, Dr. Riley Gwin. Well now, I expect you want to do some business, so we'll go into the barn and see what we have for you."

The barn smelled of hay, as a barn should. It held tools and equipment, a skinny, ancient tractor, a couple of stalls. A refrigerator that had surely been plugged in the first time in the 1950s—and, Riley imagined, held beer and snacks.

In the back, the sloping concrete floor led to a small, orderly arsenal. Rifles, shotguns, handguns stood in two large gun safes. Ammunition, and plenty of it, stacked on metal shelves. A long workbench held the tools for making shotgun shells.

"Make your own?"

Liam smiled at Riley. "A hobby of mine.

This would be your interest today." He took a Ruger out of the safe, started to pass it to Doyle. Riley intercepted.

She checked its load—empty—tested its weight, aimed it toward the side wall.

"Not to speak out of turn," Liam said, "but that's a lot of gun there for a woman of your size."

"There was a drunk in a bar in Mozambique who thought I was too small to object when he put his hands where I didn't want them." She lowered the gun, offered it to Doyle. "He and his broken arm found out differently. Can I see the other?"

"Mozambique," Liam said, chuckling, then passed her the second rifle.

"I haven't shot this model before. I'd like to test it."

"You'd be a fool if you didn't." Liam took two mags from the shelf. "Out the back, if you don't mind." He offered ear protectors. "The wife's doing some baking in the kitchen. Just let me give her a text so she knows what we're about."

They went out the rear of the barn where the land gave way to fields and stone fences, and a pair of chestnut horses grazing on the green.

"They're beauties," Riley said.

"My pride and my joy. Not to worry, as they're used to the noise, as is our Rory here. I like to shoot some skeet out here, and kill some paper targets as well."

He gestured to fresh circle targets pinned to wooden planks, backed by thick stacks of hay.

"These have a good long range as you know, but as you're not familiar with the gun itself, you may want to move closer."

"This is close enough." About fifty yards, she judged, and when it came to the real purpose, she'd want to shoot true a great deal farther. But this would do.

She slapped the mag in place, lifted the weapon, took her stance, sighted. She'd expected the kick, and the rifle didn't disappoint.

She missed the bull's-eye, but by no more than an inch.

"Well done," Liam said, pleased surprise in the tone.

Riley adjusted, fired again, hit the center. "Better," she murmured, and shot a more than respectable grouping of five.

"It's quick," she decided. "I like the hand grip, the trigger pressure. It's got good balance, and doesn't weigh me down." She glanced at Doyle. "Your turn."

He did as Riley did, loaded the second rifle, set, fired. Caught the outside of the first white ring, plugged one inside it, managed a decent grouping if not as tight or accurate as hers.

"It'll do." Doyle ejected the mag.

"Well now, since you're making it so easy, I'll throw in cases for them. Anything else I can show you for your...tournament?"

"These do the trick—along with the ammo we discussed."

"Some tournament you're having." But Liam left it at that, and the deal was struck.

They loaded the guns in their canvas cases, the ammo, in the back of Bran's car, covered it all with a blanket before saying their good-byes to Liam and the dog.

Riley kicked back in her seat. "You're a decent shot with a long gun, but you pull a hair to the left."

Since he knew she was right, he didn't respond. "Did you pull that data about his name, his mother's name out of your ass?"

"Out of my brain," she corrected. "You can look it up. I did refresh myself with his surname before we headed out—in case. Kennedy? That's an easy one. Mostly, if I read something, study something, I remember it. Or enough of it. It's interesting, isn't it, he has McCleary relations, and given the location, it's more than likely they cross with yours."

"Just a coincidence."

"You may want to believe that, but you've lived too long to believe it. Too many crosses with you here, McCleary. The land, the site of the house, the most direct connection with Arianrhod. Our prophet finds the Fire Star, our siren the Water Star. You're a sword-wielding warrior, pal. My money's on you for the ice. And if Nerezza makes the same connections, she'll come at you the hardest."

"Let her."

"We'll take her down. I damn well finish what I start, and I swear I'd like to go all Black Widow on her ass. But I'm reading the signs, heeding, we'll say, the seer, so it's most likely going to be you. A sword ends her—so says the prophet."

"If I do, it'll be the biggest pleasure of my life. And I've had more than a few."

"Really?" Since he'd opened the door, she shifted to face him. "So it's not all dour and dark in immortal land?"

"You're a pain in the ass, Gwin."

"I have a medal. Truth," she said when he flicked her a glance. "It's a silver disk with Plta engraved on it. A professor I had as an undergrad gave it to me. I wore it when I gave the valedictorian address. I worked with him on a dig about five, six years after, and we ended up sleeping together one night."

"Just one?"

She only shrugged. "Nothing there, on either side. We decided we'd been attracted to each other's brain, and the rest didn't work. It was just weird." She pointed at him. "Weirdest sexual encounter."

"No."

"Come on!" she said with an easy, appealing laugh. "I slept with my anthropology prof's brain in a tent in Mazatlán. Balance it out."

He wanted to laugh, barely restrained it.

"All right, at random. I slept with a woman who performed in a traveling circus. Tightrope walker, aerialist."

"What was weird about it?"

"She was crazy as a rabid cat, claimed she was really a snake who'd taken human form in order to procreate."

"Huh. What century?"

"Ah…" That took a little thinking. "The nineteenth, early nineteenth, if it matters."

"Just curious. What part of her did you sleep with? Yeah, yeah, all of her, but I mean like my professor's brain."

"She was fearless."

"That may have been the crazy, but fearless appeals. Pull over."

"Why?"

"Pull over," she repeated.

Though he muttered, he swung over to the excuse for a shoulder. "If you need to piss, we'll be in Ennis—"

"See that bird?" she interrupted. "On the signpost."

"I see the bloody raven."

"It's not a raven, and it's the seventh I've spotted since we left the barn."

"It looks like a damn raven." But he felt a

prickle along the back of his neck as the bird sat, the bird stared. "And there are more than seven ravens in the county of Clare."

"It's not a raven," she said again, and shoved out of the car.

When Doyle saw her pull her gun from under her shirt, he pushed out quickly. "You're not going to shoot a goddamn bird just for—"

As he spoke, the bird screamed, flew straight for them. Riley shot it in midair, turned it to ash.

"Not a raven," she said yet again, spun around, shot two others who came at them from the rear.

"I stand corrected."

"Damn right." She waited, watching, but no others came. "Scouts. She must be feeling better." After holstering the gun, Riley turned back to the car.

Doyle took her arm. "How did you know what it was? I've got eyes, same as you."

"Moon or not, the wolf's always in me. The wolf knows when a raven's not a raven." She took a moment, leaned back against the car, looked out over the near field where sheep cropped among gravestones and the ruin of what she judged had been a small chapel.

And the quiet was glorious, like a deserted cathedral.

"Don't you wonder who built that, and why there? Who worshipped there, what they worshipped?"

"Not really." But the pettiness of the lie stuck between his shoulder blades. "Yes," he corrected, "now and then, if I walk through a place. You're right when you say you can feel what and who were there before. In some places, at some times."

"Battlefields, I find, especially. Ever been to Culloden?"

"Yes, in 1746."

She pushed off the car, eyes alight, and now she gripped his arm. "April 16? You were **there**? Actually there, in it? Oh, you've got to tell me about that."

"It was bloody and brutal and men died screaming. That's any battle."

"No, but—" She stopped herself. He didn't tell war stories, but avoided them. "You could at least tell me which side you were on."

"We lost."

"You were in the Jacobite army, in the rising." Completely fascinated, she stared up at him. "Captured or killed?"

"Captured and hanged, and it's an unpleasant experience."

"I just bet. Did you—"

When he drew away, skirted the hood, she decided to detour from wars before he just shut down. "Most important societal advance," she said when she got in the car.

"I don't think about it."

"You have to live in society."

"I try not to."

"Sociopolitical movements, whether or not they spark and result from revolution, form past, present, future. The Magna Carta, the Elizabethan Religious Settlement, the Bill of Rights, the Emancipation Proclamation, the New Deal. And you can go back to—"

He gripped her shirt at the shoulders, lifted her out of her seat. The movement, completely unexpected, had her falling into him. He had his mouth on hers before she could react.

Then her reaction was elemental, as his

mouth was hot, a little frenzied, and stirred needs barely buried. His mouth was rough; so were his hands.

And that was just fine.

He'd snapped, no question, but at least now he had something he wanted. A taste, a release, however they incited more hunger. He'd known, just known, she'd grab on rather than pull away. Known she'd cover him in that wild and earthy scent.

He gripped her hair now, the carelessly sexy chop of it, and took his fill.

Then released her, plopping her back in her seat as abruptly as he'd yanked her out of it.

She'd have sworn her insides sizzled, but kept her voice steady. "Well, that was interesting."

"I had an itch, and you make it worse because you won't shut the hell up."

"Intellectual curiosity isn't a flaw in my world." Mildly insulted, she gave his shoulder a sharp poke. "I defy anyone sitting next to a three-hundred-year-old man not to have questions."

"The others don't badger me with them."

"If Annika badgered you, you'd find it

charming. And who can blame you? Sawyer, he's got a way of figuring out what he wants and needs to know with the subtle. If Bran hasn't asked you some direct questions in a one-to-one, I'm a dancing girl from Tupelo. And Sasha doesn't have to ask, but when she does, it comes off—I don't know—next thing to maternal."

He waited a beat. "Tupelo?"

"They have dancing girls. Hold on." This time she just opened the window, hitched up, and shot the black, staring bird off the sign-post where it perched.

Satisfied, she put her gun away, closed the window, sat back. "Now what?"

Was it any wonder he had this damn itch?

"Now we go pick up some pizza."

"Sounds right."

Better to pretend it never happened. That's what Doyle told himself. They drove into the village in blissful silence—since Riley took out her phone, began scrolling something or other.

It took some doing to maneuver the

narrow streets thronged with traffic, with pedestrians swimming over the sidewalks.

He supposed tourists found it charming— the pubs, the shops, the painted walls, the flowers spilling out of baskets.

For himself, he preferred the open.

Still, unlike Annika, Riley didn't exclaim over every shop window they passed— from the car or on foot once they parked.

She moved briskly, a woman on a mission, a trait he appreciated.

"Should be ready," she said as they weaved through the pedestrians taking advantage of a pretty day. "I texted our order from the road."

Something else to appreciate, he admitted. She thought ahead, didn't waste time.

She'd ordered four large, a variety, and since it was his turn to provide dinner, waited for him to pay. She carried half as they navigated back to the car.

They loaded pizza boxes with the weapons.

"I've had a lot of time to acquire funds and what I need."

She angled her head, tipped down her sunglasses, stared at him.

"I can all but hear the questions rolling around in your head. Where do you get your money, McCleary? What do you do with it? What do you think about the evolution of the tax system?"

"Didn't ask." She poked a finger in his chest. "Sir Broody."

"You will. I may have scared you off for the moment, but you'll start up again."

Now she grabbed his shirt, a fast fistful, rose up as she jerked him down. Caught him in a hard, challenging kiss.

"Do I look scared?" Flicking him away, she opened her door, got in.

He'd baited her, Doyle admitted. Deliberately baited her because he'd wanted another taste, another rush of her.

Now let that be enough, he warned himself.

He got in, pushed the start button.

"I don't badger."

He maneuvered out of the crowded lot, onto the crowded street. "It's the word that pisses you off."

"The insinuation of the term, yeah. I'm wired to learn, and you've got centuries of knowledge and experience stored up. But

I get there's knowledge and experience you don't particularly want to revisit. So it's a pisser to have what's natural to me termed as something rude and heartless."

"You can be rude, I don't mind that. I've never thought heartless."

He could breathe clear again when they drove out of the crowds, into the hills and fields.

"I admire the Declaration of Independence," he said, "as a document created from human intellect, courage, and compassion."

"I agree. Thanks." Again she tipped down her glasses, gave him a smile with her eyes. "Best era for music."

"You're daring me to say the time of Mozart or Beethoven, and it was a time xof brilliance and innovation."

"No argument."

"But I'm going to say the mid-twentieth century and the birth of rock and roll, because it's tribal, and it comes from the loins. It's seeded in rebellion."

She pushed her glasses back up, sat back. "You have potential, McCleary. You have potential."

Chapter Eight

Since Sawyer stepped out of the house when Doyle pulled up, Riley called him over.

"Mission accomplished," Sawyer said while Riley pulled out the pizza boxes. "Bran and I kicked around where to store all this—other than the pizza. We figured the sitting room, second floor, north side."

"Attack comes at night, better on the bedroom level." Riley nodded. "I've got dinner. You guys get the rest."

She carried the boxes straight back to the kitchen, saw Annika and Sasha sitting out on the cliff wall drinking wine. Deciding she'd earned herself a glass of same, she poured one, stepped out.

"You're back." In invitation, Sasha patted

the stones beside her. "Have a seat."

"Sounds good, but you may want to come in, see what we bought."

"I like pizza." Annika jumped nimbly from the wall. "But I don't think you bought something fun like a new dress. The rest is guns."

"Yeah, and I know you don't like them, but you should know what they are and where they are." Riley looked at Sasha. "And you're totally Katniss with the crossbow, but you need to be familiarized with the Rugers."

"You're right." Sasha slid down, gave Annika's hand a squeeze. "It was a nice break, to just sit for a while."

"See any ravens?" Riley asked.

Sasha frowned. "Ravens?"

"I'll explain. We actually picked up more than pizza and guns, in the information department." She led the way in, considered, then grabbed the bottle of wine to take upstairs.

"While you were gone," Annika began, "Sasha and I helped Bran. He's making a fire shield."

"Cool. Is that a shield against fire, or a

shield **of** fire?"

"Both! You're so clever."

"If he pulls that one off, I'd say Bran wins the clever award." She headed for the sound of male voices, and into the sitting room—handy between her room and Doyle's—where the three men loaded boxes of ammo into an antique display cabinet.

"Edwardian," Riley noted. "Circa 1900. Nice."

"You do know everything," Sasha commented.

"You gotta try. Not its original intent, but it works, and it'll make it easy to keep track of inventory. Still, maybe we should take a share of it to the main level."

"Doyle said the same." Bran stepped back. "Kitchen panty, I'm thinking."

"And that works, too." Riley looked over as Sawyer unzipped one of the rifle cases. "It's got a kick," she told him.

"It looks very mean."

Understanding, Riley gave Annika's back a pat. "It is mean. We're going to need mean."

"You stick with your Wonder Woman

cuffs." At Sawyer's comment, Annika rubbed the copper bracelets Bran had conjured for her. "You don't have to touch these."

For himself, Sawyer opened the terrace door, took the rifle out, tested its weight, dry fired a few times.

"We tested it at about fifty yards. We need to practice more distance." Riley unloaded the second rifle herself, offered it to Sasha. "Get a feel."

Long resigned to weaponry, Sasha took it. "It's heavy."

"Compared to your bow or a handgun, sure. But not for what it is. We'll work in some practice tomorrow, after the dive."

"We dive tomorrow." The tension in Annika's face dissolved. "This is much better. I can show you some caves, but the water will be much colder for you than the waters in Capri or Corfu."

"We'll manage." Riley topped off Annika's glass, Sasha's, then her own. "What do you say, a box of each caliber, a quiver of bolts, down in the pantry? Rotate them from here as we go."

Because he felt he'd earned a drink

himself, and hers was handy, Doyle took Riley's glass, downed half of it. "It'll do. But I think now we should have bought a third rifle—he had a Remington in stock. We could keep that in the pantry, have another on the main level if needed."

"Hindsight." Riley snatched her glass back. "We can go back if we decide we need another."

"You said you'd picked up more," Sasha reminded her. "Information."

"Yeah, we did. I vote we go down, get into the pizza. I had to smell it all the way home, and I'm ready to eat."

"Don't have to ask me twice. I'm going to take this down now," Sawyer said, rifle in hand. "I'd like to try it out after we eat."

When they started down with the main floor supplies, Sasha held Bran back.

"Something happened between them— Riley and Doyle."

"They argued? Not surprising."

"I don't mean arguing."

"Ah." Now he smiled. "I don't suppose that's something that should come as a surprise either, should it? Two healthy, attractive people in a close and intense situation. More inevitable than surprising. Why would it worry you?" He tapped a finger between her eyebrows. "I can see the worry."

"If it's just sex, that's one thing. Despite assignment charts, family meals, Annika's shopping sprees—all we do to establish a kind of order and normality, we've been risking our lives every day since we met. So sex, well, that's another kind of normality. But...he's closed his heart off, Bran. It's his only defense against living decade after decade while everyone he knows dies. Even the trust, the connection, the affection he feels for all of us is troubling and difficult for him."

"I know it. And Riley knows it as well."

"But Riley is, well, she's a pack animal. It's her nature. She needs and values her solitude, her studies, but at the core she's team and family oriented. And wolves, they mate for life, don't they?"

"I have a strong suspicion Riley mated before this."

"He's her counterpart."

Now Bran frowned. "What do you mean?"

"I've felt it all along. From her, not him.

He's so closed off, it's rare for him to send out any feelings or emotions—and I don't push in."

"You don't, no."

"It's more what I feel when I look at them together, or think of them together. He's what she wants, whether she knows it or admits it, he's what she wants for the long haul. I think she could fall in love with him, and it could hurt her."

Bran laid his hands on Sasha's shoulders. "She's the first true friend you've ever had."

"Yes. And she's the one who offered the friendship, the first who did knowing what I am."

"So it's natural you'd worry for her, worry about her. And still, Riley's a woman grown, and as smart and tough as they come. She'll have to walk her own path on this. You'll be there for her wherever it takes her."

With a nod, Sasha moved in for a hug, held on, and wished with all she had, her first true friend could be as happy as she was.

"Hey!" Snapping with impatience, Riley's voice boomed up the stairs. "Jump each other later, or we eat without you."

"We're coming now." Sasha eased back, took Bran's hand.

They'd opened another bottle of wine, and even for such a casual meal, Annika had shaped napkins into swans, draped the necks with collars of tiny flowers, set them to swimming on a pale blue plate.

"We've got your plain cheese for the boring," Riley began, "your pepperoni, your meat, meat, and more meat, and your veggie extravaganza."

"I think I'll start out boring and work my way up." Sasha sat, laughed when Bran flicked a hand over the offered pies to send the cheese bubbling again.

"Riley and Doyle have reports." Because it was so pretty, Annika chose a slice of the vegetable. "So do we. Who should go first?"

"I've more work to do on my part," Bran began, "so I'll cede the first slot to Riley and Doyle."

"Since the Lord of Few Words here will skim over it, I'll take the lead." Riley opted for meat. "It turns out my guns and ammo contact here in Clare has a half brother—

the oldest. A McCleary."

"Just like Doyle," Annika said.

"Just like. Sir Cynic wants to call it coincidence."

"It wouldn't be." Sasha looked at Doyle with some sympathy. "It just wouldn't."

"Not to say you wouldn't come across plenty of McClearys in Clare or Galway or anywhere in the country," Bran added. "But no, it wouldn't be. You knew this man from before?"

"Nope." Riley washed down pizza with wine, considered it the best of the best. "He's the cousin of a friend's ex. Interesting guy. He knew your name, Bran. And I got respect and curiosity from him there. Short version, Liam—that's the guy— Liam's mother married a James McCleary, he went off to World War II, leaving his pregnant wife, was killed in the war. She had his son, and a few years later remarried. I'm going to say I could've gone in a couple directions to get what we wanted here, but I went straight for this one. Liam made us a fair deal, didn't ask too many questions, and has a direct connection to the clan McCleary."

"Going to make a point," Sawyer said over a mouthful of pizza. "We didn't find the blood connections—the confirmations—before we got here, to this point. So I'm saying it wasn't the time and place for them before. This is."

"We were already family."

He leaned over, kissed Annika. "Damn right. And maybe we had to get there before we got here."

"Not just a team now," Bran stated. "A **clann**."

"In Irish, children or progeny. So from that clan or tribe," Riley continued, "people united by kinship, actual or perceived. It fits."

"We started separately." Sasha laid a hand over Bran's. "Formed an alliance, because we weren't a team, not at first."

"You made us one." Sawyer lifted his glass to her. "More than anyone."

"We made us one, but thanks. And Annika's right, from there we became family. And family remains even as a clan."

"We should get us a coat of arms."

Annika gave Sawyer a puzzled look. "But a coat has arms already."

"No, it's a symbol, like an emblem."

"A heraldic design," Riley supplied. "And you know, I like it. Sasha should draw us one."

"That would be a first, but I can try."

"Symbols matter." Doyle shrugged when all eyes turned to him. "It's been said often enough around this group. Clan. So it would matter."

"I'll work on it."

"We can order up matching T-shirts, but in the meantime." Riley paused to grab another slice. "Pretty sure Nerezza's feeling a little better."

"She came at you." Sasha jerked in her chair. "I didn't feel—"

"Not directly," Riley interrupted. "She sent scouts. Ravens. I took out a few of them."

"You killed birds?" Annika, clearly distressed, laid a hand on her heart.

"Birds don't turn to ash when you put a bullet in them. These did."

"Weregirl recognized them for other." When Riley sneered at him, Doyle just smiled. "Apparently the wolf knows a raven from a minion."

"Scout," Riley corrected. "Not that they wouldn't have clawed our eyes out given the chance, but they were weak—which hopefully translates to her still being weak."

"But she knows where we are," Sawyer put in.

"I'd say she does. Not ready to do much about it, but she knows we're here."

"And when she's ready," Bran said, "so will we be. A clan, a coat of arms, and for my part, a shield. When the time comes, we'll fight fire with fire."

"And firepower. Did some scouting of my own," Sawyer told them. "My take is rather than in the towers, outside on the—let's have fun and call them battlements—makes a better position for the long-range rifles. You don't have the cover, but you'd have a three-sixty, and when whatever she sends gets within, say, twenty yards, you'd get cover. Plenty of time for it."

"That's good thinking. I'd like to check it out, too."

"I already have," Doyle said to Riley. "Sawyer's right. It's a better position to target on land, sky, sea."

Riley considered. "Bran, you know how

to do those flying balls for Anni and her Wonder Woman deal?"

"I do, and yes, that's also good thinking. I can give you targets—land, sea, air."

"Very cool. We can try it out tonight, after we finish here."

"I would clean up." Annika sent an imploring look around the table. "I don't like the sound the guns make. I would stay here, clean up."

"That's okay." Sawyer gave her hand a squeeze under the table.

"We dive tomorrow." Wanting to make Annika smile again, Riley changed the subject to something her friend liked. "We should be ready to drive out by eight thirty, so we can pick up the boat, the equipment. Or a couple of us go to get the boat, pilot it back here, and Sawyer travels the rest of you down to it. We'll keep the boat here for the duration, just have to deal with getting the tanks refilled as we need them."

"More efficient." Sawyer circled a finger as he ate. "Riley and Doyle—best at piloting—go for the boat. When we spot you coming back, I'll get the rest of us on board."

"Can do. Eight thirty," Riley said to Doyle, who just nodded.

They went up, leaving Annika to deal with the debris, and outside to look over the crenelated wall into the coming twilight.

"Days are longer—calendar and geography," Riley said. "She likes the dark, but she may hit more often in daylight. It's the last round, and she lost the first two."

"Day or night, we'll knock them back." Ready, Sawyer loaded a rifle. "Give me a target, at least fifty yards out."

"Where would you like it?" Bran asked.

"Surprise me."

Obliging, Bran sent a globe into the air, out above the sea. Sawyer shifted his stance, fired, struck it dead center.

"Figures." Riley lifted the second rifle. "Give me one."

This one Bran sent high into the north. Riley took it down.

"Okay, let's make it a hundred yards, multiple targets. You game?" Sawyer asked Riley.

"I invented the game. Go."

After the barrage of fire, Riley lowered her weapon. "You don't miss, cowboy."

"You didn't either."

"I only nicked a couple of them. You hit dead-on, every one. More practice for me. You need to try it." Riley offered the gun to Sasha.

"I don't know how I can shoot what I can barely see."

"Bran's going to bring it in for you. Start at twenty yards, Bran, straight ahead over the water."

Doyle stepped behind Sasha. "It'll recoil, so you need to go with that." He adjusted her stance, put his hands over hers. "Use the sight, hold it steady. Do you have it?"

"Well, I can see it, in the cross—the crosshairs."

"Steady," he said again. "Don't jerk when you pull the trigger. You want it smooth, building the pressure, like drawing a line. Keep drawing it even after you fire. A slow pull, all the way. Take a breath, hold it, fire."

She did as he told her, let out an embarrassing squeal when the kick shoved her back against him. "Sorry. And I completely missed."

"You pulled up and to the right," Riley told her.

"Steady," Doyle repeated. "Try again."

She didn't squeal this time, but hissed. And by the third time she just dinged the bottom of the globe.

"It won't be your primary weapon," Doyle began.

"Thank God." Happy to relinquish it, she passed it to Doyle.

"But you'll learn how to handle it, clean it, load it, and use it with accuracy."

"All right." She rolled her aggravated shoulder. "I'll learn."

"And you." Doyle gestured to Bran. "Not even close to your primary weapon."

"And still," Bran agreed.

They spent twenty minutes destroying target globes before stowing the weapons.

"I'm going to take Anni down, so she can swim. It'll smooth her out after all the gunfire."

"Dawn, as usual," Doyle reminded Sawyer.

"Not likely to forget."

"I've got another hour's work in me,"

Bran decided.

"And I'll start working on that coat of arms."

Riley closed the outside door as the others filed out. Doyle stowed the rifles.

"We'll take my bike tomorrow."

"Fine with me. With Sawyer bringing everybody to us, we should be able to start diving around nine thirty. Annika's right about the water temp, so we'll have to limit underwater time. Maybe do a couple of thirty-minute dives tomorrow, get acclimated."

Since he made no move to leave, she studied him. "Have you ever dived in the North Atlantic?"

"A few times."

"You're not going to tell me you were a Navy SEAL, are you?"

"It seemed like a good idea at the time."

"Seriously?" A dozen questions popped into her mind, but she shook her head.

"Five years. Any longer than that with one group is risky."

"I can see that. But right now, we're not just a group, and we already know who you are. It should make things easier for you."

"It doesn't."

When he walked out on that, Riley let out a sigh. "It should," she murmured.

In the morning, after a sweaty hour under Doyle's training whip, a hot breakfast where they refined and confirmed the diving plan, Riley pulled on a battered leather jacket. As a hopeful sun had broken through the earlier gloom and drizzle, she pushed on her sunglasses.

She had her tank suit for diving under her sweatshirt and cargoes, her gun on her hip under the jacket, and her cell phone secured in the inside pocket.

And considered herself good to go.

She'd been quick, and walked outside at eight twenty-seven. She couldn't say, exactly, why it irritated her that Doyle waited beside his bike.

He held out a black helmet with a small emblem of the dragon that flew over the side of the bike.

"Why do you even have this?" she wondered. "A fractured skull wouldn't hold you back for long."

"It's the law in a lot of places, and you make fewer ripples if you follow local laws. And a fractured skull wouldn't kill me, but it fucking hurts." She strapped on the helmet. "Haven't had the experience, but I bet."

He swung on the bike. "Navigate."

"You could just let me drive."

"No. Lay out the route."

"South on the coast road toward Spanish Point. Should be a sign about a half kilometer this side for Donahue's Diving. Follow that down to the beach. I'm licensed," she added, swinging on behind him.

"Nobody drives my bike."

He kicked it to life. The dragon roar of bikes had always appealed to her, as had the sensation of speed and the freedom of blasting down the road open to the wind.

It all appealed less when riding pillion.

Still, his bike, his rules.

She set her hands on his hips, and **imagined** she was driving.

Down the bumpy lane, around the curves where Bran had let the hedgerows of fuchsia rise to form borders, and sassy wildflowers poked up to edge the dirt track. Around and beyond the forest where the track turned onto pavement.

While she enjoyed the speed and power, the smell of green still damp from the morning shower, she kept a sharp eye out for any ravens—for anything that struck her as **off**.

No need for conversation with the roar and buffeting wind, and no need to direct as Doyle wound them to the coast road. She imagined he'd made the journey on horseback or cart more than once.

Had he played on the beach as a boy, splashed in the waves, shouted out laughing as the chilly water rolled over him? Sailed out in a currach, fished the seas?

She could imagine it, she could see him—a tall boy with long dark hair, eyes green like the hills, running over shale and sand, through the shallows with his siblings as boys had and would.

A good life, she thought as she leaned with him into a turn.

She shifted a little, looked out over the water, a rough and ready blue with tinges of green. Gulls swooped, white or gray, and farther out she saw the roll of a white fishing boat.

He slowed through villages decked with flowers, slapped the gas again once they moved beyond.

She tapped his shoulder, pointed when she spotted the little sign up ahead. He only nodded, then slowed into the turn.

The wind kicked harder now, and brisker as they took the narrow ribbon of road down. She smelled the sea, cool and briny, and the roses from the garden of a cottage, the smoke from a chimney of another.

Chickens, she thought. Though she couldn't see or hear them, the scent of their feathers tickled her nose. She smelled the dog before it ran out and along a tumbling stone wall to watch them.

She tapped Doyle's shoulder again when she saw the blue building with the long pier. She spotted the dive boat, a fishing boat, and a sweet little cabin cruiser with a man on deck patiently polishing its brightwork.

Doyle pulled up beside a pair of trucks

and a compact, cut the engine.

"I've got this," she said, slid off the bike, and strolled toward the boat where the man stopped, put his hands on his hips.

Her deal, Doyle thought, and walked over the shale to the thin strip of dark gold sand.

It would be here, wouldn't it? he thought. Fate's quick poke in the ribs. Here, where he'd come as a boy—of nine or ten, if memory served. A cousin had lived nearby. Christ, what was the name? Ronan, yes, Ronan had been the boy about his age, son of his father's sister. And they'd come to visit, barely a hard stone's throw from this spot.

His two sisters nearest his age chasing birds. The brother who came after them splashing in the shallows while a younger sister clung shyly to his mother's skirts. His young, doomed brother barely toddling. Another babe—though he hadn't known it then—in his mother's belly.

All there, his mother and father, his grandparents, aunt, uncle, cousins.

They'd stayed three days, fishing, feasting, playing music, and dancing late into the night. And he and Ronan had plied through the water like seals.

The following winter his aunt whose name escaped him died in childbirth. His father had wept.

Death unmans us all, Doyle thought.

Riley stepped over to him. "You've been here before."

"Yes."

"With your family?"

"Yes. Did you make the deal?"

She studied him a moment longer, then nodded. "Done. We can load the equipment."

They didn't speak again, or only of practicalities as along with Donahue they carted tanks, wet suits, equipment.

Riley addressed her conversation to Donahue, some talk, Doyle realized, of the dives a mutual acquaintance had taken a few years earlier.

When Donahue asked about the motorcycle, Riley just smiled and told him someone would pick it up later. And they'd be back to refill the tanks when needed.

Since she'd made the deal, she took the wheelhouse, eased the boat away from the dock with a wave to Donahue, already heading back to his brightwork.

"Making some small talk also causes fewer ripples," she pointed out.

"You were doing enough for both of us. It's a good boat."

"The friend we small talked about is a marine biologist, and he's partnered with a marine anthropologist. So Donahue came highly recommended. The anthro's also a lycan. The daughter of a friend of my mother's."

"Small world."

"Situationally."

It was a good boat, and she knew how to handle it. She headed north, kept within sight of the coast until she spotted a cove.

"A good spot," she called out, "for dropping four people out of the air."

She navigated in, using the shelter of the cliff face for cover, then pulled out her phone.

"Latitude and longitude for Sawyer. I've got an app for that. You'd better come up here so somebody doesn't splat on top of you."

He moved up with her while she found

the coordinates.

She still smelled of the forest, he noted, if the forest grew out of the sea.

"Hey, Sawyer, we're about halfway between here and there." She read off the coordinates. "Same type of RIB we've been using. Yeah, you got that. We're in the wheelhouse, nosed into a cove, bow toward the cliff, so you've got the rest of the boat. Don't miss," she added, then pocketed the phone.

"They'll be a minute. You know, given my bloodline and line of work, I've always been open to, we'll say, the unusual. But up until recently I wouldn't have seen myself hanging out waiting for four pals to pop out of thin air."

"A small and fluid world."

"Fluid works."

Water lapped and rocked against the boat, and Doyle—who could go weeks happily speaking to no one—found himself restless with the silence.

"Do lycans tend to go into science?"

"I wouldn't say so. I know teachers, artists, business types, chefs, lazy asses, politicians—"

"Politicians."

"Yeah." Now she smiled. "We've had a few in Congress, Parliament. There was this guy about twenty, twenty-five years ago I heard about who had higher ambitions. Leader of the Free World ambitions, but the council strongly discouraged him. You go for that, people start digging pretty deep. Better not to risk it. A shame really."

"A lycan president."

"We could do a hell of a lot worse."

"And likely have."

"Definitely have," she said with a grin. "But hey, three nights a month, a lycan couldn't answer that three a.m. phone call, so no-go there."

"And a Secret Service code name 'Furry' lacks dignity."

Very deliberately, she tipped down her sunglasses, peered at him over them. "You made a joke."

"I considered a career in comedy."

"And two for two. I have to circle this day on my calendar."

The way her eyes danced with humor, so gold in the sunlight, made him want to touch her. Just touch her hair, her skin.

He started to lift his hand to do just that when with a shimmer and a shudder of air the others appeared on the boat, and saved him from what he realized would have been a grave mistake.

"Dead-Eye strikes again," Riley said. "Perfect landing."

"Practice makes perfect." Sawyer glanced around. "You picked a good spot."

"I thought so. Settle in, friends and neighbors." Riley turned back to the wheel. "Where to, Anni?"

"Oh." Annika managed to look sexy even in one of the macs borrowed from Bran's mudroom. "If you sail as if we were going back to Bran's, I'll tell you when to stop."

"Good enough. Enjoy the balmy breezes while you can."

"You call this balmy?" As Riley steered the boat out of the cove, Sasha huddled beside Bran.

"Compared to what it's going to be like under the water? This is damn near tropical."

Chapter Nine

Even with wetsuits, the Atlantic shivered in, and it swallowed the sun. Riley, armed as Sawyer was with an underwater pistol, switched on the headlamp on her balaclava so its beam cut through the dank gloom of the water.

They swam in pairs, Annika and Sawyer in the lead—with Annika turning somersaults before she swam ahead. Sasha and Bran followed, and Riley couldn't complain when Bran circled a hand in the water, added light with a swirl. She took flank with Doyle.

They all knew what could streak out of the sea, if Nerezza had the strength for it. Mutant sharks and toothy fish thirsting for blood. Both Doyle and Sasha carried harpoons.

And look at her go, Riley thought, watching Sasha cut through the water, remembering how nervous the novice diver had been on their first dive off the coast of Corfu.

She learned fast. They'd all had to shore up personal weaknesses on this quest. Maybe that was part of the whole, she mused, turning weakness into strength, and for all, learning to trust enough to become that clan.

She watched a school of mackerel—just ordinary fish—head away from them, followed Bran's silvery light toward the mouth of a cave. In front of it, Annika executed a graceful turn, waved, then slid inside.

Singly now through the narrows, and again two by two when the channel widened. Then spreading out to search for...something, Riley thought. A glow, a sparkle, a **feeling**, anything that would lead the way to the last star, the Ice Star.

Cold enough for it—that thought crossed her mind. With the patience of her calling, she searched the underwater cave inch by inch, using her eyes, her gloved fingers, doing all she could to keep her mind and instincts wide open.

But she nodded when Sawyer tapped his wrist, once again took flank with Doyle for the return trip to the boat.

When Riley hauled herself out of the water, she saw Bran holding Sasha close, laying a serious kiss on her.

"Oh, God, that's **wonderful**. I'm warm again."

"Magick mouth?"

Bran laughed over at Riley as she dripped frigid water onto the deck. "Just a personal benefit." He took Riley's arms, squeezed lightly. And warmth flooded her.

"Excellent, even without the lip-lock."

He moved to Annika.

"I like kissing," she told him, and brushed her lips to his. "And I like warm."

Bran slapped both Sawyer and Doyle on the shoulder. "No point in any of us shivering our way through this. "Anything, **fáidh**?"

"No, sorry. It's so different from where we've been before. All so shadowy and stark in a way. But I didn't feel anything. Anyone?"

"I felt good," Annika told her. "But there's no singing, like there was for me with the Water Star."

"Up for round two?" Riley asked.

Sasha turned her back to Bran so he could help her change tanks. "It's what we're here for."

The second dive of the day gave them no more than the first. In Riley's book that meant two locations checked off.

Routine, Riley told herself when they secured the boat below the cliffs of Bran's house. Part, an important part, of discovery was routine.

They took the easy way—Sawyer's way—back to the house. And she folded herself into routine by scarfing down leftover pizza, closing herself in with her books.

The rain came back in the night, lashing rain with grumbling thunder that echoed off the sea. The storm woke her from a dream she couldn't quite pull back. And with the crashing waves, whirl of wind, she doubted she'd pull back sleep either.

She dragged on a sweatshirt, flannel pants. She wanted to see the storm boil over the sea and cliffs so slipped out of her room, walked quietly down to the sitting room that faced the Atlantic.

Glorious, she thought as she opened the doors. It flashed and burned, whipped and snapped so the wind screamed with it. Like a banshee, she decided, since it was Ireland.

The wild had always, would always call to her blood, and a wicked storm whirling over the night-dark sea, the rough and rugged land heated that blood, had her stepping out just enough to let the rain pelt her upturned face.

Then she looked down, saw movement, saw a figure near the cliff wall, and instinctively reached for the gun she hadn't thought to bring.

In a flash of lightning the figure became Doyle, and her instincts took a hard turn into lust.

Dark and brooding in the storm, coat swirling, sword in hand as if prepared to strike against the elements. Gorgeous, she thought again, and primal and violently sexy.

Yeah, she'd always been drawn to the

wild.

As she thought it, he turned, lightning sizzling above him, and in its fire, his eyes met hers. He tightened those thoughts into a noose that clutched at her throat.

Pride and sheer will made her stand there another moment, meeting those eyes, holding them even when the dark fell again, turned him into a shadow.

Then she stepped back, shut the doors against the storm, against the man, and went back to her room alone.

Routine, Riley reminded herself when they went through it, step-by-step, the next day.

A dawn run through the wet forest, jumping over a few limbs brought down in the storm. Polishing it off with a sweat-popping session in the gym as watery sunlight struggled through the clouds.

A shower, breakfast, two more dives, weapons training.

She opted for a fire in the library, the books while Bran worked at the top of the tower, while Sasha used the other tower's sitting room to paint. Sawyer and Doyle drove out to refill the tanks, do a food supply run. And Annika charmed her way into going with them, as a trip to the village meant shopping.

Now and again as she worked, she'd hear something rumble up above and assumed Bran made progress. But two hours into it, she found herself restless. Fresh air, she decided. She needed to move, to think. At some point in the gathering of data, you needed to stop, let it roll while you did something else.

Since the day had turned—that watery sunlight strengthened by late afternoon— she'd take a walk in the forest. Armed, of course, she thought as she patted the gun on her hip. Aware, always, but a good walk in the woods.

Odds were long she'd stumble across the star there, but thinking time was never wasted time. She slipped on a ragged hoodie, zipped it, went out by way of the main steps, nearly turned back when she saw both the car and the bike outside.

They'd gotten back while she'd been working, she supposed, and since the back of the car remained open, supplies inside, they were still unloading.

Could probably use some help. She headed toward the car when Sasha called her name.

"Hey!" She looked over, shot Sasha a salute as her friend stood just outside the trees at the head of a path. "Looks like you had the same idea as I did. I was going for a walk, but—"

"Good. There's something—come with me."

"Just let me haul some of this in first."

"I need to show you something. I'm not sure...I need you to see."

"What?" Intrigued, Riley detoured from the car.

"It's hard to explain. I went off the path, nearly got lost. But I found these marks on a tree. Carvings. I don't know what they are."

"Carvings?" The single word had Riley quickening her steps. "Recent?"

"I don't think so." As she spoke, Sasha looked back into the woods. "I should have taken a picture with my phone. I didn't think of it, just started back to tell everyone. Let me show you, and we'll take some pictures to show the others."

"Sash, you don't even have your knife."

"Oh. I don't know what I was thinking, but well, I'll be with you now." Sasha took Riley's hand, tugged. "I really want you to see this. It must mean something."

"Okay. Lead the way."

Doyle came out, saw Sasha and Riley move into the woods. He shook his head, grabbed two bags of groceries. "Thanks for the help," he muttered, and headed in.

In the dappled sunlight Riley breathed deep. "I just wanted a break from the books, and some air. Didn't figure on finding something cool. Did you get a vibe from it?"

"What? Vibe?"

"You know, a feeling?"

"I felt it was old—older than made sense. If that makes sense." Sasha moved quickly, gestured as she cut off the track. "I just—I guess I felt pulled to go this way."

"Must be a reason. So is it letters, symbols?"

"Both. I've never seen anything like it."

"I was all over these woods, two nights

running, and didn't see it. I should have," Riley added as they skirted around brambles and brush. "I've got good night vision. That makes me think you were meant to find it. But you didn't get a strong sense, any sort of vision, so—"

She turned her head. The backhand exploded pain in her cheekbone, lifted her off her feet, propelling her into the air. She crashed hard into a tree, saw stars, felt something **crunch** in her right arm.

She screamed as her instinctive reach for her gun shot agony through her. Sasha leaped over the brush, sprang off the moss-coated trunk of a fallen tree.

Her eyes glowed.

In defense, Riley tried to roll, to reach cross body for her gun. The savage kicks to her ribs, to her back, her belly stole all breath.

Sasha laughed.

A nightmare, dreaming. Not real. Engulfed in pain, swimming in shock, Riley struggled to unsheathe her knife with her left hand.

The sound she made when Sasha's boot stomped on her hand was a high-pitched shriek. Her vision wavered; her stomach pitched.

Then her friend's artist's hands closed around her throat.

Doyle strode into the kitchen where Annika happily put groceries away, and Sawyer sniffed a fat tomato.

"Still more, right?" Sawyer set the tomato aside. "I'll bring it in."

"You going to make that salsa?"

"As advertised."

"Do that." Doyle grabbed a cold beer from the fridge, took a long pull. "I'll get the rest."

"There's a deal."

After one more swig of beer, Doyle set the bottle down, started back through the house. A beer, he thought, some chips with Sawyer's salsa would be a solid way to offset Annika's shopping enthusiasm.

In any case, they'd gotten everything they should need for a good week. And next time, somebody else would deal with the mermaid.

He glanced up, momentarily baffled when Sasha jogged down the steps.

"I didn't hear you get back. I was painting

on the other side of the house. How—"

"You've been upstairs?"

"Yes, I went by the tower library just now to see if I could help Riley, but—"

"Jesus Christ. Get Bran, get the others. Riley's in trouble."

"What? How?"

"Get them." He drew his sword from the sheath on his back, was already running. "She's in the woods."

He'd barely reached the verge when he heard her scream.

He didn't think, just moved. The sound had been agonized, and he already might be too late.

He caught the sound of laughter— horrible, gleeful—and sprinted toward it off the track. No time for stealth, and his instincts demanded he make more noise. The sound of someone coming, and fast, might stop whatever was being done to Riley.

He didn't pause when he saw Riley crumpled on the ground, bleeding, unmoving, and Sasha—or what had taken Sasha's form—standing over her with a wide, wide grin.

"She's dying," the thing said with Sasha's voice, then long teeth shimmered between Sasha's lips, claws sprang from her hands. "You'll all be dying soon."

Even as Doyle charged, it delivered a vicious kick to Riley's head. When Doyle's sword cleaved down, it struck empty air as the thing coiled down into itself and ran through the trees with preternatural speed.

Doyle dropped to the ground, pressed his fingers to the pulse on Riley's raw throat. Found a pulse, thready, but beating.

Bearing down on fear, on rage, on a kind of grief he'd sworn never to feel again, he ran his hands over her, checking her injuries. Her face, sickly gray under the bruising, bleeding, abrasions, was the least of it.

He heard running, shouting, tightened his grip on his sword, prepared to defend Riley should foe join his friends.

They burst through the trees, armed for battle. But Doyle knew the battle was done for the moment.

"She's breathing, but she's been choked, and her hand's broken, ribs, too. I think her right elbow's shattered. And—"

On a keening sound of distress, Sasha all but fell on the ground beside Riley. "No, no, no, no."

"Let me see." Bran dropped down beside her.

"We need to get her inside, heal her." Tears shimmering, Annika knelt by Riley's other side, stroked her bloodied hair.

"I don't think we move her until we know..." Sawyer's knuckles showed white on the grip of his gun. "You're not supposed to move her, right, because it can make it worse?"

"Sawyer's right. That's sensible." Calm as a lake, Bran cupped his hands on Riley's head. "Neck and spine. We should see if they're injured."

"I can do it."

Bran looked into Sasha's eyes, eyes glazed with shock. "Calmly, **fáidh**. Slowly. Just the surface now."

"All right." Closing her eyes, Sasha took in air, let it out until her breath was nearly steady. She used her hands, her heart, and with Bran's hands on her shoulders to aid her, she let herself feel.

"Oh, God, oh, God, so much broken, so

much damaged."

"Neck and spine, Sasha," Bran said quietly. "Start there."

"Bruised, jolted. Not broken."

"Then we can take her inside." Those tears streamed down Annika's cheeks. "She shouldn't lie on the ground. It's cold. She's cold."

"Yes, we can move her." When Bran started to lift her, Doyle nudged him aside.

"I've got her." She moaned when he gathered her up, and her eyelids fluttered— both of which he took as good signs. For an instant, her eyes opened—blind with pain, with shock, met his. "I've got you, **ma faol**."

Her eyes rolled up white, closed again as he carried her out of the forest.

"Straight to her room," Bran ordered. "I'll get my medical kit. Anni, towels and hot water. Sawyer, a pitcher of cool water. Not cold, cool, and a clear glass. Sasha, strip her bed down to the sheets for now."

They scattered as Sasha ran up the stairs behind Bran. Though he wanted to run himself—and could have, as she weighed nothing much to his mind—Doyle moved carefully, doing what he could not to jar her.

When he turned into Riley's room, Sasha had tossed the bedding and pillows aside.

"I can help her."

"Wait for Bran." As if she were made of thin, fragile glass, Doyle laid her on the bed.

"I can help. If she comes to before...I don't know how she could stand it."

"She's tough. She'll hold up." With great care, Doyle unzipped her hoodie, ignored the blood, removed her holster, her knife sheath. "Wait for Bran."

Fighting tears, Sasha sat on the side of the bed, took Riley's good hand. "How did you know?"

"I saw her go into the forest when I was taking in supplies. Saw her going in with you minutes before I went out for more, and you came down."

"With me? With **me**?"

"Hold it together." He issued the order with a snap. "You can't help her if you don't hold it together."

"You're right. I will. And if Bran's not here

in thirty seconds, I'm—"

"I'm here." He came in with his kit and a satchel. "I needed to get some more things. Pour a half glass of that," he told Sawyer when Sawyer came in. "I need to bring her around enough for her to swallow."

"Not like this. Bran, not like this. Let me try to help first."

He looked at Sasha. "She's gravely injured. Understand that and go lightly. Just enough, do you understand, to ease the worst."

"I'll be careful."

She laid a hand on Riley's bruised and swollen cheek, held back a hiss as she felt the pain.

"Just enough," Bran repeated.

She tried, tried to go lightly, to ease only, to skim over what she understood were critical injuries, internal as well as shattered and broken bones.

But love, and an ability she'd only just learned to use, overwhelmed.

She laid a hand over Riley's crushed one, felt the vicious bootstrike, the agony as bones snapped and shattered. And, horrified, saw her own face looming over

Riley's prone body. Her own face filled with jubilant hate.

The pain, the overwhelming pain, struck her.

Bran cursed when Sasha melted to the floor.

"I've got her, I've got her." Sawyer rushed to Sasha as Annika hurried in, towels under her arm, a kitchen pot of water in her hands.

"You can make it hot quicker than the stove. I remembered."

"Of course I can. I wasn't thinking. Set it down there," Bran told Annika.

"I'm sorry." Sasha rubbed hands over her face. "I went too deep. Let me try again."

"You'll wait. Doyle, Sawyer, I need you to hold Riley down."

"No." Sasha rocked herself. "Oh, no."

"I'll be quick, but she needs this in her now. Lift her head so she takes it in," Bran told Doyle, "and hold her still."

Sasha knelt beside the bed, took Riley's good hand again. "Just to let her know we're here. I can let her know we're all here. It will help."

"It will." Bran shoved up his sleeves.

"Annika. Eight drops from the blue bottle. Two from the red. Blue, then red."

With Sawyer holding Riley's legs, Doyle on the bed behind her propping her head up, holding her shoulders, Bran straddled her, gripped her purpling jaw in one hand.

His eyes, black as onyx, went deeper, went darker. Riley stirred, struggled. Howled.

"Damn it," Sawyer muttered, forced to add weight to his grip. "Goddamn it."

"Get it in her," Doyle demanded, and lost control enough to lower his face in Riley's hair. "Take your bloody medicine, Gwin, and don't be a baby about it."

And suffering, he murmured to her.

Bran took the glass from Annika, poured the contents ruthlessly down Riley's throat.

Her eyes shot open, wheeled in her head. Her body arched, limbs trembling as they tried to drum. Then she collapsed, shuddering, shuddering, until she lay pale and still as death.

As he eased off the bed, Bran swiped sweat off his brow. "Now we can start."

She woke in agony, she floated in dreams.

She struggled in nightmares, she searched for peace.

She found peace now and then, hearing the voices of her friends. Sawyer...reading? Yes, reading Terry Pratchett, an old one, with the female cop—who happened to be a werewolf.

Just like her.

Annika singing—opera and Adele. Curled on the bed with her, softly crooning and smelling of spring rain.

The nightmares would close in, and the pain spike. And then Sasha would be there with her, telling her she wasn't alone, and the pain would subside, a little.

Bran running his hands over her, sometimes chanting in Irish or Latin, sometimes talking to her or to someone else who talked back to him with an accent as Irish as his own.

And Doyle, so often Doyle. He read Shakespeare. Who knew he had a voice so suited to Shakespeare? And when the demons chased her, demons with the faces of friends, he held her close.

"Beat them back, **ma faol**," he told her— demanded of her. "You know how. Fight!"

So she fought, and she drifted, and agony turned to grinding aches.

Doyle was there when the woman came, and urged the contents of some vial between her lips.

"No. I don't want—"

"It's what you need that counts. Swallow it down, there's a good girl."

She had red hair and eyes fiercely green, and a beauty that had survived decades. "Arianrhod."

"No, indeed. But one of her daughters, it seems. As you are. Sleep awhile more, and this fine young man will watch over you."

"I'm older than you are, by far."

The woman laughed at Doyle's comment, stroked a hand over Riley's cheek. "Sleep," she said.

And Riley slept.

When she woke minutes later—hours, days?—Doyle was beside her, propped up on pillows, reading **Much Ado** out loud by lamplight.

"I wrote a paper on Beatrice as a feminist."

Doyle lowered the book, shifted to study her face with eyes that looked exhausted. "You would."

"Why are you in bed with me?"

"Doctor's orders. Witch doctors. You look like hell, Gwin."

"Matches how I feel. What happened? What the hell happened? I don't—" Then she did, tried to bolt up, but Doyle held her down one-handed. "Sasha. She's possessed. You have to—"

"No, that wasn't it. It wasn't Sasha."

"She knocked the crap out of me, so I ought to know...No." Riley closed her eyes, forced herself to try to remember what came in fragments. "No, not Sasha. Malmon."

"That's been our theory."

"I'm sure of it. It looked and sounded like Sasha, until it clocked me. It felt like being hit with a brick." Cautiously, she lifted her hand to her cheek, pressed. "Feels okay now. I couldn't get my gun. I couldn't...My hand." She lifted her left hand, stared at the bandage wrapped around it. "Uh-oh."

"Nearly healed. They don't want you moving your fingers much as yet."

"She—he—it—stomped on it. I think I passed out."

"A lot of bones in the hand. Passing out

would be the wise course when having them all broken or crushed."

She braced herself. "How bad am I?"

"You're not dead, and would've been without Bran and Sasha, and even then. Internal injuries—kidneys, spleen, liver—severe enough we nearly hauled you to the hospital, but Bran had another solution. His grandmother."

"She looks like Arianrhod. I talked to her. I think."

"You did, more than once, I'm told. She's a healer, an empath. Bran swore by her skill, and he didn't exaggerate. I'm not sure you'd have full use of that hand again without her."

"Then I'm grateful. How long have I been down? A day? Two?" she asked when he only shook his head.

"You walked into the forest five days ago."

"Five?"

When she shoved up, gritted her teeth against a gasp of pain, he rolled out of the bed, poured something into a glass. "Drink it."

"I don't want to sleep again. Five days?"

"Fine."

"Where are you going?" she demanded, close to panic as he turned to the door.

"To get the others."

"Don't. Just wait. I want to get up."

"I want to dance with a naked Charlize Theron. We all have to face limitations."

"I'm serious. What time is it? Where is everybody?"

"Even though you talk in your sleep, it was more peaceful when you were unconscious. It's nearly ten thirty—that's p.m.—and I imagine the rest are downstairs."

"Then I want to go down. If you could just help me up, just give me a hand."

He huffed out a breath, walked back, plucked her out of bed.

"I didn't say carry me down." Mortifying. "I don't want to be carried."

"I go down and bring them to you, or I carry you down. Choose."

"I'll take the ride. Wait—mirror."

He stepped around, turned so she could get a look in the cheval glass in the corner of the room.

She saw a big man all in black holding

her as if she weighed as much as a puppy. And she looked pale, fragile—too thin. "I do look like hell. I should appreciate the honesty."

"No point in lying about it. You looked worse even yesterday. He all but choked the life out of you."

In the mirror, their eyes met, and on the meeting his went blank. "I don't remember that. Why did he stop?"

"Best guess is he heard me coming."

"You? How did you know to come?"

"I saw you head into the woods with what I thought was Sasha," he began as he carried her from the room. "And then I saw Sasha come down the stairs in the house. Easy enough to put it together. I wasn't quick enough to stop him from giving you a kick in the head. You were seeing double every time you came out of it for the first two days. Sicked up even the broth they tried to get into you until yesterday afternoon."

"Glad I don't remember that. I hate puking. You read to me. You and Sawyer and—"

"Brigid said reading, talking, being close

enough you could feel us would help the healing. We took shifts, like we did when Sawyer was hurt."

"He was tortured and knifed and beaten and burned, and he wasn't down and out this long."

"Men did to him—that's what Bran and Brigid say about it. A creature of Nerezza's did to you. There was poison in you. Be glad Bran won the argument about a hospital. They'd never have addressed the poison."

"More gratitude." When she heard voices, she tensed.

"It wasn't Sasha."

"I know."

Doyle stopped. "She's suffered. You need to know. Whatever worry, even fear, others knew over the last days, she felt it more keenly."

"It wasn't her fault."

"Convince her," Doyle said simply, then carried her toward the voices.

Chapter Ten

When Doyle stepped in, Riley in his arms, everything stopped.

Sawyer, on the point of demonstrating to Annika the proper way to hold a pool cue, jerked upright and grinned like a maniac. Annika let out a joyous laugh, and somehow managed to execute a backflip in the relatively confined space.

At the bar pouring a whiskey into a short glass, Bran set the bottle down, stepped over to lay a hand on Sasha's shoulder. She sat on a sofa with Bran's grandmother, who crisply laid out a tarot card spread.

"She'll be fine now," Brigid said as Sasha jolted to her feet, even as Sasha's breath caught and her eyes filled.

"There she is!" Sawyer laid the cue down,

used one hand on the back of a chair to hurtle over it. He grabbed Riley's face in his hands, kissed her hard and noisily. "Yeah, there you are."

"Put me down somewhere." Riley punched Doyle lightly on the shoulder. "You're making it a thing."

"It **is** a thing. Here, give her to me." Sawyer pulled Riley away from Doyle, spun in a circle. "Ladies and gentlemen, she's back!"

"Cut it out." As Riley laughed, Sasha burst into tears. "Oh, seriously, cut it out. Down," she muttered to Sawyer. "Down, down."

He carried her around the sofa, set her—gently—down.

"Sash—"

"Sorry. I'm sorry." Even as she swiped at her eyes, Sasha dropped down to kneel in front of Riley, grip her hands. "I'm so sorry."

"You didn't **do** anything. So stop. No, that's wrong. You did. You all did. So gratitude—extreme gratitude. Can I get something to eat? Pretty much anything."

"There's soup on the simmer." Brigid continued to lay the cards on the coffee table in front of her. "Sasha had a yearning to make chicken soup, and it's just the thing."

"I'll get it. Riley, I'm so happy," Annika said as she danced to the stove.

"I'm feeling pretty cheerful myself." Still holding Sasha's hands, Riley studied Brigid. "You look just like her."

"I've seen our Sasha's sketches, and I do. But for a few decades."

"I think you saved my life. It's appreciated."

"You're more than welcome. Bran, are you going to give me that whiskey or let the glass sit half empty until the years pass?"

He poured a healthy four fingers, brought it to her. Kissed her on both cheeks. "My endless thanks, Móraí."

"My gracious welcome. You're pale yet," Brigid observed, studying Riley over her glass. "But clear of eye. Sasha?"

"Oh, I don't—"

"You do." Brigid dismissed the protest. "You know how to look, how to see. So see to your sister, and no whining about it."

Sasha took a breath—shaky—closed her

brimming eyes. "There's still pain, but it's tolerable. There's still healing to be done, but it's progressing. She's hungry, and that's a good sign. She needs to eat, carefully for now, and rest another day or two."

"And the hand?" Brigid probed.

"Ah…Will hurt when the bandages come off—Bran treated them," she told Riley, "numbed the pain. But it's all healing well. The bandages should come off tomorrow." Sasha looked over at Brigid. "Is that right?"

"It is. You've so much more than you think. She knows better in the head," Brigid said to Riley, "but she blames herself in her heart."

"Then she's stupid. That's bullshit."

"Sure it is." Brigid stroked a hand down Sasha's hair. "But love is so often full of bullshit, isn't it?"

"Here's food!" Bright as the sun, Annika brought over a tray. "Sasha made soup with chicken and noodles and vegetables, and Móraí made brown bread."

"You sang to me," Riley said as Annika set down the tray.

"You heard me? Móraí said you would

hear in your heart if we talked or sang, and we should lie with you, stay close."

"I heard." She turned to Sawyer. "Terry Pratchett."

"I found **Night Watch** in your stash. It looked like you'd read it a million times."

"Close enough." Riley spooned up some soup. It slid into her like glory. "Oh, my God."

"Slowly," Brigid warned. "Else you'll sick it up."

"Give me a minute here, then we can do a roundup, but I feel like I haven't eaten in weeks." Riley spooned up more, tried to go slow. "You sent for reinforcements," she said to Bran.

"I didn't know enough. We were losing you."

"I've seen dead men on the battlefield with more life than you had." At the bar, Doyle poured himself a whiskey.

"Way to ease into it," Sawyer muttered.

"Straight up's better." Riley ate another spoonful, sat back. "You're right. Slower's better. It was Malmon."

"You're sure?" Bran demanded.

"Pretty damn sure. I went outside—it's a

little scattered yet—but I went outside. I needed a break, was going to take a walk. I saw the car. I hadn't heard Doyle and the others come back, but I saw the car. I saw the supplies, so I started to go over, grab some. Help out. And Sasha—"

She broke off when Sasha sat back on her heels, wrapped her arms around herself.

"Not you, okay? He made himself look like you. Or Nerezza made him look like you."

"If I'd come out again, it might have been Bran, or Sasha, or you," Doyle said with a nod to Riley as he leaned against the bar. "The illusion tailored for circumstance."

"Yes." Grateful for the clarification, Riley took a careful nibble of bread. "I think...I think if I'd just headed into the forest as I'd meant to, he'd have been waiting for me inside. As Sasha, or any of you. But I detoured, started for the car, so he had to lure me in. He said he'd found something I needed to see. I didn't hesitate, why would I? I went right in. Carvings, something about carvings. On a tree?"

The memories wavered, caused her

head to ache.

"Something like that. We walked, and went off the track. Oblivious, I was just oblivious, and he sucker-punched me. I fucking flew. Hit something. A rock, a tree. I felt things cracking and breaking inside me. My arm...wouldn't work. Couldn't get to my gun, or my knife. I couldn't fight back, just couldn't, and he was basically kicking the crap out of me. I thought I was finished. Done."

"Sasha called us." Annika brought Riley a mug of tea. "She ran in, said to hurry. Doyle said you needed us, so we all ran out, as fast as we could. But..."

"He was gone when we got there," Sawyer finished. "Doyle was there first. Doyle found you. Saw him. Malmon."

"He couldn't hold the illusion, or didn't want to." Doyle shrugged. "The illusion of Sasha wavered, just for an instant. He wouldn't stand and fight. He ran."

"Doyle carried you home, and Bran got his magicks, and Sasha tried to heal you, to start, but it was so much she—what is it called?" Annika asked Sawyer.

"She passed out."

"I didn't—I didn't have enough," Sasha managed.

"Nor did I," Bran reminded her. "The extent of the injuries, how they were inflicted, and the poison that had already moved into you. Healing is not my specialty."

"It might have been." Brigid tapped a finger in the air. "But you had a bent for flashier. You're loved, **sí-mac tíre**."

Irish for she-wolf, Riley translated, amused.

"Well loved, and valued. My boy here sent for me. And none too soon. You've a strong heart, spirit, body. It served you well. And so did I." Brigid lifted her glass, toasted, drank.

"Thank you, **máthair**, for my life."

Brigid nodded in approval. "You have respect. Eat. Bran, pour our girl here a half glass of wine."

"They wouldn't even let me have a beer when I got my ass kicked," Sawyer complained, and Brigid laughed.

"Sure, you should've called for me. A beer never hurt a fine, strapping man such as you."

"Next time. We shot a couple dozen ravens while you were out," Sawyer added.

"Ravens."

"Nerezza wanted to gloat, I'm thinking. But we gave her little to gloat about." Bran brought the wine. "Your color's better. I'm glad to see you, darling."

"Yeats," Riley remembered. "You read Yeats."

"It seemed apt. You need more sleep."

"I feel better."

"And sleep will be better yet."

"I'm not—"

"Sleep now." Brigid merely tapped Riley's shoulder. Riley dropped off. "Carry her back up, Doyle, there's a good lad." Brigid stroked a hand over Riley's hair, smiled and nodded. "She'll do. She'll do well enough now."

The sun streamed when Riley woke again, and a sweet breeze scented of flowers and forest wafted in the open doors of her balcony.

For a moment all the rest seemed like some ugly dream until she shifted to sit up, felt that wave of weakness that came from a hard illness or injury.

And Sasha stepped in from the balcony.

"Wait." Immediately Sasha hurried over to pile pillows behind Riley's back. "Take it slow. God, you look better. You look so much better."

"If you tell me I slept another five days, I'm going to belt you."

"Not even one. A little more than half of one." Voice cheerful, Sasha mixed something from a vial with something from a bottle into a glass.

Riley's eyes narrowed in suspicion. "What is that?"

"A restorative. Brigid said you were clear for it when you woke naturally."

Now Riley eyed the glass with more interest. "Like the one Bran made for Sawyer?"

"Brigid tamed it down."

"Spoilsport." But Riley took it, drank it. "How long does it take to—Okay." The dragging hangover from long sleep faded off, and at last—at last—her head felt clear. "I'd like a few samples of that for the next time I go on a tequila binge."

"Riley."

"Don't start again, Sash. I may have been half off last night, but I remember enough. This isn't on you."

"I need to get it out." Sasha eased onto the side of the bed. "Do me a favor, okay? Let me."

"Okay, but if you wander off into stupidville, I'm cutting you off."

"I know it could have been anyone who walked out of the house alone—that it was random and opportunistic."

"So far, you're in the right lane."

"But it was you. I know any one of us could have been used as a false face to draw you away from the house, into the woods. But it was me. It horrifies me, and it enrages me to know you have an image of me attacking you, hurting you, almost killing you. Switch places for a minute, and tell me it wouldn't do the same to you."

Grateful her mind was clear, Riley took a moment to organize her thoughts—and feelings with them. "I thought it **was** you. When you called me, when I went with you. I thought it was you when you knocked me like a sledgehammer into what felt like a concrete wall. I thought it was you," she repeated even as Sasha's lips trembled. "And you'd been possessed, taken over by Nerezza. My bell had been rung, and hard, and right then, lying there, looking at you, I thought she'd gotten into you somehow. I tried for my gun—I remember that—I remember if my arm hadn't been useless and I could have, I'd have shot you. I'd have tried to hit you in the leg, but I'd have shot you, thinking it was you."

"Defending yourself against—"

"It horrifies me, and it enrages me to know I'd have shot you. We're both going to have to get over the horror and the rage, Sash. That's it. Move it away, or they've won this round."

"I want the rage." And it burned in the blue of Sasha's eyes. "I want to give her pain, and misery, and horror for making you think, even for an instant, I'd hurt you. For making you have to choose, even for an instant, to hurt me."

"Okay." Riley nodded. "Rage is good. We'll keep it. But we're square, you and me."

"We're square."

"Excellent. I have to get up."

"You still need rest."

"I really have to pee. I mean seriously pee."

"I'll help you."

"Let me just try to get up on my own. I feel reasonably okay."

She managed it. A little wobbly maybe, Riley considered, but the room stayed steady and her vision didn't waver. "So far, so good. It's not about modesty—I don't have that much at the best of times—but I'm going to try to empty my now desperate bladder by myself. Stand by."

She didn't bolt to the adjoining bathroom, but moved briskly, and felt grateful she could. But no amount of gratitude could match what she felt when that desperate bladder emptied.

"Success! Could a hot shower be next?" She stepped out first, held out her bandaged hand. "How about taking this off first?"

"Let me get Bran or Brigid."

"Why?"

"They're so much more experienced."

Riley just lifted her eyebrows. "I'm on my feet. I'm lucid. I pick my own healer. Take it off for me, check it out."

Understanding—the creature with her face had mangled the hand; the woman, the friend, would judge its health—Sasha unwound the treated bandage.

"Hold it still," Sasha soothed as she cupped Riley's hand between hers. "It feels...clean. Sore, stiff, but clean. You can wiggle your fingers."

Feeling them, watching them move brought Riley such intense relief she nearly couldn't speak. When she did, her voice shook. "I was afraid I'd lose use of it, or at least some use of it."

She made a fist, opened it, closed it. "Sore, yeah. Maybe one and a half on a scale of ten." Emboldened, she rolled her right shoulder, flexed her biceps, tested range of motion. "Maybe two on the scale, but that'll ease up with use."

For the major test, she walked to the cheval glass. Hollow-eyed, gaunt, she thought. Weak. "Jesus, I look puny."

"Other than the soup last night, you haven't had a solid meal in nearly a week."

"I'll make up for that. Any of it left? The soup?"

"Yes."

"I want that—after a shower, real clothes."

"I'll stand by."

The shower ranked as miraculous, as did being able to use her hands, her arms with minimal discomfort. As she dressed, she noticed Sasha's easel on the balcony, and the painting in progress of the forest.

"I was angry with the forest, too," Sasha told her. "Ridiculous really, but that's how I felt. I thought painting it would exorcise that, and it's helped. Seeing you on your feet finishes it."

"Wait until you see me eat. While I do maybe you can fill me in on what's been happening while I was out of it."

"Bran's made real progress on the shield he's creating. Doyle's been cracking the whip when he hasn't been at the books."

The idea of Doyle researching without prodding had Riley stopping short. "At the books?"

"Translating mostly. Some passages in Greek, others in Irish or Latin on the stars, and the island. No definitive answers yet there."

As they came down the back steps, Sawyer walked in from the mudroom. "Hey!

I was just going to head up to check. Look at you!"

"Don't look too close," Riley advised, but he wrapped his arms around her in a hug. "Aw, you missed me."

"Did. Nobody around here wants to discuss the details, small and large, of the cinematic pastiche that is **A New Hope**."

"You've really suffered."

"Tell me." Though he was subtle about it, he kept an arm around Riley's waist to walk her to the table. "But you're looking for food."

"Damn skippy."

"I've got this," he told Sasha. "Bran's still out with Doyle at target practice. Annika's out there with Brigid—Brigid's teaching her to knit," he told Riley as he took the container of soup out of the fridge.

"Knit?"

"Yeah, they've bonded over yarns. Anyway, they'd like to know the prodigal's returned."

"I'll go out." Sasha took a last glance at Riley, went out.

Curious, Riley sat back. "Okay, you got rid of her."

"Just wanted you to know she's worried you'll look at her different."

"Don't, won't, and we settled all that."

"Knew you would." While the soup heated, he cut her a generous slab of bread, deftly sliced up an apple, cubed some cheese. "Appetizer."

"Thanks. Missed you, too. I guess the search for the star's been on hold."

"Not altogether. We talked about maybe diving, since Brigid was here for you, but it didn't make sense—and didn't feel right. It needs to be all six of us, so we tabled that. Unanimously. Doyle and I mapped out some areas on land. Annika says he's a little bit stuck on you."

"What sort of areas…What? **What?**"

Obviously amused by her reaction, Sawyer smirked. "Could be because Sasha gave her **Pride and Prejudice** to read to you. Annika thinks Doyle's like Mr. Darcy."

"Oh, please."

"What I said." He jabbed a finger in the air. "She's romantic. Bonus for me. Still, Doyle's been pretty messed up about what happened to you. We all have been, but…"

He glanced at the door—just in case—as

he ladled soup into a bowl. "I guess I noticed some myself. We had to hold you down." Blowing out a breath, Sawyer set the soup in front of Riley. "Don't like going back there. Seriously horrible, every level. But we had to hold you down while Bran and Sasha worked on you, when we got you back upstairs. I was pretty focused on you—had your legs. Doyle's behind you on the bed, propping you up so Bran could get some potion into you, holding your shoulders."

"I don't remember...exactly. It's all jumbled."

"That's probably a good thing. Leave it jumbled. Anyway, he looked rough. He doesn't let a lot show, you know? But he looked rough. I guess we all did. I didn't think much of it until Annika started with Darcy and all that, but Doyle, he kept talking to you—mostly in Irish and low, so I don't know what he said, but it was the **way**. Just speculation, take it for what it's worth. I just figured you'd want to know."

"Anni's rubbing off on you."

"Every chance I get."

Laughing, Riley dismissed it, applied

herself to the soup. "You know what I said to you when you were brooding and sulking about being weak and hurt?"

"I wasn't sulking." And Sawyer sulked a little at the idea. "Maybe brooding, marginally."

"Just throw it back in my face if I do the same."

"Consider it done."

"How close was I to buying it? Don't hold back."

He gave her a long study first, gray eyes assessing. "You were pocketing the receipt, telling dead relatives calling to you from the light to keep the change."

Nodding, she ate. "Then I won't brood and sulk much, because hey, alive."

"A fine attitude," Brigid said as she came in with Annika. "It will serve you well. Let's have a look." Stepping around the table, Brigid took Riley's chin in one hand, laid the other on top of her head. "Clear-minded, a bit weak, a bit sore. You'll tire more quickly than you'd like for another day or so. Rest and the restorative will help there. The soreness will pass, as will the weakness. Red meat for you tonight, girl."

"And my gratitude knows no bounds."

"Can she have the biscuits? Móraí showed me how to make them. They're very good."

"A couple of sugar biscuits never hurt a soul, and some tea with it, my angel," Brigid added. "With two drops only from the vial. You're a sweet boy, Sawyer King, and a brave one. You nearly deserve her."

"I'm working on it."

As the others came in, Riley tried to block out Sawyer's speculations, return Doyle's gaze casually. It helped when Bran walked to her, repeated his grandmother's gesture. "Nearly back altogether. I'd say rare steak for you tonight."

"Already got that bulletin."

"We're having tea and biscuits," Annika announced.

"And I'm all about both. Sasha caught me up a little on what's been going on the last few days. She said you'd made progress."

Bran sat, stretched out his legs. "We'll be ready for her should she come at us as Sasha foretold. We may have lost diving time, but it's given me more time for my own work. And Doyle and Sawyer made use of that time scouting out the land hereabouts."

"A few possibilities we should check out," Sawyer added. "Annika found a couple more caves farther up the coast, so there's that."

Riley picked up one of the cookies from the tray Annika put on the table. "I hear you've been librarian," she said to Doyle.

"I haven't found more than bits and pieces, and nothing that adds to the whole. You're welcome to the position now that you're back on your feet."

Riley sampled the cookie, found it excellent. "Doesn't anyone think it's odd we haven't been attacked while we were a man down?"

"The ravens came," Annika said, still busy with the tea.

"More ravens—you said something last night. I'm vague on it."

"They hit two days after you were attacked." Doyle remained standing. "Shortly after dawn. The day after, we didn't go out."

"Bran sent for Móraí." Annika set the pot

on the table. "You were hurt so much, and we needed to help you, so we didn't have calisthenics or training."

"But when you did, she sent ravens?"

"A couple dozen." Doyle glanced out the window, as if checking for more. "More nuisance than attack."

"She's weak." Attention turned to Sasha.

"Don't be afraid of it," Brigid murmured.

"I'm not. Only that she'll find a way to use me. But I can feel...she's weak. Growing stronger, but...Ah. Transforming Malmon, the illusion to disguise the creature, it took all she had. He failed. Even with all she gave him, he failed. She wants to bleed him. But she needs him. He feeds her; he serves her. He loves beyond reason. He has no reason. She is all. And the Globe of All...Wait, wait."

Sasha held out both hands, palms out. "She drinks a bloody brew. It sustains her. And the Globe of All is murky, clears only for moments, and at such a cost. She sees the house on the cliff, and what was before. Oh, if she had destroyed what came before, there would be no now. There would be no guardians. Why did he not

finish the woman, the wolf? Take one, take all. Why did he not finish before the immortal came? Bring me her dying body, bring me her blood. The blood of the wolf, the blood of a guardian. Their blood, my blood. I will gorge on it, and take the stars into the dark."

Letting out air, Sasha sat.

"A drop in Sasha's tea as well, darling," Brigid told Annika.

"I'm all right. She felt me, and she pushed back, but she's still too weak. He— Malmon—wasn't meant to kill you, just nearly, and bring you back to her. You or whoever he was able to get to. To drain you, to bring her back to full strength—to restore her youth as well as her power. To keep you alive, draining you slowly. Blood of the living is more powerful than blood of the dead."

"So it has always been in such matters." Brigid picked up her tea. "Nasty business."

"Almost enough to put me off this cookie." Deliberately Riley bit into it.

"It's the first I've been able to get past her defenses since you were hurt. I don't know if that means I've been too distracted

or if we just needed you back. Either way."
As deliberately as Riley, Sasha chose a
cookie, bit in. "We're back now."

"We're back," Riley agreed. "Now let's
fuck her up. Sorry," she said to Brigid.

"It's a sentiment I'm behind altogether.
I'll be on my way in the morning and
leave you to it."

"Oh, don't go, Móraí." Annika wrapped
her arms around Brigid from behind.

"I'll come back when you're done with
this, and I expect you all to find a way to
visit me and mine. But I want my own bed,
and my man. More?" She patted Annika's
hand as she looked into her grandson's
eyes. "This is for you. For the six of you.
All I am will be with you. Drink your tea,"
she told Riley. "And have one of this lot
go out with you for a bit of a walk. It'll do
you good."

"Yes, ma'am."

"Móraí," Brigid corrected. "For I'm yours
as well."

"Móraí." **Grandmother**, Riley thought,
and drank her tea.

Chapter Eleven

As was his habit, Doyle took a last patrol after midnight. A soft rain fell, obscuring the waning moon, turning the world into a dark, quiet mist. It cushioned the slap of the sea so that its steady beat became the pulse of the world.

At his back, the house stood behind the thin curtain of rain with lights shimmering through here and there to give it life.

Though his route around the house had become routine, he remained alert and ready. And when he saw the hooded figure standing among the gravestones, his sword leaped into his hand.

Not Nerezza, he thought as he moved closer, silent as a cat. Too slight for that. For a moment, he thought: Riley, and his temper spiked at the idea of her standing in the rain when she'd barely gained her feet.

But the figure turned. His first jolting thought was: Ma.

The spirit of his mother rising out of the mist. To comfort? To torment? At times one felt the same as the other.

Then she spoke, and he knew her for flesh and blood.

"You move like the air," Brigid commented. "But your thoughts are a shout."

"I took you for Riley, and more than my thoughts would have shouted. You shouldn't be out here either, in the rain and the dark."

Rain beaded on her hood, forming a dark, wet frame for a face of strength and enduring beauty.

"I'm an Irishwoman, so rain doesn't trouble me. And what witch is worried about the dark? The sweet girl leaves tributes for your dead."

Doyle glanced down. Annika had added shells to the stones, brought fresh flowers. "I know."

"They live on in you, and in the others as

well. In me and in mine. You favor my uncle—my father's brother, Ned. A rebel he was, and died fighting. I've seen pictures of him when he was your age."

"I'm more than three hundred years old."

Brigid let out a hooting laugh. "You hold up well, don't you? From what I know of Ned, he lacked your discipline, though he believed in his cause, gave his life for it. I've tried to see if your lives will be given, and I can't. I don't have the power that Sasha holds."

Seeing his surprise, she smiled. "Myself? I'm for the science of magicks. I like to think Bran took that from me. And I'm for healing. The cards can guide me to some answers, but Sasha is the most powerful seer I've known in my long life, and she's yet to tap the whole of her powers. And you, my boy, I know only that you won't reach the whole of your own until you break down the borders you've put up yourself."

"I don't have powers."

Brigid ticked her finger in the misty air. "There you are, that's one of your borders. Each of you has what you were given, willing or not. I've loved a man more than a half century. That may not be such a thing for one of your great age, but it's no small business. I've borne children, known the joys and sorrows, the frustrations and delights, the pride and the disappointments children bring with them into a mother's world. I can tell you, standing here on this holy ground, you gave your mother all of that, and it's all a woman asks from a son."

"I wasn't her only son."

"And evil took him, your young brother. She took that grief to her grave. But not for you, boy. Not for you." She lifted her chin toward the house, smiled. "Your wolf is restless."

He glanced back, saw the light had come on in Riley's room. "She's not my wolf."

Brigid only sighed. "One who's lived as long as you shouldn't be so boneheaded. But that's a man, I suppose, be he twenty or two hundred and twenty. I wish you a good journey, Doyle, son of Cleary, and happiness along your way. Good night."

"Good night." He watched her go, saw her safely into the house.

Then continued his rounds. Before he went inside for the night, he saw Riley's room was dark again, and hoped she slept.

Riley rose at dawn, determined to get back to routine, to push herself through training. When she stepped outside, she aimed I-dare-you looks at the others.

Maybe basic stretching brought on some pings and twinges, but she assured herself her muscles thanked her. And maybe shuffles, squats, lunges had her heart laboring, and those muscles quivering, but she gritted her way through them.

And through nearly a dozen push-ups before those quivering muscles simply gave up and sent her face-first into the damp grass.

"Take a break," Sasha began.

"Don't baby me." Hissing out a breath, Riley struggled back to plank position. She lowered halfway down, and sloppily, when she felt her arms giving up again.

She cursed when Doyle shot a hand under her hoodie, grabbed her belt and pumped her up and down. When he dropped her—not too gently—she shoved up to her hands and knees, ready to snarl and bite.

Sawyer crouched in front of her, poked a finger between her sulky eyebrows. "Do I have to give you The Talk?"

For one soaring moment, she wanted to punch him. Then her anger deflated as completely as her biceps. "No. Tantrum avoided."

"You did more than anyone in your point of recovery has a right to," Sasha pointed out. "It sort of pisses me off."

"Okay, that's something."

"Three-mile run," Doyle announced.

"We do five," Riley countered.

"Today it's three."

"I can do five."

"Bollocks. And pushing it to five only means you'll be in worse shape tomorrow. Three, and we pace you."

She started to bitch, caught Sawyer's arch look, decided she really didn't want her own words shoved in her face. She got to her feet.

"How about this? The five of you run the usual. I'll use the machine in the gym, keep it to three miles. I'll only slow you down."

"I can stay with Riley," Annika said.

"No need for that. I'll be in the house, in

the gym. Treadmill, three miles." Riley crossed a finger over her heart.

"Done. Let's move," Doyle ordered.

She hated that he was right, already knew she could only manage five miles if she'd limped or crawled through it. Better to keep it to three, moderate pace, and try for more next time.

She barely made the three, even with music to distract her.

Dripping sweat, she sat on a bench, guzzled water. She made herself stretch, consoled herself she already had her breath back.

And eyed the weight rack.

She hadn't promised not to lift.

She picked up a pair of twenty-pound weights, set, began a set of curls.

"Take it down to ten," Doyle said from the doorway.

"I can do twenty."

"And you'll strain muscles instead of building them back up."

Sheer stubbornness had her doing another rep before she racked them, picked up the tens. "You're right." She reset her position for triceps kickbacks. "I don't need a spotter."

"A keeper's more like it. You're too smart for this, Gwin. You know you'll set recovery back by overdoing."

"I won't overdo, but I need to work it some. I've never really been sick, not seriously. A couple of days, stomach bug, a cold, whatever. Hungover, sure. But I bounce back. I need to bounce back."

Saying nothing, he walked to the rack, took a fifty. He sat, smoothly curled.

"Show-off."

She switched to shoulder raises, moved to chest curls, onto flies, found a simpatico rhythm with him working nearby.

"That covers it," Doyle announced when she finished a second set.

She'd have argued, for form, but a third set was beyond her. "I just want to do one set of bench presses. One set. I'm a little sore, but it's a good sore. You know what I mean."

He walked to the bench. "One set."

She replaced the free weights, swiped her face with a towel, then crossed over to lie down. "I won't say I don't need a spotter, because I'm not an idiot."

He set the weights, nodded. "I've got you."

Something tapped at her memory at his words, stirred something, then slipped away. Riley focused, fixed her grip. "Okay, I felt that," she muttered as she pressed one. "One set of three. That's all I've got."

And the third rep was shaky, but gave her a lift of satisfaction.

"Okay. Okay, that's it. That's good enough." It wasn't until she sat up she noticed the weights. "You cut it down to ninety."

"I'm impressed you could manage that. Day after tomorrow you can try for a hundred. Stretch it out."

She decided ninety wasn't mortifying given the circumstances. And besides, she felt good, accomplished, healthily fatigued rather than exhausted.

"I'm bouncing."

"According to Bran's grandmother, the wolf accelerates your recovery time."

"Probably. Like I said, I've never been down like that before."

She stretched, and so did he. When he did, she noted, everything rippled and bulged and sleeked out in exactly the right way.

She had to give it to him, the man was shredded.

What if he did have a kind of a little thing going for her? She had her own lusty—perfectly normal—thoughts in his direction.

They'd even managed a gym session without busting each other's balls. It followed, logically, another form of healthy exercise—mutual—might just cap it all off.

"We could have sex."

He had his left arm across his chest, cradled in the crook of his right for the stretch. And moved only his head in her direction. "What?"

"It's not like it hasn't occurred to you." She went for another bottle of water, then studied him as she would a potential bootie buddy.

Sweaty, as she was, the mass of dark hair curling a little from the damp. Green eyes watched her suspiciously out of a face with hard planes and angles.

And the body? Well, Jesus, what woman wouldn't want to play with that?

"I'm single, you're single. I'm here, you're

here." As she spoke, she wagged a finger toward him, toward herself. "We've already had a lip-lock that wasn't half bad."

"Half bad."

"I'm good at it. I'm just saying." She swigged water. "Or so I'm told. I'm betting you're pretty good at it, too. Straight sex, Doyle, which I haven't had for eight months and five days."

"That's very specific."

"I was on a project in Brittany, ran into an old friend, scratched an itch. My record for a dry spell is eight months, twenty-three days. I'd hate to set a new one, frankly."

"You want me to help you keep your current record intact?"

She shrugged. It didn't trouble her he'd continued to stretch, continued to watch her. If you couldn't be straightforward about sex, what was the point in being an adult?

"Unless I'm reading you wrong—doubtful but possible—you could use a roll the same as me. It also occurred to me we're going to be right back in the bloody thick of it anytime. I don't want to go down without getting laid if I can help it. So I'm saying you could scratch my itch, I could scratch yours. No frills, no worries."

She capped the bottle. "Think about it. If it doesn't work for you, no problem."

She got halfway to the door when he gripped her arm, spun her around. "People spend too much time thinking about sex."

"Well, it's an endlessly fascinating and diverse activity."

He fisted a hand in her shirt, hauled her to her toes. "Thinking and talking about sex means you're not having it."

"There's a point of agreement."

Both amused and aroused, she sprang off her toes, jumping lightly to hook her legs around his waist. "So? Want to think and talk some more?"

"No."

He took her mouth, that clever mouth that talked entirely too much. She tasted of cool water and hot salt, and the sound she made wasn't words—thank Christ—but transmitted pure pleasure.

Her body, warm, limber, damp, pressed against him as he gripped her hips, as she gripped his hair.

Not enough, he thought. Not close to

enough. They'd finish this, start and finish what had been wound tight inside him for far too long.

He turned with the single idea of carting her to his room.

And Sasha stepped in. "Oh. Oh, I'm **sorry**! I'm—Oh, God."

Before a vibrating Riley could react, Doyle dropped her to her feet. "I'd say breakfast is ready. You need to eat," he said to Riley, and walked out.

"Riley. God, Riley, could I have timed that any worse?"

"Well, we could've been naked." She waved a hand in the air. "It's okay. Shouldn't have started that in a public area, so to speak. You know, I think I'm just going to sit down for a second."

Which she did, right on the floor.

"I didn't know—I mean I knew." Babbling, Sasha came to sit beside her. "But I didn't know. I just came in to tell you we're about to eat, and...I should've **known**. I felt—I thought you were working out, like...pumped up."

Now Riley lowered her head into her hands and laughed. "We did, we were. We will again, absolutely. No way we're leaving this undone. I am officially both shaken and stirred, and by God, I'm gulping down that martini."

"What?"

"Popular culture reference. Don't worry about it." She patted Sasha's shoulder. "I definitely need to eat. I'm going to need to be in top form for the next rounds."

She stood, offered a hand to Sasha. "What's for breakfast?"

She ate like a wolf. Along with the others, she said her good-byes to Brigid, then took herself off for some time in the library before weapons training.

Doyle didn't join her, which she didn't find surprising. He'd know as well as she did with the unfinished business between them they'd be rolling around naked on the floor inside ten minutes once they were alone behind closed doors.

She'd wait, he'd wait. They'd wait. If he didn't come to her room that night, she'd go to his.

Situation settled.

Anticipation gave her an edge, one she

used as she selected books, opened her own notebook.

In it she puzzled over Doyle's notes. Apparently a few centuries of practice hadn't given him clear and legible handwriting.

> **Look to the past to find**
> **the future.**
> **It waits in the dark, cold**
> **and still.**
> **Blood of the blood frees it.**
> **And so the ice will burn bright**
> **as a sun.**

She read his notes again, read others.

At least he'd marked down the books and the pages so she could verify.

As she worked, she frowned over some of his translations, wrote down questions and her own interpretations.

When she needed it, she bolstered herself with a ten-minute nap, made more coffee, dug deeper.

"See the name, read the name," she muttered as she read. "Speak the name. What name?"

As she read on, Annika burst into the room. "Sasha says something is coming. To hurry."

Riley leaped up, left the question unanswered.

By the time she got downstairs, ran out, the others were armed and waiting.

"From the sea." Sasha gestured. "It's not her—she's not ready—but she's sending plenty. A dark cloud. I see a dark sweep of cloud, blocking the sun."

"We can take the towers. Me and Sawyer."

"Not this time." Doyle searched the pale blue sky, the stacks of white and gray clouds. "We save that tactic for when she comes full force. This is a test run." He gestured with the sword in his hands. "There, due west."

They came, swirling into a funnel that spun the clouds, darkened them. Until they became the clouds, black and alive. They spun, a kind of whip and wave inking the pale blue to midnight.

"Impressive." Sawyer drew both his sidearms. "But what's the point?"

At his words that whip cracked, a sonic

boom that shook the ground, and smothered the sun.

"That's the point," he said when the world fell into dark, absolute. "Can't hit what we can't see. Bran?"

Then came the thunder of wings, the cyclone of wind. Bran struck against the dark, turned the black into a murky, green-tinged gray.

"That'll do." Riley fired with her right, gripped her combat knife in her left. Red-eyed ravens, long-toothed bats with oversized heads and twisted bodies.

Their wings, she knew, would slice like razors if they met flesh.

But the bullets Bran had enchanted hit home. Nerezza's winged army flashed in fire, fell in a rain of bloody ash. To her left, Annika shot light from her bracelets, pounded into a handspring, and shot again. Sasha's bolts flew, accurate and deadly, while Bran burned a swath with twin lances of blue lightning.

And all the while, even over the scream of wind, she heard Doyle's sword sing and strike, the brutal music of the battlefield.

Were they slower than before? she

wondered. A multitude, no question, and even with skill, they'd be overcome without Bran's powers. And still, she'd nearly misjudged a couple of targets, moving more sluggishly than others.

She dived and rolled to avoid an attack, reloading as she moved, firing from the ground. She sprang up, punching out with her knife as one veered close. Then the wind gripped her like a hand, tossed her up and back. Her body, not quite healed, knew fresh pain.

Winded, she fired again, fought her way to a crouch. Her blood froze when a swarm within the swarm peeled off, arrowed toward her.

Not enough bullets, she thought, but made what she had count. She rolled, slowed to a crawl by the force of the wind. She felt the bite of a wing graze her calf, another bite into her shoulder as she kicked and slashed.

Dozens fell around her as her comrades destroyed them, and still they came.

She fired again, stabbed one before it could slice wing and talon over her face. Three coalesced, eyes bright and mad, lancing toward her as she struggled to reload.

Doyle's sword sliced through them, cleaved and struck as he shoved through that crazed wind. With one hand he reached down, gripped her by the neck of her sweatshirt, and dragged her behind him.

"Stay down!"

She didn't believe in staying down. Using his body as a windbreak, she pushed up, reloaded. She stood with him, back-to-back, half mad herself as she peppered the air with bullets.

Annika leaped through, bracelets flashing, then Sawyer, then Sasha.

"Bran?" Riley shouted.

"He said to get here, stay here," Sasha shouted back, sent a bolt through one creature that continued through another. "And he'd—"

For an instant, the light blinded. It carried a flood of heat, a burn of power that scorched the air. What died didn't have the chance to scream.

Overhead the sky bloomed blue again.

Shaken more than she liked, Riley bent over, braced her hands on her thighs as she caught her breath.

"You're hurt." Annika hugged arms around her.

"No. Just a couple of nicks."

Though it did no good, she protested when Doyle yanked her sweatshirt off her shoulder, studied the wound. "A graze."

"Like I said." She jerked the shirt back in place.

"They swarmed you." Sasha lowered her bow, looked back as Bran strode toward them. "I didn't realize it until it was nearly too late."

"Quantity over quality, that's what I was thinking." Sawyer swiped a splatter of blood from his cheek. "Enough to keep us busy, but on the weak side."

"Yeah." Riley nodded. "I thought the same. Then the wind picked me up, tossed me—like getting slapped by a tornado. A couple hundred of them banked toward me." She snarled out a breath. "She knew I'd been hurt, figured I was the weak sister. Well, fuck that."

"We were too far away to help." Annika rubbed Riley's arm. "If Doyle hadn't been closer, if he hadn't…"

Realizing she still held her gun in an iron grip, Riley made herself holster it, look at him. "Yeah. Thanks for the assist."

"All in a day's."

His eyes said something different, she thought, something not so cool and dismissive. She kept hers locked with his as Bran checked her shoulder.

She heard him speak, didn't register the words. He and the others might have stepped into another world. Hers raced, pumped with adrenaline and lust.

Doyle gripped her arm, said, "Now."

She sheathed her knife. "Now."

She moved with him toward the house. Apparently she didn't move fast enough to suit him, as he plucked her off the ground. Since that was fine with her, she wrapped her legs around his waist, dragged his head down to hers.

"Oh." Delighted, Annika hugged her arms. "They're going to have very good sex."

Sasha watched Doyle carry Riley up the terrace steps. "Shouldn't we treat her wounds before..."

Bran simply took her hand. "She'll be fine

for now. Let's get cleaned up, have a beer, and let them...tend each other for the moment."

"Clean up. Good idea." Sawyer grabbed Annika's hand.

"Oh, we're going to have sex, too."

Laughing, Bran wrapped his arms around Sasha. "Sounds brilliant," he said, and winked her straight up to bed.

Doyle ignored the bed. The minute he kicked the terrace door closed, he spun around, slapped Riley's back to the wall.

"No frills, you said."

"Not necessary." She took his mouth again, added a testing bite as she fought to remove his sword and sheath.

She wanted flesh, the scent, the taste, the **feel** of it, and let the sheath fall with a thud so she could drag off his shirt and find it.

He'd already found her, his hands streaking under her sweatshirt to close around her breasts. Big, rough hands— exactly what she was after.

But more, more, she wanted **penetration**. Wanted invasion, hot and hard. The unspeakable thrill of life after near death.

He had grazes and nicks of his own. Together they smelled of war—of blood and sweat and battle.

Impatient, he didn't pull her shirt off, but hooked his fingers where it was torn and ripped it—or most of it—away. The violence of the act, the rending, pumped through her blood, had her fighting with his belt as he dragged at hers.

Need growled in her throat, tied quivering knots in her belly.

He yanked her jeans over her hips, and then—thank God then—drove ferociously into her.

A pause, a beat, a breath. Absorbing the shock, the **glory**, and once again her eyes met his.

Held his while her breath tore through her lungs, while he plundered. She came in a torrent, release, blessed release, then fisted her hands in that thick hair, let him whip her up again while she pumped against him to take him in turn.

When it struck her again, the hot lash of a whip, she felt his body shudder as he fell with her.

Chapter Twelve

She didn't have to hold on. She was trapped between his body and the wall, still suspended off the floor. But she held on anyway. After a flight like that, she wasn't at all sure she wouldn't just spin off like a dust mote.

The fast and the furious, she thought, more than pleased. And a job damn well done. The fact that he was winded added an extra layer of satisfaction.

She took pride in her work, after all.

Since she was holding on for a bit longer, she explored the muscles of his back. Speed had eliminated some of the finer details. And he had a really exceptional back. A really fine chest, too, which was currently pressed hard—a rippling steel door—against hers.

In fact, on a strictly physical level, she'd never seen a finer specimen, much less had one. Bonus points, she decided, and at last opened her eyes to find his on hers.

"Nice work, Sir Studly. Let me know when you want to put me down."

He managed to hold her in place and hitch his pants back up. Turning, still carrying her, he walked to the bed, dropped them both.

She let out an **oof**. The exceptional physical specimen had some weight to him.

"Sorry." He rolled off, lay flat on his back a moment. "No frills," he said again.

"Do I strike you as the frilly sort?"

"You don't, but there are certain details... I didn't think, wasn't thinking, about protection."

"Right. I've recently broken an over-eight-month fast. I'm clean. I assume the same goes."

"I'm immune to any sort of disease or disorder. There are other reasons for protection."

"I use LARC—long-acting reversible contraception. Not to worry."

"Good."

She looked down at herself, and the tattered remains of her shirt. "I liked this sweatshirt."

"It was ruined anyway. And you didn't complain at the time."

"At the time I was a little wound up, and ripping clothes adds to it. Just saying, I liked it."

Gone now, she thought, and pulled away what was left. "I'm going to want to borrow something until I can change. Not that everybody doesn't know what we just did, but I hold the line at flashing Sawyer or Bran."

"Borrow what you need." He rolled up to pull off his boots, glanced back over his shoulder. Turned the glance into a long study as she lay bare, with her jeans still caught around her knees.

"You lost some weight."

"I'll get it back."

"You will. You have a strong, agile body. Compact, efficient."

Amused, she fluttered her lashes. "Girls

love to hear how efficient their bodies are."

"It's a compliment when it comes to war and warriors. I've wanted it. Wanted you."

"Same goes—except for the compact part. You're just ripped."

"I'm going to want you again."

"That works for me. In fact." She sat up to untie her high-tops. "Why don't we go another round after you have a little recovery time."

"I heal, and recover, quickly."

"Even better, so..." Her eyebrows shot up as he stood to remove his pants. "Oh, well. Hello." Laughing, she tossed her shoes to the floor. "I bet that's a benefit to immortality you don't brood about."

"We'll see if you can handle it."

"Oh, I can handle it," she told him when he straddled her.

She handled it, and handled it again when they showered off sex and war. Not sure if she could handle a fourth bout, she grabbed one of his shirts, dashed over to her own room.

She changed, tossed his shirt over a chair to return later, then turned to the mirror to take stock.

To her own eye she looked about as relaxed as a woman could outside of a coma. And more than a little used up. In fact, she thought she could flop on the bed and sleep for hours—except she was starving.

Add to that, they all needed to talk about the battle before the bouts.

She tugged her fresh shirt away, studied her shoulder. Doyle had treated it and her leg with Bran's balm—and she'd done the same for his minor wounds. Since it already looked better, she gave it a little poke, felt no twinge.

Barely a scratch, she thought. A sky filled with death, and barely a scratch.

They'd been weak. A test run, just as Doyle had said.

But the run had been focused on her, and that burned. Twice now she'd been a target. She intended to reap some payback before she was done.

She put on her belt—gun on one hip, knife on the other—and went down to find food, drink, and friends.

She found them all in the kitchen, hit the post-battle snack platter first, grabbed a deviled egg.

"Sasha made Bellinis!" Annika immediately poured one for Riley, who made approving noises over a cracker topped with salami and cheese. "Did you have good sex?"

"Yes, thanks." Riley sent Doyle—already sipping a beer—a wide, exaggerated smile.

"Sawyer and I had good sex, and so did Bran and Sasha. I think it's nice we're all having good sex now. Móraí said it's good for the body, the mind, and the spirit, especially on a quest."

Bran choked. "What? My grandmother?"

"She's very wise. I miss her. She taught me to knit. I'm making everyone scarves. When we're not together like this, they'll be like a hug."

Riley gave her a one-armed one. "Wherever you go, I'm coming to see you. Where's Sasha?"

"She wanted to finish something," Bran said. "She won't be long. Do you have pain?"

"Absolutely none. The couple of nicks are already healing. Let me just say, I know

I'd have been in it deep if it wasn't for all of you. Not just because I wasn't a hundred percent—because I'd say I was closing in on ninety—but because she turned it on me, specifically. Even at a hundred, I couldn't have defended myself."

"She doesn't understand us, the unity of us." Bran gestured with his beer to encompass the room. "That we don't just fight together, don't just search together. We defend and protect each other, no matter the threat."

"We do." Carrying a canvas, Sasha walked in. "And we will. I wanted to finish this because, as we've said, symbols matter. This, I think, is a symbol of that unity. Of what we are, each of us, and what we are together."

She moved to the table, turned the canvas around, propped it against a vase of flowers cut that morning from the garden.

"A coat of arms," Sawyer said.

"Actually, it's an achievement, as it displays all the components, not just the armorials on the escutcheon, and..." Riley trailed off when she noted the puzzled looks—or in Doyle's case the cool stare.

"We'll just go with coat of arms." Riley lowered her glass, walked closer. "An amazing coat of arms."

"This is me, the mermaid." Annika linked her hand with Sasha's, squeezed, gestured to the painted woman with iridescent tail, with copper cuffs on both wrists, perched on a rock in a lapping sea. "And this stands for Sawyer."

The man had a gun on each hip, and the compass he held in an outstretched palm seemed to glow against a shimmering sky.

"And you, Riley!"

"Yeah, so I see."

Sasha had painted the image of a woman with her face thrown up to a full moon, her body a wolf.

"I told you I wanted to paint you transforming," Sasha reminded her. "This called for it."

"You captured it. I mean, I've never actually seen myself change—a little busy—but there's a joy to it you've captured. Got you, too, Doyle. All broody look, billowy coat, and the sword in your hand."

"It's not brooding. It's thoughtful. And there's herself," he added with a rare Irish idiom, "with crossbow and paintbrush, and eyes full of visions."

"And you." Sasha turned to Bran. "The sorcerer on the cliffside, riding the lightning."

"Each of us as individuals in the panels," Bran observed, "and here, under the crest, six together, standing together, as one."

"Dragons for the supporters," Doyle added.

"I liked the look of them." Sasha studied her work. "Wanted something strong and mystical."

"The three stars and the moon make the crest," Sawyer noted. "Bull's-eye, Sasha. What's it say? The, you know, motto. Is that Latin?"

"It says: **To seek the stars. To serve the light. To guard the worlds.**"

Sasha looked at Riley with relief. "I got the Latin right? I was afraid I'd bungle it — then I couldn't decide at first. Gaelic, Latin, Greek. But I kept coming back to the Latin, so I went with it."

"It's perfect."

"And beautiful," Annika added. "The colors are strong, because we are. And it has six sides, because we are six. Even the..." When she couldn't find the word, she traced the edge of the coat of arms.

"Border," Sawyer told her.

"Yes, the border. It's three strands of two—yes—braided together. Because we are. Can you make drawings—like the sketches—for us all?"

"I think I can do something else," Bran put in. "Leave it to me. This, **fáidh**, is magnificent, and it's powerful. Will you let me use it?"

"Of course."

"You took strangers and brought them together, for purpose, for family."

"I didn't—"

"Your vision," he interrupted. "And your courage. I think we'd have come together, we were meant to. But without you, not when and where we did. Or, I believe, how."

He turned to her and kissed her gently. "I had intended to do this when we were alone. Tonight, with candles and wine under a quiet moon. But I think now, here, together."

He reached in his pocket, took out a small white box with the symbol for eternity etched in silver on the top.

"Bran."

"Móraí gave this to me before she left this morning. I had thought to create one for you myself, but this was her grandmother's, created by her grandfather in love, in magick, in pledge. Will you take it, wear it, this symbol of always?"

"Yes. Of course, yes." She took his hand. "I love you."

When he opened the box, she gasped. The ring caught the light, showered the room with every color, before it shimmered into quiet, steady shine.

"It's beautiful. It's—"

Magnificent, elegant, the center stone a heart of pure white framed in tiny round diamonds that glistened like a rainbow.

"I give you this heart because you're mine."

"I'll wear it because you're mine. Oh, it fits. It fits."

"Magick," he said, drew her close, kissed her long.

"Okay, break it up. Let's get a good look." Riley snatched Sasha's left hand. "That's some rock. Nice," she told Bran.

"How's a guy supposed to follow that one?" Sawyer wondered, and gave Bran a light punch in the shoulder.

"I would like a ring from you. I'm so happy." Tearfully, Annika embraced Bran and Sasha in turn. "I have so much happy."

"It looks right on you."

Sasha smiled at Doyle. "Feels even better." Then she turned into Bran's arms. "I have so much happy, too. And it makes me feel strong." She drew away. "It makes me feel valiant. It makes me believe, more than ever, we'll do what it says on our crest. We'll seek the stars."

"And serve the light," Bran said.

"And guard the worlds," the others said together.

Riley stepped back, picked up her drink. "To do those three things means fighting, surviving, and destroying Nerezza. Not just her minions and whatever the hell Malmon's become."

"Agreed. Since we're all here now," Bran began, "why don't we sit down and talk about this last fight."

"Do that, but give me five." Sawyer pulled open a drawer for kitchen scissors. "I need some stuff out of the herb garden for this marinade. Didn't realize when I decided on rack of lamb we'd be celebrating an official engagement. We're going fancy tonight, boys and girls."

As he went out, Riley moved into the lounge area to sit. Propped her feet on the coffee table.

"I'm always up for a celebratory meal," she said, "but it seems particularly timely tonight."

Sasha sat beside her. "Really?"

Catching the subtext, Riley laughed. "Yeah, we're all having sex. Drop the confetti. What I mean was Sasha's got a ring, we've got a coat of arms and a kick-ass motto. Best, we're all alive."

"Barely scratched," Bran pointed out.

"They were slow and weak. Sawyer said—" Pausing, Annika glanced toward the door. "Should we wait to say—but he knows because he said. They were slow and weak."

"I wouldn't have thought so if it had

been the first attack." As she drank, Sasha curled up her legs. "There were so many this time, more than we've had before. But without the—without the same ferocity. Except toward Riley."

"We should—Here he is," Annika said as Sawyer came in with a basket of herbs.

"Keep it going. I'm multitasking."

"All right. I want to say first, I didn't sense, not initially, their focus on Riley. And when I did..." Sasha laid a hand on Riley's outstretched leg, rubbed. "It was nearly too late."

"They—or Nerezza—figured I was off my game."

"You were," Doyle responded, mercilessly.

She wanted to bristle, made herself shrug. "Marginally. I'd like to see you take on a few hundred mutant birds from hell all determined to slice and peck you to death."

"He pretty much did." As he spoke, Sawyer continued to chop herbs. "The rest of us were too spread out."

"Okay, point, and again, thanks for the save."

"I'm not looking for thanks. You were off your game," Doyle repeated. "A soldier still fights. It's more to the point we **were** spread out. Nerezza may be off her game as well, but she had the tactics here. She pulled us away from each other, or more accurately, pulled us away from Riley, in hopes of eliminating the one she believed was most vulnerable."

"It came too close to working." In his chair, Bran studied his beer. "We can't forget to protect each other."

"We did. Not arguing about how close she came to turning this around," Sawyer continued. "But we did protect each other. And we won. She went for the shock and awe, right? Blocked out the freaking sun. And it worked—temporarily. Each one of us was so busy cutting them down we didn't have each other's backs. But then we did."

"I saw you fly," Annika murmured. "The wind, it was alive. It wrapped around you, and threw you."

"Felt that way," Riley admitted. "It was like—not that I've had the experience— being sucked into a tornado."

"It threw you," Annika said again, "even more away from us. I saw you fall, and I was afraid. But I was even more very, very angry."

"I was a little pissed off myself. You came running. All of you. She doesn't have that in her bag of tactics. That all-for-one deal. And I'm feeling a hell of a lot better."

"She'll be feeling better, too," Sasha pointed out. "Whatever she sends next won't be as slow or weak."

"We work on positions." Doyle nodded when Sawyer pulled another beer out of the refrigerator, waggled it. "No one gets cut off, separated, or pulled away. They may have been slower, weaker, but we weren't sharp. Not sharp enough."

"If I'd sensed the intent, even five seconds sooner—"

"It's not all on you, Blondie," Doyle said. "We got flanked."

Since one of Sasha's sketch pads sat on the table, he picked it up, took one of her pencils. He drew quickly.

The structure, to Riley's eye, looked more like a barn than Bran's house, but it made the point. So did the curved lines, the squiggles to represent garden paths, shrubs, trees, the cliff wall.

And as far as she could tell, he had everything in its place, and nearly to scale.

"We started here." He used first initials—and an SK for Sawyer—to note positions. "Annika shifted here, Bran here." Now he used dotted lines to note the change in positions, for each. And again until he laid them out when Riley had been tossed.

"How do you know where everyone moved, during the thick of it?" Sasha demanded.

"I know where my people are."

Studying the diagram, Riley leaned closer. "Impressive. And assuming this is accurate—and I do," she added before Doyle could snap at her—"it illustrates how easily she drew us apart. Bran—magick man—is the full length of the field from my position when I hit my ass. Whatever she thinks of the rest of us, she respects power, his power. Sawyer's closer, but again, pulled way back. Lowers the chances of him pulling out the compass, getting me out of there."

"Sasha is back against the wall above

the sea."

"And facing away. I was facing away. That was probably deliberate, too."

"I was closer, but..." Annika looked at Doyle. "She would think me stronger in the sea than on the land. Yes?"

"She'd be wrong, but yes."

"And you, here, closer than all but me. But still far. It helps to see it like this, like a picture. Can you draw what we should have done? The positions?"

Doyle smiled at her. "Yeah. The thing is, those positions have to be flexible. You have to react in the moment. You could take a hit, or need to move to help someone else. But."

As Doyle sketched out, explained, battlefield strategy, Riley rose to get another drink, watched Sawyer finish rubbing his herbs and garlic—and she thought maybe mustard—over the big rack of lamb.

"That smells really good."

"A couple of hours in this?" He slid the rack into a huge plastic bag, poured olive oil over it. "It'll taste even better," he promised as he turned the bag to coat the meat.

"She conned us." He said it to Riley, then repeated it for the others. "Nerezza conned us, and so we underestimated her. Lesson learned."

"This has value." Bran gestured to the sketches. "And so will the drills I believe Doyle will exhaust us with."

"Starting now."

"Now?" Riley nearly choked on the olive she'd popped in her mouth. "Been drinking," she pointed out.

"And if an attack came now, you'd have been drinking. We need to know how to break off into teams. We've been over that, but it went to hell today. So we drill."

"How long before you have to deal with the rest of that meal you're making?" Bran asked Sawyer.

"I've got an hour."

"An hour then." He pushed to his feet, pulled Sasha to hers. "Then I need an hour of my own with the painting."

They drilled. Riley hated to admit Doyle was right, but they needed to. Maybe it was weird to think—and feel—battles with evil forces had become a kind of routine, but as she'd nearly had her ass handed to her, she had to admit that as part of the issue.

She'd gotten sloppy, and she hadn't been alone.

When he called it, she slipped off. Not to hit the books, but to give in to recovery. She stretched out on the sofa in the tower library, fire snapping, and took a much-needed nap.

Refreshed, she wandered back into the kitchen, and into the marvelous scents of roasted meat and potatoes.

"Good timing," Sawyer told her. "Lamb's resting. We eat in ten."

Glancing over, she noted Annika had already set the table. She'd fashioned a bride and groom out of salt and pepper mills, draping a train of white linen for Sasha, creating a bow tie out of a black ribbon for Bran. She'd even created an arbor of flowers over them.

"Sweet," Riley declared.

"She is that. I thought aquamarine."

"Huh?"

"For a ring. For Anni."

"Oh. Because it represents the sea. Nice,

Sawyer."

"I don't suppose you know where I can get one—the stone. Just the stone. I'm thinking Sasha could help me design a ring, and maybe Bran could..." He wiggled his fingers.

Sweet, she thought again. "I'll make some calls."

They had their celebratory meal, with the bridal tablescape and champagne. Doyle might've preferred beer, but he figured some moments deserved the sparkle.

They didn't talk of war but of wedding, and as a man who'd lived lifetimes as a soldier, he knew there were moments as well to put the blood and the battles aside and give over to love and life.

He might not have had much to say about either, but his companions didn't appear to need him, as conversation never lagged.

"Would you marry me here?" Bran asked. "When the stars are returned, and our lives are our own again?"

"Here? I can't think of a more perfect or beautiful place. My mother—"

"We'll bring her over, and my family will come in droves, believe me."

"Móraí." The idea delighted Annika. "I can show her the scarves I've made. But..."

"You're worried you won't be able to come, that you'll be back in the sea," Sasha said. "Bran?"

"I'll make you a pool," he promised. "If your time on land is up, you'll have a pool, and be part of the day."

"You'd do that for me?"

Bran reached over to take her hand, to kiss her knuckles. "You're my sister."

"And mine. Both you and Riley. So you'll be my maids of honor. You'll do that, won't you?"

"Couldn't stop us, right, Anni?"

"Oh, we will be so happy to be maids of honor. What is it?"

As Sasha laughed, Riley reached for more potatoes. "Like attendants. It's a tradition with a long history—which I'll refrain from recounting."

She ignored the applause that rounded the table.

"But to bring it current, we stand up for Sasha, help make the day perfect for her.

Then we party."

"I would like that very much."

"And I have my best men here, with Doyle and Sawyer. It's very like what you and Riley will be for Sasha."

"You can count on us, bro. You can count on us to throw you the mother of all stag parties, right, Doyle?"

"You will have deer?" Annika wondered.

"Stag parties are an excuse for the groom and his pals to drink themselves stupid and hire a stripper," Riley told her.

"They have too much class for strippers," Sasha objected.

"No, we don't." And Doyle reached for more champagne.

"We'll have our own version," Riley assured her.

"You'll make some calls," Doyle assumed.

"I've got some contacts."

Bran waited until the meal wound down.

"I'd like everyone to join me outside in an hour. For a kind of ceremony, you could say. You'll need your weapons."

"If it's another drill after that meal..." Riley groaned as she pushed back from the table.

"Something else. In an hour," Bran said again, "by the seawall."

Riley spent the bulk of the hour making those calls, then pocketed her phone to go gather weapons. Since Bran hadn't been specific, she decided to haul out all of them.

When Sawyer walked into the sitting room turned armory, she realized he'd had the same idea.

"I was going to hunt you up after I took down the first load."

"No hunting required, and with two of us, we should be able to handle it in one trip."

"Speaking of trips," she said as she slung the long-distance rifle over her shoulder. "I've got a source for your aquamarine."

"You—Already?"

"We deliver. Bran didn't say ammo, but..." She shoved extra mags in her pockets.

"Wait. Where? How?"

"How is I know a guy who knows a girl whose family owns a jewelry store in Dublin. They make and design as well as sell, so they have loose stones."

"In Dublin."

"Yeah, the other side of the country, but I don't see that as a big for a shifter like you. The uncle of the girl the guy knows can have some stones to show you in a couple of days. If that's the way you want to go, we zip over there, take a look, zip back."

"Yeah, I...I didn't expect it to be like now."

"Your move, Cowboy."

"Right. My move. I'm in. Wow."

"Good. Load 'em up. Let's see what Bran's got cooking."

Cooking wasn't far off, Riley noted, as Bran had a cauldron hovering over the ground. Sasha's painting of the coat of arms floated over it.

"You started the show without us," Riley said.

"You ain't seen nothing yet." Bran looked over as the others crossed the lawn. "We've talked of unity. We've shown our unity. Sasha's given us a symbol of unity. We take another step here, if all are willing."

"We're with you," Sawyer said simply. "Every one."

Riley nodded. "So say we all."

"Then here I cast the circle." Taking an athame from his belt, Bran pointed it north, south, east, west. "On this land, at this hour, we cast our light, we lift our power. Spark the fire, stir the air."

Under the cauldron, fire burned. The wind rose to shimmer the circle of light around the six.

"Against evil conspire, to stand in times foul or fair. Earth bloom, water spill. Both sun and moon defeat the gloom, so against the dark we test our will."

Flowers tumbled out of the grass within the circle. Pure blue water fountained out of the air and into the cauldron.

"We are kinsmen, of blood and heart. As one together or apart. This symbol we create, our unity to celebrate."

The air thrummed. Riley felt it beat in her own blood, felt the wolf inside her open to the power, to the sheer beauty as Bran held his hands over the cauldron. As he turned them up to the sky. In them now were two vials, gleaming white.

What poured to them to her eyes was liquid light.

Mists rose, and what stirred inside the cauldron hummed.

"This was passed to me, hand to hand, magick to magick, son to daughter, daughter to son." Bran held up the athame, then slid it into the cauldron. "Your bow, **fáidh**."

Sasha held it out to him. In her eyes Riley saw not only the love, the absolute faith, but a great deal of the wonder she felt herself.

When he'd put the bow in the cauldron, he turned to Annika, who wordlessly held out her arms. He took the cuffs, added them.

In full trust, Riley gave Bran her guns, even the knife at her hip. Sawyer did the same, then pulled out his compass.

"You should take this, too."

"Are you certain?" Bran asked him.

"Yeah. Passed to me, hand to hand."

Adding it, Bran turned to Doyle, took his bow. "Will you, again, trust me with your sword?"

"You, and all within this circle, as I've

trusted no others in three hundred years."

Bran lowered the sword, impossibly, into the cauldron.

"We fight for light, our might for right. All we are in body, in spirit, in mind bound beyond the stars we find. On this night, by this mark, we are **clann**, and under this symbol united stand."

The mist above the cauldron stirred and formed the symbol of the coat of arms.

"Do you will this to be?"

Rather than speak, Riley took Sawyer's hand, then Doyle's. And all six joined around the circle.

"Then by our wills, so mote it be."

In the smoke, the replica of the coat of arms burned bright, flashed into flame, then lowered into the cauldron.

And all went still.

"Wow. Can I hear an amen?" Sawyer asked.

Riley blew out a breath. "Amen, brother. You got some major chops, Irish."

"Well, we do what we can." Bran drew out Doyle's sword, held it to the moonlight. Just below the hilt, the coat of arms was etched into the steel.

"It's ours," Annika murmured. "Our family."

Bran lifted out her cuffs, slipped them back on her wrists. She traced her fingers over the new symbols. "They're only more beautiful now."

"And potentially more powerful." Bran handed Riley the guns. "Unity is strength, and I believe that will translate."

Sawyer took his sidearms, studied the symbol on the grips, like Riley's. "It's a good thing." And took his compass, now bearing the coat of arms. "A real good thing."

Let her come, Riley thought, and searched the sky. Let her come and test the Clan of the Guardians.

Chapter Thirteen

Nerezza didn't come that night, or the next. She sent no vicious creatures to attack when they dived the cold waters of the Atlantic to search.

Nothing lurked in the forest, hovered in the sky.

Sasha had no visions.

Riley used the time to her advantage. She drilled, she practiced, she worked out until her body began to feel like itself again. She spent hours with books, computers, notes.

And hours more with Doyle in bed. Or on the floor.

She went with Sawyer to Dublin, using a trip for supplies as cover. Leaving a sulking Annika behind. Since they were there, she replaced the ruined sweatshirt.

And since they were there, she dragged a somewhat shell-shocked Sawyer into a pub for a pint.

"Maybe I should've just bought a ready-made."

"This way means more."

"Yeah, but...then it would just be done."

Riley settled back to enjoy her Guinness, as to her mind there was nothing quite like a well-built Guinness, savored slowly in a dimly lit Irish pub.

Add a plate of chips still hot from the fryer and drizzled with salt and vinegar? Perfection.

"Getting cold feet?"

"No. No, it's just..." Sawyer took a fast, non savoring pull from his own pint. "I'm going to get engaged—ring and everything. It's a moment."

Happy to drink to that, Riley hefted her pint. "Here's to the moment."

"Yeah." He clinked glasses with her, glanced around as if he'd forgotten where they were. "It seems weird to be here—all these people—just sitting here having a beer. Nobody knows what the fuck, Riley, except you and me."

Biting into a chip, Riley looked around herself—the buzz of conversation, the energy and color.

Low lights on a day when the sun couldn't make up its mind, air smelling of beer and fried potatoes and pureed vegetable soup.

Voices—German, Japanese, Italian. American, Canadian, Brit, Irish accents.

She'd always considered a good European bar a kind of mini UN.

"I missed people," she realized, "and that's not usually true for me. But I've missed the noise and the vibe. The faces and voices of strangers. It's good they don't know what the fuck. They can't do a damn thing about it. So it's another moment, just sitting here like normal people, having a normal beer in a normal pub."

"You're right. You're right. At the bottom it's what we're fighting for."

"A world where anybody can have a beer at four o'clock on a Tuesday afternoon."

"Or get engaged to a mermaid."

"That might be stretching it for most anyone but you in this pub, or in Dublin. But yeah, I can drink to that." She glanced over at the waitress, a young, fresh-faced girl with deep purple hair. "We're good, thanks."

"When I'm done, and this world is dark, I'll drink your blood."

The girl had a quick smile, a pretty lilt in her voice. And her eyes were blind and mad. Riley slid a hand under her jacket, snapped open her holster.

"Don't," Sawyer whispered, gaze fixed on the waitress's face. "She's innocent."

"You're weak. Did you think what you hold could destroy me? I grow stronger."

As they watched, the purple hair grew, went smoke gray streaked with black. Blue eyes went black as they shifted to Riley. "I may keep you as a pet, and let Malmon have you."

Though she kept one hand on her gun, Riley picked up her glass. "Yawn," she said, and drank.

The table shook; the chairs rattled. And the other patrons drank on, talked on, feeling nothing.

Deliberately, Sawyer twirled a finger in the air. "Hey, if you're playing waitress—nice look for you—maybe you could get us some beer nuts to go with the pints and chips."

Rage stained the creamy Irish skin florid pink. "I'll peel the flesh from your bones, feed it to my dogs."

"Yeah, yeah. Beer nuts?"

"The storm comes."

The waitress blinked, pushed dazedly at her purple hair. "Beg pardon, my mind went somewhere. Can I get you something more?"

"No, thanks." Riley took a deep drink, waited until the girl wandered off. "That was fun."

"No beer nuts."

On a laugh, Riley offered her fist to bump. "You've got stones, Sawyer. And I'd say we'd better get our asses home, spread the word. Nerezza's on the mend, and on the prowl."

Sawyer sighed as they slid out of the booth. "Now we've got to tell them we've been in Dublin."

"No way around it," Riley agreed. "Let

me take the lead there."

"Happy to follow."

Given the situation, Sawyer had no problem letting Riley take point. When they got back, wound their way back to the kitchen, he just slid his hands into his pockets—and over the jewelry pouches he'd stuck there—and kept his mouth shut.

Sasha worked alone, forming dough i nto baguettes. "Hey, you're back."

"Yeah, something smells really good."

"I've got the sauce going for lasagna, and trying my hand at making Italian bread. It's fun. I hope you found the ricotta and mozzarella."

"Oh." Shit. Now Riley's hands found their way into her pockets. "About that—"

"Need some help bringing in the supplies? Annika's up with Bran, and—I don't know where Doyle is." Choosing a knife, Sasha made diagonal slices on the loaves. "Just let me cover these to rise, and I'll help."

"We didn't actually get supplies."

"What? Why? Where have you been?"

"Annika's in the tower, right? Sawyer

wanted to bag some stones for an engagement ring, so—"

"Sawyer!" Tossing the dishcloth aside for the moment, Sasha raced over, hugged him hard. "This is so...Stones? Not an actual ring?"

"See, I was thinking you could help me design one, then maybe Bran—"

"Oh! That is the best idea!" She hugged him again. "She'll love it. I can't wait to start. Tell me what you have in mind."

"Actually, we need to wait a minute on that. Right?" He appealed to Riley.

"Right. When we were in Dublin, we—"

"Dublin?" Sasha gaped, actually gave Sawyer a little shove as she stepped back from him. "You went to **Dublin**."

"Long story short. I had a contact, so we zipped there, got the stones, and we were having a drink when..."

When Sasha held up a finger, Riley trailed off. "The two of you went all the way to Dublin—it doesn't matter how quickly you got there and back—" Sasha said, effectively cutting off Riley's main argument. "You didn't tell anyone you were going. Then you stopped for a **drink**?"

"Maybe you had to be there. And okay, I bought a sweatshirt. I needed a sweatshirt. It wasn't like we were trolling Grafton Street."

"Anyone who leaves the property needs to make it clear where they are. Obviously something happened while you were gone. I'll get the others, and you can explain yourselves."

As Sasha carefully covered the loaves with the towel, Sawyer shifted his feet. "Can we leave out the why we went? At least when Anni's around?"

Sasha sent him a cool stare. "All you had to do was tell me, or Bran or Doyle. We know how to keep a secret. I'll get them."

Alone with Sawyer, Riley let out a long breath. "Mom's very disappointed in us."

"I feel like an idiot. How did she make me feel like an idiot without raising her voice?"

"Skills. I'm opening wine. We never finished that pint, and I have a feeling we're going to need some adult beverages."

"We didn't get the supplies either. How did we forget the supplies?"

"We were in a little bit of a hurry to get back," Riley reminded him. She opened a bottle of red, set out glasses. And prepared to face the music.

Annika danced down the back steps— sulks long forgotten—as Doyle came in from the outside.

"Are we having wine? Bran and I have been working very hard. Wine is good." Annika wrapped arms around Sawyer, snuggled in. "So are you."

Stroking her hair, he shot Riley a wan smile over Annika's head.

"Show some solidarity," Riley said to Doyle before he could go for a beer. She poured six glasses.

Before he took one, he studied her face. "What's the deal?"

"All at once, everybody at once." And she noted from the look on Bran's face as he came in with Sasha he'd already been partially briefed.

"Okay, here's the deal." To fortify herself, Riley took a glass, took a gulp. "Sawyer and I shifted to Dublin."

"What is Dublin?" Annika asked.

"The capital of Ireland." Doyle's gaze hardened. "On the east coast of the country."

"That's very far for food supplies. It's a city?" Annika continued, drawing back from Sawyer. "But you didn't take me?"

"No, I...Well, we—"

"He needed to go there to do something for you. A surprise for you."

Far from mollified, Annika frowned at Riley. "A surprise for me? What is it?"

"Anni, a surprise means you don't get to know yet. I went to help him with it."

"Regardless," Bran interrupted, his tone as dismissive as Sasha's had been. "Traveling that far, for any reason, without telling the rest of us, is directly in opposition to everything we've done and become."

"It's my fault—" Sawyer began, but Riley cut him off.

"No, we're in it together. And you're right. I'm going to say we got caught up and leave it at that. Sawyer can grovel later."

"Hey."

"I just think you'd be better at groveling than me. We can keep talking about how stupid or irresponsible or whatever we were. Or we can tell you what happened that's a hell of a lot more important."

"You suck at groveling," Sawyer muttered.

"Told ya."

"Nerezza. It was Nerezza." Sasha stepped forward. "I can feel it now."

"Alive and in person. Or in the person of a waitress at this pub off Grafton."

"You went for a pint?" Doyle demanded.

"Oh, like you wouldn't have done the same. We finished our...business, went for a beer before heading back. And I've barely gotten a good start on my Guinness when the waitress comes over. At first, it was her own face and body, her own voice. But the words?"

Riley closed her eyes a moment to bring it back. "She said: 'When I'm done, and this world is dark, I'll drink your blood.'" Riley glanced down at the red wine in her hand, considered, then drank it almost for spite. "And if you don't think it's a jolt to hear some pretty young waitress say that in an Irish accent, let me tell you, it is."

"People are just going about their business," Sawyer added. "We can't go at her. She's just a girl. Nerezza's using her, so it's not like we could knock her on her ass."

"Or shoot her, as Sawyer pointed out to me. She said we were weak, and she was growing stronger."

"To prove that, she showed us. The girl changed, and there she was, standing in this crowded pub. Her hair's not all gray now. It's got black streaks through it, and she's got some age on her, but not like she did when I had a grip on her over Capri."

"She's healing," Sasha murmured. "Regaining her strength and powers."

"Riley dissed her. Pulled the 'bored now' bit."

"Bad Willow. Buffy reference."

Doyle gave Riley a light shove. "Do you mind?"

"Look, seeing as it was, in reality, some innocent girl, dissing was all I could do. All we could do."

"She said maybe she'd make Riley a pet, give her to Malmon."

"As if."

"Don't toss that off," Sawyer argued. "For whatever reason she's gunning for you right now. When she got pissed at

Riley, the pub shook. Bottles, glasses rattling around. Nobody noticed."

"Then Sawyer took a solid dig at her, said maybe she could get us some beer nuts. Pissed her off more, so then it was all peeling our skin off, feeding it to dogs. Since we couldn't go at her, we shrugged it off. The last thing she said was: 'The storm comes.' Then the waitress was back, looking dazed and confused."

"She didn't try to harm you." With a nod, Bran finally picked up the wine, passed one glass to Sasha. "She had you down to two, in an enclosed, public space where you'd have hesitated to use force or violence, but she didn't strike at you."

"Because she couldn't," Sasha concluded. "She's not strong enough for that yet. For illusions, for using other means. But not striking out herself."

"She wasn't actually there. Do I have that right?" Doyle turned to Bran. "The illusion of her only."

"That would be my take on it, yes."

"If she had been stronger, we wouldn't have been with you." Annika stepped over to Sasha—away from Sawyer. "We wouldn't have known you were far away. And if you were taken or hurt, we wouldn't know."

"We weren't." Sawyer felt it vital to point that out. "I'm sorry, bad judgment, but we weren't taken or hurt. And all of us are alone or with only part of the team all the time."

"Not alone or in part in bloody Dublin," Doyle snapped.

"Hence the bad judgment. It was the wrong way to go about it, but we pulled in some information. You can keep slapping us back for the bad judgment, or we can use what we brought back."

"You suck at groveling, too," Riley commented.

"Apparently. Look, what I went to do was really important to me. I went about it wrong, and I'm sorry. Mea culpa squared, sincerely. That's it."

"Maybe we should all just cool off a little, then we can talk about this more reasonably." Sasha moved over to stir the sauce. "And we still need those supplies."

"You didn't get the buggering supplies."

"We got a little distracted," Riley snapped back at Doyle. "We'll go get the buggering supplies now."

"No, Annika and I'll go get them."

"Yes." Annika linked her arm through Doyle's. "We will go, and I will get cool so we can talk again."

She held her hand, palm up, to Sawyer. "You have the list of what we need to buy."

He pulled it out of his back pocket, handed it to her. Said, "Balls," when she sailed out beside Doyle.

"She'll get over it. You're all going to have to get over it," Riley said. "We did what we did, copped to it. If you're going to scold us some more, I want more wine."

Sasha glanced back from the stove. "It was unnecessarily risky."

"It didn't feel like it." Riley shrugged.

"Until you were waiting for the dark god to bring you beer nuts?" Bran suggested.

"Even then. It was clear intimidation, Irish. Did it give us a jolt? Sure. But what was she going to do? She doesn't, or hasn't, come to fight on her own. We should have told you guys—sans Anni. Not doing that was stupid, just stupid. I can only say

I guess we were so into the secret mission we didn't think of it."

"Shortsighted, impulsive. And understandable."

"Under—" Shocked nearly speechless, Sasha swung around, gaped at Bran.

"**A ghrá.** A man in love often thinks with heart instead of head."

Sawyer tried a winning smile in Sasha's direction, patted his hand over his heart.

She sniffed. "Riley's not a man in love and should've known better."

"For friendship one also does the foolish."

"Foolish isn't—I'll shut up," Riley decided. "Come on, Sash, all's well that ends with everybody breathing. And you know you want to see the rocks. You really want to see the shinies Sawyer bought for the ring."

"I really don't—Damn it, of course I want to see them."

Grasping the reprieve, Sawyer pulled the pouches from his pocket. "This one's the big kahuna."

He poured the stone into his hand. Perfectly round, beautifully blue, it gleamed there like a small pool.

"Aquamarine." Smiling, Bran rubbed a

hand on Sasha's shoulder. "As legends say the mermaids once prized the stones."

"Blue sea—the name means blue sea, so it fits," Riley added.

"It's lovely, Sawyer. Can I?" Sasha lifted it, held it up. "Oh, look how many shades of blue in the light. You couldn't have chosen anything more right for her."

"You think? I've got these little stones." From the second pouch he poured a stream of tiny diamonds, pink sapphires, more aquamarines. "I was thinking you could come up with something, and I got these." From a third pouch he took two bands of platinum. "And then maybe Bran could put it all together."

"I'd be happy to."

"And I've already got a couple of ideas." Sasha took another study of the stone, handed it back. "That doesn't mean I'm not still annoyed."

"Down to annoyed's progress." Sawyer repouched the stones, the bands.

"In the name of progress, I'd like to add one thing. When the bitch said a storm's coming, the hair on the back of my neck stood up."

Sawyer looked at Riley. "You, too?"

"Oh, yeah. Something there, something big. That wasn't just bluster. For me, it was slipped in out of pique, but it had weight. Maybe it'll springboard something for you."

"Not right now," Sasha told her.

"Something to think on. I'm going to think on it while I hit the books. That's my penance."

"Researching isn't penance for you. Making a salad, however—"

"I'm better at that; she's better at the books." Sawyer tried that winning smile again. "Let's play to our strengths."

"Good plan. I'm in my room, digging in if needed." Riley escaped while she had the chance.

Maybe she didn't like having Doyle and Annika still pissed, but she figured Annika wasn't wired to stay mad for long. And she had a plan where Doyle was concerned.

As she had her balcony doors open, she heard them come back. Biding her time, she continued to work, take notes. It didn't take him long.

When he walked in, she sat at her desk. Wearing nothing but his shirt.

He closed the door with a decisive snap. "That's your research outfit?"

"This?" She swiveled in the chair. Yeah, still pissed, but...interested. "I figured you'd get around to wanting your shirt back. Just wanted to have it handy."

"You think you can distract me with sex?"

"Sure." She rose. "I get wanting your shirt back, but it seems a little redundant when you're already wearing one."

While he stood, she took off his sheath, stood the sword beside the bed. Came back and began unbuttoning his shirt.

"You're that sure of your allure?"

"Allure? Please. I've got all the necessary girl parts. That's allure enough, especially with a man who's already cruised them."

She tossed the shirt aside, gave him a little nudge toward the bed. "Sit down, big guy, and I'll get you naked."

"It didn't trouble you that Sawyer or Bran might have walked in rather than me?"

Another nudge. "First, I'm covered. Second, you're the only one who'd walk in without knocking. Sit," she repeated.

"I didn't come in here to have sex." But he sat on the side of the bed.

"Life's full of surprises." She pulled off his boots, smiled as she unhooked his belt. "Surprise."

"I can have sex and still be pissed at you."

"Handy for both of us." She gave him a shove to push him onto his back. Moving quickly, she tugged his jeans down, kicked them across the room.

Then climbed on to straddle him.

"What do you say we talk later?"

He gripped her hair, none too gently, to haul her down. As her mouth met his, he flipped her onto her back.

She expected him to simply take her, just pound away—and wouldn't have objected. Instead he changed his grip from her hair to her wrists, yanked her arms over her head.

Instinct had her trying to tug free. "Hey."

"Shut up."

He ravaged her mouth, spinning her system into overdrive. She struggled—not in protest, but in the desire to get her hands on him.

She'd have to say no, tell him outright to stop, or she'd take what he gave her.

Temper still burned in him, and burning with it was a scorching lust. She thought she could play him—and by God she had—but she'd know the full force of what he wanted from her before he was done.

He liked her helpless, for once, pinned under him, her hands cuffed by his. Her body quivering and bucking when he closed his mouth over her breast. When he used his teeth to hint at pain.

She could tie him into knots with those eyes. Now she'd know what it was to feel choice dissolve in outrageous desire.

He yanked her arms down, kept her wrists clamped in his hand. And moved ruthlessly down her body. She cried out when he used his tongue. Arched and writhed and cried out again when he didn't relent.

But the word she cried wasn't no.

It was yes.

She knew what it was to burn. Knew what it was to give in to needs, however feral. But this, now, spurred her beyond the known. He shoved her over the edge only to whip her onto another. And again until her lungs seared and her heart beat to bursting.

When he released her hands so he could use his own on her, to press and grip and plunder, hers could only grip the sheets and let what he did rage through her.

Everywhere, everywhere those rough hands moved shuddered, as if her nerves lived over her skin now.

When he jerked her up, her head fell back. Her body quivered, every inch, at the threat of more. At the welcoming of it.

"No, no, you'll look. You'll open your eyes and look at the one who takes you as you're meant to be taken. Look at me, damn you, look at the one who knows what lives in you."

She opened her eyes, looked into his, so fiercely green they were nearly blinding. But in them she saw that need and that knowledge. For her, of her.

She gripped his hips. "I see you."

Half mad, he thrust into her. He plundered her as his blood burned and his heart leaped where it had no business falling. Because he saw her, he knew her, and she him.

And so he feared both of them were

damned.

Taken over, she thought when they'd both gone limp as wax. That one step she'd never allowed with another, she'd allowed him. To take her over—body, mind, and all she was.

Once that step was taken, how did she go back?

How could she go back?

When he rolled away, to lie on his back beside her, her instinct was to curl in. But she quashed it, stayed as she was.

Keep it light, she warned herself. She knew how to address facts and keep it light.

"Maybe I'll keep that shirt. It obviously works on me."

"You can have what's left of it."

Puzzled, she looked down, noted the torn remains of it at the foot of the bed. "We keep this up, we'll both be walking around mostly naked."

He rolled, grabbed the bottle of water from her nightstand, drank half of it down. Almost as an afterthought, he offered her the rest. "I've marked you."

She took stock. Bruises on her wrists, a

couple more here and there. "Nothing much."

But he got up and brought her jar of balm back to the bed.

"You pissed me off," he said, even as he stroked the balm onto the bruises.

"Bitch at me all you want because nothing's going to reach the level of Sasha's stern disapproval." Now Riley hissed out a breath. "It flattened me. We should've told somebody what we were doing, where we were going. Sawyer wanted to get the makings of an engagement ring for Anni, and—"

"I figured that out on my own, though I figured you'd gone for a ring altogether. Doesn't excuse it."

"Message received, loud and clear. It was a slap to the whole unity thing, and thoughtless. Even with that, all of this…old habits. I'm sorry. Best I can do is I'm sorry."

Because she still felt just a little fragile, she got out of bed, pulled on his torn shirt. "I'm going to—Wait. You said you figured out why we went. Has Anni?"

"She might have, as she's no idiot, but I steered her in another direction. I suggested the two of you'd gone so he could find her a new dress, maybe some earrings. A present."

"Good thinking."

"It mollified her, as did the half a torturous hour she spent in the little shop that sells various trinkets."

"I'd say I owe you for that, but considering recent activities, I claim paid in full. I'm going to grab a shower, then head down to finish the amends by helping with something domestic."

When he made no move to join her, she went into the bathroom, closed the door.

Closed her eyes.

He'd shaken everything inside her, she realized. Shaken it, tossed it in the air so it fell back in an order she didn't understand.

She'd figure it out, she assured herself. Whatever the puzzle, the problem, the code, she figured it out eventually.

She took off the shirt, realized it smelled of both of them, a mix of them. A blend.

And folding it onto the counter, she felt ridiculous because she knew she had no intention of tossing it away.

Chapter Fourteen

After days of quiet, the routine of training and diving, Doyle calculated it was time, past time, to mix things up. He tracked Bran down in the tower, stood a moment watching as his friend wrote in the thick spell book.

It wasn't all whirlwinds and calling the lightning, he thought. Some of magick was—well—toil and trouble, and more was, apparently, as pedestrian as pen and paper.

Bran set the pen down, studied what he'd written. Then he laid his hand on the page. Light flashed, held. Dissolved.

And a great deal, Doyle considered, was sheer and stunning power.

"Got a minute?" he asked when Bran

glanced over.

"I do now. Things must be written down and the magicks sealed. For ourselves, and for those who come after."

Curious, Doyle walked over to see what Bran had written.

"In the old tongue."

"The language of my blood—and yours. Of the old gods, of the old powers."

"A kind of locator spell," Doyle said, translating. "Using the coat of arms as... a homing device."

"More or less. Let's have some tea." He rose, leaving the book open, and walked over to plug in an electric kettle.

"You don't need electricity and teapots."

"Well now, the gods help those who help themselves, we could say. No point in being lazy about basic practicalities."

"Others would."

"And have. It's not how I was taught. The spell," Bran said, winding back to it as he measured tea leaves. "I thought of what happened to Riley, and again what she and Sawyer did. So this will find any of us who might become separated. I've given it some work since Annika and Sawyer were taken in Capri, but other matters bumped ahead of it until now."

"Because we've had a little more time on our hands in the last few days."

"For as long as it lasts. Impatient?"

"Brother, I may have all the time in the world, but if this is the time—and we all believe it is—we shouldn't waste it."

"I'll agree, though I'll tell you it's been pleasant having Sasha settle in here, have that time to paint without being plagued day and night with visions."

He made the tea, offered Doyle a mug. Setting his own aside, he locked the spell book. "Let's sit so you can tell me what you have in mind."

"Sawyer's huddled up with Sasha in the other tower."

"Working on the design for the ring, yes." Bran smiled and sat back. And reading the smile, Doyle shrugged.

"I respect the women without qualifications. I'm more used to talking war with men."

"There are none of us, put together, who has the experience in battle you do."

Though he'd have said the same once,

Doyle shook his head. "That doesn't fly, not now. But putting that and gender equality aside—"

"Sometimes a man must talk to a man. And a woman to her own."

"It's no great change. The exploration of underwater caves has given us nothing but locations to cross off."

"Agreed. We found the same in Corfu and Capri."

"It feels different here." Restless, Doyle glanced toward the window. "I don't know if it's my own feelings about being here, or if it **is** different."

"Would you go back?" Bran asked. "It's something I've wondered. Would you, knowing you couldn't save your brother then, do differently if you could go back to that day?"

"Not try? Sure I'd have a normal life span, but what measure of life would it be, knowing I'd done nothing for him, and all for myself? I've had more than enough time to resolve I did all I could. I failed, and that will never leave me, but I did all I could do, and would do it again."

Doyle studied his tea, dark and strong.

"You wonder why I haven't asked Sawyer to take me back so I could kill the witch before she harmed him—or try. Sawyer would, as there's little he wouldn't do for a friend. I'll ask you, wizard, could I change the fates?"

"I don't know, but I know this. You might save one brother and lose another. Or start a war that takes the lives of thousands. The past, to my mind, isn't to be meddled with. The gods themselves let it lie."

"Change a moment, change an eon." Doyle stared into the fire, the shadow and light. "I've thought the same. I failed, and the man he might have been was lost. The man I might have been was lost with him."

"The man you are is enough. We're here, you and I, and four others, blown by the winds of fate to some extent. But more, I believe, through every step we've taken, every choice we've made along our way. So we're here."

Bran waited a beat, arched his scarred eyebrow. "What do you want to do?"

"I've thought of the words spoken, Sasha's visions. Of coming here of all the places in the world. The gods make us pay, for all those steps, all those choices."

And this, Doyle knew, would be one of the most painful he'd ever made. "I know the cave where my brother died. It's time I went back. Time we looked there."

Doyle's eyes narrowed on Bran's face. "You've thought the same."

"Whatever I thought, it had to come from you. If you're ready for it, we'll go together."

"Tomorrow."

"Tomorrow," Bran agreed. "I've thought of other words, ones spoken to you, you told me, by a redheaded witch. How love would pierce your heart with fang and claw."

Doyle nearly laughed. "Riley? She's not looking to pierce my heart. We understand each other."

Bran might have spoken again, but Sasha rushed in.

"Oh, sorry. I'm interrupting."

"No, we've finished." Doyle started to rise.

"Just sit a minute, and you can add your opinion. After considerable attempts, I've got a design Sawyer's about ninety-eight percent sold on. Have a look. He's gone to make sure Annika's occupied. And to think about it."

She flipped through pages in her sketchbook, each holding several designs that all looked more than good enough to Doyle's eye. Then stopped on a page holding a single design in the center.

She'd used colored pencils to enhance it, the deep-water blue of the center stone, surrounded by a halo of white diamond chips, and those flanked by two pink sapphires. The band held the sparkle— pink, white, blue—repeated in the wedding band.

"It's lovely, and very like her. Unique," Bran added. "As she is."

"It's hard not to push him on it, because I think it's right. I want to show it to Riley. What do you think?" she asked Doyle.

"Not my area. It looks fine to me. Plenty of sparkle, which she'd appreciate."

"I hear something." Sasha pointed at him. "I hear a but."

"Not my area," he repeated. "I was just thinking how she liked the design around the coat of arms, the braids. If the bands were braided—"

"Oh!" Sasha gave him an enthusiastic punch on the shoulder. "Oh, that's perfect. That's inspired. I'm going to fix it right now. And if Sawyer doesn't say go, something is **wrong** with him."

She rushed out as she'd rushed in.

"Well then, that's settled." Bran eased back with his tea, smiled at Doyle. "And it seems each of us has a hand in it. Things are meant as they're meant."

Contemplatively, Doyle rubbed his shoulder. "Your woman's got a firmer punch than she once had."

"In all things."

It didn't take her long, and Sasha decided she'd hit the mark when she found Sawyer working with Riley in the tower library.

"Annika?"

"Doing laundry. I've never seen anybody as happy with laundry." Sawyer set his compass on a map, shook his head. "And she's having better luck with it than I am with this."

"I've had tremendous luck. I've added another touch to the design."

"I was pretty well sold on the other."

"But not a hundred percent. I think Doyle's idea will change that."

Riley looked up from her book. "Doyle?"

"He had a suggestion. Look here, Sawyer. The bands, we can braid the bands with the same design I used on the coat of arms."

"I don't know if that's…" Then he looked. "Oh, yeah. Score. It's like—**it**. It's it. Why didn't we think of that?"

"Don't know. Riley?"

"If she doesn't do handsprings over this, it's because she's doing backflips. You rang the bell, Sash. You going for it, Dead-Eye?"

"I'm so going for it."

"You ought to take it to Bran, get him started on the mojo."

"Right. You're right." He pocketed the compass, took the sketch when Sasha tore it from her book. "Thanks."

Sasha watched him go. "You wanted to move him along."

"We're not getting anywhere here. Everything feels stalled. I need to move. Maybe we drag Anni away from laundry, work on those handsprings and backflips."

"I still suck at both."

"Exactly."

"There's something more."

Riley pushed back from the table, rolled her shoulders. "Maybe we'll talk about it after I move."

She'd been twitchy, Riley admitted as she dragged her friends outside. She hadn't been able to shake it—not with work, with diving, with sex, with sleep. The minute her mind wandered from the task at hand, the twitchiness started.

So maybe some time away from men altogether, and some solid sport that required a mind-body connection.

The sky held blue and nearly cloudless, and the sun beamed. Pleased, Riley tossed aside the hoodie she'd grabbed on the way out, stood with her hands on her hips, wearing a faded red T-shirt that said DIG IT!

It wasn't Capri or Corfu, but this taste of Irish summer—that might actually last an entire day—just shined.

She took a running start, executed triple handsprings, stuck the landing.

Oh, yeah, she was coming back.

And Sasha didn't suck as much as she had. Sure her landings were still shaky, but she was getting more height. Then there was Annika—nobody could come close. She might as well have wings instead of a tail.

Following Annika's orders, Riley hit a back handspring, pivoted into a side kick. God, she wished she had someone to **fight**.

Annika's next order had Sasha looking a little sick, but she charged Riley, who basketed her hands. When Sasha's foot slapped the basket, Riley pushed up hard.

The soaring backflip was more than decent, the landing rough to Riley's eye, but Sasha steadied quickly, punched a fist in the air.

"I did it! I'm going to do it again. Better."

This time as she flew up, Sasha mimed shooting her bow. Riley found herself grinning, even as Sasha lost the landing, fell back on her ass.

"One more time," Riley shouted.

On one more time, Sasha stuck it, then did a little Rocky-at-the-top-of-the-steps victory dance.

After an hour, Riley had worked up a nice sweat, her muscles felt well used, her brain clear. And the twitchiness snuck back in.

"Okay, we moved. Boy, did we move." Sasha sat on the ground to stretch. "Now, what's the more?"

"I don't know exactly." Riley rolled her shoulders as if trying to get to an itch.

"Do you still hurt?"

"No." Shaking her head at Annika, Riley stretched her calves, her hamstrings. "I'm good, and back to fighting weight. I guess ready for a fight. The waiting's getting to me. We're so close. I want to finish it."

As she stretched her quads, she glanced up. Doyle stood on the terrace, the breeze in his hair, his eyes on her. After a long moment, he slipped back inside.

"Crap."

"Did you fight with Doyle?" Already sympathetic, Annika rubbed Riley's arm. "You like to fight with Doyle. It's like the foreplay."

"Yeah. No. I mean we're not fighting. We probably will, and that's okay. It's…" She looked at Sasha. "You've already got an inkling."

"I'm sorry. It's hard not to. You have feelings. Why wouldn't you?"

"I'm all right with feelings. But I have more than I want or know what to do with. I wasn't after this kind of a thing, and now it's kind of got a hook in me."

"Oh! You're in love. This is wonderful!" Annika threw her arms around Riley.

"It's not wonderful for everybody."

"It should be."

"And I don't know if it's like that. I'm just...Why can't it just be sex? There's nothing complicated there. I know what to do about that. I don't know what to do about this."

"You suit so well."

Riley gaped at Sasha. "What?"

"You do, so well. Just fit. I'll admit I've worried about it because you're both combative, and hard headed."

"I'm not hard headed. I'm rational."

"And feelings aren't. You helped me resolve mine for Bran, to see my own potential, alone and with him. So I'm telling you, if Doyle's who you want, go get what you want."

"I've sort of got him."

"I like sex," Annika said, and flipped her long braid behind her back.

"We've heard." Riley rolled her eyes. "Literally."

"It's joyful, and exciting. But with Sawyer, I learned it's more. With love it brings more, means more. When I no longer have the legs, we can still mate. I'm glad. But I'm sad to know I won't be able to walk with him, or make food with him, or lie in bed and sleep together."

"Oh, Anni." Sasha moved in to hold her. "It's so unfair."

"But we'll be together. I mean to say that. We've found a way to be as much together as we can, and will be happy. If Doyle would make you happy, you should listen to Sasha."

"How am I supposed to know if he'll make me happy?"

"Find out," Sasha said. "You're too smart—and yes, you are hard-headed—to do otherwise. He needs you."

"He—**What?**"

"He may not know it, may not be able to accept it yet, but he needs you. And when the man meets the boy, when the boy sees the man, the dark echoes, old blood spills fresh."

"Anni," Riley ordered, "go get the others. Quick. What do you see, Sasha?"

"Memories and grief, faced anew. Old scabs, old scars torn open. She feeds on the pain, stirs the old to rise and strike. She lies. Hold strong, hold true, pass this test. For the star waits in the dark, in the innocent. Bring back the light to the man, to the boy. See the name, read the name, say the name. And find the bright and white."

Sasha closed her eyes, held up a hand. "Need a second. That was intense." When she felt Bran's arm around her, she leaned into him.

"Do you remember what you said?" Riley prompted.

"Yes, and what I saw. A cave, but it's not clear. It changed. Maybe it was the light. Your light, at first, so clean, so white," she said as she reached down for Bran's hand. "But then the shadows. Not shadows. And she came. Nerezza. But not her. Not exactly. I'm not making any sense."

"Let's go inside," Sawyer suggested.

"You can sit down, take a minute."

"No, actually, the air feels good. It got so cold. A cave, but not underwater. I'm sure of that. It seemed big at first—then small. But big enough for us all to stand. It's a bad place. A very bad place." Her fingers whitened on Bran's. "Terrible things there, old and terrible. Just what she wants and needs. But...God, then it's just the opposite. It's happy and quiet."

"Maybe we take out what's old and terrible, and that changes things."

Sasha nodded at Riley. "Maybe. I just don't know. I only know we have to go there." Now she turned to Doyle. "I'm so sorry. We have to go there. To where you lost your brother."

"I know it. I spoke to Bran about it."

"Making plans without the whole class?" Riley snapped.

"To start. I know the cave, and how to find it. It's less than fifty kilometers from here."

"You can show me on the map," Sawyer said, "so I've got it logged. In case."

"We'll map it out." Bran rubbed Sasha's shoulder. "Steady now?"

"Yes."

"I'd say some food would be in order. And wine."

"Won't argue with either."

"Soup's on. Anni, why don't you check on that? I'll get the map." Sawyer gave her hand a tug, and left Doyle alone with Riley.

"I don't like explaining myself," he began.

"Then don't." She started to walk away; he gripped her arm.

"I wanted to talk to a brother, and a witch, because I'd be talking about going back where I lost a brother, and killed the witch who cursed me."

"Okay."

"That's it?"

"Jesus, Doyle, buy a clue. We all know it sucks, we all know it's brutal. So you needed to lay it out to Bran first. Fine. I— We're with you."

"I'd have spoken to Sawyer before you."

"Now you're pissing me off again."

"Why did you come out here with the other women?"

"I wanted some practice. Sasha needs the practice." Then she mumbled a curse.

"And okay, I wanted the female for a while. I get it."

He hesitated, then gentled his hold on her arm. "If I had a life to lose, I'd put it in your hands. That's trust and respect."

"I could be an asshole, claim that's easy for you to say. But I'm not an asshole, and I know it's not. We're cool." She held out a hand to shake on it.

He gripped her elbows, hauled her up, kissed her. "You're not a sister to me."

"Good thing."

"But you are...essential. Going where we're going tomorrow, I want you with me."

Struck, touched, she laid a hand on his cheek. "I will be."

He dropped her to her feet, considered a moment, then took her hand. Rather than shake it, he held it as they walked back to the house.

Well armed, they set out early in the morning. Riley rode with Doyle on his bike as they traveled away from the coast, wound through land where the hills rolled green and serene into a sky that held in a sweet summer blue.

She imagined Doyle taking a similar route on that very hard day, on horse-back. Hooves striking the ground, Doyle's cloak flying as he pressed for speed. A faster trip now, she thought as they whizzed around curves where wild lilies sprang yellow as the sunlight they danced in. But a harder one for him. Before he'd believed he'd save his brother, bring him home to family.

Now he knew he never would.

But if they found the star...

Did that place that had once held such evil now serve as the resting place for the Ice Star?

Either way, they rode toward a fight. And she was more than ready for one.

Essential. He'd said that to her. She tried not to think too much of it, just as she tried not to probe too deeply into her own feelings. Far from the priority right now, she reminded herself. Whatever she felt, whatever he felt, didn't rise up to the fate of worlds.

He slowed, veered off onto a narrow, bumpy track.

"We walk from here," he told her. "Bran's

car can't handle this."

She swung off. "How far?"

"A little more than a kilometer."

He paused, looked left over a stone wall to a small farm where a spotted dog napped in the sun and cows grazed in a field beyond.

As he stood, the farmhouse with its blue trim, the outbuildings, an old tractor, even the spotted dog faded away.

There on the field and up the rising hill sheep cropped. A shepherd boy sat dozing, propped against a rock. He opened his eyes, pale blue, and looked back at Doyle.

"Do you see him there?"

"The dog?"

"The boy. He watched me that day. He watches me now."

"There's no boy." Riley kept a hand on his arm, looked back as Bran walked up with the others.

"His hair's almost white under his cap. He's half asleep, with his crook over his lap."

"There's a smear over the air." Bran lifted a hand, pushed. Narrowed his eyes against the resistance, pushed again.

The pretty farm sat quiet, and the dog slept on.

"She's working on you, man."

Doyle nodded at Sawyer's words. "Up this track, about a kilometer. The cave's in a hillock of rock and sod. There's a small pond outside it. It swam black that day."

And what lived in it, he remembered as they began to walk, had slithered under the oily surface like snakes.

Now along the narrow track were the yellow lilies and overgrown hedgerows dripping with fuchsia. A magpie winged by.

One is for sorrow.

As they neared he saw the signs and talismans—carved in wood or stone, fashioned from stick and straws. Warnings and protections against evil.

As the others said nothing, he knew they saw only the rambling stone wall, the wildflowers, the scatter of cows in the field.

A raven swooped down, perched on the wall. As Riley reached for her gun, Doyle stayed her hand. "You see that, at least." He pulled his sword, cleaved the bird in two.

Trees sprang up, and birds called from them. The cheerful, country birds that did no harm. Through the trees, he caught the glint of water from the pond. He angled right, strode through the sheltering grove.

Dark blue water amid wild grasses and choked with lily pads.

Then black and oily, rippling with what lived beneath.

"What do you see?" he asked Riley.

"A lily pond that needs some clearing out."

"Another smear." Once again Bran held up a hand. "And through it, the water's thick and black."

"The cave." Sasha gestured to the high, dark mouth. "Blood and bones. A cauldron bubbling with both. It's not clean, not clean. She lies, and everything inside is a lie." Sasha let out a breath, steadied herself. "She's waiting."

"I should go in alone. Alone," Doyle repeated before anyone could protest. "There's nothing she can do to me."

"What bullshit."

"I'm with Riley on that," Sawyer said. "All

or nothing. I vote all."

Riley drew her gun. "Maybe you could hit the lights, Bran. It'd be nice to see where we're going."

The mouth of the cave flooded with it, bright and white. Together they moved toward it, into it.

High and wide as he remembered. Leaves, pine needles had blown in to litter the floor. Animals who'd used it for shelter left droppings behind. Bumpy skins of moss, bony fingers of weeds grew over the rock walls.

"I guess we spread out," Riley said. "Look around."

"Stay close," Sasha warned. "It's not... right."

"Two by two for now, we'll say. As Sasha's on the mark." Bran peered through his own light. "It's not right."

They searched. Riley crouched down to study the cave walls inch by meticulous inch. No more than two feet away, Doyle ran his hands over it, crumbling moss.

Tension gripped the back of his neck like clawed fingers. The muscles of his belly coiled as they might before a leap into battle.

He could hear Annika talking quietly to Sawyer, hear Riley's boots scraping the ground as she moved along the wall.

The light changed, going to a dirty gray, and the air chilled with it. He turned.

Bones littered the floor, and he smelled the blood that seeped into the dirt. In the cave center, a black cauldron smoked over a fire red as a fresh wound.

The witch he'd killed stood stirring with a ladle fashioned from a human arm. Her hair was mad coils of black, her face blinding beauty as she smiled.

"You can save him. Take back the time here and now. He calls for you."

She gestured.

There, sprawled on the floor of the cave, pale as ice, bleeding from a dozen wounds, was his brother.

He held out a hand that trembled. "Doyle. Save me, brother."

With sword in hand, Doyle swung back to strike the witch, but she vanished in laughter. He ran to his brother, dropped down beside him as he had so long before. Felt the blood run on his hands.

"I'm dying."

"No. I'm here. Feilim, I'm here."

"You can save me. She said only you could save me. Take me home." As a trickle of blood slid between his lips, Feilim shivered. "I'm so cold."

"I need to stop the bleeding."

"There's only one way to stop it, to save me. Strike them down. It must be their blood for mine. Strike them down, and I live. We go home together." His brother's hand clutched at his. "Don't fail me again, **dearthái**r. Don't let me die here. Kill them. Kill them all. For my life."

Holding his brother in his arms, Doyle looked back.

The others battled, gun and bow, light and cuff, knife and fist as winged death flew through the smoky air of the cave.

He couldn't hear them. But he heard his brother's pleas.

"I'm your brother, one you swore to protect. I'm your blood. Take the witch first. The rest will be easy."

Gently, Doyle laid a hand on his brother's cheek. And rising, lifted his sword.

Chapter Fifteen

In him the rage held cold, an iced fury as the hot licks of blood and madness swirled around him. His brother. Young, innocent, suffering. The life draining out of him, out of a body wracked with pain.

The war screaming around him.

Always another war.

Through the fetid air he saw Riley slash through an attacker with her knife, then another as she shouted something at him that he couldn't hear.

Didn't she know, couldn't she see he wasn't part of them now? He was removed, for that moment removed and separate. Away.

Bran's lightning couldn't penetrate the distance, nor Sasha's bolts.

His brother, he thought. His blood. His failure.

"Save me."

Once again Doyle looked down at the face that had haunted him through the centuries. So young, so innocent. So full of pain and fear.

Images flashed through his mind, etched in joy and grief. Feilim toddling on unsteady legs on a seaswept beach. Struggling not to cry when Doyle sucked a splinter out of his thumb. How he'd laughed when he'd ridden a chubby brown pony. How he'd grown so slim and straight, and still would sit with avid eyes around the fire when their grandfather told one of his tales.

And now this image overlaying all, Feilim, face bone white, eyes mad with pain, bleeding at his feet.

And the boy lifted a trembling hand to the man. "This one thing, only this one thing, and I live. Only you can save me."

"I would have given my life to save my brother. You're not my brother."

And cased in that ice, Doyle rammed the keen point of his sword into the heart of the lie. It screamed, piercing, inhuman. Its blood boiled black, went to ash.

Now the sword was vengeance, cold and slashing as Doyle cleaved all and any that came. If they clawed or bit, he felt nothing. Inside him was another scream, a war cry, ringing in his ears, pumping in his heart.

A thousand battles whirled in his head as his sword slashed and thrust. A thousand battlefields. Ten thousand enemies as faceless as the mad creatures created by a vengeful god.

No retreat. Kill them all.

He saw one of the black, murderous beasts hook claws into Sawyer's back. With one bare hand, he tore it away, stomped its vicious head to dust with his boot.

He spun away to destroy more and saw nothing was left of them but blood and gore and ash. He saw Sasha lower to her knees, waving a hand when Bran rushed to her side. Annika embracing Sawyer as much to hold him up as hold on.

And Riley, her gun lowered, her bloody knife still gripped, watching him.

His breath was short, Doyle realized, and his head filled with tribal drums. And he who'd fought those countless wars wanted to tremble at victory.

He made himself turn to Bran. "Purify it."

"Sawyer is hurt."

"I'm okay." Sawyer closed a hand over Annika's arm, squeezed as he studied Doyle. "I'm okay."

"Purify it," Doyle repeated. "It's not enough to strike them down."

"Yes." Bran helped Sasha to her feet. "Your hand, **fáidh**. And yours. And all. Flesh to flesh, blood to blood."

He cupped the blood from their wounds in his palm, reached up with another. Pure white salt filled it.

"With bloodshed we rebuke the dark." He walked a circle around the others, spilling their joined blood on the ground. "With salt now blessed we make our mark," he said as he retraced his steps, letting it sift through his fingers. "With light to spark." He held his hands over the ground. "Now fire burns the unholy lie, rise up the flames to purify."

The fire snapped, sparked, spread

around the circle he'd created. It burned hot red, cold white, then at last, pure, calming blue.

"So evil is banished from this place, defeated by valor and light and grace. We six stand witness willingly. As I will, so mote it be."

The circle of fire flamed up, turned the air a soft blue, then shimmered away.

"It's done."

Doyle nodded, sheathed his sword. "If the star's here, it'll wait. We have wounded to tend."

"Just like that?" Riley asked as he stalked out. Bran stayed her when she would have stalked out after him.

"That's for later. We're all more than a bit battered. I've a small kit in the car, but... Sawyer, are you able to shift us there? I'd rather not even attempt that short walk."

"He's hurt. His back, his arm."

"Not that bad," he assured Annika. "I can handle the shift."

Sasha limped out with Bran's help. Riley ignored her own wounds, though the back of her shoulder burned like a bitch, and stepped out.

Doyle stood, his face a mask under spatters of blood.

"We're shifting to where we left the car, the bike," Bran told him. "We do have wounds to tend."

"Move in," Sawyer requested. "Easier that way."

With a hand not altogether steady, he took out his compass. Breathed in and out a moment, nodded.

Riley felt a quick bump, then found herself standing beside Doyle's bike. She noted Sawyer didn't object when both Annika and Sasha helped him into the car.

"I'm driving," she told Doyle.

"Nobody drives my bike."

"Today I do. Look at your goddamn hands." She pulled a faded bandanna out of her back pocket, shoved it at him. "Wrap that around the worst one, and don't be a complete fuckhead."

She got on the bike, kicked it into a roar.

"It'll be healed before we're back."

"I don't give a rat's ass. Get on or walk."

Because he knew he wasn't as calm as he wanted to be—needed to be—he swung on behind her.

She drove the bike as she drove everything else. Recklessly fast. But he was in the mood for reckless. She knew how to handle it, which didn't surprise him, and took them snaking around curves and turns, sweeping by stone walls, skimming by hedgerows.

The blur was fine with him, as was the sting and burn of his healing wounds. It masked, for now, his own ugly and intimate nightmare.

By the time she roared up to the house, cut the engine, he judged himself healed and calm. It took seconds to understand she was neither.

"Did you forget there were five other people in that cave?" she demanded. "Or did you just decide you were the only one capable of getting the job done?"

"I did what needed doing." He walked away from her as his own words brought back his brother's face, the killing edge of the sword on his back.

"Bullshit, bullshit, bullshit." When she would have torn after him, Sasha called her name.

"Riley. He's in pain."

"He stopped bleeding before we were halfway here."

"Not that kind of pain."

"Help with Sawyer, will you?" Bran scooped Sasha off her feet. "Let's heal the flesh, then deal with the spirit."

"I'm okay. Just a little..." Sawyer swayed in Annika's hold. "Rocky."

Since he was pasty white, and his pupils wide as saucers, Riley realized he was far from all right. "Gotcha, dude."

Grateful for the support, he swung an arm around her shoulders, felt the wet. "That's not my blood, Doc. It's yours."

"I took some hits. Anni?"

"I have some hurts, but it would be worse. Sawyer blocked them from me, and one dug into his back. Then Doyle..."

"Yeah, saw that part."

They dragged themselves in, and back to the kitchen where Bran already tended wounds on Sasha's leg, her arms with Doyle's help.

"Want a beer," Sawyer managed as he slid onto a chair.

"Who doesn't? Get his shirt off, Anni. I

bet you know how."

Annika sent Riley a wan smile as she gently drew off Sawyer's torn and bloody T-shirt. "Will you help me...Oh! Oh, Bran, it's very deep."

Riley took a look, hissed. "Looks like a raging infection already."

"One moment. Drink this, **a ghrá**."

"It's already easing." She drank. "Honestly, it's better. Deal with Sawyer."

"Annika, work with Doyle—and, Doyle, help Annika treat herself as well. She just needs the balm now, Anni," Bran told her. "Even the small cuts. There's poison."

He stepped to Sawyer, sent Riley a grim look over his head. From his kit he took a knife, a vial, three candles. He lit the candles with a thought, then reached for a small bowl.

"I have to drain the poison first."

"He's shocky," Riley said as Sawyer's teeth began to chatter.

"Hold on to him, as this is going to hurt like a thousand hells. You brace yourself, Sawyer."

"Right. Yeah."

"Look at me." Riley gripped both his

hands. "I've got a question. Iron Man versus Hulk. Who wins?"

"Iron Man."

Riley shook her head. "Hulk smash."

"Yeah, sure. Stronger, but no strategy. Iron Man's got the smarts, the intellect."

"Hulk's got the instincts. Primal."

"That doesn't—**B'lyad.** Holy fuck. **Fuck!**"

"Hold on." Bran spoke between his teeth as he used the treated knife to drain poisoned blood into the bowl.

On a sob, Annika broke away from Sasha, threw herself down beside Sawyer.

His hands clamped so fierce on hers Riley imagined bones crushing, but she kept talking. "Intellect versus instinct. It's a hard call."

"So says the—**fuck me, fuck me**—the werewolf."

"Yeah, so I ought to know. Think about it. You put Mr. Spock against the Hulk."

Breath labored, body shaking, Sawyer set his teeth. "You're crossing the streams. Motherfucker!"

"Nearly done," Bran promised. "It's washing clean now."

"Okay. Okay."

Riley watched Sawyer's color come back, felt his crushing grip ease.

"Just the balm now."

As Bran applied it, Sawyer closed his eyes, breathed out. "Oh, yeah, that works. Don't cry, Anni." He drew a hand from Riley, stroked it over Annika's hair. "I'm okay. You let Sasha finish fixing you up now."

"It's all right." Annika raised her head, lifted drenched eyes to Bran.

"It is, I promise you. You'll use the balm on the wounds every two or three hours for now, and I'll check again before bed. But it's clean and already healing. I can tell you it would have been worse, a great deal worse, if that bastard, buggering thing had gone any deeper or dug in any longer."

"Thanks."

Doyle jerked a shoulder at Sawyer. "No problem. Beer?"

Sawyer just gave a thumbs-up.

"You're my heart." Annika stood, bent down to kiss Sawyer softly. "And you are all my heroes. I have only little hurts now, Sasha. Riley has more."

"Shit. She's got a bad one on her shoulder." Sawyer got, a little shakily, to his feet. "Switch it, pal."

Resigned, Riley took his seat, yanked off another sweatshirt that would never be the same, and sat in her black tank and jeans while Bran studied the wound.

"I'm happy to tell you it's not nearly so serious as Sawyer's, and I won't need to use the knife to drain it."

"Yay."

"Beer?" Sawyer asked her.

"Tequila. Double shot."

"You got it."

It hurt, and hurt enough that once she'd knocked back the first shot, she held up the glass. "And again."

As it eased, she downed the second, sat while Bran treated her lesser cuts and gashes.

"All right now, your turn." Sasha pointed at Bran. "Now you sit. Anni, let's heal the healer."

"Wouldn't mind a beer myself."

Doyle pulled out one for Bran. His curse healed him, he thought. The others? They healed each other. He stood there, as separate as he'd been during that horror in the cave. Turning, he headed for the door.

"Nobody leaves," Riley snapped.

"I want some air."

"It'll have to wait."

"You don't give me orders, Gwin."

"Then I will." Her voice cool as she treated Bran's wounds, Sasha glanced toward Doyle. "Nobody leaves until we talk about what happened."

"What happened?" He wanted to peel it off as he peeled off the bloody cloth around his hand. "We walked into a fight, not unexpected, and we walked out again."

"That's hardly all. She blocked you from us," Bran continued. "She used that place, and your memories of it against you."

"Mind-fucked you, dude. Or tried," Sawyer qualified. "And we couldn't get through. Like a wall, or a freaking force field. Us on one side, you on the other with..."

"You saw him?"

Riley decided on one more shot. "A man—boy really. Young, bleeding. We couldn't hear, but you were talking. It's like you were in a trance. The minions, they swarmed, but they left you alone. You were..."

"Trapped," Sasha said. "I think the whole reason we were drawn there was to separate you, to pull you away from the rest of us. To take you back to before."

"If you could go back, I asked you, and save him, would you?"

Doyle shook his head at Bran. "It wasn't him." Doyle gave up, sat. "It looked like him, sounded like him. And at first...It was being back, it was having another chance. I couldn't hear you, and even when I saw you fighting, it seemed vague and unimportant. To save my brother, to take him home, it's what mattered."

"Then why didn't you?" Riley demanded.

"He said to save him I needed to strike you down. Your blood for his, and he'd be spared. I'd failed him before, but I could save him now. Just do this one thing. I've killed more than my share. What's five more for the life of a brother I'd sworn to protect?"

"He asked you to do an evil thing," Annika

stated.

"That's right. And I knew what I already knew. It wasn't Feilim. He'd never have asked it. Never. He was full of heart and sweetness. His name, it means ever good, and he was. He...He was like you," Doyle realized. "So I did what I had to do."

"What?" Riley slapped down the shot glass. "One minute you were standing there in a trance, the next you were wading into the fight like a madman."

"I put my sword through his heart."

"Its heart," Sasha said gently. "Its heart, Doyle."

"Yes. Its. And its heart had my brother's face." He shoved up. "And I need some goddamn air."

Sasha set the balm aside, kissed the top of Bran's head. "If you don't go after him, Riley, you'll disappoint me."

"He wants to be alone."

"What he wants and needs are different things."

"I don't know what to—"

"Then figure it out, but go after him."

"Hell." Riley grabbed her ruined shirt, dragged it on as she went out.

"You're wise and kind, **fáidh**." Bran drew her hand to his lips.

"I know what it is to feel apart. And I know what it is to love when love seemed impossible."

Riley didn't feel particularly loving. In Doyle's place, she'd have kicked and punched at anyone who got in the way. She reminded herself she could take a punch, shoved her hands in her pockets, and crossed the lawn to where he stood at the cliff wall.

"I've said all I have to say. I don't want to talk to you, or anyone."

Fair enough, she thought, and said nothing.

"Go the hell away."

Going the hell away would be the easy route, and preferable, she admitted. She took the hard one, sat on the wall, looked at him in silence.

"I've nothing to say to you." His fury lashed out, stung him more than her. "I don't have to justify anything to you, to anyone."

When she said nothing, her silence only enraged him. He gripped her by the shirt, dragged her off the wall. "I did what I had to do. That's all there is to it. I don't need anything from you."

He'd yet to wash off the blood—but then neither had she. His face was rough and shadowed beneath a couple days' growth of scruff. And his eyes were shattered.

Instinct, she considered, versus intellect. She went with instinct. He shoved at her when she wrapped her arms around him, so she just held on. When it jarred her healing shoulder, she set her teeth, gripped tighter.

And instinct proved the right course when he went still, then dropped his head on the top of hers.

"I don't want your sympathy."

"You're going to have to take it. And the respect that goes with it."

"Respect, my ass." He broke her hold, stepped back.

"I've got something to say, and you're going to have to listen."

"Not if I gag you."

She planted her feet, lifted her chin. "Try it and you'll bleed. She exploited your grief, she pulled you back to the moment when that grief was the sharpest, and she offered you a lie. The lie was changing what was, and it came from the image of someone you loved, you lost. She hooked you, Doyle, the way she did me in the woods, the way she went at Sasha in that first cave on Corfu, but not with violence, not for you. With cruelty."

"I know what she did. I was there."

"Don't be a dick. Especially when I'm going to point out something essential you seem to be too pissed off to latch on to. You were stronger than she was. You did what you had to do, yeah, but you did it because you were stronger."

"It wasn't my brother," he began, and she moved in, short-jabbed a fist to his chest.

"Bullshit. It looked like him, sounded like him, bleeding and dying in the same cave where you lost him. You had a choice, and don't tell me, don't fucking tell me, that for one fraction of an instant you didn't wonder if you'd done what she wanted, you'd have had him back. You'd have broken the curse. Don't tell me that in all the years you've lived the choice you made today wasn't the hardest."

"To save him, I'd have cut my own throat when cutting it would've mattered. Today? Even if it had been a real choice, even if it had been my brother, I wouldn't have sacrificed you, or anyone in that house."

"I know it."

It mattered that she did, more than he could say.

"She separated me, and made me feel that distance so I could stand back, watch you fight, and think, what's the point of it all? They'll live, they'll die, and I'll just go on. That's the difference."

"Three nights a month I'm pretty different myself."

"Not the same."

"Oh, boo-hoo. I've got to live forever, feel my pain." Deliberately dramatic, Riley clutched at her heart. "I've got to live forever, young and hot and strong, feel my torment. Get over yourself, old man."

"You have no idea what—"

"Blah, blah, blah. Blah, blah, blah. Why don't you take a rest from the I'm cursed for a century or so. You've got the time."

"Christ, you're a pain in the ass."

"Want some there-theres, some cheek pats? Let me go get Sasha or Annika."

She started to turn, smiled to herself when he grabbed her arm, swung her around. She met his furious look with a sneer, and enjoyed—very much—how he wiped the sneer off her face.

The way his mouth crushed down on hers, hard and hot. The way his hands pressed, molded, possessed.

Just as it shook something inside her when that mouth, those hands gentled. When for one trembling moment there was real tenderness.

She squeezed her eyes tight when he held her, when his hands glided light and easy over her back.

"I loved him more than I can tell you."

"I know that. Anyone could see that."

"When he'd barely learned to walk, he'd follow me around like a puppy. So full of light, and...delight. If I shook him off, I'd feel like a bully. He was like Annika. It occurs to me that's why she struck a chord with me right off."

"It wouldn't have anything to do with being blow-your-pants-off gorgeous?"

"Bonus. I couldn't hear you, and in that fog, through that wall, you seemed very far away. But I knew you." He eased back, studied her face. "She couldn't reach that."

"She doesn't **get** that. That's how we'll win. Plus, we're just smarter. Or I am anyway. A lot smarter."

"Now who's being a dick?"

"Truth's truth. Had enough air?"

"I could use another beer."

"I could use food. It's my round for lunch, so it's sandwiches. You can help me with that."

"I'm on dinner tonight."

"So I'll help you get the pizza."

He looked back at the house, down at her, and felt something just let go. "Deal."

In her chamber beneath the earth, Nerezza raged. The creatures she'd created skittered and scattered. Only Malmon stood, prepared—even happy—to take her abuse.

"He should have slayed them like pigs. He should have done as I bid! Where is this human love? Where is this human grief? It's weak, weak and false."

She tore the head off a bat, hurled its still fluttering body against the wall.

"You'll tire yourself, my queen."

She flew at him, fingers curled into claws to gouge. An inch before his sickly yellow eyes, she stopped. Her hand gentled, stroked the cold, rough cheek.

"I'm strong again. You tended me well."

"You are my queen. You are my love."

"Yes, yes." She flicked that aside, paced the chamber. In the faceted mirrors of the walls she could see herself reflected, again and again.

Her hair was more black than white now, and nearly as silky as before. Yes, Malmon had tended her well. She'd skimmed the glass so the lines in her face softened, even vanished to her eye.

She'd have her full youth and beauty back, and more. She would have all.

"Wine," she ordered Malmon. "Just wine. For soothing rather than strengthening."

Sitting on her jeweled throne, she toyed with changing her skirts from black to red, to black again. A child's trick, but after her fall, she'd been unable to do even that.

Now, she thought as she sipped the wine. She was strong enough.

"I've allowed my thirst for revenge to cloud purpose. I will kill them, of course. Kill them all and feast on them. The immortal? Nothing but a toy to torment for eternity. But first, the stars. I lost sight of the stars."

"You were so ill."

"But no more. I will reward you one day, my pet. We will go to them. I am stronger, but it costs too much to send power over distance. We need to be closer to be on them when they find the Ice Star."

"Travel will tire you."

"Their deaths, when the stars are in my hands, will rejuvenate me. I have plans, my pet. Such lovely plans. Soon, soon now, the worlds will scream in the dark. Soon, the stars will shine only for me. And I will return to the Island of Glass, drink the blood of the gods, the false sisters who banished me. I will rule all from there."

She picked up the Globe of All, smiled into it.

"See how the mists clear for me, how

the dark swirls in? We'll dig our fortress deep, and we'll strike with a force of power that will rend the ground and crack the sky."

She turned that fierce smile on Malmon. "Prepare."

"My queen? Will I go with you to the Island of Glass, and sit beside you?"

"Of course, my pet." She waved him away.

Until I have no need for you, she thought, or worse, until you bore me. But on that day she would reward his loyalty by giving him a quick, clean death.

Chapter Sixteen

A couple days of drenching rain boosted color and bloom in the gardens, and made for wet, muddy training. It didn't stop six determined guardians from exploring caves and historical sites. In the plethora of books, Riley found references to stones, a name—never specified—carved into them that "marked the bed of the star." Following that lead, they scoured ruins, cemeteries, cave walls while the incessant rain pelted them and turned the hills to shining emerald.

With rain dripping off the brim of her hat, Riley stood on the bumpy grass of a graveyard, boot-deep in ground mist. Behind her, the ruins of an old abbey stood stark gray above a winding curve of the river, tea colored under sulky clouds.

Atmosphere-wise, in her opinion, it hit every glorious gothic note. She hoped, as she'd hoped on every rain-washed stop of the last two days, that atmosphere would nudge Sasha into a vision.

"Early twelfth century," Riley said. "Fertile ground for crops and animals, fish in the river. Not a bad spot. So, naturally, the Cromwellians had to sack it."

"Nice, spooky feel. And could it **get** any wetter?" Sawyer looked up at the sky.

"I like the rain." Annika gestured toward the purple spears arching out of crevices. "It makes the flowers grow in the stone."

"It keeps up you'll be able to swim on land. In or out," Sawyer added. "Though in, in this case, is out."

"Name in the stone," Riley reminded him. "I'd say headstones first."

"It might help if we knew the name we're looking for," Doyle pointed out.

"Blame the cryptic gods and their messengers." Since complaining about the weather wouldn't get them anywhere, Riley began to walk, to read headstones, to wonder.

It didn't seem egocentric at this point to wonder if the name they searched for would be one of theirs. An ancestor's. That connection. Certainly on a headstone or grave marker that made the most logical sense.

Barring that, she wondered if they would—at some point—find the names of the three goddesses, or the young queen—on some carving.

Or...

"Maybe it's the name of the star." Crouching, she ran her fingers over the faded name in a lichen-covered stone. "Most likely in Irish—**réalta de orghor**—since it's from Arianrhod. But possibly in Greek or Latin."

"It seems unlikely we're going to find it somewhere so open," Doyle began. "And as wet as it is, we might as well have dived."

"Stones, names, water—this place has all three. It's worth a look. And it's not what I'd call overrun by tourists."

"Any self-respecting tourist would be spending a day like this in a pub."

Hard to argue, Riley thought, and wound her way toward the ruin.

She understood the old, had always been drawn to it and the foundation it laid for the next to come. She could imagine the life here, inside the stone walls. One of prayer and intellect, of husbandry and service.

And superstition.

Some had been laid to rest inside, under slabs of stone where the names and dates were faint fingerprints, eroded with time and weather. But for her, it echoed of life and death, of fires burning, pots simmering, voices hushed in prayer.

Smells of incense and smoke and earth.

She started up a narrow curve of stone stairs, noting where the joists—long gone— had once held up the second floor, and the third.

She stepped through an opening, onto a wide ledge overlooking the lazily flowing river. She spotted the bird huddled in a tree, reached under her jacket for her gun.

Then relaxed.

Just a rook, idling on a rainy afternoon.

Below, she saw Annika turning a circle, hands held up as if to catch the rain.

"She makes her own fun."

"Wherever she goes," Doyle agreed from behind her.

Riley turned her head. "Boots ought to make more noise on stone steps."

"Not if you know how to walk. There's nothing here, Gwin."

"There's history and tradition, there's architecture and longevity. We're standing here where some buried below once stood. That's not nothing. But no, I don't think this is the place."

She watched Sasha walk into the ruins with Bran.

"She's feeling the pressure—from all of us. We've been here nearly three weeks now."

Riley followed his gaze, back to Annika.

"She's got time. She has more than another month. We haven't gotten this far together to stall, to just tread water so she'll have to go back before we finish."

"In Nerezza's place, from a tactical standpoint, I'd hold off until that time was up—until one of us, by nature, is separated from the rest." Resigned to the rain, Doyle scanned the mists and stones. "Even if we find the star first, we have to find the island, get there. And the clock's ticking."

"Screw tactics."

"That could've been Custer's motto."

"Yeah? Were you in the Montana Territory in 1876?"

"Missed that one."

"Then I'll point out Custer was an arrogant egomaniac, and part of an invading force that didn't quibble at genocide. Got his ass handed to him. I think Nerezza's got a lot more in common with him."

"The Lakota won the battle, but they sure as hell didn't win the war."

Tipping back her hat, she angled her head to study that hard, handsome face. "You know, maybe it's not the pressure of our combined thoughts blocking Sasha. Maybe it's your consistent pessimism."

"Realism."

"Realism? Seriously? I'm a lycan standing here with a three-hundred-year-old man. There's a mermaid down there skipping around a graveyard. Where does that fit in with realism? We're a fucking mystic force, McCleary, and don't forget it."

"Three hundred and fifty-nine,

technically."

"Funny. Now why don't you—Wait, wait." Eyes narrowed, she turned to him. "In what year were you cursed? In 1683, right?"

"Yes. Why?"

Struck, she thumped a fist on his chest. "Do the math! Three hundred and thirty-three years ago. Three-three-three. Three's a number of power."

"I don't see how that—"

"Three." Snapping out the number, Riley circled her hands in the air. "How the hell did I miss that?" She grabbed his arm, pulled him toward the stairs. Stopped halfway as Bran and Sasha had started up.

"Doyle's three hundred and fifty-nine."

"He holds up so well," Sasha began.

"And he was cursed in 1683. Three hundred and thirty-three years ago."

Now Bran angled his head, laid a hand on Sasha's shoulder. "Now how did we miss that?"

"See!" Riley jabbed a finger at Doyle. "We didn't think about the exact number because, hey, immortal to round things off. But it has to apply."

"You've lost me." Sasha glanced back

as Annika and Sawyer stepped up.

"Three," Bran repeated. "A magickal number, one of power. As we are. Three men, three women, in search of three stars."

"Created by three goddesses," Riley finished.

"Next year it'll be three hundred and thirty-four."

"**Now** is what matters. Don't be a blockhead." Dismissing him, Riley waved the others back so she could come down. "This time, this year. Three, three, three. And this place—Ireland, Clare, where the house sits. You were born there, right? In the house?"

"The birthing center at the local hospital was full up at the time."

On a roll, Riley just slapped the back of her hand on his chest. "Maybe it ends where it began. Or Doyle began, and the clock started on the day he was cursed." Riley demanded. "What month? When in 1683?"

"January."

"Do you hear that click? Sasha, when did you first start dreaming of us, of the stars, of this?"

"You already know, because I told you. In January, right after the first of the year."

"Exactly. Click, click. You started being pulled into this when Doyle hit his triple threes as an immortal. And you pulled us all together." She looked at Bran now. "It's not nothing."

"It's not, no. Signs are meant to be heeded."

"There's a graveyard—stones—back at the house. Sorry, man," Sawyer added.

"Where we've been living," Doyle pointed out, "training, walking for weeks now."

"But not looking, or digging." Riley held up a hand at the flare in Doyle's eyes. "I don't mean digging literally."

"We would never disrespect your family," Annika added. "Is it possible your family helps protect the star? Is that the possible Riley means?"

"That's exactly the possible. Look." Now she turned to Doyle. "What I do, even the literal digging, is because I respect and value who and what came before. I don't desecrate, ever, or support anyone who does, even in the name of science and discovery. We need to check this out. We just go back and check it out for now. Okay?"

"Fine. We'll get out of this filthy weather. And tomorrow, as the chances of the last star popping out of my mother's headstone are thin, we dive, whatever the weather."

Since she figured everyone was entitled to mood, and she wanted to think, Riley said nothing as they trooped back to the car, squeezed in.

She spent the drive back using her phone to gather more data on the number three.

"Three divisions of time," she mused aloud. "Past, present, future. From the first three numbers, all the others synthesize. What makes up a man—or woman—mind, body, spirit. Three. Most cultures use three as a symbol of power or philosophies. The Celts, the Druids, the Greeks, Christianity. Art and literature."

"You had to say Beetlejuice three times," Sawyer commented.

"There you go. Third time's the charm. Actually—didn't think of it—the Pythagoreans believed three was the first true number."

"They were wrong, weren't they?" Doyle replied.

She lowered her phone, met his eyes. "Plato divided his Utopian city into three groups. Laborers, Philosophers, Guardians—who were, essentially, warriors."

"And in his Utopia, laborers equaled slaves, philosophers rulers. Only Utopia for some."

"The point is three," Riley insisted.

The minute Bran parked, she shoved out. "We have to look. We know it's personal for you, we all do. But that may be part of it. So we have to look."

"So we look."

When Doyle started back, Bran signaled to Riley, then lengthened his own stride to catch up.

"Most of my family rest in Sligo," he began. "But those here are family all the same. For all of us."

"You didn't know them."

"I know you, as we all do. Tell us about them."

"What?"

"One thing," Bran said. "Tell us one thing

that strikes your memory about each. And we'll know them."

"How will that help find the star?"

"We can't know. Feilim. This is the brother you lost. You've told us he was kind and pure-hearted. So we know him. What of this brother?"

"Brian? He was clever and good with his hands. Beside him is his wife, Fionnoula. She was pretty as a sunbeam, and he fell for her when he was no more than ten. Loved her all his life. Steadfast, that was Brian."

"And their children here with them?" Bran prompted.

"Three more than the two here. I barely knew them."

Doyle moved to his last brother. "Cillian, he liked to dream, to make music. He had a voice like an angel that drew the girls like bees to honey. My sister Maire's not here, but buried with her husband and children in a churchyard near Kilshanny. Bossy, opinionated. Always a scrapper."

He found a kind of solace, finding something about each of his brothers, his sisters. His grandparents. Paused at his father.

"He was a good man," Doyle said after a moment. "He loved his wife, his children, the land. He taught me to fight, to build with stone and wood. He didn't mind a lie, if it was entertaining, but he'd tolerate no cheating.

"My mother. She ran the house, and all in it. She'd sing when she baked. She liked to dance, and when Maire had her first child...I still remember her holding the baby, looking at its face. She said whoever you were, now you're Aiden."

Annika laid her head against his arm. "We believe when one of us dies they go to another place. One of peace and beauty. After a time, there's a choice to stay there or to come back again. It's harder to come back again, but most do."

Solace, Doyle thought again. "I never thanked you for the flowers, the shells and stones you put on the graves."

"It's to honor who they were. Even if they choose to come back, we might not know them."

"That's who they were, or a part of it. I've said their names. There's no star here."

"We just need to figure out how to pick the lock. I'll work on it," Riley promised. "Maybe not here. Maybe in or around the house, or the old well. Somewhere in the woods. There's too much weight not to think it's right here."

"Let's go in, take a break. It's been a dreary couple of days," Sasha added. "We could all use a break."

"We can have wine, with cheese and bread. Sawyer said I could be chief cook tonight, and I could make...What am I making?"

"Baked potato soup—in bread bowls. Good for a wet day."

"Bread bowls? How am I supposed to think about research when I'm going to eat bowls of bread?"

Sasha took Riley's arm. "By having wine first."

"That could work."

Wine usually worked, in Riley's opinion. And she didn't mind having some in front of the fire, her feet up while she worked on her tablet. Especially when the air began to smell of whatever Sawyer taught Annika to chop, stir, or mix.

It seemed to her Sasha felt the same as she sat in the kitchen lounge sketching. Doyle had said something about a hot shower and disappeared. Since she thought he wanted space, she provided it.

She noted idly that Bran was absent for at least an hour, came back in, left again. Shortly after helping Annika form balls of bread dough, Sawyer told her to cover them with a cloth, time it for an hour.

He slipped out.

Riley lowered her tablet. "What if we tried something like a scavenger hunt?"

"Why would you hunt scavengers?" Annika wondered.

"No, it's like a game."

"I like games. Sawyer taught me one with cards, and when you lose, you take off a piece of clothes. Oh, but he said we only play it for two."

"Yeah, that's better as a duet. It's when you have a list of things to find, and you hunt for them."

"Like the stars. So it's a quest."

"In a way."

Sasha glanced up from her sketch. "How does a scavenger hunt help us find the star?"

"It's a way to get us to comb through the house, to look for the unexpected. I don't know. Reaching," Riley admitted. "Doyle's family built on this spot. He was born here. Bran built, three hundred years later, on this spot. We've been driving and hiking around Clare, diving in the Atlantic. But it's making more sense, it's just more logical, the answer's right here."

"Don't you think Bran, being Bran, would have sensed it?"

Because Riley had rolled that around, she had a theory. "I think, somehow, it didn't really begin for us until January—and Doyle's unwilling rebirth. Yes, everyone but you already knew about the Stars of Fortune before we hooked up on Corfu—and that's another in the mix. We all knew; you didn't. The clock started when Doyle hit the magic number."

She pushed up, poured more wine. "It's a solid theory. January starts the clock, you start having visions about us, about the stars. It takes you a while, but you go to Corfu—and so do the rest of us. Same time, same place."

"Riley is very smart." Annika poured more wine, too.

"You bet I am." She clicked her glass to Annika's, and feeling generous, took the bottle to where Sasha sat, topped off her glass. "You're drawing the house."

"I love the house. I don't think it's any more than that. But I do follow the theory. And...Bran brought the other two stars here, into **this** house. So maybe this is why."

"Good point. So we could go through it, top to bottom. Your visions, so far, say it's somewhere cold, talk about a name on a stone. First on the hunt list is a name, a stone. You talked about the boy seeing the man, the man the boy."

"We have three men," Annika pointed out.

"Right you are. One of them was born here, was a boy here. That could be it. Or..." Riley sipped. "It could be symbolic again. Something in the house from Doyle's time, or that represents—"

She broke off when Doyle came in.

"Who knew it was that easy to shut you up."

"She doesn't want to poke at a sore," Sasha told him.

"Nothing sore." He looked at the wine, and since it was handy, got a glass. "You had a point before. The whole whims-of-fate deal pisses me off. It wasn't you, but like this wine, you were handy."

"Riley wants to hunt scavengers to find the star." Annika peeked under the cloth, pleased to see the balls were bigger.

"A scavenger hunt?"

"A form thereof," Riley said to Doyle. "We compile a list of things, symbols, possibilities that may apply, and we start looking. Hell, what else have we got to do on a rainy night?"

He shifted, caged her back against the counter. "Seriously?"

"You can have sex now," Annika suggested amiably. "There's time before dinner."

Doyle smiled at her. "Gorgeous, are you sure I can't talk you into tossing Sawyer over for me?"

"Nice." Not too subtly, Riley lifted her knee, pressed it firmly against Doyle's crotch.

"He's making a joke because he knows Sawyer is my only true love."

"Good thing," Sawyer said as he came in with Bran behind him.

"Sawyer, the balls are bigger!"

"Not mine." Doyle eased Riley's knee down.

"No, yours, too—Oh." Tossing her hair, Annika laughed. "You made another joke."

"He's a laugh riot." Riley shoved Doyle's chest, didn't budge him. "You're blocking me."

"I'm thinking of time before dinner."

"I'm using the time before dinner," Sawyer announced. "Anni—"

"But we can't have sex now because I have to make the dinner. It's my turn."

"Anni," he said again, and went to her, cupped her face, kissed her.

"Sasha could watch the balls of dough," Annika murmured, and circled his neck with her arms.

"I love you. Everything about you. Everything you are."

"Is this happening now?" Doyle muttered at Riley.

"Shut up."

"Do you remember when Riley and I went to Dublin?"

"It hurt my feelings you didn't take me with you, and the others were angry because—"

"Yeah, let's skip over that," Sawyer said quickly. "I went to get something for you, and Riley helped me."

"The surprise, but you never gave me the surprise."

"I'm going to give it to you now, because you like the rain, and we're making soup, and this is family. You're my family. Stay my family, Annika."

He took a pair of polished shells out of his pocket.

"It's beautiful."

But when she reached for it, Sawyer lifted the top shell.

Gasping, she pressed her hands to her lips. "A ring. Is it mine?"

"Made for you. We designed it—we all had a hand in that. Riley helped me find the stones, and Bran, well, made the magicks. The blue stone—"

"I know this stone. It's precious. It holds the heart of the sea."

"You hold mine. Always. Marry me."

"Sawyer." She laid a hand on her heart, her other on his. "Will you put it on, the way Bran put Sasha's on?"

"I take that as a yes." He slipped it on her finger.

"It's more beautiful, more precious than anything I have. Except you. I will be your mate, always."

She slid into his arms to seal it with a kiss, held tight, tight. "I thought I already had the biggest happy, but this is bigger."

"And that's our Anni." This time Riley elbowed Doyle aside. "Show it off."

"It's so beautiful. It holds the sea, and the pink is for joy, and the bands are for all, for family. Thank you for helping." She kissed Riley's cheek. "Thank you." Then Sasha's, then Doyle's. "And you, for the magick." She hugged Bran, swayed.

Then swung away, holding her ring hand high. "Look! It's so, so pretty. It's the best of any surprise."

She leaped into Sawyer's arms, laughing as she took his mouth.

"Mmm. Sasha will finish the—" She jumped back when the timer buzzed. "The balls!"

"Brother." With a shake of his head, Doyle lifted his glass. "You'll never have a dull moment in the rest of your life."

Sawyer watched Annika whip the cloth off the dough, like a magician completing a trick. "I'm counting on just that."

They ate soup, drank wine, talked theories.

"Interesting," Bran considered. "The idea the star might be in, or even of, the house."

"Your builders might have mentioned it," Doyle commented.

"He's had three centuries to hone his skeptic creds." Deciding to ignore Doyle, Riley tore a chunk off her bread bowl, enjoyed it. "The hypothesis, like this quest, like everyone here at this table, is founded on the unarguable fact that alternate realities, para-realities, exist. Accepting that, we move to other facts. Doyle was changed in January three hundred and thirty-three years ago. In January, Sasha began to have visions about the Stars of Fortune, and about us. Conclusion, that's the kickoff."

"We were all drawn to Corfu," Bran continued. "Three of us met on the day we arrived, at the same hotel. Within days the six of us fought together, for the first time, against Nerezza. In our time there, a bond was formed." He lifted Sasha's hand to kiss. "Of varying degrees."

"A bond," Sasha repeated. "And each one of us came to the point where we were able to share our own heritage. I think, I really do, we're where we are now because of that bond. It didn't exist in January. It didn't exist when Bran built this house, or when Doyle was cursed. But...the potential of it did."

"Yes." Delighted, Riley slapped a finger on the table. "That potential began the minute the stars were created, and evolved. The stars fell, and the research on when's sketchy, but indicates they fell before Doyle was born. His birth—and the mystical rebirth from the curse? Another step in the evolution. The rest of us fill in. And don't you have to wonder at the mix? Witch, mermaid, immortal, lycan, seer, shifter. Why not six witches, six immortals?"

"The diversity brings strength," Bran

surmised. "And challenges to overcome."

"You've got to admit—you said it yourself," Sawyer added as he looked at Doyle. "The closest you came to finding Nerezza was in that cave on Corfu, with us."

"I'll buy the timing mattered, the six of us mattered. It's the idea the Ice Star is behind the baseboard that doesn't ring for me."

"If we follow the dots." Lifting her wine, Riley spoke to the table at large rather than Doyle specifically. "What holds the most weight is the stars can only be found by the six of us—and couldn't be found until the six of us came together. Ergo, the Ice Star might have been hidden in the house where Doyle was born, and might be hidden in or around this one now. The house is stone, and the data and the visions speak of stone. And the sea, which is right out there."

"The man sees the boy, the boy sees the man. No, not a vision," Sasha said quickly. "Just remembering. A mirror, a glass?"

"Now you're thinking. And the bit about the name. Maybe something written down, something in a book."

"A painting. The signature of the artist," Sasha explained, "or the person in the painting."

"Memorabilia," Sawyer suggested. "A keepsake. Something engraved."

"I'm going to write this down." Riley rose to grab her tablet from the lounge. "Mirror, glass, book..."

"You make the words so fast." Annika angled over to watch them come on screen. "Can you teach me? I like to learn."

"Sure." But Riley said it absently as she finally looked at Doyle. "Why did you choose the bedroom upstairs?"

"It had a bed."

"Stop the smart-ass. Why that particular room?"

"And no particular reason except..."

"Except what?"

"It faced the sea. My room as a boy here did the same."

"Okay. That could matter. Talk among yourselves. I want to play with this." Riley took her tablet back to the lounge.

Doyle rose, followed her over. "You pissed about something?"

"No. Clearly, I'm working something out, whether or not you support the theory."

"You're pissed because I don't buy in?"

"No." She looked up now, held a level gaze. "Theories are meant to be debated and challenged. It's why they're theories. I'm a scientist. I worship ideas, even when they're contrary to mine."

"Then what's the attitude?"

"I'm working something out," she repeated. "This, and something personal. If I were pissed, I'd say so."

"Okay." He went back to the table, sat with the others.

Riley went back to ignoring him. It seemed the best course while holding an internal debate on whether or not to tell him she was in love with him. And if she told him, when. And if and when, how.

A lot of questions, and no clear answer.

She had a lot to work out, so let those questions circle in her mind while she added items to the hunt list, and let the conversation across the room wash over her.

Chapter Seventeen

At the table Annika admired her ring, wiggled her fingers to make it sparkle. She thought she would most like to marry Sawyer on the island where he'd taken her—where one of her people had given his ancestor the compass. Where he'd told her he loved her the first time.

Everyone could come, the land people who were family, the mer-people. She hoped, so much, she could marry Sawyer while she still had the legs. Then she could wear a beautiful dress, and dance with him.

She caught Sasha smiling at her while the men talked of battle plans and hard things.

"I like to look at it, and to feel how it feels on my finger. Do you with yours?"

"All the time."

"You will come to the wedding, and stand for me, you and Riley, the way we will for you?"

"I thought you'd never ask." Sasha laughed.

"I think, would like so much, if we could marry on the island. Our island."

Sawyer slid an arm around her. "I was thinking the same."

"Really? Oh, then everyone could come. Our family, your family, my family. We would have flowers, on the land and on the sea, and music. And wine. It's more than I can imagine. More than I ever did, and I used to dream of the rite, the promise when I was a girl. I had a place for dreaming special dreams, and that was the most special."

"What kind of place?"

"In the warm waters of the south where the water is so clear the sun strikes through it, I had a secret place just for me. A garden of coral and sea plants. I would curl there and dream my best dreams."

Now she had the dream, she thought, and snuggled against him. "Did you have a secret place?"

"A tree house."

Her eyes widened. "You had a tree for a house?"

"No, it's a little house built in a tree. Up in a tree. My dad and my grandfather built it, for the kids. We all hung out there, but I'd climb up, especially on summer nights, by myself. I guess I dreamed some pretty good dreams there."

"Especially after pawing through porn mags," Riley said from across the room.

"Different kind of dreaming."

"What are porn mags?" Annika wondered.

"I'll explain later. How about you, bigmouth?"

"Me?" Riley glanced over again. "We traveled a lot, so I found places wherever. Books were my place, not so secret, but my place. Plenty of dreams inside books. But now that I think about it, there's this old storm cellar back home. I guess that was my version of a tree house or sea garden."

"Sasha." Enjoying the conversation, Annika turned to her. "Where was your secret place?"

"I was going to say I didn't have one, but that's knee-jerk. Something you say without thinking first," she explained. "The attic. It was very secret for me, somewhere I'd go to be alone, when I had to get away from everything, everyone. I'd draw, and imagine being like everyone else. I wasn't happy the way I am now."

"I wish I could have been your friend when you were a girl."

"We're making up for that now. Let's keep it going. You're up, Bran."

"There's a stream a fair walk from our home in Sligo. I'd set off for it when I was a boy and had deep thoughts to think. I'd sit with my back against an old, gnarled rowan tree, watch the fish in the stream, practice magicks, and dream of being a great sorcerer."

"And you are!" Annika pressed her hands together. "Doyle, where was your place?"

"Days were full of work when I was a boy. Firewood to gather, peat to dig, stock to tend."

"Walking barefoot through snow ten miles to school. Uphill," Riley added, and earned his bland stare.

"You had no shoes?"

"She's talking in smart-ass clichés," Doyle told Annika. "I was the oldest, and so had more responsibilities...Knee-jerk," he said with a glance at Sasha. "Old habits. We were forbidden to climb on the cliff, so of course, nothing appealed more. If I could slip away from my siblings, from the chores, that's just what I'd do. I liked the danger of it, the sea crashing below, the wind whipping at me. And when I found the—"

He stopped, shocked, stunned. All along? he wondered as his mind struggled to grasp it. Had it been there all along?

"Not in the house. Not in the graveyard. The star's not here, not there."

Riley had already gotten to her feet. Now she set the tablet aside, walked over to the table. "But you know where."

"I don't—" The fact that he had to settle himself infuriated. "I may," he said, calmly now. "A theory, following your dots. I climbed the cliffs, a bit, then a bit more, and when I didn't get caught and hided, more still. Even at night, by moonlight, and Christ knows if I'd lost my footing... But that was part of it all. That thrill, that risk. I was the oldest, after all, and Feilim, he'd just been born, and my mother distracted, my father besotted. He was beautiful, even a boy of nine could see how beautiful he was. He was days old when I found the cave.

"I could use a whiskey."

"I'll get it." As he rose, Bran glanced at the sketch Sasha worked on, quickly, skillfully, in her lap.

"A cave in the cliff wall," Riley prompted.

"Aye. It was like a treasure. I went right in, as a boy with no sense would. The sea echoed in it. Here was something no one knew of but me, no one would have but me. I was a pirate, claiming my prize. Over the next weeks and months and years, it was my place. I took an old horse blanket, tinder, tallow, a small boy's treasures. I could sit on the ledge outside it, look out to the sea and imagine the adventures I'd have. I whittled a pipe to play, to call my dragon. I'd settled on a dragon for my spirit guide long before. Thanks."

Doyle lifted the glass Bran set in front of him. "I carved the symbol of one into the cave wall, and above it my name."

"Doyle Mac Cleirich, writ the boy in the stone, and dreamed of the man to be. Warrior, adventurer." Sasha set the sketch pad on the table.

On it she'd drawn a cave lit by a single candle held on a rock by its own wax, and a boy—dark, shaggy hair, dirt-smeared shirt—his face intent as he carved letters into the stone wall.

"Dreaming of what would be, he doesn't see the fire and the ice. Nor feel the heat and cold. That is for the man, one who knows war is blood and death and will still fight. The star waits for the boy, for the man. See the name, read the name, say the name and its ice burns through the fire. One for the seer, two for the siren, three for the soldier. Dare the storm, children of the gods, and take them home."

Sasha shuddered out a breath, reached across the table for Doyle's whiskey. "Mind?" she said and downed it. Shuddered again. "Wow. That was probably a mistake."

"You did well." Bran laid his hands on her shoulders. "You did brilliantly."

"You saw it?" Doyle tapped the sketch pad. "You saw this?"

"As soon as you started talking about the cliffs. It's been like a film over my mind—hard to explain. And when you started to talk, it just lifted. And I saw you— I saw you as a boy in this cave. I felt..."

Doyle picked up the bottle of whiskey Bran had brought to the table, tipped more in his glass. "Go ahead."

"Determination, excitement, innocence. Power all around you. You nicked your finger with the knife, and when you traced the letters you carved, your blood sealed them."

Doyle nodded, drank. "Here, all along. Just as you said." He looked at Riley. "I never thought of the cave. I even went there after we came here. Climbed down, went to see it again. I thought nothing of it. I felt nothing."

"You were alone. Next time you won't be."

"It isn't the easiest of climbs."

Riley arched her eyebrows. "Getting to the other two wasn't a stroll in the park either."

"I'd say give me the coordinates, but if you're off by a foot or two." Sawyer scratched his head. "It's a long way down."

"We'll use rope." Bran looked toward the window. "But not tonight. Not in the dark, in the rain. In the morning then—please the gods we get a break in the weather—and together."

"Say we find it, and I say we will. What do we do with it?" Sawyer asked. "Where do we put it until we figure out how to take it home?"

"Well, according to the established pattern..." Riley looked toward Sasha.

"A painting. I've been painting when I've had the chance, but nothing's **compelled** me like the other two. Maybe, now that the film's gone, I'll be compelled. Otherwise, maybe a more ordinary painting will work as well."

"And question after that, where the hell is the Island of Glass? I'll keep hitting the books on it," Riley promised. "But I'm starting to think I'm not going to find that answer in the library or the 'net. Still, I'll keep digging. Starting now."

"If we climb, we climb at first light," Doyle told her.

"I'll be ready," she said and walked out.

She worked until after midnight, played with a couple of theories. Discarded them.

She wrote a long email to her parents, catching them up with where she was, how she was, asking them if they knew of any lines to tug she'd missed.

Time to shut it down for the night, she told herself. Time to get some sleep—or try to. If tomorrow was the big next step, they all needed to be ready.

Not just ready to find the star, to protect it, but to fight. The minute Nerezza got wind they had the last star, she'd come calling.

Thinking just that, she left the library, made her way to the sitting room where they stored weapons. Doyle sat quietly by a low fire, polishing his sword.

"You should get some sleep," he told her.

"Heading that way. Same goes."

"Soon as I'm done here. I didn't think of the cave. I should have. I didn't."

"I didn't think to ask if anywhere around here had particular meaning for you. I was hung up on the graveyard because I knew it did."

"I thought you were right at first. I hated it."

She sat across from him. "You're entitled to want your family to rest in peace. I think...Do you want to know what I think?"

"When has that ever stopped you? Yes," he admitted when she said nothing. "I want to hear what you think."

"I think this is a gift. I think this is something given to you hundreds of years ago to help you resolve the rest. Every boy wants to be a hero, right? And now you are. You are," she insisted when he shook his head. "They just gave you the choice to be one or to walk away. You didn't walk away. You went back to the—gotta say evil—place where your brother was killed, and when Nerezza tried to use your grief against you, all of us, you kicked her ass. You didn't want to stand in the graveyard today, and talk about your family. But you did. That's not battle heroics, Doyle, but it's stepping up. So—"

She got to her feet. "Like I said earlier, I've been working some things out."

"On finding the island."

"Goose egg there. I mean the personal

business. We made sort of a deal, and I'm sort of reneging."

He frowned at her. "What deal?"

"Just sex, just good, healthy sex. No sticky stuff. But things got a little turned around on me. In me."

He set the sword aside, very carefully. "Are you pregnant?"

"No. Jesus. You're irritating a lot of the time, and you're moody. And pushy," she decided.

"What does that have to do with sex?"

"It doesn't. It has to do with the sticky part that wasn't supposed to happen. I don't know why it happened. I like to know why, so that's irritating, too. I can hang some of that on you, too, as getting anything out of you is pulling teeth. Like I didn't know until today you were twenty-six when you were cursed."

"How do you know that?"

"I did the math, for God's sake. How old you were when Feilim was born—nine—how old you'd said he was when he died. Seventeen. Which makes you—excluding the immortality—a couple years younger than me. That hit strange."

Saying nothing, Doyle reached for his sword again.

"No, just hold off on that, and listen. I'm going to say that despite all that—and I could say you have qualities that balance out the bullshit, but this is already taking too long. Despite it, or maybe I'm twisted up because of it—I haven't worked out which—I'm in love with you."

"No, you're not."

Of all the responses she'd imagined, she'd never imagined a cool, calm dismissal. She'd prepared herself for hurt feelings, even a solid punch to the heart. She hadn't prepared for insult and anger.

"Don't tell me what I feel. Don't tell me what I have in here." She thumped a fist on her heart. "I'm telling **you** even though I'd rather not. Do I look happy about it? Am I doing the happy dance? Am I doing the cartwheel of joy?"

"You're caught up, that's all. We're sleeping together, and everyone else is talking weddings and flowers. You've conflated them."

"Bullshit. Insulting bullshit. Did I say anything about weddings and flowers? Do

I **look** like somebody who can't wait to run out and buy some big white dress and grab a bouquet?"

He felt the first trickle of alarm. "No, you really don't."

"I don't like this any more than you, but it is what it is. I'm giving you the respect of telling you. You give me the respect of not accusing me of being some sentimental **girl**."

He thought he should stand. "I'm saying I think we're in a strange and intense situation. We added sex to that. We... respect each other, trust each other. Obviously we're attracted to each other. You're a smart woman, a logical woman, a rational woman. A woman who has to know—"

"I'm smart enough to know that logic and rational thinking mean dick-all when it comes to who you fall for." Beyond pissed, she slapped her hands on her hips. "What do you think I've been telling myself? But I feel what I feel. God knows why."

"I can't give you what love asks for."

She shook her head as the temper in her eyes dimmed to pity. "Moron, love doesn't ask. It just is. Deal with it."

"Riley," he said when she started out, and she turned back.

"Don't tell me you care about me. That's cheap. That's beneath us both."

"There are reasons I can't—"

"Did I ask you for anything back?"

She'd asked for nothing, he thought. And what was he supposed to do with that? "No."

"Then leave it. Just leave it. I told you because whatever else I weighed in, I don't like regrets. I'm not going to regret telling you what I feel. Don't make me feel less for feeling it."

He let her go—that was best for both of them. But he knew in three centuries, with all he'd done, all he'd experienced, she was the only woman who'd managed to turn him inside out.

She slept well. She'd said her piece, Riley thought, solved the internal issue nagging at her by saying it. So she'd thrown off that weight and worry.

He hadn't hurt her, and she'd expected him to. After all, she'd never been in love before. In lust, in fairly serious like, but she'd never slipped over that very essential line.

No, he hadn't hurt her, Riley considered as she dressed for a rugged cliff climb. She was a smart, educated woman, reasonably attractive, healthy, well traveled. If Doyle couldn't see and accept love from her, that was absolutely his loss.

She'd never dreamed of weddings and marriage and happy-ever-after. Not that she stood against any of that. But she led a full and interesting life—even before waging war against a god. If she survived that war, she fully intended to continue leading a full and interesting life.

Doyle could be a part of it, or not. Choice entirely his.

But the priority of now outweighed the priority of maybe later. She strapped on her guns—don't leave home without them—clipped on her knife sheath, and took the back stairs to the kitchen.

Coffee—number one priority—scented the air, along with grilling meat, toasted bread.

"Omelettes," Sasha told Riley as she

skillfully folded one in the pan. "Loaded. Annika set the table before I got down so Sawyer could take her down for a quick swim."

She'd built a cave out of napkins, Riley noted, set it on a stand above a flowing blue napkin obviously representing the sea. Inside the cave she'd placed six figures made out of pipe cleaners. They circled a dragon made of the same that held a small white stone.

"Let's consider that a prophecy." Riley poured coffee, and decided to take advantage of the moment. "I told Doyle I'm in love with him."

"Oh!" Quickly, Sasha slid the omelette onto a platter. Her smile faded. "Oh."

"Listen, I didn't expect him to sweep me up like the studly hero in a novel. I just needed to say it so thinking about saying it—or not—wasn't clogging up my brain. I did, so it's clear."

"What did he say?"

"Not much, but one of the standouts was how I must be conflating—**conflating**—sex and all the wedding talk. That was insulting."

"Yes, it really is. To your emotions and your intellect."

"Boom." Riley tapped a finger on Sasha's shoulder. "Mostly he was stunned and annoyed—more heavy on the stunned. I'm not going to hold the stunned against him. We had a deal."

"Oh, for—"

"We did," Riley insisted. "I reneged."

Sasha made a **ppfft** sound. "As if you can make a deal about love."

"I get that. But I didn't get that when I made the deal. It's my first time in the arena." With a shrug, she hooked her thumb in her front pocket. "Anyway, by the time we'd finished up I felt sorry for him because of what he doesn't get. Love's precious, isn't it? It's not something you can find by digging, searching, reading. It just is, or it just isn't."

"Sorry for him, my ass."

On a laugh, Riley drank coffee. "No, really. And I didn't tell you so you'd be pissed at him."

"You're my friend. You're the first real friend I've ever had. What kind of friend would I be if I wasn't pissed at him? Of

course I'm pissed at him. The jerk."

"Appreciate it. But if you can't make a deal not to fall in love, you can't make one to, can you? It just is, or it just isn't," Riley repeated. "I'm okay. More, a lot more important, we've got to hang together. No internal conflicts, especially today."

"I can be pissed at him and hang together with him." Scowling, Sasha poured beaten egg into the pan.

"Reverse the order. Hang together first."

"For you." Sasha added grilled bacon and peppers, shredded cheese. "I'll do that for you."

"I love you. I don't think about saying it very often. Today's a good day to say it."

"I love you, too."

Riley heard feet on the stairs. "You're going to tell Bran—no problem. Maybe just wait on that until after we get back. With the star."

"I can do that."

It wasn't Bran, but Doyle, and Riley gauged her reaction. She concluded she hit borderline amusement to see the big, sword-wielding immortal looking awkward and braced for female ire.

Maybe the reaction was small of her, but she didn't mind being small.

"We're fueling up on loaded omelettes before the climb." Riley spoke **very** casually, topped off her coffee. "According to Annika"—she gestured toward the table with her mug—"we make it just fine."

"Good."

He glanced back, his relief just visible enough to tip Riley over the borderline into full amusement when Bran came down.

"Ah, just the man I wanted to see. I want to get the rope from the garage. We've time for that, Sasha?"

"You've got ten minutes."

"Time enough. Give me a hand, will you, Doyle?"

Riley held her snicker until they'd gone out.

In the garage, Bran lifted a coil of sturdy rope from its hook on the wall. "Well, now I know why I felt I had to have all this." He passed it to Doyle, lifted off a second coil.

"It's more than enough for this. The cave's about fifteen feet down."

"I could get us there without the rope," Bran considered. "Though I'd feel better about it if I'd been there first myself. It's orienting, really. Sawyer could do the same, once he logged it, but..."

"You have the rope," Doyle finished. "And think there's a reason for that."

"Tied together, rather than me taking us down one or two at a time. I think it has to be tied together, yes." Bran angled his head. "Are you worried then?"

"No. No, it's a tricky climb, but nothing this lot can't handle."

"What then?"

"It's nothing. It's other. It isn't relevant." Bollocks. "Riley says she's in love with me."

Bran merely nodded. "Then you're a fortunate man."

"That might be, if I were just a man. And even then, we've got more pressing matters. If she's pissed off at me because I didn't—couldn't—" He broke off with a curse. "If she's distracted by what she thinks she feels..."

"I'd say Riley knows herself very well. That's one. And to add, she didn't seem pissed or distracted just now to me."

"She's canny," Doyle contested, and

made Bran smile.

"That she is. And still from where I'm standing it's yourself who seems distracted and pissed. You have feelings for her."

"Of course I do. We're sleeping together."

"To borrow from Sawyer, just let me say: Dude."

That surprised a laugh out of Doyle. "All right, no, I haven't had feelings for every woman I've slept with. But we're part of a unit, we're connected." He studied the rope. "Tied together."

"I'm a man in love, and that love increases every day. It's amazing to me. So I've seen your struggle. We're connected—tied together—so I'd wish you happy, as I've seen, clear enough, she adds to you, and you to her. But it's for you to know, you to decide."

"There's nothing more to know, and no decision to make. And more pressing matters to deal with." Doyle took the last coil of rope off the wall.

Once they'd eaten, they stood at the seawall.

Sasha looked over and down, paled. "It's

a long drop."

"Mister Wizard isn't going to let you fall." Expertly, Riley looped rope around Sasha's waist. "Plus, as discussed, Sawyer, Doyle, and I all have rock-climbing experience. All you have to do is watch your step, follow our lead."

"And don't look down," Sasha said.

"If the bow feels awkward, leave it here. You can take one of my guns. You're a better than decent shot."

"I'm better with the bow. I can handle it."

Riley secured a knot. She might have wished for some sturdy carabiners, a couple of belay devices, and some good harnesses, but you couldn't have everything. And the rope was first-rate.

She measured a length, moved to secure Bran.

"She'll be fine," Riley said quietly, "but if she gets jiggly, talk to her. That'll calm her down."

She shifted her gaze, noted Doyle looped Sawyer in beside Annika. Satisfied, she began securing herself.

"Let me check that." Doyle moved to her.

She took a mental survey as his hands

brushed here, there. Yeah, she could handle it.

"The first real climb for me was in Arizona, studying the Ancestral Puebloans. Hot and dry," she added, glancing up to the soft blue of the morning sky. "Windless." She looked back at him, met his eyes. "Sasha's jittery, but she'll handle it."

"Okay. Secure the end."

He waited while Riley wound the rope around a tree trunk, tied it off.

"Want to check it?"

Doyle shook his head. As in most things, she knew what she was doing.

Though he didn't need the rope, he used it. And took the lead by vaulting over the wall. With her usual enthusiasm, Annika leaped over with him.

"Easy," Sawyer warned, and landed on the narrow edge of soft sod. "Not every-body has your balance."

"He means me." Sasha swung over. "I've got it. Don't worry."

Riley waited, let Doyle start the climb down, then rolled over the wall.

She considered the first five feet the kiddie slope, and would have enjoyed the challenge to come—along with the crash and spume of waves, the light swirl of wind, the feel of the cliff face—if she wasn't worried about Sasha.

"Doing great!" she called out as Sasha carefully lowered a few more inches, with Sawyer advising her to ease right, plant this foot.

It surprised everyone when ten feet down it was Annika who lost her hand-hold as a rock gave way under her fingers. She teetered, nearly overbalanced. Riley braced, dragged up slack, then breathed again when Sawyer pulled Annika back.

"I'm apology!" she shouted. "I mean sorry."

"Climb now," Riley called back. "Swim later."

With her own heart drumming still, Riley continued down.

She looked up once, saw the ravens perched on the wall above.

"Fire in the hole." She let go with one hand, toes digging in hard, pulled her gun. She managed to hit two before the others took wing.

Below, Sasha lowered to the ledge.

"She's watching. I can feel it."

"Nearly there." Doyle gestured. "Just watch your footing."

Even as Riley reached the ledge, she saw him ease into the cave. Getting back up again was bound to be more complicated. So she'd think about it later.

She moved carefully over the ledge, followed the others into the cave.

"Tight fit." She squeezed in between Sasha and Annika.

"It's pure, like the boy. Can you feel it?" Sasha wondered.

It echoed with the sea, smelled of sea and earth, and when Bran held his hand over a rock, Riley saw the old wax pooled there liquefy and glow so the cave washed with soft gold light.

"I'd've made a fort in here," Sawyer commented as he looked around. "Irish cave version of a tree house. What kid could resist it?"

"It was for him, the boy, the boy who dreamed of being a man. It is for him, the man who remembers the boy." Sasha reached out, laid a hand on Doyle's back. "It waits, and its time is now. The time of the six. Of the guardians. See the name, read the name, speak the name."

He saw the name he'd carved into stone so long ago, above the dragon symbol. He read the name, his own name, so it etched in his mind as it did on the wall.

And he spoke the name.

"Doyle Mac Cleirich."

The light changed, burned from warm gold to ice white, and with it the air went cold as winter.

The name, his name, blazed in the rock, each letter spilling fire. The dragon roared with it.

Heart at a gallop, blood all but singing, Doyle dropped to his knees, reached into the flame. And from the mouth of the dragon took the star.

It blazed like the fire—but pure and white, blinding bright. Cupped in his palm, its power sprang free.

"It's not cold." Doyle stared at the beauty in his hand. "Not now. It's warm."

And so was the air.

"We have it." He pushed to his feet, turned, held it for the others to see. "We have the last star."

Chapter Eighteen

As he spoke, the ground shook. Loose rocks tumbled in front of the mouth of the cave, fell into the sea.

"I'd say she knows." Riley tried to angle around, face the mouth of the cave. A beam from Annika's bracelet struck the first bat that swooped in.

"I'd say that's our cue to get the hell out of here."

"But not the way we came in." Sawyer pulled out his compass. "Hold on."

The shift shot them into the light, the wind. Riley heard a hammerblow of thunder, saw something streak and flash. Then she felt herself falling helplessly, tumbling.

Not thunder now, she realized, but the waves crashing on rock. And she fell straight toward them.

The cold, the wet slashed across her face. Her hand groped for her knife. Cut the rope, cut the rope before she dragged the others with her.

Then her body jerked as that rope snapped taut. She flew up again, fighting to breathe, and landed in a wet, boneless heap on the lawn.

"Anni, everybody. Is everybody all right?" Sawyer's hoarse voice clawed through her stunned mind. "Sash—Jesus, Riley."

She waved away the hands that tugged at her. "Okay, not hurt. What the hell, Sawyer?"

"Inside! We can't risk the star in a fight." Doyle scooped Riley up. "Run," he ordered, and charged for the house as what had poured into the cave poured over the seawall.

Ignoring, for the moment, the indignity of being tossed over Doyle's shoulder, Riley reached back for her gun. "We're secured to the damn tree."

"Not anymore."

She got off a few rounds before Doyle shoved into the house.

He swung her off his shoulder, dumped her onto the kitchen island so they were eye to eye. "Are you hurt?"

"No. I'm wet." She shoved him back. "Again, what the hell, Sawyer?"

"She walloped us. Best I can say." He shoved his gun back in his holster. "Knocked me off balance. I lost my grip, so to speak, for a couple seconds."

"I was falling, toward the rocks." Riley pushed at her dripping hair. "I think I almost hit."

"Would have," Doyle told her. "Without the rope to haul you back."

"I don't know what she threw at me," Sawyer added, "but I bet she's been waiting to do just that. I'm sorry. I lost it."

"Not your fault, and you got it back." Steadier, Riley looked to the window into the deep gloom, the lash of rain. "The storm."

"No." With a shove at her wind-ravaged hair, Sasha shook her head. "That's just anger. She's gathering more. Right now, Riley needs dry clothes, and as grateful as I am for the ropes, they have to go."

Bran merely waved a hand, whisked

them away.

"Dry clothes can wait. I want another look at the star."

Once again, Bran waved a hand. Riley let out a sigh as her clothes, her hair, even her boots went warm and dry. "Gratitude."

"My pleasure. We'll take the star upstairs, with the others. Secure it."

"We've got no place to put it yet," Sawyer reminded him.

"We do." Bran slid an arm around Sasha. "Our **fáidh** painted until nearly half two this morning."

"You didn't tell us," Annika said.

"Bran and I talked about it, after I'd finished. We both thought we should focus on getting the star. Until we did..."

"What did you paint?" Riley hopped down from the counter. "Let's go see. And..." She wiggled her hand at Doyle.

He drew the star from his pocket, offered it.

"Weight and heat without mass. It's just amazing. And the light. Clear and pure as Arctic ice. It pulses," she murmured as they walked upstairs. "Like a heartbeat."

She looked at Doyle, grinned. "We

did it."

He pushed her back against the wall, and with the star pumping between them, kissed her like a man possessed.

"I saw you fall. You were no more than a foot away from the rocks when I—we—managed to drag you back. You were going to cut the rope. You were going for your knife."

"Of course I was going to cut the rope. I thought I'd gotten knocked loose, and I'd drag everybody down with me. You'd have done exactly the same."

"I don't die," he reminded her, and walked away.

She looked down at the star, hissed out a breath, and stalked after him. "Is this really the time for attitude? We've just found the last star. We have in our possession something no one ever has but the gods. We—"

"Looking to put them in a museum with a plaque?"

She flinched—something he'd never once seen her do no matter the threat. Hurt looked out of her eyes at him, and that, too, was new. "That's not right."

"No, it's not. It's not. I apologize. I'm sorry." He paced two steps away, paced back. "Very sorry. That was stupid and undeserved."

She nodded slowly. "Bygones."

"Riley." He took her arm before she could walk away. "I saw you die in my head, saw you crushed on the rocks. In my head. It... screwed with my mood," he decided.

"Still here. So adjust. The others are waiting for us, and the star."

"Right." He walked with her, in silence, into the tower.

Riley rolled her eyes as conversation stopped, everyone turned. "Excuse the delay. We were just...Holy shit."

The painting glowed. Riley would have sworn it pulsed almost as visibly as the miracle of the star still in her hand.

"That's...breathtaking. Sasha."

"I don't know how much I can actually take credit for."

"All," Bran told her. "All."

She touched a hand to his cheek. "I was explaining, it came on around midnight. I'd prepped a canvas, just in case, and that was a damn good thing, as the need to paint this just blew through me. I didn't just see it. I was **in** it. I could smell it, touch it, hear it. Every other vision or image I've had of it was pale, indistinct compared to this."

"I just have to say it, okay?" Sawyer gestured elaborately toward the canvas. "Behold, the Island of Glass."

On a gleaming indigo sea beneath a star-struck sky that held a wild white moon, it floated. Floated as if free to go and come on the wind. Its beaches shimmered white, diamond dust against the frothed edge of the sea. Its hills rolled, shadowed green with blurred color from wildflowers blooming.

On one such hill stood a palace, shining silver. On another a circle of stones, gray as the fog they swam in.

Small details came to life as Riley studied the painting. A gentle curve of a stream, the long spill of a waterfall, gardens lit as if with faeries in flight, a fountain where a winged dragon spewed water rather than fire.

"We have got to get there. And when we do, they have **got** to let me have a couple of samples. Some pebbles, some sand, a little dirt. There **must** be fossils. I mean—"

"Take it easy, Indiana." Sawyer gave her a poke. "Star first."

"Yeah, star first, but later." Riley looked down at the star, up at the painting. "It makes you realize why, doesn't it? They need to go back, need to be protected. It all does. The world gets screwed up regularly, routinely. But this one. It holds together. Maybe because it does, the rest of us don't go off the edge."

She held the star out to Bran. "Your turn, magick man."

As he had with the other two, Bran enclosed the star in glass. They formed the circle, performed the ritual as guardians, to send the star safely into the painting. Away from Nerezza's grasp.

"Now, gee, all we have to do is find the island, get there—with the stars—destroy the evil psycho god, and..." Riley shrugged. "Then the first round's on me."

"Hold you to it," Sawyer said.

Riley frowned toward the window when thunder cracked. "You're sure this is just a hissy fit?"

"I'm sure," Sasha told her.

"Then I'm going to work on the next step. I'm damn well going to find the island. It's what the hell I do."

The ugly weather continued, so holing up in the library surrounded by books near a snapping fire wasn't a hardship. Riley understood the patience required to meticulously sift through layers, but frustration tightened her shoulder blades.

They'd fought, they'd bled, they'd searched, they'd found. And none of it mattered if the island remained out of reach.

She sat back, rolled her shoulders to release the tension, scanned the walls of books. So much here, she thought, so many avenues. Any one of them might hold the answer, or at least a signpost toward the answer. But how long would it take to find that answer? How much time did they have?

She glanced toward the window as thunder cracked. And how long could six people camp inside one house—even a pretty spectacular house—without wanting to punch each other?

They'd need action, movement, progress.

She rose, wandered the shelves, reached for a book at random.

Doyle walked in.

"I got nothing," she told him. "Nothing I didn't have two hours ago. Two days ago, for that matter. If you want to dive in, be my guest. Maybe we should start a book club—and everyone takes a book each day."

She paused, frowned. "Actually, that's not a bad idea."

"We've got the stars."

"Yeah, but we don't have the island." Riley gestured toward the window with the book she held. "It's a pretty sure bet Nerezza can keep that temper tantrum going, and fighting her now, without an exit plan, doesn't make sense."

"We fight when we need to fight."

"No argument, but tactically it's going to be to our advantage to find the route to the island before we take her on. What?" Riley rubbed a hand over her face as if brushing at a smudge. "What are you staring at?"

"I don't understand you."

"You're not the first." But she understood, and set the book down. "Do you really want to get into this? Doesn't seem like your style."

"We have the stars," he repeated. "But we're not finished. We have to work together, fight together, plan together."

"Yeah, that's no problem." She arched her eyebrows. "If it's one for you, that's your damage. My feelings are my feelings. The fact that they're out there doesn't change anything. And like Bogart said, more or less, the issues of two people don't much mean dick in the big picture."

"That's wildly paraphrased."

"And true." She let out a sigh, sat on the arm of a sofa. "Not everybody gets what or who they want. That's just reality. We may be dealing with gods and magick islands and stars, but every one of us understands reality. Do I look like somebody who's going to screw up something this important—or worse, pine away—because some guy from the seventeenth century doesn't love her back?"

"No."

"Good, because I'm not. Get this, okay?

I own what I am, who I am, what I feel. You do the same, and we're square. Clear enough?"

"Yeah. I've got you."

As he turned to leave, she got to her feet—slowly. "Wait a minute. Wait a minute. What did you say?"

"I said it's clear."

"No." Her heart began to thud as she walked toward him. "You said, 'I've got you.'"

"Same thing."

"No." She took a risk, lowered her defenses long enough to look at him, really look. And saw. "You **asshole**!" Her short right jab landed hard, center chest. "You complete dick. I've got you, **ma faol**. You said that to me when I was half conscious, bleeding, broken, and you carried me out of the forest. I've got you—my wolf. **Your** wolf?" She punched him again, added a shove.

"You were hurt," he began.

"That's right, that's right." Now she jabbed a finger in his chest, drilled. "And when Bran worked on me, you held me." God, it flooded back now, over and through the memory of pain. "You told me to be strong, to come back. Come back to you. In Irish. **Teacht ar ais chugam, ma faol. You coward.**"

The word dripped with derision.

"You said those things to me when you thought I was out of it, but you can't say them to my face?"

He caught her fist in his hand before it connected. "Hit me again, and we'll see who's the coward."

"Emotional midget work better for you? You're in love with me, and you can't say it when I'm conscious because you're afraid. That's pathetic. You're pathetic."

Temper hot and visible, he hauled her to her toes. "Watch yourself."

"Screw that. I say what I feel, remember? You're the one who lies about it."

"I haven't lied to you."

"Let's just test that. Are you in love with me?"

He dropped her to her feet. "I'm not getting into this any deeper."

"Yes or no. That's simple. If you've got the balls."

"It doesn't matter what—"

"Yes or goddamn no. Pick one."

"Yes!" And the word bellowed like the thunder. "But it doesn't—"

"Yes works," she cut him off. "So good." She opened the door for him, gestured to show him he was free to leave.

"It can't go anywhere."

"Oh, for God's sake, it already has. And if you're going to fall back on the immortal's lament, it doesn't fly. Yeah, I'm going to die. Could be today." She flicked a hand toward the storm outside the window. "Could be fifty years from now. Could be next week or I could live to be a hundred and four. Five of the six of us have that to face, and it sure as hell isn't stopping Bran and Sasha or Sawyer and Annika from grabbing what they have for as long as they can have it."

"None of them have stood by and watched the other die."

"But they will."

"It's not the same, not remotely."

"Grief is grief, but you hold on to that if you need it. I'm not asking or expecting you to hang around should I hit a hundred and four. I just wanted the truth. However long it works, it works."

"Marriage is—"

"Who said anything about marriage?" she demanded. "I don't need pledges and rings and white dresses. I just need the respect of the truth. Now I've got it, and we're back on even ground. That's enough."

She sighed, and this time laid her palm on his heart. "That's enough, Doyle, for me. Give me the truth, and stick with me as long as it works, and that's enough."

He closed his hand over hers. "I swore I'd never love again."

"That was before you tangled with me."

"It was. There's no other like you. Your eyes lured me, your mind fascinates me, your body...didn't hurt a thing."

She let out a half laugh. "You forgot my sparkling personality."

"It doesn't sparkle. I'd rather the edge than the shine."

"Lucky for you."

She moved into him, rose to her toes, felt his hands grip her hips. And heard someone running down the swirl of stairs.

"You need to come!" Annika clasped her hands together. "To the top. I have to get

Sawyer. You need to come."

With no questions asked, they raced up.

Bran stood beside Sasha, a hand on her shoulder as she stared through the wet glass of the terrace doors.

"A vision?" Riley asked.

Even as Bran shook his head, Sasha spoke. "Not exactly. It's...Something's out there, but I can't see it or hear it. I just know it."

"Nerezza?" Riley walked up to stand at Sasha's other side.

"She's close—too close, but that's not it. In the sea, through the storm or beyond it. I can't tell."

"There's more." Bran turned to where the three paintings stood on the mantel.

They pulsed with light. A deep strong red through the painting of the path through Bran's forest, a pure rich blue through the painting of the house, a clear brilliant white from the Island of Glass.

"It's—I think it's their hearts," Sasha said. "The heart of the stars beating. And there's something out there we can't see. In the heart of the storm."

"Wait." Riley pressed her fingers to her

temples as Sawyer and Annika hurried in. "In my notes...Let me think. I've got references. The heart of the stars, heart of the sea, heart of the storm."

"I'll get your notes."

"Just—" She held up a hand to hold Doyle off. "References to the stars' resurrection—the fall and the rise. Silent breath, blah, blah, beating hearts. They pulsed when we found them, so I put it down to that, but there's references to the heart calling to heart, leading them home. And...ah...when the stars wake full, the storm breaks, land and sea. Ride the storm to its heart, and there the heart of the sea, the heart of the worlds waits."

"The Island of Glass?" Sawyer moved closer to a window, peered out.

"It's a theory. And Sasha talked about the storm, riding it. We sure as hell have the storm."

"Ride it to where?" Sawyer wondered. "Visibility is complete crap out there."

"We wouldn't be the first to follow a star. And we have three." Bran scanned the faces of his clan. "Do we trust in the fates, in the stars?"

"If I'm going to ride into that, it would be with the five of you, and with them." Doyle looked at the paintings. "The fates are bastards, but I'm in."

"I would be in, too." Annika reached for Sawyer's hand. "If it's with all of you."

"I say go for it," Sawyer agreed.

"Yes." Sasha turned from the window. "Yes. Riley?"

"Let's make us a plan, and do it."

In the deep twilight, while the storm screamed, Sasha and Annika walked outside toward the seawall. They might have been patrolling, and the black slickers turned them to little more than moving shadows.

Sasha took Annika's hand, squeezed hard. Then, wrenching her bow off her back, shot a bolt high. It exploded with light, illuminating the swarm streaming silently across the blackened sky.

From both towers gunfire erupted. On the parapet Bran hurled lightning.

Agile and quick, Annika ran to place the vials of light where Bran instructed, leaping to avoid keen wings and vicious beaks.

Doyle charged to clear her path, sword lashing.

And the ground began to quake.

From her position on the battlement, Riley reloaded, fired, fired. She hissed when black lightning struck a tree at the verge of the forest, exploded it. As shrapnel rained, the ground burst open to swallow it.

Damned if Nerezza would destroy this place. Damned if she would. Eyes fierce, she took out a swath of flying black death.

She caught the blur of movement to her left, swung around. What had been Malmon grinned at her even as she shot him.

Thick green liquid trickled down his chest.

"She made me stronger. She gave you to me."

Her next shot missed as he seemed to vanish from one spot, appear in another. Before she could shoot again, he closed a hand around her throat, choked off her voice, her air.

"She is Nerezza. She is my queen. She is all. Give me the stars for my queen, and you may live."

Riley managed to choke out, "Fuck you," when he eased his grip.

Now he squeezed harder, lifting her off the ground so her heels drummed the air. "She gave me my pick. I chose you." Those reptilian eyes barely blinked when she plunged her knife into his belly. "I can take you back, feed off you. I have hunger."

His tongue snaked out, slid horribly over her cheek.

"The others die here, and the immortal—"

"Hey, asshole."

Malmon's head swiveled, front to back. As he blinked, as his clawed fingers loosened fractionally, Riley sucked in air.

Sawyer shot him between the eyes.

"That's for Morocco." Dead center of the forehead.

Choking, Riley lifted her gun again, saw there was no need.

"And for Riley." As Malmon stumbled back, eyes clouding, claws clicking, Sawyer took aim once again. "And that, you son of a bitch, is for Annika." The last shot simply blew away the face of what the man had become.

Sawyer gripped Riley's shoulder as she wheezed air in and out. His face was stone, his gray eyes hard as flint. But his voice soothed. "Works for zombies, so you had to figure."

"Yeah, thanks."

Malmon didn't go to ash, but seemed to dissolve, scale, blood, bone, to simply melt into a stain on stone. Riley swallowed, winced. "I gotta say ick."

"I'll go ditto. Okay?"

On a long breath, Riley nodded. Then looked up. "Shit, shit, here come the big guns."

Nerezza rode the sky on her three-headed beast. Her hair, streaked with gray, flew in the roaring wind. Armed with sword and shield, she sliced the air with black lightning that turned to a rain of fire. Bran hurled his own as Riley and Sawyer ran down to the others.

The ground sizzled, gardens burst into flame. Beneath them, the quaking ground cracked, opening with fissures where fire spewed.

"Come on, Bran, come on," Riley urged as she dodged tongues of flame, fired her sidearm. "We've got to get her away from here. Sash!" She leaped, grabbing Sasha's arm and propelling them both aside as the ground split.

Above their heads, like a shield, the coat of arms burst. Blue, white, red in flames to mimic the stars. Fiery rain struck against it, sputtered out.

"That's our cue. We gotta go."

Sasha shook her head at Sawyer, watching as Bran stood atop the parapet, drawing Nerezza's wrath. "Bran."

"He'll make it. Trust him." Riley gripped Sasha's hand, nodded to Sawyer. "Go."

Riley kept her hand gripped on Sasha's during the shift. She knew love now, and knew the fear that came with it. When they dropped into the boat, Doyle moved fast to take the wheel. All around them the wind and rain lashed. The roar of the storm masked the roar of the motor as he aimed from shore to sea.

"He'll make it," Riley repeated. "He's just keeping her off us until we can—"

Bran landed lightly on the boat, his arms filled with glass-shielded stars. Sasha threw her arms around him.

"Are you hurt? Bran."

"Just a bit singed here and there. Take the stars, **fáidh**. If they're to guide us, it would be in your hands."

The boat reared up on a wicked wave, crashed down. Wind and water whipped and churned.

"I can swim if I need to," Annika shouted. "But—"

"Hold on." Sawyer held on to her as the next wave threatened to swamp the boat.

Riley fought her way to the wheelhouse where Doyle stood, feet planted, muscles straining. "Get back with the others, and hold the hell on."

"I'm with you."

He glanced at her, saw the raw marks on her throat. "What the hell—"

"Later." She braced herself as the sea tossed them like rags.

"She's coming!" Sasha shouted. "And the stars..."

Not pulsing now, Riley realized as the next wave drenched her. Beating faster and faster, and beams of light shot from them like beacons.

To show them the way. And showing

them would show Nerezza exactly where they were.

"Ten degrees starboard," she told Doyle.

"Christ. Do you see what's out there?"

A waterspout, swirling up, black against black. And the rain again turned to flames. Arrows of it sparked in the air, hissed like snakes in the sea.

As Bran lifted his arms to form the shield, Nerezza dived out of the sky.

Her lightning crashed against Bran's, and power screamed through the storm.

"Take the wheel," Doyle ordered as Sawyer's shot went wide when the boat tipped. He yanked Sasha and the stars into the wheelhouse. "Take us where we need to go. They need help." He kissed Riley, hard and brief. "Don't lose it," he added, then fought his way back to stand with his friends.

"Heart to heart, light to light." Sasha struggled not to fall as the vision flowed through her. "This moment in all the moments in all the worlds. Risk the storm, ride the storm, and open the curtain."

"Doing my best here." Teeth gritted, Riley wrenched the wheel, doing what she could to ride the mad curl of the next wave. And with her heart, and her faith, in her throat, set course for the waterspout.

Madness. Like an uncontrolled shift, a dive off a cliff. The whirling water caught them, spun them. She lost her grip on the wheel, nearly went flying before she managed to curl the fingers of one hand on the wheel again.

She glanced at Sasha, back braced, arms cradling stars like babies, and her face luminous with their light. "The guardians ride the storm, guided by the stars. The curtain opens, the storm dies. The sword strikes. And it is done."

"Your mouth to all the gods' ears," Riley screamed. "Because I can't hold it much longer."

"Look, Daughter of Glass, and see."

Dizzy, half sick, Riley squinted through the wall of water, the sheering wind.

It gleamed. Clear, shining, still in a beam of moonlight. The door to another world.

When the bow pitched up, she clung to the wheel, looked back.

Doyle stood in water nearly to his knees. Sawyer all but sat in it as he braced his feet against a bench and fired at the Cerberus.

"I can't get a shot at her," he shouted as Bran struck lightning against her shield and Annika attacked the beast.

"I can." Doyle leaped onto the bench even as the sea rocked. He struck the Cerberus, all but cleaving the center head.

And his sword met Nerezza's with a clang that shook the air.

Shook the worlds.

One of the heads snapped out toward him, and met Bran's lightning. Doyle thought nothing of it, nothing of the mad sea, the gunfire, the slash of power.

His eyes, his thoughts, his all centered on Nerezza, and the need that had lived in him for centuries to end her.

He feinted, saw the triumph in her eyes as her blade slid past his guard, gashed his shoulder.

And on that triumph, he thrust his sword into her heart.

Those mad eyes wheeled with shock. Her shriek joined the third head's howl as Sawyer's next bullet hit home.

She fought to fly up, escape, but with the

beast, she tumbled into the black, boiling sea, and was swallowed.

With her fall, the storm died. Stunned and breathless, Riley guided the boat through the door where the Island of Glass floated like a quiet dream.

Then she collapsed.

"Riley!"

At Sasha's call, Doyle whirled, bloodied sword raised.

"No, no, it's the moon. It's changed. And so am I. Damn it, damn it."

"I've got her. Somebody start bailing or we'll sink before we make shore." Doyle dropped down, helped Riley pull off the slicker, her sweater.

"I've got you." He pressed his lips to her temple as she began to change. "I've got you, **ma faol**."

She let it take her, let him lift her above the swamped deck. And when they glided to shore as if over a quiet lake, she let him carry her to the beach where she took her first steps on the island as a wolf.

Chapter Nineteen

In all her life, Riley had never regretted her lycan blood. She'd never cursed the moon or resented the change. But finding herself standing on the Island of Glass, a place of mystery and magicks, of age beyond the knowing, and not being able to speak had her cursing the damn timing.

She smelled flowers and citrus, sea and sand, the cool green of grasses, smoke from torches flanking a path winding up a high hill where a castle stood, shining silver, beaming with light. Felt the warm, soft breeze—a balm over the chilly wet.

And the desperate need to run as the feral energy of the change churned inside her. She quivered with it even as Doyle crouched beside her, a hand light on her neck.

"Don't run, not yet."

Instinct, intellect crashed and clashed inside her, yet another battle. But his eyes, strong and green, held her still. Then she braced, muscles coiled, prepared to attack and defend and she scented something...other.

Beside her Doyle reached for his sword.

They flowed from dark to light, the moon goddesses of Sasha's vision and art. Still gripping his sword, Doyle straightened. Bran laid a hand on his arm.

"Sheath your sword, **mo chara**. They're of the light. Can't you feel it?"

"Just how do you say hi to a god?" Sawyer wondered. "I mean one who's not trying to kill you."

Annika solved the puzzle by running forward, wet braid flying. "Hello! We're so happy! You're so beautiful. You look like my mother, and like Móraí. Like the pictures Sasha drew. We're very wet, and, oh, I have some blood." As if brushing lint from a lapel, Annika rubbed at the blood on her arm. "I'm sorry we're so messy."

"That's one way," Sawyer murmured.

Luna smiled. "You are very welcome here, Sons and Daughters of Glass." And she laid a hand on Annika's arm, healed the gash as she kissed her cheek.

"Oh, thank you. We brought the stars for you. Sasha has them. She has some blood, too. And Sawyer—he's my mate. And Bran has blood and burns. The moon is full here, so Riley had to change very fast to her wolf. And this is Doyle. He stabbed Nerezza with his sword and she fell into the sea. Now the fighting is done, and we're here. I have such happy."

"You are joy," Luna told her. "And you are loved," she said to all.

"You are courage." Arianrhod stepped forward. "And you are valued. We will talk," she said to Riley, "but you must run. Be free." Then she looked at Doyle. "On my honor, she will be safe, and she will come back to you."

The wolf turned her head, looked at Doyle. Then bounded across the sand and into the dark.

"She will always find her way to you, and you to her."

"You are strength and valor." Celene

stepped to Bran, kissed his cheek. "Power and light. You are respected, and have all our gratitude."

"We are your children."

"Blood of our blood, bone of our bone. Heart," Celene added, laying a hand on Bran's, "of our hearts. Daughter." She turned to Sasha. "Will you give us the stars?"

"Yes."

Each goddess held out a hand. As the glass around the stars shimmered away, each star floated to the hand that created it.

Pulsed, pulsed, stilled. Vanished.

"Are they back in the sky?" Annika looked up.

"Not yet," Luna told her. "But safe."

"Don't mean to tell you your business," Sawyer began, "but wasn't the whole deal about putting them back up there?"

"We're not done," Sasha said. "It's not finished."

"I didn't end her," Doyle said as he studied Sasha's face. "She's still out there."

"Your sword struck true." With one hand on the hilt of her own, Arianrhod faced

Doyle, warrior to warrior. "As you are true. But your steel was not the sword that brings her end. Until her end, the stars wait."

"She cannot reach them now," Luna assured them.

"But she can reach us, even here," Sasha said as truth pumped through her. "Now the rage heals her wounds, and once healed, her madness will be complete. She will crave our deaths like wine."

"But not tonight." Celene raised her arms high. "See what I see, know what I know. This night is pure, and the Children of Glass are welcomed home."

"To take another journey." Sasha's eyes darkened as she saw, and she knew. "Beyond the circle of power where the Tree of All Life shelters the stone, and the stone shelters the sword. One hand to draw it, one to wield it, all to end what would swallow worlds."

"But not tonight," Celene said again. "Tonight you will have food and drink and rest. Come. We will tend to you."

"She is safe." Arianrhod laid a hand on Doyle's arm when he hesitated. "And will be guided to you."

As he glanced toward the hills, shadows under a star-dazed sky, he heard the wolf howl. The sound of joy and triumph echoed after him as he took the winding, torch-lit path with the others.

The palace, rising high into the night sky, was as Sasha had foreseen. Gardens of color and scent, musical fountains, rooms with a fairytale gleam that glowed with light and glinted with sparkle.

No one approached them as they followed three goddesses up a sweep of silver stairs strewn with flowers and white candles as tall as a man. Jeweled ropes dripped from the ceiling, raining light as they traveled along a wide corridor into a large chamber.

An elaborate sitting room, Doyle supposed, decked out with curved sofas and chairs in the same jewel colors as the ropes of light. Tables held food—platters of meats and fruit and bread, cheeses and olives and dates. Desserts all but bursting with cream. Wine and crystal goblets.

He thought of Riley's fast. Her hard luck.

He didn't question that his clothes, his hair and body, so thoroughly drenched by the storm and the sea, were now dry and comfortably warm.

They didn't walk in a world of logic now.

A fire crackled invitingly, and though light seemed to emanate from the walls, candles flickered.

From somewhere, soft as a whisper, came harp song.

"You have questions. But the body, mind, and spirit must be fed." Celene poured wine into goblets. "And rested. Your chambers are prepared for you, when you're ready."

"There is beer." Arianrhod poured from an amber bottle, offered it to Doyle. "There will be food for her in the chamber you share when she wakes."

"And if I go out to look for her?"

"You are free to go as you please, as she is. As all are. Might I see your sword? And you mine," she added when his eyes narrowed. She drew hers, held it out to him. "I forged it when I was very young, tempered it with lightning and cooled it in the sea. I named it Ceartas."

"Justice?"

She smiled. "I was very young."

He accepted her sword, gave her his own.

"It has good balance and weight," Arianrhod decided. "It still carries her blood."

"Apparently not enough of it."

"My sword, despite its name, was not meant to bear her blood. I envy you that. I would like to spar with you."

Doyle arched an eyebrow. "Now?"

He saw a warrior's gleam in her eye before she glanced back where the others filled plates, tended wounds. "My sisters would object, but perhaps tomorrow."

"You'd have an advantage."

She exchanged swords with him, sheathed her own. "Warrior to warrior, not god to immortal."

"No. You look like my mother."

That warrior gleam shifted to a compassion he hadn't expected. "I hope a time comes when you find comfort there instead of grief. Eat, soldier, the food is good."

Now she turned to Sawyer. "The demon,

the human she turned, is dead."

"Yeah."

Doyle's head whipped around as the others stopped to look at Sawyer. "Malmon's finished?"

"We've been a little too busy for the recount." Sawyer rubbed the back of his neck. "He went at Riley."

"The marks on her throat," Doyle added.

"She shot him, knifed him—body hits. I went for the head shot." He gulped some wine, struggling a little. Malmon had been human once. "It took three. Magick number."

"He is no more?" Annika asked softly.

"Melted into a pile of goo." Sawyer sent Bran a wan smile. "You're probably going to have to clean that up."

"We are sworn not to do such evil." Luna lowered her head, then lifted it. "But she has broken all oaths. And he became her evil. She turned him because she saw what he was. What was human, she destroyed. Not you, Sawyer King. You ended a demon."

"To save a friend, a sister." Now Arianrhod turned back to Doyle and from her pocket she took a key. "This will guide you to your bedchamber when you retire."

"How will she find me?"

Surprise, and perhaps a little disappointment, moved over Arianrhod's face. "You should trust, son of Cleary, Son of Glass. As long as your heart beats, she will find you."

"Now you have food and drink and comfort," Luna began, "we will give you privacy. If you have a need for anything, you have only to ask. Eat and rest well, and we will be with you on the morrow."

"No harm will come tonight," Celene vowed. "And nothing will disturb you. Be welcome here."

When they were alone, Doyle picked up the beer, sampled it, decided he sure as hell couldn't complain about that.

Sawyer lifted a hand. "Can I just say, holy shit? I'm not sure my brain's caught up with the rest of me, but we're sitting at our own personal banquet in a castle on the freaking Island of Glass. A castle, in case you didn't notice, that's made of glass."

"Bollocks," Doyle said.

"Back at you, dude. I had a good look, a

good—if sneaky—feel. Plus I tapped on it. Glass. Magick glass, I bet, but wow. Plus, a god just poured me a drink."

"They're very nice. We made them happy, too." Annika bit into a little cream cake. "I like this food."

"She's right about the food," Sawyer told Doyle.

"Yeah, I could eat." But he walked to the glass doors, opened them to look out on the hills.

"She's fine. I can feel her." Sasha leaned against Bran, sipped wine. "She's more than fine. She's thrilled. This is a world few have seen, much less explored, and there's still an archaeologist inside the wolf." Rising, Sasha filled a plate, walked over to Doyle. "Eat."

"Eat, drink, and be merry?"

"Tomorrow's coming either way."

She went back to Bran.

He stroked her hair. "We found the stars, we found the island and returned them. And we should have known, I suppose, such things come in threes. So we've one more leg to go."

"I must have missed the heart." Disgusted,

Doyle sat, brooded over the food.

"I don't think so." Now Bran brushed his lips at Sasha's temple.

"It's the sword," she said. "Yours could hurt her, and enchanted, make her bleed, but can't end her. We have to free the one that can, and will, from the stone."

"Somebody'll play King Arthur," Sawyer supposed. "Hope it's you, man, as you're the best here with a sword."

"We will have one more battle."

"Don't say one more," Sawyer said to Annika. "It's bad luck. Let's just say, we're taking a hike tomorrow."

"I like to hike."

"We'll make our own fun."

They talked late into the night, or what felt late, and still Riley didn't come back. Doyle let the key guide him—it simply drew him along the corridor to a wide, arched door that opened when he stepped up to it.

He hoped to find her there, waiting for him. But there was no wolf curled by the fire or stretched out over the enormous bed.

Once again he went to the doors, flung them open to a balmy, almost tropical breeze perfumed with night-blooming jasmine and citrus. The room held a curved love seat in a nook, two wing chairs in front of the fire, a sturdy writing desk—she'd like that—under a window. And the massive bed with a soaring headboard carved with symbols. He recognized some—Irish, Greek, Latin, Aramaic, Mandarin.

If his translation could be trusted, all symbolized peace.

He wouldn't have minded some damn peace.

He took off his sword, leaned it on the side of a chair. Poured himself a couple fingers of what he discovered was whiskey in a slender bottle, and settled down by the fire to wait for her.

He should've been annoyed, and couldn't figure out why he wasn't—or not particularly. She'd have run off that energy by now, and should have come back. But she was still out there, sniffing around, he supposed—literally—exploring her brave new world.

So he sipped his whiskey, brooded into

the fire, and with a soldier's mind went over every step of the battle looking for mistakes.

He didn't hear her so much as feel her, and turning his head saw her standing just inside the terrace doors, scanning the room with those amazing eyes.

"About bloody time."

He rose, walked to the bed, tossed the bedding aside. He stripped to the skin, and rolled in. A moment later he felt her leap up, land beside him. Curl against him.

And finding his peace, he put an arm around her and slept.

The change came at dawn with the sun breaking the night with soft pinks, strong reds, rich golds. It moved through her, pain and beauty, helplessness and power. She shuddered with it, gave in, gave all as one became another.

And on a sigh opened her eyes to find Doyle's on her.

"What?"

"Beautiful. You're beautiful."

Still half dazed, she blinked. "Huh?"

He rolled onto her, covered her, and his

mouth was hot, indescribably tender on hers. Her system, her spirit, her body, barely through the glory of the change, trembled anew at the fresh assault on her senses.

She could barely breathe and his hands stroked over her skin, molded her breasts, skimmed down to her hips. His mouth followed.

She flew up, clung, clung, clung to that edge of impossible pleasure, then let it go to take the fall.

Helplessness and power, pain and beauty.

All she was responded, gave back. Here, too, was change, a merging of two into one. They rolled over the bed, grasping, finding, taking.

He could still smell the wild on her, all but feel it beat inside her. When her mouth met his again, strong and fierce, he surrendered to all she was.

And all she was, was his.

Lust burned. Love shattered. Need beyond the physical overwhelmed.

When she straddled him, those eyes like melted gold, her body taut and glowing in those streaks of morning, he was lost.

So she took him, slow, slow, glorious torture. Then stronger, deeper, until her breath caught on moans and her heart thundered under his hands. And driving, driving, fast, wild, and straight into the heart of the storm.

She slid bonelessly down on him, rested her head on his chest. Her lips curved when his arms came around her, as they had around the wolf before they'd slept.

She'd have slept again, warm and content, if not for the sudden and desperate hunger. She hoped to God there was food of some sort close by.

"You watched me change," she told him.

"It's not the first time." He stroked her hair. "It's magnificent. Oddly arousing."

She snickered at that, then her head shot up as she sniffed the air. "Food."

"There's a kind of sitting room where—"

"No, here." She rolled off him, leaped up.

On a table were platters—that hadn't been there—eggs, grilled meats, bread, glossy pastries.

He pushed up to his elbows. "Tell me that's coffee."

She sniffed a pot as she stuffed bacon in her mouth. "Tea, but it's strong. I'm starving."

He watched her eat, still naked, still flushed from sex, her hair tousled and shaggy, her hands grabbing greedily.

"I'm in love with you."

She glanced back. "Hey, you said it right out loud."

"I'm in love with you. Damn it."

"Sounds more like you. Better get your ass up if you want any of this."

"I've been married. Twice."

Riley paused, deliberately poured tea. "That's not surprising in three centuries."

"The first was about forty years after... after. She was young and sweet-natured. I shouldn't have touched her, but I did, and more than once, and with that she— She got pregnant. I couldn't ruin her. I had ruined her."

"So you married her. Did you tell her?"

"No, I didn't tell her. And I didn't need to, as it turned out, as both she and the baby died in the birthing."

"I'm sorry." In that moment, she felt his grief as her own. Dull and deep. "I'm so sorry."

"Not uncommon in those days. I swore I'd never touch an innocent again, such as she had been. And didn't. More than a hundred years and I married again. She was a bit older, not innocent. A widow. Barren. We enjoyed each other. Her I did tell, though I doubt she believed me. Until she grew older, and I didn't. And she grew bitter with it. I had soldier's work to do, but I always came back to her. And one day I came back to her too late. She'd hanged herself, and left a letter for me. Cursing me."

Riley nodded, sipped some tea. "I'm sorry. It sucks. For the first, if I got pregnant, it's now the twenty-first century. I'm strong and healthy. For the second, I'm not vain, and I'm not stupid. And over all that, I don't need marriage."

"I do. With you."

She choked on the tea. "What?"

"It's stupid. It's a mistake. We'll both regret it."

And looking at her, just looking at her, he didn't give a damn.

"I want the pledge. For a day, a week, for

fifty years or if you live to a hundred and four."

"You're serious? You're asking me to marry you?"

"That's what I said, isn't it?" He rolled out of bed, stalked over. "Give me the damn tea."

"But I'm all aflutter."

He shot her a viciously dark look. "I didn't love them. I cared for them, both, and I pledged to them. I honored the pledge, without love, as I thought love wasn't necessary. Or possible. I love you, and I'll damn well have the pledge and make it."

"I could say no."

"You won't." He slammed the tea down. Then closed his eyes a moment. Opened them with his heart in them. "Don't. Don't say no. Give me this one thing."

She reached up to frame his face. "Do you understand I don't need this to stay with you, to love you, to accept you'll go on after I stop?"

"Yes. I don't need it to stay with you or to love you. I need it because I will and I do. I need it because in three and a half centuries, you're the only woman I've loved."

"Okay."

"Okay? Just...okay? That's your answer?"

"Yeah, okay. I'm in."

He shook his head, then lowered his brow to hers. "What a pair we are."

"It works."

"It works," he agreed. "I guess you'll want a ring."

"**Treweth**—the Anglo-Saxon root of betrothed. Means truth. The ring's a symbol of the promise. I appreciate symbols."

"I'll find something." He drew her in. He'd found her, hadn't he?

"It'd be nice to stay here." Skin to skin, heart to heart. "But." With reluctance she drew back. "I've got some questions, and the first is, where are the damn stars?"

"Safe, we're told. I'll fill you in. We should get dressed, find the others."

"Great. Where are my clothes?"

"Couldn't say."

Her brows knitted. "Didn't you get them?"

"Considering the situation, I didn't think to pick up after you."

"Well crap." At a loss, she looked around

the room, then walked to a delicately carved wardrobe. Stared at the contents. "You've got to be kidding me."

Doyle studied in turn, smiled. Inside hung a pair of leather breeches the color of cowhide, a simple shirt, a leather jerkin, and his own coat and boots.

And a dress the color of old gold with silver laces and piping along with kid boots.

"Seriously? You get the cool leather pants and I get a Maid Marian dress?"

"It's that or naked."

"Let me think about it a minute."

She wore the dress—and scowled at herself in the mirror. "Where am I supposed to put my gun, my knife? Where **are** my gun and knife?"

"We'll sort it out." Doyle strapped on his sword. "You look beautiful."

"I look like I'm going to a Renaissance fair." She tugged uselessly at the bodice. "That's a lot of landscape. Why are breasts such a thing?"

"I'll show you later," he said and went to answer the knock on the door.

"Good morning! Oh, Riley!" Annika swirled in. "You're **beautiful**! Oh, how pretty. Do you like my dress? Isn't it wonderful?"

She did a spin, sending the skirts flying out, all sea green and silky. "Sawyer said it's like my eyes, and yours is like yours. Sasha's is so pretty and blue. Everyone is in our sitting room. We're to wait until they come for us. We're going to meet the queen." She took a breath, focused on Doyle's face. "You're happy! I can see your happy. You're with Riley!" She threw her arms around him. "You must get Riley a ring now."

"I'll work on that."

"Will I do the stand-up at your wedding?" she asked Riley.

On a laugh, Riley stopped feeling awkward in the dress. "You bet your ass."

"Come, come. There's more food. And coffee."

"Coffee? How'd you get coffee?"

"Sasha asked." Grabbing Riley's hands, Annika tugged. "We have only to ask."

"I missed that memo."

In the sitting room the others stood, Sasha in flowing blue velvet, Bran in the dignified black of the sorcerer, Sawyer in brown tanned pants and a hip-length jerkin over a cream-colored shirt.

"Nice threads," he said to Riley.

"Middle Ages prom dress." She studied him as she beelined for the coffee. "You got a Han Solo deal going."

"I know, right? I'm digging it."

"So, sorry I had to change and run last night, but Doyle's caught me up. Nerezza's like a bitch cat with nine lives, and the stars don't go up until we finish her off." She gulped coffee. "And so a pilgrimage to the sword stone, an Arthur the Young twist. Then we freaking end this thing."

"That sums it up," Bran agreed. "May it be so simple."

"I need my weapons," she began, then turned when a young man in trews and doublet stepped to the door.

"My ladies, my lords. Queen Aegle requests the honor of your presence."

It wasn't every day you met a queen, Riley thought as they followed the page up the wide stairs. It wasn't every lifetime you met the queen of a magick island who'd ruled for more than a millennium.

NORA ROBERTS

She'd expected the huge double doors, but had assumed to find them guarded. Instead they were flanked by glass urns of flowers.

She'd expected a kind of throne room, and the size met that description, along with what seemed like acres of clear glass floor. But the decor struck as simple—flowers, candles, colorful fabrics—and a throne, clear as the floor—more like an elegant chair than royal.

Then again, a chair of gold and jewels might have seemed simple compared to the woman who graced it.

She was radiant.

Topped by a diadem of jeweled glass, Titian hair spilled luxuriously over the shoulders of a white gown. The tiny clear stones scattered over it sparkled like diamonds. Perhaps they were. Her beauty stole the breath. Luminous perfection in a sculpted mouth, in vividly green eyes, and high, keen cheekbones.

When she smiled, Riley would have sworn the light shimmered.

The three goddesses stood at her right side. On her left sat a massive white wolf with eyes of bright gold.

Annika swept into a fluid curtsy. "Mother of magicks, queen of the worlds, Aegle who is radiance, we are your servants."

"You are welcome, Children of Glass. You are welcome, Guardians of the Lights."

She rose, glided down the three steps from the throne, crossed to them with her hands outstretched. She took Annika's, kissed Annika's cheeks.

"Wonder of the sea, you have our love, our thanks. Traveler of time and place." She kissed Sawyer. "You have our love, our thanks. Child of the moon." And Riley's. "You have our love, our thanks. "Warrior of forever, you have our love, our thanks."

She moved from Doyle to Bran. "Son of power, you have our love, our thanks." And last to Sasha. "Daughter of visions, you have our love, our thanks. I would give you more than this, but your journey is not yet complete. Will you finish it?"

Sasha answered as Aegle's hands still held hers and the words rose up in her. "We will travel the path of the gods to the circle of power, and beyond to the Tree of All Life and the stone and sword. We will fight the last battle, light against dark.

"I can't see who wields the sword, or if the sword strikes true. I can't see the end of Nerezza, or our end."

"You cannot see, but you will take the journey?"

"We've pledged to it," Bran answered.

"It's an oath," Annika added, then looked at Sawyer.

"All in." He kissed her temple. "Ah, Your Majesty."

"We could stay here." Riley drew Aegle's attention. "The guardians are on Glass, and the stars, and it's within your power to move the island to another place, even another dimension. We could stay, potentially without interference from Nerezza for a couple of centuries. Or so I've read in several records."

"You are a scholar and a seeker, and what you say is truth. Is this what you would wish?"

"No, I just wanted verification. No disrespect."

"I would give you time. You would enjoy learning more of us, more of this world. Digging."

"Very much. But there isn't time, not here and now."

"Not here and now."

"Then we finish the journey." Riley looked at Doyle. "So say we all?"

"We finish. My woman needs her weapons."

Riley's eyebrows shot up—not just at the **my woman**, but because he spoke in Irish.

"In the chamber you share when you return, and garb suitable for what is to come." Aegle laid a hand on Doyle's arm. "You have only to ask. Such is our love, our gratitude. Only ask."

The queen stepped back. "It is our greatest hope that you will return here, victorious, and together with all of Glass, we will watch the stars shine."

Chapter Twenty

As they started back, they passed servants, ladies-in-waiting, courtiers—as best Riley could figure. Each would stop, bow, or curtsy. It struck her as awkward as the dress.

"So that was our royal pep talk."

"Wasn't she beautiful?"

"I'll give her that." Riley nodded at Annika. "She lives up to her name. And she looked about what—sixteen? Had about two miles of red hair."

"But it was like Sasha's," Annika said. "Like sunlight, in many braids."

"Black." Sawyer twirled his fingers. "Curls."

Riley stopped on the stairs. "Red—Titian red, long and loose. Emerald green eyes.

Sasha?"

"Black, but swept up. Her eyes were more like yours, Riley, but a few shades deeper."

"All things to all people." Riley nodded as they continued. "We saw her as we imagined her—or somewhat. You spoke to her in Irish," she said to Doyle.

"She was speaking in Irish."

"English and Russian," Sawyer said.

"She spoke to me in my mind once, in the language of the merpeople."

"Of all the strange, I guess it's not the strangest," Riley considered.

"And it wasn't just a pep talk. She gave us something." Sasha looked down at her own hand. "She gave us light. Didn't you feel it?"

"I felt something," Riley admitted. "Let's hope it works."

"We make it work. We're ending it, and Nerezza, today."

Riley turned to Doyle. "Sir Pessimism's taking a turn on the Optimistic Highway."

"She looked like you," he said shortly.

"She what?"

"I saw you. That's who she was, the form,

for me. Whatever the hell it means, we make it work. We're not losing this. I'm not losing you. So we end it. Gear up. Let's get moving."

He stalked off.

"Doyle's happy," Annika said. "He loves Riley. He's going to get her a ring."

"We'll worry about the last part after we end the bitch. And I'm damned if I'm doing it in a dress."

She peeled off, followed Doyle.

He stood studying the new items in the wardrobe. "You'll be happier with this."

"She looked like me?"

He took out Riley's gunbelt, set in on a table. "I didn't know you when you were sixteen, but yes. Your face, your hair, your eyes. Those are eyes I trust, and that's what I felt. We're not going to lose this."

"All right then." Riley put her hands on her hips, scanned her wardrobe choices. "This is more like it."

In sturdy trousers and a leather vest with pockets for extra clips, she went back to the sitting room with Doyle. She picked up a hide canteen, sniffed the contents. "Water." And strapped it on cross body. "Couldn't hurt."

Sasha and Bran joined them. Bran patted a leather satchel. "Salvaged from the boat. A few light bombs."

"Water." Riley offered Sasha a skin. "Any idea how long a hike?"

"I don't know." She turned when Annika and Sawyer came in. "I guess this is it. I thought—it seemed—as if we came together to find the stars, get them here. But this is it. We're guardians, and it's always been leading here."

"We will guide you to the path."

The three goddesses stood in the doorway of the terrace, backed by the warm light of the sun.

They walked together, two by two, down to a courtyard where a fountain spewed rainbows, where flowers soared and spilled and fruit dripped from trees like glossy jewels.

People stood in silent respect. Children raced and waved.

They moved through a gate, past a grove, then a green field where a man and the boy working with him stopped, doffed their caps.

Riley heard the cluck of chickens, the coo of doves, the throaty hum of bees. A woman with a little girl on her hip smiled at Riley, dropped a quick curtsy. The little girl blew kisses. Others stood outside of cottages, tidy as postcards, hats in hands or hands on hearts.

In a small bay, fishermen stopped casting their nets and saluted.

"The people of Glass are with you." Luna gestured as they crossed a stretch of white sand toward the path. Flowers and baskets of fruit, glinting stones, pearly shells heaped at the verge. "Offerings to the guardians, and wishes for a good journey."

"On this day, at this time, the path is only for you." With her sisters, Celene stopped. "Only you can walk it. What waits at its end is only for you."

"Brave hearts," Luna said. "Walk in light."

Arianrhod set her hand on the hilt of her sword. "And fight the dark."

And they were gone.

"I'd say that's god-talk for you're on your own." So saying Riley stepped onto the path, started up.

The first quarter mile was paved with stone, lined with trees, a gentle rise. It turned to hard-packed earth as the trees thinned and the rise steepened.

How many miles had they walked together since they'd started? she wondered. She should've kept a log.

In places the path narrowed so they went singly. In places it roughened so they navigated ruts, climbed over rock. On one outcropping Riley stopped, turned to look back.

The island went absolutely still below her, like something caught in a ball of glass. All color and shape without movement. A painting spread over sea and sky.

A bird caught in mid flight, a wave frozen above the shore.

When the worlds still, she remembered. And so it had.

Then a deer leaped over the path, a bird took wing. The standard on the palace waved in the breeze.

At the end of the path, she thought, lay the end of the journey.

She leaped down, continued the climb.

The path wound, and a little stream bubbled beside it. Water spilled over rock, tumbled into a small pool where the deer drank.

"I ran this far last night," she told the others. "Part of me wanted to keep going up, but something just told me not yet. I stopped by that pool, the water so clear I could see my reflection, and the moon's."

"Let's hope we get up there, get this done before you see the moon again and go furry."

Riley shook her head at Sawyer. "Last night was the third night here. But I'd sure as hell like to get it done before dark."

She fell companionably into step with him. "I was thinking about Malmon."

"Gone and no regrets."

"That's something I was thinking about. She chose him, lured him, seduced him, and turned him into a demon. One who worshipped her. He didn't just kill for her, he very likely saved her life, at the very least nursed her until she got herself back."

"And?"

"She did nothing to save him. Because he meant nothing to her. Look, he was a bastard when he was human, as evil and twisted as they come, but she ended that human life. As somebody who knows about change, I'm telling you **that** change had to be agony."

"Hard to wring out any sympathy there."

"With you," Riley agreed. "The thing is, she didn't have to change him to get what she wanted out of him."

Sawyer stopped, narrowed his eyes. "I hadn't thought of that, but you're right. One hundred percent."

"She did it for fun. And when he failed, even after he saved her miserable existence, he was just a kind of diversion. Yeah, he tried to kill me, but she sent him in to pave the way for her. And after all that, bang, you're dead. Thanks to you. Odds are she could've given him what Doyle has, instead it's over like a finger-snap for him. And she doesn't care."

"You thought she would?"

"I'm saying if she didn't give him a thought—someone—something that fed her, nursed her, did her bidding, worshipped her, fucking died for her, she sure as hell doesn't care about any living thing. Dark or light."

"I could've killed him if he'd still been human, but not the way I did. I couldn't have just...not if he'd been human."

"I know." Riley gave him an elbow jab. "That's why we're the good guys."

A few paces ahead on the rugged path, Annika began to sing.

"And that," Sawyer said.

"And that."

They climbed while the sun wheeled past noon with the stream rising with the path. Quick, frothy waterfalls poured over ledges of rock, but nothing came to drink. No bird soared overhead or darted through the trees.

Riley scented nothing but the water, the earth, the trees, her companions.

When the worlds still—she thought again.

Then there was...something. Something old, potent, alive. But not human, not beast, not fowl, not of the earth.

"There's something—"

But Sasha had already stopped, was reaching for Bran's hand as he reached for hers.

"Do you feel it?" Sasha's words were

barely a whisper over the music of the water.

"Power," Bran said. "Waiting." Bran glanced back at the others. "Let me have a look first."

But Sawyer shook his head. "All for one, man. That's how it is."

Doyle's sword slithered out of its sheath. "Together."

And together they crested the high hill.

There the path ended, and there stood the stones, a perfect circle, graduated in size from one on each side no higher than Riley's waist to the king stone, taller than two men.

They stood, quiet gray, under the strong afternoon sun, swimming in a shallow sea of mist.

"Not as massive as Stonehenge, but more symmetrical," Riley observed. "I bet when I measure them, each set is precisely the same in height and width, and an exact ratio."

The archaeologist led the way, moved straight up, laid a hand on a stone. Pulled it back. "Did you hear that?"

"It...grumbled," Sawyer said.

"No, it sang!"

"Annika's closer. More a hum, right?" Riley asked. "And it gave me a little jolt. Not painful, more like: Think about it."

"Here stand the guardians, placed here by the first." Sasha held her hands out to the circle. "The circle, the dance, the source. Light and dark, as one must have the other. Morning sun and dark of moon. Joy and sorrow, life and death. Here is truth. And from it springs the tree, and beneath the tree the sword. Walk through, and wake the sword."

She lifted her face. "Oh, I can barely breathe. It's so strong, so beautiful. Walk through!"

Bran walked between the stones. They hummed, soft and quiet, the sound building when each of the others walked in, stood with him.

Light lanced out of the sky, struck the two smallest stones. Like a chain of fire, light streamed around the circle, struck the king stone. Voices rose like the wind in one strong, soaring note. The stones pulsed with it, shined silver with it. The mist burned away, revealed the ground of glass.

As the stones quieted, the sun showered over the hundreds of bare branches of a great tree that stood alone. Beneath it sheltered a gray spear of stone with a naked sword carved on its surface.

"Looks like step two." Because her skin still quivered, Riley cleared her throat, sucked in a breath, then started across the circle to once again walk between the stones.

"Of the stone." Riley walked around it, crouched in front of it. "Any idea how to get it out?"

"Reach in. Wake it. Free it. It's all I know," Sasha told her.

Riley straightened, stepped back. "Doyle makes the most sense. Agreed?"

That got nods all around.

Doyle studied the carving. A bit smaller, slimmer than his own, but a fine-looking blade with a simple, unadorned hilt. He gathered his faith, his trust, his hope, reached for it. Hit solid stone.

"I feel nothing. Should I? Only that it's not for me to take it."

"Then Bran. I'm sorry," Annika said

quickly.

"No need." Doyle stepped back. "Your go, brother."

Bran laid his hand on top of the stone, used what he was to try to **feel** through it. Shook his head. "Like a locked door," he murmured, skimmed his hand down, laid it over the carved hilt. "Or a power sleeping."

"Well, it needs to wake the hell up. Maybe there's a code or a pattern. Maybe some sort of incantation. We just need to figure it out. Give me a minute to..."

Riley ran her hand down, fingers tracing the carving for a clue.

The stone trembled, sang in a sound like rising joy. When shocked, she pulled back her hand, she held the sword.

"Oh, shit."

Immediately she swung to Doyle, held it out.

"It's not mine." He wondered if she felt the light beating around her. "It's yours."

"What am I supposed to—"

It all but leaped in her hand. Against her closed fist the rough stone hilt began to change, to smooth. Light streaked up the blade so she instinctively lifted it up to protect the others.

The sun struck it, searing. Before her stunned eyes the stone became clear polished glass.

"Did everybody see that?" Her heart thudded, her ears rang as she lowered the sword. And still its power raced up her arm, through her body. "It's glass."

"Like the palace." Sawyer reached out, ran a finger over the flat of the blade. "You've got a magickal glass sword, Riley."

"It sparkles," Annika murmured. "And makes rainbows."

"And holds power. Can you feel it?" Bran asked her.

"Oh, damn skippy. It's like the stars. There's a pulse in it. And it...it feels like mine, but let's be practical. I'm no swordsman. I know the basics, but that's it. I'd love to nail Nerezza with it, but I'm going to need a lot of training."

Sasha gripped Riley's shoulder. "She's coming."

Doyle ranged himself beside Riley. "Learn fast," he told her, and drew his sword.

She came with a swarm, turned day to

night.

Riley shifted the sword to her left hand—she'd need to get a lot closer for it to do any good—and pulled her gun.

They spilled out of the sky, slithered and shambled out of the trees, dark, twisted things with snapping fangs, swiping claws.

Bolts and beams and bullets struck against the dark. Shrieks tore the air as light exploded.

On the beast mangled by Doyle's sword, Nerezza rode with them, pure madness now, her beauty gone, her hair a tangle, wild gray snakes, her eyes sunken, burning black.

Her lightning crashed with Bran's, and the aftershocks knocked Riley off her feet. Something crawled burning over her boot. Even as she jerked back, Annika turned it to ash. Firing, firing, Riley flipped to her feet. Almost without thought, she slashed with the sword. The thing she cleaved screamed, vanished in a flare of light.

She felt the pump of power now, the thrill of it, and slashed, struck, jabbed, hacking her way through a swarm.

"I need to get closer. I can do it, I can

take her. Can you get me up there, behind her?"

Sawyer shook his head. "Trying to bring her ride down, but these things block it. They keep coming."

He slapped in another clip, and Riley saw blood dripping down his hand.

"We need cover. We need to—"

"Die here!" Nerezza screamed. "Die here, and I feed on your power. All that you are is mine. This world, and all die with you."

She shot down flame. Annika deflected the first, but the second ball exploded in front of her, sent her flying back. Sawyer rushed to her as one of Sasha's bolts killed the creature before its sharp wing scored Annika's face.

"Into the circle. Lure her into the circle," Sasha shouted. "I think—Bran!"

"Yes, yes. The power. i'll draw her in."

"Leave that to me. What's she going to do?" Doyle demanded. "Kill me? Keep her off Riley." He fought his way closer to the circle, managed to turn to meet Riley's eye. "This isn't Malmon. Aim for the heart. Drive her to me, push her to me. Some magick wouldn't hurt."

"You'll have it." Bran hurtled lightning at Nerezza's flank. "Keep the pressure on her."

"She'll go for Doyle." Teeth gritted, Riley fired. "Once she sees he's alone."

"But he's not alone," Sasha reminded her.

Bran leaped on one of the stones, hurled a vial of light. As it exploded, the Cerberus screamed in pain. The slash of its tail missed Bran by inches as he jumped clear. But the maneuver turned Nerezza toward Doyle in the heart of the stone circle.

"Immortal. Burn and bleed."

He rolled away from the fire, jumped clear of that lashing tail. Closer, he thought. Just a little closer.

"Bitch," he called back. "This time I'll cut out your heart. Sword to sword. God to god!"

"You are no god." When she swooped, he struck, but her quick turn had him slicing the side of her beast. The sword he'd carried for centuries snapped in two like a toy. "And that is no sword."

Bran threw lightning to draw her off as

Doyle pulled his knife. As he pivoted, the Cerberus clawed his back, struck him down.

The others rushed toward the circle. As the blood of an immortal, a guardian stained the glass, light burst like a bomb. It sent Riley sprawling, had her ears thundering, her breath lost. Through the haze she saw Bran struggling to his knees, heard Sawyer cursing. And saw Doyle unarmed, alone.

Overhead Nerezza laughed. "Can you grow your head back, immortal?"

She dived, a sword raised over her head.

Like Bran, Riley struggled to her knees, knew she'd never make it. "Doyle!"

When he turned his head, she saw the pain in his eyes, the regret. "Bullshit on that. Catch!"

She threw the sword, and all her faith.

He lifted his hand, closed his fist around the hilt. With a warrior's cry, he sprang up, whirled away from Nerezza's sword. He drove the Sword of Glass through her heart.

She didn't scream. The beast beneath

her, all those that flew or crawled sizzled away like water in the sun or melted like ugly chalk drawings in the rain.

Day burst back to life.

She fell into the circle, the mother of lies, eyes glazed with fear and madness.

"I am a god." She croaked it out as her hair thinned, as her flesh shriveled.

Doyle gripped the sword in both hands. "You're nothing." And plunged it into her heart again.

The blood bubbled black. Her fingers became bones that clacked together. "I want. I want." Black eyes wheeled as the flesh of the face flaked away.

Doyle gripped Riley's hand when she limped to him. Looked around once as the others, bruised, burned, bloody, came with her. "We ended you."

She withered to bone without a sound, and the bone went to ash.

"She can't come back?" Annika hugged close to Sawyer. "She's gone?"

"Look." Bran gestured.

The hundreds of branches of the tree leafed out green, bloomed with fruit and flowers. The air, so full of the sounds of battle only moments before, now sang with birds and breezes. A doe wandered out of the woods to crop at the grass.

The stones stood silver and shining on the hill of Glass. The king stone bore the guardians' coat of arms.

"Good answer." Then Sawyer dropped to his knees. "Sorry. Ow."

"Let's have a look. We'll do what we can here," Bran added, "then—"

"We've only to ask," Sasha remembered. "I'm asking for us to be brought back. If we've done what we were meant to do."

"You really think they're just going to—Oh," Riley said as she found herself, and the others, standing at the start of the path. "Excellent."

They began to limp and wince their way toward the palace.

"We couldn't just wish to be healed?" Annika wondered.

"People should see their warriors. They should see what it costs to stand for the light," Doyle told her, and put an arm around her to support her. "To do what's needed."

They wept, and they cheered as the six

passed by. And wept and cheered all the way to the doors of the palace where the goddesses waited.

"We will tend you now." Celene stepped forward, raised her voice. "Tonight, there will be celebration. Tonight is for music and dancing, for wine, for joy. Tonight is now and forevermore, the Night of the Guardians."

"I'm going to bleed all over the floor," Sawyer began.

Luna stroked his wounded arm. "You will not. Come now to be tended and fed and bathed and rested. We are your servants today."

It wasn't so bad having a goddess as a servant. At least not when, Riley decided, it included luxuriating in a sunken tub full of hot water that a pretty young maid scented with jasmine. Or having every ache in your tired body rubbed out with oil.

She didn't even mind—too much— putting the dress on again. Not when she had permission to explore, take samples. Some stones, some scrapings, a little dirt, some sand. A couple of flowers she'd never seen before.

When she rushed into the sitting room to find the others, she was all but flying. "You won't **believe** what I've seen. They have chickens that lay colored eggs. I saw a baby dragon—the adults prefer caves. A freaking baby dragon."

She grabbed a bottle, poured a glass not caring what it might be.

"And the library in this place? It makes yours look like the book turnstile at a gas station, Bran. Every book ever written, in every language. I mean freaking Hogwarts doesn't have what they have."

She gulped down what proved to be wine. "And their society? No war, not since that whole uprising with the Bay of Sighs—which, by the way, is back. People like their work, whatever they choose. Farmers farm, weavers weave, bakers bake. If they need to cut a tree, they plant another. Always. And—What?"

"We got around some, too," Sawyer told her. "Annika got to swim with some merpeople in the Bay of Sighs. Sasha's done half a million sketches. Bran, he's been holed up with other magic types."

"We went up," Bran told her, "consecrated

the ground within the circle."

"Doyle's been busy, too." Sasha continued to sketch.

"Yeah? With what?"

"Nothing much."

Sasha lifted her head, stared holes through him.

"Fine. Al! right." He stood up, pulled something out of his pocket. "I got this."

Riley stared, dumbfounded, at the ring. The pure white stone sat in a simple band. Its brilliance needed no adornment.

"You don't like fuss," he said.

"No, I don't. But how did you..."

"Just ask, right? I just asked if there were any jewelers, and I had about a hundred rings pushed at me."

"Sasha and I helped from there," Annika told her. "Because it was confusing."

"I don't happen to have any money on me that works around here anyway. And they didn't want any. But..."

"He had in his pocket a pipe—a musical pipe—he made as a boy," Annika said helpfully. "He traded."

"That's...Jeez, that's sweet."

"It gets sweeter," Sasha told Riley. "He

asked Bran to engrave it."

"Engraved." Riley snatched the ring from Doyle's hand, turned it to look inside the band. **"Ma Faol."** Her throat simply closed as her heart leaped into it. All she could do was look at him.

He took the ring back. "Are you going to give me your hand?"

"Damn right I am."

"It's called the Stone of Glass. I don't know what the hell it actually is."

"I'll be finding out." It astonished her that her eyes stung, that she had to fight back tears. "And I can tell everybody you're a cheap bastard, and it's glass."

"Bet you would." He slid it on her finger. "You're stuck now."

Annika applauded. "Kiss her, Doyle! You need to kiss her now."

"Yeah, kiss me, Doyle." Despite the dress, Riley boosted up, wrapped her legs around his waist. "And make it good."

He made it very good.

Epilogue

A royal celebration required fancy, Riley discovered. She also discovered Annika was a force of nature when the mermaid's mind was set.

She banished the men, decreeing the women would dress together.

"It's special," Annika insisted as she patiently fastened what seemed like half a million buttons on the back of Riley's gown. "When we have a special celebration, my sisters and I prepare together. You're my sisters." She rested her cheek on the back of Riley's head. "I'll miss you so."

"Don't cry." Alarmed, Riley turned. "We won. We saved the worlds."

"We're still going to see each other." Sasha moved in for a hard group hug.

"We're a clan, remember? We'll come to your island, and Bran will make your pool so you can come to us. And we'll all go to wherever Riley and Doyle are."

"It's an oath."

"Pinky swear." Riley held up her pinky. "A very serious oath." She took Annika's, hooked it, and Sasha added hers. "Done. I love you guys, sincerely. And I'm going to need regular Sawyer and Bran fixes."

"Could I have a favor?" Annika asked.

Sasha kissed her cheek. "You have only to ask."

"I'm very excited for the celebration here, but...Could we have one of our own? Just us, when we go back to Bran's? A night for the six of us, without worry and weapons, before I go back to the sea?"

"That is a most excellent idea." Riley looked at Sasha. "You up for that?"

"Absolutely. Biggest and best celebration ever."

"And done again. Okay, Anni, how about the big reveal?" Riley gestured to the mirror Annika had covered with a tapestry.

"Oh, yes." But first she gave her friends a long study, and a nod of approval. Then swept the tapestry aside with a flourish. "We are beautiful!"

"Whoa." Riley blinked.

She'd seen her companions, of course, Annika in a gown of blues and greens as iridescent as her mermaid's tail with her hair a glory of sleek braids streaming down her back. And Sasha, hair in long, soft waves over a fluid gown of silvery blue. But she barely recognized herself in the fitted gown the color of crushed rose petals with a glimmering gold underskirt.

She touched a hand to her hair—Annika had managed to fluff and curl and add some style.

"We're rocking it." She slid an arm around Sasha's waist as Annika did the same. Joining them. "We're badasses who clean up really well."

"Badasses," Annika repeated and laughed. "Beautiful badasses."

"That's who we are." Riley shot a finger at their reflection. "Let's go party."

She figured the endless primping time worth the effort when she saw Doyle's face. And more when he took her hand, bowed over it, kissed it. "Warrior queen.

Mine."

"You look pretty good yourself." She brushed her fingers over his doublet of dull silver. "Ready to do this thing?"

He offered his arm, and though she laughed, she laid hers on it so they walked, all six, up the wide stairs.

People in their finery crowded the ballroom where tables groaned with food on platters of silver and gold. Lights sparkled from the ceiling, massive candles glowed, and jeweled trees shined in air scented with the perfume of masses of white flowers.

Doors and windows stood open wide to bring the sound of music and celebration from outside in.

As the six entered, conversation stopped. At some signal, the happy din from outside stilled. Men dropped to one knee; women swept into deep curtsies. And the queen rose from her chair, walked to them.

"Tonight we honor heroes." She curtsied before them, head bowed. "Your names, your deeds will be remembered for all time, and celebrated on this night through the ages. You, and all who come from you, will be welcome here, always."

She rose, took Bran's hand, took Sasha's. "Bran Killian, Sasha Riggs. You have only to ask."

"I've been given more than I ever dared to wish. I found myself," Sasha told her. "And love. And family."

"I have my heart." Bran brought Sasha's other hand to his heart. "Brothers, sisters. What I am, what I have, is stronger for it."

"You are well matched. When it comes my time for a life mate, I hope to find such harmony. Our blessings on you."

She turned to Sawyer and Annika, took their hands. "Sawyer King, Annika of the waters, you have only to ask."

"Everything I could want is right here with me," Sawyer said. "I don't travel alone anymore."

"I wished for Sawyer, with all my heart, and my wish was granted. I kept my oath, and my people can have pride. I have a new family, and we have promised to come together."

"Child of the sea, your heart is so kind. Would you not ask for the one thing still held inside it?"

Now Annika bowed her head. "The moon must turn, my lady, for the worlds to be. I can't ask."

"The moon will turn, and you may ask."

"But I..." She lifted her head, eyes wide and full of hope. "The legs? I could keep them, walk with Sawyer?"

"If this is your wish. Daughter of the sea, and of the land. Would you wish to be of both worlds?"

"Oh, yes! Sawyer."

"Wait. She wouldn't have to give up her parents, her sisters, her people?"

"She has, as you have, given all. She gives up nothing. Yes," Aegle said, smiling back at Annika. "There can be children."

Tears sprang to Annika's eyes as she laughed, flung her arms around the queen. Riley braced, waiting for lightning to strike at the breach in protocol. But the queen only laughed in turn.

"You are joy, and deserve to have it."

"Thank you, thank you. Sawyer!" Annika whirled, threw her arms around him. "I can walk and dance with you. We can make children."

When she whispered in his ear, he cleared

his throat. "Yeah, we can do that, right after the party." Heart in his eyes, he looked over Annika's head to the queen. "Thank you."

"You would not ask it for yourself. You are well matched. Our blessings on you."

She turned to Doyle and Riley. "Doyle McCleary, Riley Gwin, you have only to ask."

"I have a million questions," Riley began, and made Aegle smile.

"This is not a wish, but study. You may stay or come back as you will, and learn. The Island of Glass is forever open to you. If you stay, time is different here. You would have more."

"No. No," Doyle said, firm. "You have work, you have your pack. We're fine," he said to Riley.

"It is for her to ask or not. Would you give up the moon, Riley Gwin, the change and the wolf?"

"I—" Everything inside her knotted. "It's who I am. Doyle—"

"It's who I love." To cut her off, he gripped her hands. "You thought I meant to strike you down that night, the first change, after the battle. But I **was** struck. And began to change. Those eyes, **ma faol**. No, you give up nothing."

"It's who I am." Content, Riley turned back to the queen. "Having the door open here, that's a great gift to me. Thank you for it."

"I would have been sorry if you'd chosen differently."

As Aegle spoke, Riley saw the deer leaping over the path, the doe who came out of the woods, the woman holding a little girl on her hip, the rosy-cheeked maid who'd filled her bath.

"You're a shapeshifter."

"I am in all, of all. I was always with you. And you," she said to Doyle. "Will you ask?"

"I have family again, and with them succeeded where I'd failed for three centuries. I have my wolf."

"The dark marked you, giving you what some men seek, knowing it would bring you grief. Light can lift it. Would you cast away immortality?"

"It can't be done. Even Bran—" Doyle caught the look in Bran's eye. "It can?"

"I asked, and was shown. It can be done."

"Hold on. Not for me," Riley insisted. "And not on impulse. Dying's no picnic, and—"

"Three centuries doesn't qualify as impulse." Hope, real hope brought a kind of pain.

Bittersweet.

"A life with you? A real one? Really living, knowing a day is precious and finite? It's what I want. It's more than I ever thought to have."

"Then you must accept." Aegle held out her hand. A servant rushed forward, gave her a glass goblet. "From your brother."

Bran took the goblet, and a vial of clear liquid from his pocket. "This is the water of life, conjured of light. Its purity defeats the dark, breaks the curse." He poured the water into the goblet. "If you choose to be mortal, drink."

Doyle studied the water, thought of his life, the deaths, the battles, the long roads traveled alone.

He lifted the goblet to Bran, then to Sasha, to Annika and Sawyer in turn. And last to Riley. To the love of his true life.

"I want a pack of kids," he said, and drank.

"Wh—What?"

"You heard me." He waited a beat. "I don't feel any different."

"Be glad you didn't do a Nerezza and age three centuries. Define pack."

"We'll talk about it." He turned to the queen. "The first girl of our pack will have your name. However many days I have from this night, I'll be grateful."

"Well matched. I see an adventurous life ahead. Blessings on all of you. A queen may reign with kindness and care, with wisdom and justice, people may prosper, but without those who will risk all to stand against evil, no world can flourish."

There was music and feasting, wine and joy. The color of sweeping skirts, the sparkle of light. Late in the night, amid the celebration, the queen and her goddesses led the way to the beach.

Arianrhod held out the sword cased in a simple leather sheath. "This is yours."

"Seriously?" Riley stared at it. "I'm allowed to take it?"

"It is yours."

"She was our sister," Luna said. "We will mourn what she might have been."

"And grieve for what she chose to be," Celene added. "And cherish what has come home. For Aegle, the radiant, the Fire Star."

"For Aegle, the radiant, the Water Star." Luna turned with her sister.

"For Aegle, the radiant, the Ice Star." Arianrhod lifted her hand with the other goddesses. In them the stars whirled and pulsed.

And flew, streaking into the sky, leaving their trail of light on their journey to the moon. The people of Glass roared as the stars settled, a perfect curve, to shine.

"And there they will ever be, for all the worlds to see, to wonder, to hope." Once more Aegle held out her hands. "Safe journeys, Guardians of Glass. The door will always be open for you."

"Go in joy." Celene crossed her hands over her heart.

"In love." Luna laid a hand on hers.

"In peace." Arianrhod tapped a fist on hers.

And Riley found herself standing with the others by the seawall of Bran's home.

"Wow," Sawyer managed. "That just

happened."

Laughing, still wearing the ball gown, Annika turned cartwheels over the lawn.

"Home again." Bran drew Sasha close.

"And all's well."

"I have a magick sword."

Doyle glanced down at Riley. "You're going to need training."

"Yeah, yeah, but I've got a magick sword." She drew it, lifted it toward the sky. "And look."

The sword glinted as it pointed to the three stars under the moon. "There they are. We did that. And what do you think astronomers are going to have to say about it?"

"Only you," Doyle said with a shake of his head. Then he cupped her face, looked into the eyes he loved. "Only you."

"I call for a moment. Gather up, team." Sawyer managed to grab Annika.

"A major moment." Riley clasped Doyle's hand, slid an arm around Sasha's waist. Waited while the others moved in close, joined.

So the guardians could stand, above the sea, under the Stars of Fortune.

United.

HARVARD EAST ASIAN SERIES

1. *China's Early Industrialization: Sheng Hsuan-huai (1844–1916) and Mandarin Enterprise.* By Albert Feuerwerker.
2. *Intellectual Trends in the Ch'ing Period.* By Liang Ch'i-ch'ao. Translation by Immanuel C. Y. Hsü.
3. *Reform in Sung China: Wang An-shih (1021–1086) and his New Policies.* By James T. C. Liu.
4. *Studies on the Population of China, 1368–1953.* By Ping-ti Ho.
5. *China's Entrance into the Family of Nations: The Diplomatic Phase, 1858–1880.* By Immanuel C. Y. Hsü.
6. *The May Fourth Movement: Intellectual Revolution in Modern China.* By Chow Tse-tsung.
7. *Ch'ing Administrative Terms.* Translated and edited by E-tu Zen Sun.
8. *Anglo-American Steamship Rivalry in China, 1862–1876.* By Kwang-Ching Liu.
9. *Local Government in China under the Ch'ing.* By T'ung-tsu Ch'ü.
10. *Communist China 1955–1959: Policy Documents with Analysis.* With a foreword by Robert R. Bowie and John K. Fairbank. (Prepared at Harvard University under the joint auspices of the Center for International Affairs and the East Asian Research Center.)
11. *China and Christianity: The Missionary Movement and the Growth of Chinese Antiforeignism, 1860–1870.* By Paul A. Cohen.
12. *China and the Helping Hand, 1937–1945.* By Arthur N. Young.
13. *Research Guide to the May Fourth Movement: Intellectual Revolution in Modern China, 1915–1924.* By Chow Tse-tsung.
14. *The United States and the Far Eastern Crisis of 1933–1938 (from the Manchurian incident through the initial stage of the undeclared Sino-Japanese war).* By Dorothy Borg.
15. *China and the West, 1858–1861: The Origins of the Tsungli Yamen.* By Masataka Banno.
16. *In Search of Wealth and Power: Yen Fu and the West.* By Benjamin Schwartz.
17. *The Origins of Entrepreneurship in Meiji Japan.* By Johannes Hirschmeier, S.V.D.

HARVARD EAST ASIAN SERIES, 17

The Origins of Entrepreneurship in Meiji Japan

The East Asian Research Center at
Harvard University administers projects
designed to further scholarly understanding
of China, Korea, Japan, and adjacent areas.

THE ORIGINS OF
ENTREPRENEURSHIP
IN MEIJI JAPAN

Johannes Hirschmeier, S.V.D.

HARVARD UNIVERSITY PRESS

1964 · CAMBRIDGE, MASSACHUSETTS

Distributed in Great Britain by Oxford University Press, London

Preparation and publication have been aided by a grant from the Ford Foundation

Library of Congress Catalog Card Number: 64–20973

Printed in the United States of America

TO MARY

PREFACE

This book has grown into its present shape over a period of five years. When I started to write a dissertation on Meiji entrepreneurship, I had only a vague idea of the problems involved. In the course of my research my own viewpoints changed repeatedly, and my material and its arrangement had to be altered accordingly. I know of no research works of a similar kind that might have served as a model, and in Japan the study of entrepreneurship is still in its infancy.

One of the greatest difficulties was to find a meaningful balance between writing a general history of Meiji industrial development and presenting detailed biographical data on individual business leaders. I became increasingly convinced that the two must be synthesized because Meiji industrial development was contingent upon the dynamism of its entrepreneurs, while the entrepreneurs themselves were a product of the social, political, and economic conditions of their time. It therefore became my primary objective to point out this interplay between outside forces and the initiative of individuals. The first two chapters and part of Chapter Four stress the social and political conditions of the late Tokugawa and early Meiji periods. Chapter Three and the second part of Chapter Four put greater emphasis on economic development. The rest of the book focuses on private entrepreneurship.

I am indebted to many who helped me during my research and writing. First of all I want to express my gratitude to Professor Alexander Gerschenkron who as thesis adviser provided firm guidance, especially during my initial groping with unfamiliar material. I am equally indebted to Professor Edwin O. Reischauer, who was of great help in redressing imbalances of interpretation.

While rewriting for publication I received untiring help from Professor Albert M. Craig of Harvard University. I profited greatly from discussions with Professors Henry Rosovsky and William W. Lockwood, both of whom I had the pleasure of meeting in Tokyo. I am grateful also for very useful suggestions given me by Professors Benjamin I. Schwartz, Fritz Redlich, and Arthur H. Cole, all of Harvard. I should also like to thank the East Asian Research Center and notably Mrs. Elizabeth Matheson for all their help in editing and preparing the manuscript.

During my prolonged research in Japan I had the pleasure of frequent discussions with Professor Tsuchiya Takao, and I also received good advice from Professors Miyamoto Mataji and Yamaguchi Kazuo. My colleague and friend Suma Chikai of Nanzan University was always ready to help out with his vast knowledge of the Tokugawa period.

Through the most pressing months of thesis writing I enjoyed the generous hospitality and stimulating discussions of my friend Robert L. Hamman, who at that time was working on his own dissertation.

I thank Yasuike Masuya for so ably assisting me for a year in the collection of material. Library facilities were generously extended to me by Tokyo University and Hitotsubashi University. Special thanks are due Kato Chiye for her patience in typing and retyping the manuscript.

Finally, I am grateful to the Society of the Divine Word for financing my trip to Japan and my stay there from 1957 to 1959. Without that generous sponsorship I could not have written this book.

JOHANNES HIRSCHMEIER, S.V.D.

CONTENTS

INTRODUCTION   1

I   THE MERCHANT CLASS   7

The commitment to the past. The merchants after the Restoration.

II   THE SAMURAI CLASS   44

The economic impasse of the samurai. The drafting of samurai for modern enterprise.

III   RURAL ENTREPRENEURSHIP   69

Rural entrepreneurs in Tokugawa Japan. The rural manufacturers after the Restoration.

IV   THE INITIATIVE FROM THE CENTER   111

The *bummei kaika*. The transfer of technology. The transportation system. Other government enterprises. Indirect subsidies to private industry. Japanese industry in the mid-Meiji years.

V   THE SPIRIT OF ENTERPRISE IN THE PRIVATE SECTOR   162

The entrepreneur, a new status. The low profit rates. The question of economic rationality.

VI THE ZAIBATSU BUILDERS 211

The House of Mitsui and Minomura Rizaemon.
Masuda Takashi. Nakamigawa Hikojirō. Iwasaki Yatarō, the builder of Mitsubishi. Hirose
Saihei, the modernizer of Sumitomo. Yasuda
Zenjirō, the banker. Ōkura Kihachirō, the
trader and industrialist. Furukawa Ichibei, the
builder of a mining empire. Asano Sōichirō,
the courageous innovator. Conclusions on the
zaibatsu builders.

VII FIFTY LEADING ENTREPRENEURS 245

Formative influences. The entrepreneurial performance: Biographical notes.

CONCLUSION 287

NOTES 295

BIBLIOGRAPHY 323

GLOSSARY 343

INDEX 349

THE ORIGINS OF
ENTREPRENEURSHIP
IN MEIJI JAPAN

Nor is new wine put into old wine-skins; if that is done, the skins burst, and there is the wine spilt and the skins spoiled. If the wine is new, it is put into fresh wine-skins, and so both are kept safe.　　　　　　　　　　Matthew, 9.17

INTRODUCTION

The economic development of Japan since the Meiji Restoration of 1867 has caught the imagination of the Western world, because Japan has been the only non-Western nation to succeed in breaking through the barrier of backwardness that still entraps most of Asia. Less than a hundred years have passed since the dawn of Japan's new era, and yet this dynamic nation is beginning to extend a helping hand to her Asian neighbors in an effort to lead them, too, on the road to vigorous economic growth.[1]

The economic development of Japan has many fascinating aspects, and the literature on modern Japan, particularly on its industrialization since the Meiji era, has assumed monumental proportions. This book is not intended to repeat or improve on existing accounts of the course of Japan's development. It will focus instead on entrepreneurship, in the broadest sense of the word. All the material presented is designed to throw light on the important question of how Meiji Japan generated the power to make her economy run uphill, leap unbelievable hurdles, break down centuries-old barriers, and finally arrive at self-sustained industrial growth. Japan succeeded so well because she had exceptional leadership in both the government and the private economic sector. The combination of governmental guidance and private industrial initiative has many facets, and I am aware that I have been able barely to scratch the surface of the matter.

The role of entrepreneurs in economic development is today a much discussed subject, but unfortunately it is an unwieldy one. We cannot limit the discussion of it to quantitative variables but must also include sociological and political forces. This is particularly necessary in the early phase of economic development, prior to the industrial "take-off," when statistical data are hard to come by and when cool economic rationality is often swamped by political and social upheaval. If the economist is to treat of entrepreneurship, he has to examine the bewildering kaleidoscope of variables and from them derive a coherent theory of economic development. He cannot willfully restrict his model to those variables that are statistically tractable if others also occupy a strategic position in the developmental process. Myrdal remarks on this problem: "Also, the distinction between 'economic factors' and 'noneconomic factors' will likewise have to be discarded as illogical and, consequently, misleading. Economic analysis will have to deal with all the relevant factors if it wants to be realistic; general economic theory will have to become social theory. I believe that the main hypothesis for this new theory will then be the assumption of circular causation between all factors in the social system resulting in a cumulative process." [2]

For a long time it was thought that lack of capital was the real villain preventing economic growth. Once sufficient capital was provided — from within or without — to overcome the "low-level equilibrium population trap," economic growth would issue forth and feed on its own impetus, so the argument went. If nations provided loans and grants to underdeveloped countries, all would be well.

Recently increasing attention has been given to entrepreneurship as a key factor in the entire process. The will to develop, to invest, to take risks, and to break with traditional business attitudes may be of greater strategic importance than the availability of capital. Of course, a minimum of savings is required to set in motion modern economic growth, but this does not mean that savings hold a logical or causal priority. Hirschman thinks that capital supply may often behave passively and that it is, over a wide range, a positive function of entrepreneurship.[3] Sufficient potential capital for a vigorous start may already exist in various disguised forms. A classic example in support of this theory is Japan, where sizable amounts of disguised capital were activated by vigorous entrepreneurship. Then, as the developmental process gained momentum, more capital was formed as a result of economic and social reforms, and also as a result of the initial success of the pioneering ventures. All this was done without any foreign capital to speak of.

According to this theory, whether a country succeeds in making its big leap forward will depend largely on its ability to supply sufficient "entrepreneurship" — the determination and ability to invest, independent of the question of private versus public initiative. The government can and should, in the initial phase, go a long way not only to provide guidance, but also to build the social and economic overhead. But unless the country intends to acquire a completely planned economy, in the Soviet style, its planners must recognize the need to stimulate private entrepreneurship of a high quality and make it one of their chief tasks to do so.

Entrepreneurship, seen in this context, becomes at once a matter of paramount importance as well as one that resists quantitative analysis. It is not enough to insist that entrepreneurs are necessary for economic development; we need to know more about the factors that influence the supply of entrepreneurs. Is there anything that can be done to stimulate the emergence of business leaders in backward countries? What are the main obstacles preventing capable young men and potential industrialists from devoting their energies to private business pursuits?

Schumpeter assigned the key role to the entrepreneur in his theory of economic development. The entrepreneur is the Faustian element in the economy; he disrupts the equilibrium circular flow by introducing new combinations and thus drives the economy to ever higher levels of performance. He destroys the old and builds the new, and it is he alone who reaps profits in the proper sense.[4] There appears to be no particular scarcity of the Schumpeterian type of entrepreneur in the economically advanced countries. Even where the individual innovator is being replaced by research teams and decision making is being delegated to a managerial group,[5] the will to innovate and the eagerness to exploit all possible profit opportunities cannot be said to be in short supply. Modern capitalist societies not only provide monetary rewards for economic success but often make idols of their successful businessmen. Societies in which generals and civic leaders of the first rank retire into top business positions without any loss of prestige will easily draw capable and ambitious men into industry and business. The economically backward countries, on the other hand, frequently have an almost diametrically opposite scale of values, in which business pursuits automatically cause a man to lose his social respectability. In countries where the merchant class has been notorious for cheating and ruthlessly exploiting its customers, the very idea of business easily becomes abhorrent to the most talented people in the society. In the course of this book we shall see that this inherited value system presented one of the most persistent obstacles to the formation of a dynamic business leadership in Meiji Japan.

The approach adopted in this book represents a middle way between what can be termed macroanalysis and microanalysis. The Japanese literature abounds in biographies of all types and degrees of reliability on the Meiji "heroes," among whom are many of the top business leaders. But we gain little by simply compiling biographical sketches without attempting a macroanalytic view of the whole entrepreneurial situation. We need, above all, conclusions that are neither complete generalities (as, for example, "entrepreneurship is necessary for economic development") nor too closely limited to the conditions existing in a particular industry at a particular time. We cannot answer the question of who introduced "the new mode of production" to Japan with clichés, for then it is possible to get bogged down in attempts to find out who or which class was really "bourgeois" in Meiji Japan. The whole bourgeois or not-bourgeois problem must be left aside for a while so that we may start fresh, without looking all the time for Western prototypes.

Despite this rejection of a pat class model, my first three chapters will deal with the economic and entrepreneurial function of the three groups that occupied key positions in the process of growth prior to the Meiji Restoration and afterward. At the same time, these chapters are intended to provide general background information on the economic and social conditions of the period. The third and fourth chapters examine the all-important initiative and help that came from the center, as well as the need for and the emergence of private pioneering and independent entrepreneurship. ("Center" stands here for government in the broadest sense: it includes direct investments as well as policies, political pressures as well as official and semi-official influence on popular attitudes; particularly significant is the influence of the Restoration itself.) The last two chapters provide numerous examples of the unique interrelationship between the center and the private sector. The ample biographical material also serves as a basis for a few generalizations on the prerequisites for the emergence of modern entrepreneurs in Meiji Japan. The choice of individual entrepreneurs has been made with considerable care to lend my conclusions as much general validity as possible.

A final word needs to be said on the use of the term entrepreneur throughout the book. I use it to denote all businessmen of the modern type who excelled in some way in the fields of industry, trade, or banking. The test is their actual contribution to the building of Japan's industrial economy. It may require no less ingenuity and daring to introduce imported methods of business or production into an economically backward country than it does to introduce the primary innovations into advanced countries. Thus, such a broad use of the term seems well justified even in the Schumpeterian sense.

I

THE MERCHANT CLASS

Feudal Japan shared many social and economic features with feudal Europe. There was an aristocracy whose power was based on the ownership of all land and which lived on taxes levied on the farming population. There was also a merchant class that collected in the castle towns (*jōkamachi*) of the feudal lords (*daimyō*).[1] In these castle towns the townsmen (*chōnin*) organized their trade by supplying the consumers in the towns and cities with the products of the primary producers and craftsmen in the villages. They developed guilds with objectives and characteristics similar to those of medieval Europe.[2] If things had gone according to the European model, the merchants eventually would have become an energetic and progressive element, introducing innovations and gradually spearheading a complete change of the social as well as the economic system.

But history did not run that way in Japan. The merchant class did not rise to the top and did not display the requisite leadership; instead it succumbed to the stagnating influences of tradition and to the rigidities of Tokugawa social policy.[3] In the early seventeenth century, just as the merchant class became crystallized, Japan's military dictators (*shōgun*) closed the country to foreign intercourse, and it remained protected from external influences for almost two hundred and fifty years. When the forced seclusion was terminated by Admiral Perry's arrival in 1853, the merchants were caught unprepared for the enormous task of bridging Japan's economic backwardness. The entrepreneurial task put before the Meiji industrialists required attitudes and capabilities that the merchants, by and large, were untrained for.

This should surprise no one. It is one thing to move ahead step by step, using previously acquired skills and experience as a foundation; it is quite another to face, all at once, a set of completely unknown variables. Entrepreneurs in a country that is a latecomer to industrialization have to tackle formidable problems, and business experience may not be the best answer. We know that in latecomer countries in Europe leadership in the pioneering of large modern enterprises fell to the banks and the state, since the traditional merchants or manufacturing groups lacked the necessary capital and experience. The greater the backwardness that has to be overcome, the greater will be the guidance and help required from the state; correspondingly, the wider will be the difference between the type of entrepreneur who can be expected to pioneer successfully in the private sector and the European prototype of the bourgeois merchant. At least, this is what the case of Japan would suggest. In the following section we shall see why and to what degree Japan's "bourgeoisie" remained committed to the past and why it failed to assume economic leadership in industrialization.

THE COMMITMENT TO THE PAST

The Guild System

The guilds in England, and even in France and Germany, had lost their importance and power before they were finally dissolved officially. New products and new methods of manufacturing sprang up which did not fit into the traditional guild structure and therefore could not be regulated by the guilds. The new spirit of liberalism and a revolutionary critique of the established political and social hierarchy undermined the strength of the guilds from within. In Japan, at least in the cities, the guilds were not eroded by economic changes or undermined by a liberal ideology; they continued a relatively vigorous existence until the Meiji Restoration. The essential character of the guilds was the same as that of their counterparts in medieval Europe: they exercised regulatory functions with regard to the prices and quality of goods, and guaranteed the stability of the market by restrictions on membership and on output or sales per enterprise. Finally, they were social groups which protected the interests of the group and gave the individual a place in society. The guilds exercised a stabilizing influence on economic and social relations, and in this respect they were welcomed and protected by the shogun's government (*bakufu*).

Throughout the two hundred and fifty years of its existence, the bakufu's overriding objective was to keep the country at peace and all social groups in obedience and contentment. Japan was to remain like the dream castle in the Sleeping Beauty tale, ever unchanged and undisturbed by the evil influence of the Western "barbarians." Actual changes in economic conditions were ignored, and the classes remained forcibly frozen in their seventeenth-century molds. The guild system was not only tolerated but was promoted as one of the best expedients to keep the merchants under control and to preserve their conservative attitudes. The bakufu even sold guild charters and monopoly rights for hard cash, which was but one of its many ways of extorting money from the prosperous merchants.

The bakufu did not mind the merchants' becoming rich

through monopolies, so long as it could benefit from those riches. By the beginning of the nineteenth century, the guild merchants had succeeded in accumulating great wealth simply by relying on their chartered rights and their exclusive trading privileges; they had offered almost nothing in the way of innovations or productive contributions. But they had also earned the hostility of the hard-pressed samurai (the military class) and of the peasant population. A series of natural disasters and famines in the 1830s caused large-scale peasant uprisings and general social unrest, which was directed mainly against the merchants. The bakufu gave way to pressures and abolished the guild system in 1841–42, after it had tried in vain to make the merchants lower their high prices. But the cure turned out to be worse than the disease. Abolition of the controlling guilds was followed by chaos in the business world, with adventurous business undertakings, rampant speculation, and frequent bankruptcies. The bakufu was forced to reintroduce the guilds in 1851, and they lasted from then until their second and final abolition in 1872. Decrees against monopolistic practices and restrictions on membership were issued repeatedly, but without noticeable effect.[4] Yet from 1851 on there existed merchants outside the guild system, and their numbers increased rapidly after the opening of Japan's ports in 1858.

The opening of the ports to foreign trade, which was enforced by the Western powers, introduced a wedge into the protective guild system. The port cities attracted new men from all strata of society, men with daring and imagination, adventurers and moneymakers who cared little about rules and traditions. Former samurai without a coin in their pockets or seasoned rural manufacturers would start a business in Edo or Yokohama, fascinated by the prospects of trade with the barbarians.[5] Leading entre-

preneurs like Asano Sōichirō, Yasuda Zenjirō, Ōkura Kihachirō, and Amamiya Keijirō started their careers in Yokohama.

The guild merchants suffered heavy losses through these
new adventurer-merchants of the port cities because the
latter would buy their supplies directly from the producers
without following the usual route from local wholesaler
to city wholesaler, then again to local wholesaler, and
finally to the retailer. In their distress the guild merchants
of Edo appealed to the bakufu, which decreed that a number of export goods must be moved to Yokohama via the
Edo wholesalers, notably raw silk, seaweed, oil, wax, and
fats.[6] This decree was also aimed at the control of exports
and at price stabilization. In the last decade of the Tokugawa period, then, the guilds did break down in practice
before they were officially abolished by the Meiji government. But they had been able to exercise a determining
influence on the nature of the merchant class until ex-
terior forces destroyed the protective system.

The support accorded the guilds by the bakufu, however,
only partly explains their long, unchallenged continuance.
We may well ask why economic opportunities arising outside of the rigid system did not weaken the guilds much
earlier, as they did in most European countries. If the re-
strictive and conservative character of the guilds blocked
the emergence of vigorous entrepreneurship, why did not
a counterwave of entrepreneurial innovations shatter the
confining chains of an ancient, clearly outdated system?
The answer to this question reveals some of the marked
differences between Japan's economic development and
that of the advanced Western countries. It also brings into
relief the salient features of the Meiji entrepreneurs, who
emerged only by breaking radically with business traditions. Entrepreneurs are, to be sure, innovators by defini-

tion, and therefore also "new men"; but we usually visualize them as building at least in part on the experiences and traditions of the existing business leadership. In Japan entrepreneurship emerged through an emphatic break with all that might have constituted such a line of continuity. Because the economic and the ideological situation within the merchant class was hostile to change, the guilds were able to continue and any major innovational drive was stifled. What were the conditions primarily responsible for the stagnation of the entrepreneurial spirit among the bourgeoisie of Tokugawa Japan?

Osaka: The City of Wealth

The heavy stress on capital availability as a necessary condition for economic development tends at times to obscure the other requirement — that potential investment capital must become available to men who are able and willing to initiate productive investments. The mere concentration of wealth in terms of gold, banknotes, or debt holdings in the hands of a certain economic group may not in itself set economic development in motion, since such claims against national income can be used in a variety of ways: they may be hoarded, squandered in luxury consumption, reinvested in traditional trading, or lent out as consumer loans. None of these uses of capital is conducive to economic growth. As long as such avenues of unproductive investment remain attractive, merchant wealth may not become available for real capital formation. It is therefore necessary that productive investments become more attractive; where the difference in profit rates between productive and unproductive uses of wealth does not become convincingly large, other strong inducements in terms of prestige or power may be needed in order to channel wealth into capital formation.

The merchants of the big Japanese cities, where the nation's wealth was centered over the Tokugawa period, generally preferred to invest unproductively in trade and in consumer loans, and they conspicuously shunned the risks of innovations. There were exceptions — merchants who invested heavily in land reclamation and in rural manufacturing. But the tendency was to stick to the easy and well-trod path of monopoly trade and consumer lending. How did the accumulation of wealth take place, and what proportions did it assume?

At the turn of the seventeenth century, the merchants became the beneficiaries of the separation of the large samurai population from its rural base and its concentration in the castle towns.[7] Trade relations between town and village necessitated the spread of money, and with it came possibilities to make profits. The merchants knew how to handle money and how to use it for the spread of luxury consumption. The monetization of the economy thus moved the economic power away from the feudal class (daimyo and samurai) over to the growing merchant class. Contemporary writers warned against this trend, as the following passage shows:

Because everyone from the greatest feudal lords down to the lowest samurai uses money, the merchants make huge profits. In prosperity they far outstrip the samurai class, and enjoy far more conveniences and amenities of life. Without moving an inch, they supply the necessities to all provinces, they act as official agents of the ruling classes down to the lowest samurai, changing money, handling rice and all other products, even military equipment, as well as providing facilities for travel, horses and trappings, etc., and merchants are indispensable for any kind of ceremony.[8]

But the trend toward urbanization, and with it the great opportunities for the merchant class, could not be stopped by such critics.

Three cities became consumer centers: first there was Kyoto, the emperor's seat; then Edo, the shogun's administrative capital; and finally Osaka, a city of trade and commerce. Edo grew rapidly from a small town into the world's largest city by the beginning of the nineteenth century, with a population of between 500,000 and a million.[9] About half of its population were samurai attached to the daimyo residences,[10] and the other half were merchants. Osaka came next in size after Edo, with a population of some 350,000 at the outset of the nineteenth century.[11] At the shogun's court in Edo the daimyo and the samurai vied with each other in displaying their importance through pomp and extravagances. This was all to the benefit of the merchants, who throve on luxury trades. The merchants of Edo themselves started to dissipate their easy profits, and they became proverbial for their amusements and gay life.

Osaka was different. It was a city of merchants with few samurai, and there the merchants developed an almost puritanical sense of thrift. Osaka became the main supply center, storehouse, and trading entrepot for the whole country. The city's favorable position on the shore of the Inland Sea gave it a unique advantage as a wholesale center; rice and other staples were transported by ship from all parts of the country to Osaka's storehouses, and from there they were channeled to the main consumer centers, notably Edo and Kyoto. Wholesale trade was the mainstay of the Osaka business world.

In 1715 Osaka had no less than 5,655 wholesale establishments (tonya).[12] Among the various wholesaler groups the Twenty-Four Wholesalers Union gained national fame and through its financial power dominated the Osaka business world. Along with trade came finance, the second pillar of Osaka's economic strength. Toward the close of the Tokugawa period, popular opinion had it that about 70 percent of the nation's wealth was concentrated in the hands of the Osaka merchants and financiers.

Osaka gained unchallenged leadership as a financial metropolis during the Tokugawa period because of the close relationship between wholesale trade and banking that developed out of the monetary confusion of the time. There was a bewildering variety of paper and coin money in existence: the bakufu had its own gold, silver, and copper coins, and so did the various han. The printing of paper money and the debasement of currency added to the confusion and made long-distance trade extremely difficult.[13] This is why the merchants welcomed the services of specialized money exchanges (ryōgaeya) which would reliably and expertly exchange one type of coin for another. These money exchanges came also to serve as clearing houses in large business transactions and as deposit banks. Finally, they issued their own notes, which circulated like money in the cities and even throughout the whole country, like present-day bank notes. It is said that the notes of the very large money exchanges enjoyed higher prestige and confidence than the official government money. For one thing, the wealth of the leading exchanges seemed to provide perfect security and, for another, the bakufu was always ready to back up the money exchanges by prosecuting, with top priority in the courts, any case of counterfeiting.[14] Among the 1,340 money exchanges that existed in Osaka around 1850, the top group of Ten Money Exchanges had the best reputation. Its services were requested for official transactions by the government or the han; it enjoyed such privileges as tax exemption; and its notes circulated throughout the country.[15]

The high degree of liquidity and confidence among the Osaka financial institutions had its effect on the interest rates in that city. When the rates in the rest of the country varied between 10 and 15 percent, the large merchants and money exchanges of Osaka kept them as low as 5–6 percent.[16] The bakufu knew well that it should accord protection and favors to the Osaka merchant princes and financial magnates. Whenever the bakufu's coffers became depleted, it sought of these men forced loans (*goyōkin*) and special "donations" (*myōgakin*), and obliged them to buy up rice for the sake of price stabilization. A few examples will illustrate the magnitude of these various forms of taxation, which in themselves are a measure of the wealth of the Osaka financiers.

When the price of rice dropped to rock bottom in 1806 and threatened to cause unrest and misfortune among farmers and samurai, the bakufu ordered 318 Osaka merchants to purchase and store up over 1.2 million koku of rice (one koku equals 4.96 bushels). On that occasion the house of Kōnoike was forced to buy no less than 73,000 koku.[17]

In 1843 a large forced loan was demanded from a group of Osaka merchants, amounting to 1.14 million ryo, which corresponds to about 1.14 million koku of rice, or the sustenance of over a million people for one year.[18] Although such levies were imposed on the merchants of other cities too, Osaka always bore the heaviest burden. The curious fact is that many wealthy merchants or money exchangers actually became embarrassed if their portion of the levy was too small relative to their importance. These widely publicized contributions to the government were viewed by the merchants as the best advertisements of their financial soundness and of public confidence in them.[19]

The accumulation of so much wealth among the top echelons of the Osaka financiers and merchants might lead one to expect that these same groups would have initiated economic advances and social change. But the truth is that we find no major efforts among this city bourgoisie to break the constraints of the feudal economic system, one which had assigned them the lowest rank in society. Instead of becoming strongly antifeudal, the city merchant class tended to become even more conservative toward the end of the Tokugawa period.

At the beginning of the seventeenth century, the bakufu had divided the population into four classes: samurai, peasants, artisans, and merchants (*shi, nō, kō, shō*).[20] The rigidity of this status division was enforced by various devices and was given an ethical sanction through the Confucian doctrines on social relations. These were promoted by the bakufu and became something like an official ethic of Japanese feudal society. In the West in the Middle Ages, the merchants had also stood at the bottom of society, but they eventually succeeded in acquiring not only wealth but also prestige and a liberal outlook. In Japan a number of factors combined to prevent such a development, among them the seclusion of the country from foreign influences and the impossibility of engaging in foreign trade. Another factor was the control system devised and operated by the bakufu, with its detailed prescriptions governing all aspects of living, down to food and clothing, for the various classes of society. In spite of shifting economic power, social positions had to remain unchanged and they had to retain their basic characteristics and external appearance. Frequent decrees proscribed luxury among the merchants and tried — apparently in vain — to force upon them frugality and simplicity, as befitting the lowest social class.

With the help of the feudal class, the bakufu did succeed in denying the merchants access to a social position commensurate with their economic strength. Money was power, power over the samurai and the daimyo, but money remained something "dirty," and the merchant class in Tokugawa Japan could not rid itself of the stigma of social inferiority. Consequently, the merchants were most attracted by any kind of activity or investment that might open the way to social recognition and even to the ranks of the feudal class itself. Two avenues of escape presented themselves to the rich merchants and financiers: lending money to the daimyo and samurai, and land reclamation. I shall now examine the lending activities, leaving land reclamation until Chapter Three.

Lending to the Daimyo

One of Osaka's chief sources of revenue was the management of warehouses and trade transactions connected with warehouse goods. The warehouses were usually owned by merchants, but many were rented out to daimyo who wanted to store their han products, especially rice, in Osaka either for sale in the market there or for shipment to Edo. These daimyo warehouses (*kurayashiki*) were like extraterritorial castles of the han, and samurai were placed in charge of them. The number of warehouses in Osaka kept increasing, from 25 in the 1760s to 125 in the 1830s. By the beginning of the nineteenth century, an annual average of some 3 million koku of rice, or 10 percent of the total rice production of Japan, thus came into the Osaka warehouses as daimyo rice and wholesale rice.[21]

The merchants who handled the business transactions of the daimyo warehouses (*kuramoto*), and the merchants who acted as financial agents of the daimyo (*kakeya*), came into a quasi-retainer relationship to the daimyo. Such merchants not only reaped handsome profits from their monopolistic business deals with the warehouses, but they frequently were accorded special honors and privileges: they might, like samurai, receive rice stipends and be permitted to assume family names and carry swords similar to those of samurai (this was called the *myōji taitō* privilege).[22] Family names and swords were highly coveted by the merchants, as titles of nobility had been by the European bourgeoisie.

The *kakeya* had to extend loans to the daimyo on request. The interest rates charged were usually lower than those prevailing on the market; sometimes, instead of interest, a new right or privilege was granted. Repayment of the loans was usually assured — so long as the daimyo was solvent — by the particular economic hold that the merchants had over their daimyo creditors. If a merchant sensed a danger of default, he might confiscate and sell the warehouse goods. Nevertheless, cases of default increased considerably toward the end of the Tokugawa, when the han economies were in trouble. Occasionally, when the daimyo and samurai were in great distress, the bakufu decreed total abolition of samurai and daimyo debts to merchants; the merchants countered this danger by lending under the name of some temple, since temple debts could not be nullified. Despite the insecurity involved in daimyo loans, the advantages seem to have remained great enough to induce an ever-growing involvement of the Osaka merchants in feudal lending.

The House of Kōnoike is typical of such a development. Starting as peddlers and sake brewers in the rural districts, the Kōnoike family extended its trading activities throughout the country and became one of the wealthiest merchant families in Osaka. Gradually they concentrated on daimyo lending and turned away from pure trading. The Kōnoike records show that in 1670 credits to merchants constituted 59.3 percent of the total loans extended, against

only 19 percent in daimyo loans. By 1706 the daimyo loans
had risen to 65.8 percent, and by 1795 they were as high
as 76.9 percent of the total loans extended.[23] Kōnoike at
one time was involved with 32 daimyo and received stipends of 10,000 koku of rice, more than many a daimyo
could boast of having. The interest rates on the Kōnoike
loans to daimyo varied widely from as high as 8 percent
a month on short-term loans to no interest at all on long-
term loans that were to be repaid in installments over 10
or even 30 or 70 years. Of 338 loans negotiated by Kōnoike,
56 were interest-free.[24] On the whole, interest rates were
low in comparison with the current rates of between 10
and 15 percent a year. It is therefore quite obvious that
the chief attraction of daimyo lending lay in the honors,
privileges, monopoly rights, and stipends that the daimyo
extended to their creditors.

The negotiation of the loans was a constant source of
annoyance to the feudal lords. The merchants were not
always willing to grant the requested loans; they haggled
and often split the total loan among each other. The
daimyo had to send their highest samurai administrators
to negotiate a loan, and these agents had to treat the
chōnin to elaborate geisha parties and make deep bows to
them before they would consent to the loan. Such humilia-
tion of samurai by *chōnin* drew criticism from writers of
the time, but this had little effect on the merchants themselves.[25]

Whereas daimyo lending was considered a safe investment in the earlier part of the Tokugawa period, it became
risky toward the close of the eighteenth century, when
the han economies were pushed to the wall and when
defaults or cancellations of outstanding loans by the bakufu
often occurred. Some sober Osaka financiers warned against
involvements in daimyo lending, but the extramonetary
considerations of economic power over the feudal lords,

acquisition of a family name and the sword, continued to attract a large stream of capital into further consumer lending.[26] By the time of the Restoration, the House of Kashimaya of Osaka had some 9 million ryo in outstanding loans with daimyo and samurai; [27] and the entire economy of Sendai han is said to have been controlled in this way by the House of Masuya of Osaka.[28]

The merchants, by extending loans to the feudal leaders, not only gained a strong hold on the oppressive and overbearing warrior class; in the end, many a merchant succeeded in entering the samurai class through his creditor position. Numerous samurai sold their status privileges to merchants when they were unable to pay the interest on their heavy debts, or they adopted merchant children and obliged the merchant father thus honored to bail them out. Actually, samurai positions had something like established prices in the last decades before the Restoration — 50 ryo for the adoption of a commoner's son into samurai rank of 100 koku of (nominal) rice stipend.[29]

It may be entirely possible to conclude that the merchants had little vested interest in the abolition of the feudal system. Indeed, when feudalism was abolished, and with it most of the daimyo and samurai debts, many creditor merchants were ruined. A good deal of the merchants' passivity toward the Restoration movement,[30] and their outright hostility to the modernization policies of the Meiji government, can probably be explained by the peculiar financial and trade relations that existed between the merchant and the feudal class. Economically the merchants did not stand to gain much from a change which they were not prepared for and did not understand.

The Ideology of the City Bourgeoisie

European capitalist development received a vital stimulus from an economic ideology which Max Weber has associated with the Protestant ethic. Whether or not the Protestant ethic was the real cause of the change, there can be no doubt that this new capitalist spirit gave a tremendous impetus to economic development. Without the scientific and rational approach to economic problems which Rostow calls post-Newtonian thinking, Western capitalism as we know it would have been unthinkable.

It has been suggested that the development of a spirit of capitalism, of economic rationality, and of a "sensate" value system should be viewed as a universally valid condition for effective economic development in any country.[31] It is therefore meaningful to ask if a similar break-up of feudalism and of traditional values and thinking patterns occurred in Japan before the Meiji Restoration, and, if so, who was responsible. If things had gone according to the Western model, it would have been the city merchant class, the bourgeoisie, that championed a liberal and individualist economic rationality. However, the official Tokugawa Confucian ideology retained a very strong hold on all of Japanese society because of its strict political enforcement and because Japan lacked direct contact with foreign countries. Confucian philosophy decreed that the hierarchical structure of society was unchangeable, God-given, the expression of a divine plan.

Filial piety and adherence to the wisdom of the ages were embodied in the sacred traditions, and to break with tradition was an offense against these two highest virtues of the Confucian ethical code. Loyalty found its loftiest expression in the relation between feudal lord and retainer, daimyo and samurai; but ties of loyalty pervaded the whole of Japanese society and gave unique social coherence to the nation even when it was torn by civil warfare. Finally, the institution of the imperial throne gave a sense of family fealty to the nation: although many of the emperors were obscure and insignificant persons, they were symbols of authority, embodying a line of tradition down from the gods.

Loyalty to one's class and profession and adherence to tradition were sanctioned by the fixed division of society into the four classes of samurai, peasant, artisan, and merchant. Peasants were associated in groups of five families (*gonin-gumi*) which were responsible for one another. The guilds similarly united the merchant class, strengthening loyalties to class and tradition. To fulfill one's duty as a merchant meant to discharge one's obligation to the whole of society; this justified the protection and the other benefits that one received in the feudal scheme.[32] Within the individual merchant enterprise, loyalty found eloquent expression vertically in the *oyakata–kogata* (parent–child) relation through which the master commanded absolute respect among clerks and apprentices. The *oyakata* not only exercised his leadership in business matters, but remained a person of authority for life: the former clerk made courtesy calls on him, assisted him in times of need, and gave him respectful precedence even in social and family affairs.[33]

The master in the enterprise was also the living embodiment of ancestral wisdom. Confucian precepts demanded that the teachings of the ancestors, and hence of the head of an enterprise or family, never be questioned. Rational criticism and the introduction of new ideas were out of place. To say that a merchant had deviated from the practices of his ancestors and "innovated" was to cast an aspersion upon his honor. The Mitsui family rules contained the following prohibition: "Do not put your hand to any type of activity that has not been done before." [34] The rules of many other merchant houses included similar statements. According to merchant ideology, all things were to remain unchanged.

Honesty and business ethics within the guilds were a

direct outgrowth of feudal class consciousness and group spirit. In loyalty to his group and to his inherited store, the merchant had to keep his good name. If the merchants were socially the lowest and most despised group in Tokugawa Japan, they nevertheless found self-respect in the big cities — in Osaka, for example, they were "honorable townsmen" (o-chōnin-san). They made a point of being absolutely honest with one another and of fulfilling contracts whether or not they were put in writing. Among often-quoted principles governing merchant behavior, we find strong exhortations to honesty: "It is on the straight road that the god of happiness comes; evil and dishonest ways are shortcuts to hell." [35] A merchant had to keep the name of his store (kanban and noren) [36] undefiled as an obligation to the guild and to his ancestors. How strong this sense of obligation to the past was can be gleaned from the fact that members of the old merchant houses that had been located in Osaka for centuries still put their rural place of origin on official documents as late as 1868.[37]

The merchants' group consciousness created a double standard: honesty toward the fellow merchant, notably of the same guild, and unscrupulous exploitation of the outsider. According to contemporary critics, the merchants had no scruples about cheating outsiders and charging them arbitrary prices. Thus, to many the merchants were known for their cheating and dishonesty. None of this could fail to discourage public confidence in tradesmen and commercial activity. And this in turn hampered business growth.

The remarkable fact about the Tokugawa bourgeoisie was that it perpetrated the kind of stifling atmosphere that effectively prevented the rise of energetic innovators. Even the great houses of Kōnoike, Mitsui, Sumitomo, and Hirano, which had entered the merchant class from the ranks of the samurai before the four classes had been frozen, produced no outstanding business leaders in the two centuries before the Restoration. The great enterprisers who built up the fame of these houses lived in the early part of the Tokugawa.[38]

Emphasis on practical business training and an avowed aversion to book learning became additional deterrents to entrepreneurship in the merchant class. It was mainly through books that Western ideas and industrial technology were introduced into Japan before the Restoration and during its first decade. Entrepreneurship required not only an understanding of a single technique, but a grasp of the whole idea of industrial production, of a new economic organization for Japan. Recognition of this need required a level of education and intelligence for which the routine activities in the merchant stores were poor preparation.

The merchants scorned book learning not only as useless but as downright harmful. A man who engaged in scholarship was regarded as playing with bankruptcy. There was nothing about business to be learned from books; all was laid down by tradition. Thrift, calculation, and business talent (*shimatsu, sanyō, saikaku*) received paramount attention. Thrift was the fundamental virtue, as indicated by these rules for merchants: "simplicity and thrift are the ground on which house and barn are built"; "luxury and splendor prepare the banquet for the god of poverty." [39] To invest savings profitably and to calculate profits, the merchant had to know how to use his abacus: "consider the abacus as your only child and embrace it even in your sleep." [40] Business talent, of utmost importance for entrepreneurial activity, did not go much beyond a clever handling of customers, shrewdness, and politeness. "Do not quarrel with anyone, no matter what a man may say; do not lose your temper or use harsh words, but address him always in polite terms." [41] This sentence from the Sumitomo house rules may perhaps be considered typical. Careful study and loyal observance of all inherited rules and practices was the "way of the merchant"; learning and theoretical education were for the samurai. Scholars were given lip service but were actually regarded as "hungry gods." When a few entrepreneurs after the Restoration built schools for business and industrial education, the merchants laughed at the whole idea.[42]

It cannot be denied that Osaka had its own Confucian scholars and that they did find interested students among the merchants. In 1725 a group of five wealthy merchants built the Kaitoku Dō, the largest private school in Japan, and invited the famous Confucian scholar Miyake Sekian to teach there.[43] Many merchants did achieve a high level of education in the late Tokugawa period. They were often criticized for indulging in such luxuries as private teachers for their children. But education was not their status symbol; on the contrary, they sought education in emulation of the feudal class, to gain self-respect. Learning remained essentially unconnected with business practices; it had no direct bearing on day-to-day commercial activities, which remained pointedly tradition-bound.

The *shingaku* philosophy represented a major effort to better the education and raise the social standing and self-esteem of the merchants. Originating in the first half of the eighteenth century, its first purpose was to rehabilitate the merchants' ethics after a time of luxury and dissipation in the preceding Genroku period (1688–1703).[44] It had been customary for Confucian scholars to deride the merchants' activities and call them parasites because they made profits out of others' toil.[45] The scholars could not grasp the idea that selling was a service and that a samurai in Edo could not live on the rice that a peasant in northern Japan kept in his barn. Japanese Confucian scholars were not unique in regarding commercial transactions as exploitation; the scholars of medieval Europe thought in quite the same way and attached a moral stigma to buying and selling. In a stationary feudal society based on agricultural self-sufficiency, merchants were a disruptive element and the objects of suspicion; the elite of society defended its position with the only weapon that was left — contempt. But the *shingaku* philosophers proclaimed that the merchants' profit was as much a reward for service to society as was the samurai's stipend. They even turned the tables and called the aristocracy merchants: "To sell rice is nothing more or less than a commercial transaction. It may therefore be said that all the people, from the feudal lords of the great provinces down, are in a sense engaged in commerce. . . . Commerce is absolutely indispensable in daily life, hence it is wrong to despise money or hold commerce in contempt. There is nothing shameful about selling things. What is shameful is the conduct of men who fail to pay their debts to merchants." [46]

For a while the *shingaku* philosophy seemed to initiate liberal thinking and to inspire something akin to the Western spirit of capitalism. It did enhance the self-respect of the city bourgeoisie, but it was no match for the deeply ingrained Confucian traditionalism. Even at its best the *shingaku* movement did not go beyond the confines of status concepts. Ishida Baigan equated the "way" of the samurai and the "way" of the merchant by insisting that in either class the degree of fulfillment of one's divinely predetermined obligations decided a man's worth. In effect the *shingaku* was nothing but an adjustment in Confucian thinking designed to incorporate the merchant class into the feudal framework, to make it follow with closer steps, albeit with more pride, the beaten path of tradition. Filial piety, honesty, loyalty, were its central themes; loyalty meant faithfulness to tradition and to the ancestors; thus loyalty and filial piety had a common base.[47] With the beginning of the nineteenth century, the bakufu used the *shingaku* schools to inculcate its own political doctrines and to teach the merchants their duties to the central government. Even the central objective of the *shingaku* movement, to establish the view of business activity as a service to society, was not achieved. The leading entrepreneurs of the Meiji era still found it necessary to proclaim that their activities had no connection with the profit making of the merchants of old.

The Merchants after the Restoration

General Reactions

The Meiji Restoration of 1867 was the important step toward the modernization of Japanese society and toward the building of large-scale industry.[48] But the opening of Japan to foreign trade had preceded the Restoration by fifteen years and had already stimulated efforts by the bakufu, and by some daimyo, to push ahead with various modernization programs. Moreover, prior to 1867 it had been the bakufu that had pursued a policy of intercourse with foreign nations, forced by the ominous presence of American, British, and French warships. The sharp turn of the Meiji government toward the West could not have been clearly anticipated by the people prior to 1868, because the slogan of the antibakufu forces prior to the Restoration had been "restore the emperor; expel the barbarians." It would be a mistake to think that those who fought against the bakufu in the Restoration movement were all progressives favoring the opening of the country and the modernization of the economy. On the contrary, many of the most vocal elements within the Restoration movement were intransigent reactionaries.

As far as the merchants and the people were concerned, there was no way to resolve the contradictions that arose from loyalties to the established government and loyalties to the emperor, from han rivalries and hatred for the barbarians, and it was even more difficult to perceive constructive plans for reform. A collection of letters written by merchants in the years of the Restoration struggle reflects the perplexity and confusion that prevailed among the people. The merchants sensed that the old peace and security were crumbling, but they could not see the new horizons. They prayed for peace and order, and placed the increasing hostilities in the same category as previous peasant or samurai revolts or as natural disasters from which the gods should save them.[49]

Attempts have been made to assess the merchants' attitudes as progressive or conservative on the basis of their financial contributions to the bakufu or to the Restoration party prior to its final victory. But we know too little about the motivation behind those more or less forced contributions. Most contributions were undoubtedly made under pressure, out of former han loyalties, or because of previously established creditor connections. The Osaka merchants had become accustomed to heavy forced loans to the bakufu in times of emergency. Since Osaka was bakufu territory, it was quite natural that most merchant contributions went, at least initially, to the support of the bakufu army. The House of Mitsui, which had its stores in Osaka, Kyoto, and Edo, did make a genuine decision in favor of the Restoration party, but this decision resulted almost exclusively from the political acumen of Mitsui's head clerk, Minomura Rizaemon, and his personal friendship with Inoue Kaoru, one of the leaders of the Restoration party.[50]

The first few years following the victory of the Restoration party proved disastrous for the merchants of the cities, particularly in Osaka. They had suffered greatly from the opening of the ports and the rise of the new merchants; heavy taxes and forced loans had been demanded of them for the armies of both sides. After the Meiji government was established, the guilds were dissolved and the daimyo warehouses disappeared with the abolition of the han system. (The han were abolished in 1871 and the country divided into prefectures, in order to facilitate central control over the country.) Osaka's local silver coins were abolished when the national gold standard was established. Finally, the large daimyo debts were almost completely nullified: debts contracted by the han prior to 1843 were abolished; debts originating between 1844 and 1867 were to be repaid by the government within fifty years at no interest; and han debts contracted after the Restoration and before 1871 were to be repaid within twenty-five years at 4 percent interest. All this spelled ruin for the financiers and merchants of the cities. In Osaka twenty-six of the old established merchant houses collapsed in the early years after the Restoration.[51]

After the abolition of the guild system in 1872, the merchants and the money exchangers were very much at sea. They were told to compete, to start foreign trade, and not to band together for group security. But they were not used to competing; they had been brought up in a world of stability and order, where each merchant was assured his livelihood and his profits. The merchants' habits of mind were still worlds away from assuming a belief in a "harmony of interests" and an "invisible hand" that would make competition mutually beneficial. Normally they were peace-loving people, and now business was supposed to be a fight (*kyōsō*, the newly adopted word for competition, means "running and fighting"). Suddenly insecurity was to be the basic principle and struggle the means to survival, a situation that could not be expected to spark much enthusiasm among the former guild merchants.

After the abolition of the guilds, the government tried to establish a new company system. Apparently most of the small shopkeepers, and even managers of merchant enterprises of all sorts, had not the vaguest idea of what this meant. They understood little more than that from now on their stores were to be called "companies"; there was nothing simpler than to change the *kanban* from *dō* or *ya* (store) to *kaisha* (company). A "company-foundation boom" swept the cities, especially Tokyo and Kyoto, but little is known of the actual details. Each company had to secure a charter, which gave it official backing and increased prestige. In Kyoto some three hundred companies were chartered in the first few years following the Restoration, but they simply continued trade as before, dealing in cotton, salt, copper, and similar articles. These companies banded together, as they had under the guild system, and in 1871 the Kyoto city administration dissolved them all because of their monopolistic policies.[52] Among forty applications for company charters in Tokyo in 1873, we find such names as Roadsweepers' Company, Singing Girls Managing Company, Translating Company, Beef Trading Company, Carrot Company, Umbrella Company.[53] The applications apparently became so numerous and nonsensical that the city administration asked the Ministry of the Interior whether all must go through the cumbersome chartering procedure or whether masseurs, fortunetellers, and the like could be left to call themselves "company" without application.[54]

At the same time, the merchants made a strong effort to reintroduce some guildlike organization in order to stop the confusion, and this resulted in the establishment of *kumiai* (unions). Business morale was sinking to a new low, if we are to believe the assertions of Shibusawa Eiichi, an entrepreneur of the new type. Shibusawa complained of the dangerous abuse of trade names, especially in the sale of foodstuffs and medicines.[55] He wrote about the attitudes of the older merchants, exaggerating drastically in order to drive home the point that there was a difference between new "entrepreneurs" like himself and the merchants: "The merchants of the time [early Meiji] were men who had almost no feeling for things like rules and written regulations. Furthermore, it seemed as if the officials of the Meiji government and the merchants of Tokyo, Osaka, and Kyoto were men of an entirely different kind. One had only to look at their faces to recognize that they were almost like beings of a different species. It was only too clear that this work [economic modernization] could not be carried out with such people [the merchants]." [56]

The Drafting of Merchant Capital

Immediately after the Restoration, the government faced a pressing need to establish trading and banking facilities that could cope effectively with foreign trade. The Japanese were perplexed and disturbed by the fact that in the port cities the initiative was left entirely to foreigners. As late as 1874, Japan's foreign trade was conducted by foreign companies for 99.97 percent of her imports and 99.45 percent of her exports.[57] Specie was flowing out at a rapid rate, and the balance of trade moved increasingly against Japan. The experienced merchants with capital showed little desire to take risks in direct dealings with foreigners; and the adventurer-merchants who thrived in Yokohama,

Nagasaki, and Hyogo (Kobe) lacked the necessary experience and capital. When the government established an official exchange market in Yokohama, it summoned Osaka
men to teach the Yokohama merchants the rudiments of
the exchange business. It did the same in Hyogo, for the
new merchants had "nothing but courage." [58] The British
consul wrote in a report of 1869 on the passivity of the
Osaka merchants: "Few of the wealthier native merchants
have turned their attention to foreign trade: indeed, this
class of the people in Osaka is the last to recognize any
benefit in foreign relations. They do a good business
among themselves by advancing money on produce, and
trading in other ways; and their fear seems to be that foreign merchants will deprive them of a portion of the profits
that have hitherto accrued to themselves alone." [59]

Actually, the Meiji government expected much of Osaka
as a port city (it was opened to trade in 1868). Osaka was
to become the center of foreign trade as it had been the
commercial metropolis in the Tokugawa period. Some officials even suggested making Osaka the administrative capital instead of Edo because of the city's economic strength.
Ōkubo Toshimichi [60] and others expected that Osaka
would become the nation's center of trade and modern industry.[61] In 1868 the government set up a trading center
in Osaka that was to operate with official inconvertible
notes; the notes were to be loaned out to han trading companies and official han merchants. This scheme would have
been a repetition of what the individual han were already
doing, but now under the auspices of and coordinated by
the new Restoration government. The scheme failed because the han did not trust the government paper money
which they were supposed to repay with specie.

A more ambitious trading operation was started in 1869
under the auspices of the Ministry of Transportation and

Trade (Tsūshōshi).[62] This time reliance was to be placed on private initiative among the merchants. In eight key cities, exchange companies were set up to finance this large foreign-trade drive. Associated with these finance companies were trading companies that were to direct, assist, and finance the operations of many subordinate trading enterprises in company form. According to a survey of 1872,[63] the exchange company of Tokyo had a total share-capital of 948,500 ryo, that of Osaka 197,800 ryo, and that of Kyoto 238,500 ryo. The main participants were the rich merchant houses, chief among them Mitsui, Ono, and Shimada, which had become the official government financiers in the first years of the Meiji. Mitsui paid up 145,000 ryo, Ono 135,000 ryo, and Shimada 90,000 ryo. How much capital the trading companies had is not known, but their composition was similar to that of the exchange companies.

The government used both the carrot and the stick to push through its foreign-trade program. The members of the trading companies received various privileges, among others that of borrowing from the exchange companies without security deposit and that of monopolizing the lucrative importation of rifles; the exchange companies had a monopoly on transporting and marketing the han products, former functions of the daimyo warehouse merchants.

Of special importance were the social distinctions granted to the presidents and main shareholders of the new companies. The presidents were given the privilege of the sword and family name. They were appointed by the government, as officials were. A president could walk directly into the room of a government official while common people had to wait and squat outside the building. Many other minor privileges were granted. Indeed, the government encouraged anyone who entered foreign trade. Yet for the most part the merchants remained unenthusiastic, and many of them participated in the scheme only under pressure. In Tokyo the government threatened noncooperating merchants with exile to Hokkaido.

There was much misunderstanding about the objectives of the trading and exchange companies. The merchants had received so many blows from the new policies and developments that they assumed a capital contribution to these companies to be nothing but a disguised *goyōkin* (forced loan). Katō Yukichi, a government official, tried to promote the new idea and wrote that one should not think it difficult to contribute to these companies: it would be like contributing to the building of a shrine or a temple. Shrines and temples were for the purpose of strengthening the faith and thus giving happiness to each individual; the trading companies would stimulate trade and thus earn immediate profits for everyone.[64] It is doubtful that this comparison had encouraging effects.

Eventually more than seventy trading subcompanies came into existence in Osaka. Most of them were not directly involved in foreign trade and were similar to the old establishments of the guild period in that they joined their stock only partially. The actual operations of the scheme are not of particular interest here. The strong government controls apparently discouraged free initiative and, at the same time, encouraged irresponsible action. The exchange companies initially printed bills without restrictions, and it was understood that the final guarantee, as well as the resulting losses, were to be carried by the government. Thus the shareholders were to take only the honors and the profits. After approximately two years, the entire scheme collapsed in bankruptcy for all but the Yokohama exchange company.

Once more the central government drafted merchant

capital and experience, this time to establish joint-stock banking in Japan. It was decided to establish national banks in an effort to introduce order into the confused monetary situation. Many kinds of debased coins were in circulation. Furthermore, the government, in the first year after the Restoration, had issued 32 million ryo of inconvertible notes as loans to daimyo, merchants, and wealthy peasants and later had paid the army with an additional 14 million ryo of such notes.[65] The depreciation of these inconvertible notes and, above all, strong protests from foreign consuls induced the government to set up a new system of national banks in 1872, on the American model; the banks were to deposit 60 percent of their share capital in inconvertible notes with the government and receive the same sum in bonds with 6 percent interest attached. These bonds were to be deposited with the government as security for the issue of bank notes. Forty percent of the capital was to be kept as reserve in specie.[66]

The government had received many applications for the establishment of private banks before 1872, but when the wealthy merchants were invited to establish joint-stock national banks, they were reluctant. The House of Shimada, one of the three official money agents of the Meiji government, flatly refused to cooperate, and it was only as a result of considerable pressure that Ono finally joined with Mitsui and other Tokyo merchants to set up the first national bank with a total of 2.44 million yen, of which 2 million came from Mitsui and Ono.[67] Three other national banks were established in a similar fashion: one was a direct continuation of the Yokohama exchange company; one was established in Niigata with a rich landowner as its principal spareholder; and one was founded by a group of nobles and samurai from Satsuma.

The merchants of Osaka and Kyoto did not establish national banks of their own, although an attempt was made by Kōnoike and ten other merchant houses of Osaka; they failed to reach an agreement and abandoned the project. Their application for a charter, however, is full of flowery phrases on the new era and the need for cooperation to build up the national economy:

As we live presently in the era of civilization and enlightenment we feel ashamed to follow the old foolish practices of each one considering nothing but his own profit. Now we have to be of one mind and unite for the building of a solid foundation of great enterprises. We have been cherishing already for some time the desire to shoulder our share, as far as our weakness permits, of the burden to promote the progress of civilization. When we consider, in all humility, the national banking act, we are overwhelmed with joy because of the unification of the system, the public as well as private advantages and the building of solid enterprises, that will result from that act. Instead of empty applause, however, we, enlightened by the banking act, shall immediately work for the establishment of a bank, and we hope to raise about 1.5 million yen in all. We shall, as always, observe strictly the rules of the banking act and never deviate from it.[68]

These phrases indicate sufficiently that the establishment of a bank was thought to be a burden and at variance with the "old foolish" profit-making idea. In spite of their assertions to the contrary, men who had been brought up with the abacus could not be expected to feel enthusiasm and to exercise entrepreneurial initiative.

Modern Industry in Osaka

Manufacturing had never been important in Osaka during the Tokugawa period. Merchant capital had flowed into cotton spinning and weaving and other domestic manufacturing in the rural areas, especially in the vicinity of

Osaka, but not in the city itself. There are records of only a few minor manufacturing establishments in Osaka: sake breweries, bleacheries, and establishments producing wax, soy sauce, and soybean cheese (*tōfu*). In connection with the economic reforms of the han induced by the pre-Restoration military threats and the impasse reached in the daimyo economies, some modern enterprises had sprung up in and around the city, such as the Sakai Spinning Mill, founded by a Kagoshima samurai and financed by the daimyo, or the Hōrai Company, which started modern paper manufacturing, founded by Gotō Shōjirō, one of the economic reformers of Tosa han.

A strong influence on the modernization and industrialization of Osaka was exerted by Godai Tomoatsu, a government official from Satsuma han who took up residence in Osaka in 1868. He was not only a capable and energetic entrepreneur but a pioneer of the era of Civilization and Enlightenment (*bummei kaika*), who had gathered information on the operation of modern industry during a study trip to England before the Restoration. He initiated the construction required to open the Osaka harbor to ocean-going vessels and the building of residences for foreign consuls and trade representatives. When some of his opponents succeeded in effecting his transfer to Yokohama, he resigned his government post so that he might stay in Osaka and help to make it a flourishing industrial city.[69] Godai established a refinery in which he separated the silver and gold content in coins bought up from the han and then delivered the gold and silver to the government mint, at considerable profit to himself. He achieved his greatest success in mining, buying up and modernizing a string of copper and silver mines. For the administration of his growing mining empire, he erected a large office building in Osaka, the Kōseikan, which, with its modern methods and over two hundred employees, became one of the wonders of Osaka.[70] Godai's most outstanding pioneering enterprise was the building of an indigo factory with a government loan of 500,000 yen in 1876.

The government mint, established in Osaka in 1869, became the center and rallying place of all modern and progressive elements. The machines for the mint had been brought in from Hongkong. The bricks for the buildings also had to be imported, and the problem then arose of finding bricklayers, since nobody in Osaka had ever built a brick house. When the building was finished, after two years of construction, a grand banquet was given for which the cooks were brought from Yokohama and Kobe. The men employed at the mint had to wear Western dress and had to cut their hair short, as symbols of the new era.[71] Although its main purpose was to coin a standard currency that would be acceptable at home and abroad and would replace the debased coins still in circulation, the mint soon became involved in a whole string of associated enterprises.

In the process of refining copper, sulphur was obtained, and this the mint marketed. Since the mint had to use large quantities of fuel, it built a plant that produced coke and gas — the coke it used for fuel. The gas was used for lighting the mint buildings and the streets of Osaka; 65 lamps were put upon the streets and 621 in private houses, mostly the homes of officials and foreigners.[72] The mint initiated construction of a telegraph and a telephone line and a horsedrawn railway line that connected the important points of the city. A school for the children of mint employees and of other townsmen taught English and physics, and thus constituted another important modernizing factor in this city of tradition and practical training.[73] All of this happened rapidly, during the first few years after the Restoration, when the rest of the city was still very much weighed down in the slump of a depression.

It is typical of Osaka that, until about 1892, almost all the initiative in the building of modern industry came from outside — through direct government enterprise as in the case of the mint, through men from Tokyo or other places, and through foreigners. Westerners and Chinese were prominent as entrepreneurs in Osaka during the first fifteen years of the Meiji era. A steel factory with 240,000 yen capital, established in 1881, was planned by an American named Hunter, living in Kobe; he also supplied most of the capital, but was wise enough to make a Japanese the formal owner.[74] Some Chinese established a match factory which was also nominally owned by a Japanese. Fujita Denzaburō and Ōkura Kihachirō entered the Osaka industrial world from outside; each established a large tannery, in 1877 and 1879 respectively, and later they combined them into a single factory with over three hundred workers.[75] Fujita became one of the industrial leaders of Osaka in the second decade after the Restoration, together with Godai, Sumitomo's Hirose Saihei, Matsumoto Jūtarō, Nakano Goichi, and others.

One can, of course, exaggerate the point that outsiders were predominant in Osaka until the industrial breakthrough was achieved. A survey of 1886 showed that only forty of the more important businessmen in the city were natives; the majority of the leading men in all fields of business and industry were immigrants.[76] This survey included men like Hirose Saihei and Matsumoto Jūtarō as immigrants. But Hirose had been with the Sumitomo Besshi copper mine in Osaka since boyhood, and Matsumoto Jūtarō had been a merchant's apprentice in Osaka since he was thirteen. They were not born in Osaka, however, and perhaps had a somewhat different outlook for this reason, taking a certain pride in the fact that they were different men, progressive men. As mentioned earlier, Osaka's real swing toward industry came only in the 1890s, primarily in cotton spinning, and this was a result of the great success of the Osaka Spinning Mill, founded by another non-Osaka man, Shibusawa Eiichi.

In addition to those already mentioned, there were a few other large-scale enterprises in Osaka prior to the mid-1880s: the Osaka Copper Manufacturing Company, established by Hirose Saihei and Godai Tomoatsu in 1881 with a capital of 200,000 yen, foreign technicians, and imported machinery; a paper mill that struggled on close to bankruptcy for many years; the Osaka Printing Type Manufacturing Company (Ōsaka kappan seizō sho), established by a native of Osaka who had traveled to China to study printing processes and had been influenced by the pioneering work of Hirano Tomiji and Motoki Shōzō of Tokyo.[77] Shipbuilding was at first entirely in the hands of foreigners who either built new yards or were invited to take over and modernize existing yards. It was not until 1886 and 1891 that two large modern yards were built by Japanese in Osaka, who were inspired by the great success of Mitsubishi's Nagasaki shipyard.[78] Small workshops multiplied in the manufacturing of matches, leather, and soap. At one time there were forty-four workshops producing leather bags; by 1892 their number had increased to over one hundred.[79] Soap and match production came under the control of merchant capital, and Japan began to export these two articles as early as the 1880s.

If we compare the industrial development of the country as a whole during the first two decades of the Meiji era with that of Osaka, the former merchant metropolis, we find that Osaka lagged. In terms of industrial capital, only

10–12 percent was invested in Osaka between 1885 and 1890. In 1891–1892 the percentage rose to about 25; in 1895 it rose again to about 27 percent of the nation's total industrial capital investment.[80] The remarkable thing, however, is that at the same time that the percentage of Osaka's industrial capital relative to the rest of the country moved up from 10 to 25 percent, its relative share in trading capital also jumped from a previous 16–18 percent in the years 1888–1890 to 34–35 percent in 1892–1893, and to almost 50 percent in 1894–1896.[81]

The reason for the overall rise in Osaka's participation in industry and trade after 1890 is rather obvious. The source from which my figures are drawn indicates only the capital of corporate enterprises, meaning that Osaka's capital moved into corporate enterprise relatively late; this was especially true in trading. A jump from 16–18 percent of the national total to 50 percent within six years signifies a tremendous change. It indicates Osaka's final turn toward a modern form of enterprise, and the eventual success of the early efforts to establish joint-stock trading. While Osaka thus remained primarily a trading city, its share of the nation's industry was an impressive 25–27 percent in the 1890s, second only to Tokyo; at the same time, it retained an absolute lead in the field of trade. These figures are also a commentary on the frequent assertion that Osaka lacked capital for large-scale enterprise. It may be assumed instead that large amounts of Osaka capital were held back and used in the traditional forms of merchant business, and that they were poured into large-scale enterprise only after pioneering efforts had proven beyond doubt that these were safe and profitable investments.

Osaka, then, did rebound after its period of slump. But it never gained leadership as a center of industry and capital; the position was ceded to Tokyo. This was, of course, not solely because of the merchants' traditional outlook. For one thing, Osaka's harbor proved unsuitable for large ships, and foreign merchants soon turned to Kobe. Thus one of the most stimulating influences — foreign trade and contact with Westerners and their ideas — all but bypassed Osaka. Furthermore, the very fact that the Meiji government made Tokyo its administrative capital concentrated the progressive elements in that city. In the first two or three decades of the Meiji era, when political connections and motivations were highly important stimuli for starting industrial enterprises, Osaka was in a severely handicapped position. If Ōkubo's suggestion to make the city the center of trade, as well as the political capital, had been carried out, the Osaka bourgeoisie might have bestirred itself to show more initiative.

But even when all this is said, the main point of my argument remains unshaken. The Osaka bourgeoisie — and we may take this group as representative of the Tokugawa city merchants in general — lacked most clearly the required set of attitudes, the mentality, for launching modern business. This stifled the emergence of entrepreneurs from their ranks. Entrepreneurship must be viewed as a result both of individual personality and of the favorable economic and social conditions provided by the group and the cultural milieu. If there is too wide a distance between the new goal and the established standards of the group, even strong and talented persons will achieve the goal only with great difficulty: "Changes must be accepted. New habits and attitudes must be learned. New relationships to people must be established. If personality and culture are unfavorable to such changes, economic development may take place only slowly, if at all." [82] What is to be remembered about the city merchant class of Tokugawa Japan is that its mentality and its culture both resisted change; and this made the emergence of entrepreneurs all the more difficult.

II

THE SAMURAI CLASS

To many Westerners — and to many Japanese, for that matter — the samurai have become something of a legend. Together with the few samurai swords that are handed down as family treasures go tales of battle and harakiri, of feudal loyalties and chivalry. The Meiji Restoration was wrought by this same knightly class, which rose renewed from the ashes of its own decay and rejuvenated a nation as well. The samurai not only fought the battle that made Japan a new country; they imbued her with a new spirit, which somehow seems to live on — from the self-immolating kamikaze fliers of World War II down to the intricately detailed code of honor in daily life.

Unquestionably the samurai — the lower samurai, the experts will add — carried out the Meiji Restoration; they also supplied the administrators for the new government. It was the samurai who provided the essential dynamic force that turned Japan away from the Tokugawa status-quo policy and toward rapid modernization. Further, the "spirit of the samurai" not only determined official policies but during the Meiji era also became something of a standard public attitude: a happy mixture of militant patriotism and economically rationalized Confucian ethics.

The striking differences between the merchants and the samurai and their role in the Restoration have led to conclusions about their relative contributions to economic growth in Meiji Japan. Lacking detailed knowledge, which is indeed difficult to come by, one is tempted to construct a theory. The trouble with general statements of this kind is that they are as difficult to verify as they are to refute; they only leave the reader with an uncomfortable feeling of over-simplification. What I propose to do here is to examine the actual contribution made by the samurai class to the entrepreneurial achievements of Meiji Japan, particularly in the first half of the Meiji era when things were the most difficult for the new entrepreneurs.

Two principal schools of thought exist on this subject, and they flatly contradict one another. The first is expressed in the words of Herbert Norman: "The lower samurai . . . could not embody any new mode of production. The representative of the new mode of production which was gradually supplanting feudalism was, of course, the great *chōnin* class. Its members were, however, so immature as industrial entrepreneurs and so inexperienced in statecraft that they had to rely on the state to develop industry and on the members of the former feudal class, especially the samurai, as administrators and statesmen." [1] How could the samurai introduce a "new mode of production" when capitalism is supposed (by definition) to be spearheaded by the bourgeoisie? But since Norman, with his vast knowledge of Japanese history, could not deny the backwardness of the bourgeoisie, he had to offer the formula that the state coached the bourgeoisie until it was ready for its historically predetermined role.

The second line of thinking is expressed by George B. Sansom: "It was these men [samurai], and not the bourgeoisie, who laid the foundations of a capitalist structure and at the same time developed a political system that bore little resemblance to those which came into force in the advanced industrial countries of western Europe under the influence of a powerful moneyed class." [2] For Sansom it is not a matter of course that Japan must have repeated exactly the Western model, and he is ready to agree that the samurai played a dominant role in the private sector as well as in the government. Many present-day students of economic development will be in basic agreement with Sansom's statement.

The theory behind the statement might be drawn up something like this: The samurai had suffered continuous impoverishment throughout the Tokugawa period. Many of them had become economically ruined while still maintaining their social and educational advantages. The events following the Meiji Restoration did not improve their economic condition; on the contrary, they were robbed of almost everything by being made common citizens, with no special economic advantages. As a class that had enjoyed high standing and was trained for achievement, they were bound to compensate for their losses by striving for economic power. Yet traditional types of business were barred to them because of their deep-seated prejudice against engaging in trade and also because of the greater business experience of the entrenched merchants. The obvious avenue, then, was the new enterprises, for here the samurai had a twofold advantage over the merchants: the superior education that was essential for learning new techniques and better connections with samurai officials in the government. Working closely with the government in modern enterprises could provide prestige in the eyes of the public at a time when the building of industry was proclaimed as a supreme national duty. The samurai, therefore, were motivated by a unique combination of economic necessity and patriotism.

Although this theory seems neat and almost flawless, it will not stand up. Facts have an unpleasant way of destroying nice theories. The chief flaw in this one is that it assumes the samurai class to have been strictly homogeneous both in background and in reaction. In some directions the samurai did react very much according to the theory — as in the founding of the national banks, which will be discussed later. But in other areas one would tend to pick the rich peasants or even the merchants as "typical" representatives for introducing the "new mode of production." The last decades of the Tokugawa period had done much to blur class distinctions with respect to education, patterns of thinking, and economic activity. And even where class images and handicaps did remain, they were not the only factors that decided entrepreneurial activity.

Instead of working out another theory, I shall proceed with a review of the relevant historical facts. In this way we may see in proper perspective the development of the samurai class and its contribution to the process of economic modernization in Meiji Japan. Ultimately we may be obliged to abandon altogether the notion that Japan's entrepreneurs derived from any one social class.

The Economic Impasse of the Samurai

It is ironic that the class of professional men-of-arms was officially established by Hideyoshi (in power from 1582 to 1598) only at the end of a long period of internal warfare and at the beginning of the Great Peace which was to last two hundred and fifty years.[3] Many former peasant-militiamen now became members of a feudal class that gathered in large numbers around the castles that had begun to be built under Oda Nobunaga. This new class developed its own code of ethics, in which the principal virtue was absolute loyalty to the feudal lord. Obligations of feudal loyalty were extolled to the extent that they even took precedence over filial or paternal duties. A samurai worthy of his name had to be ready to give not only his own life but the lives of his family to protect the honor of his daimyo. The Japanese recount with awe and admiration stories of dutiful samurai who lived up to this code, unflinchingly allowing their whole families to be slaughtered by the enemy rather than utter a word that might compromise the safety of the lord. These ideals were developed during a century of warfare. In the prolonged peace, however, the martial virtues lost their original and practical meaning to a great extent, as did the two samurai swords that were symbols of their status. The ties of loyalty between samurai and daimyo became increasingly theoretical. Many samurai of low rank never even met their lords and had no occasion to demonstrate their loyalty with heroism. The samurai became a cultured leisure class whose main purpose was to justify their superior social position by physical prowess, literary pursuits, and adherence to an elaborate code of ethics. Benevolence, honesty, and erudition became important virtues.[4]

For the service rendered to their lords, the samurai were entitled to regular payment in rice. Their lives were devoted to the preservation of peace and order, a pre-eminent social duty. This public function, according to Confucian teaching, raised them high above the common crowd of those engaged solely in economic pursuits. The peasants ranked next to the samurai because it was through their labor that the samurai could live. The samurai were strictly forbidden to engage in any kind of mercantile activity for it would degrade the men of the sword. There were occasions when the bakufu meted out severe punishment for infringements of this rule.[5] Any association with business activity, even with such a simple act as shopping, was considered by the samurai as unclean and unworthy of his class. Fukuzawa Yukichi wrote: "According to the convention among the warrior class, they were ashamed of being seen handling money. Therefore, it was customary for samurai to wrap their faces with small hand-towels and to go out after dark whenever they had an errand to do. — I hated having a towel on my face and have never worn one. I even used to go out on errands in broad daylight, swinging a wine bottle in one hand, with two swords on my side as becomes a man of samurai rank." [6] Fukuzawa also observed that his father did not want his children to be taught arithmetic because numbers were the "instruments of merchants." [7] It is doubtful whether these attitudes were general throughout the whole samurai class. Much of the disdain for handling money and engaging in any sort of business seems to have vanished toward the end of the Tokugawa period.

It was severe economic pressure that led to the gradual crumbling of the samurai code of ethics. The daimyo became unable to pay the stipulated amounts of rice to their samurai. In the course of the Tokugawa period, the samurai were caught in a squeeze, especially after the Genroku era (1688–1703) which became known for its luxury and the rapid rise of the merchant class. Various devices came into vogue for cutting the samurai stipends — for example, the *hanchi* system, whereby the daimyo "borrowed" half of the samurai's stipend. Sometimes the samurai would receive only 40 percent of the amount due them.[8] Luxury consumption, which spread through the *sankin kōtai* system of alternate residence in Edo,[9] and the increasing monetization of the economy led naturally to the transfer of economic power from the feudal class to the merchants.

Exhortations to the samurai to practice simplicity and forbearance increased. The spartan frugality of the warrior class became proverbial, but it had physical limits. They tried to maintain pride and dignity: "Even if a samurai has nothing to eat he will pretend with a long toothpick" (*bushi wa kuwanedo takayōji*) runs a proverb from the late Tokugawa. They were obliged to sell their household treasures, paintings, even their armor, ceremonial dress, and furniture, and to dismiss their servants.[10]

Those samurai who resorted to borrowing became completely dependent upon merchant moneylenders or rich peasants and saved themselves in the end by selling their samurai titles or adopting merchant children as heirs. Both practices were in vogue before the Meiji Restoration and were severely criticized by contemporary writers. These developments varied somewhat according to the general economic positions of the individual han. Some han managed to carry out drastic reforms and started their own trading and even "industrialization" programs.

The social cleavage between upper and lower samurai gradually became complete.[11] The two groups almost never intermarried; they used different styles of speech and writing; and they built their houses differently (the houses of the upper samurai had *genkan* [porches]). The telling difference, of course, was the size of their rice stipends. According to Fukuzawa's description of his own han of Nakatsu, Kyushu, the upper samurai received 100 koku of rice or more; since some 20–30 koku were needed for the sustenance of one family, they could live comfortably on their allotments. The lower samurai in the same han received only 7 to 15 koku.[12]

Although the fortunes of all samurai declined drastically in the later Tokugawa period, the lower samurai had to work. The upper samurai could go on living as a leisured class, though with fewer luxuries and less display. The more impoverished samurai were forced to start some kind of home employment perhaps as early as the middle of the eighteenth century; it was already common practice in the first decade of the nineteenth century. They sold goldfish and carvings, made paper fans and lanterns, lacquer ware, umbrellas. They also entered widely into the production of sugar and tea and the manufacture of porcelain. Silkworm raising, spinning, and weaving were their most common occupations.[13]

Some samurai who did not find their way into these forms of production severed their allegiance to the feudal lord and became *rōnin* (roaming men), offering the service of their swords to anyone who would pay them. Or, as reckless political fanatics, they threw their support behind the opposing forces in the Restoration struggle. The plight of the samurai after the opening of the ports in 1853 is vividly described by a contemporary critic: "Although cheap money is abundant in the world, the Shogun's sustenance rate to his direct retainers remains the same. Driven to the wall, these samurai are now given to greed, cheating their superiors and tyrannizing over the common people. They have no time to show loyalty to the Shogun. They are in mind baser than merchants." [14]

Although the Restoration cannot be regarded as an achievement exclusively of the lower samurai, it cannot be denied that the success of the movement and the post-Restoration ascendency of many lower samurai into leading governmental posts kindled great hopes for economic betterment among the poor samurai. Restoration meant for many, first of all, the return of the emperor to power; with this, it was thought, the old glory of feudal Japan would be restored. These hopes were ruthlessly crushed by subsequent events. The government had no intention of restoring the old; it moved with determination into a new era, using the Western countries as its model. In the new Japan of the Meiji government there was to be no room for feudal privileges. The swords had become obsolete when guns decided victory or defeat.

The brief Restoration war and the ensuing changes in Edo spelled ruin for those samurai who had remained in Edo even after the *sankin kōtai* travels of the daimyo had been abolished. The merchants had left the city in a hurry and thus the central rice supply was all but cut off. Many samurai followed the abdicated shogun to Shizuoka (his family domain) as a matter of loyalty. Those who stayed set up teahouses in their front yards or little shops and sold their last possessions to prevent outright starvation.[15]

From the very start, the new government aimed at a strong central administration, and in 1871 the han were abolished and replaced by a prefectural system. Thus, by the stroke of a pen the old loyalty relationships were suspended: there were now neither feudal lords nor han for the samurai to belong to. Instead, they were citizens of prefectural units. For the time being they retained their titles, though even these were treated rather haphazardly by the new government, with willful regroupings and simplifications of the elaborate scales and degrees of rank.[16] However, the samurai were now free, like all other citizens, to pursue any type of work.[17] They still received their rice allotments, although these were sharply reduced. The central government took over the burden of paying the samurai and urged them to accept commutation of their stipends into lump sums in cash.

The cash awards were granted at about five times the market value of the rice stipend. With their new capital the samurai were supposed to start some kind of business.

Only a few were willing to trust this new approach, how-ever. Economic conditions were not at all promising for new enterprises, and the samurai's deep antipathy to busi-ness remained strong. When the commutation became law in 1876, there were still 312,775 samurai families on the stipend system,[18] probably close to 75 percent of the total samurai population. One could argue that voluntary com-mutation by some 25 percent indicates a considerable de-gree of initiative to start new business enterprises. But the disappearance of samurai from the list of stipend receivers by no means indicates that these men had received com-mutation payments before they were enforced by law. Many simply disappeared from the samurai registers with-out applying for commutation of stipends; they were ab-sorbed into the ranks of artisans, small peasants, and em-ployees. Their stipends had fallen to such a pittance that they did not consider registration and collection of the allowances worth the trouble. It is claimed that, for this reason, the number of samurai in Sendai dropped to but a few families of stipend receivers by 1873.[19] All the evi-dence points to a great reluctance to commute and to enter business. It also indicates that there was no vigorous spirit of enterprise among the samurai class as a whole.

In the early years after the Meiji Restoration, the real income of the average samurai continued to decline. In view of the back-door exodus from the samurai ranks on the one hand, and the steep rise in consumer prices on the other, it is most difficult to determine any exact per-centage for the fall in real income per capita. The follow-ing list gives the unadjusted totals of samurai incomes between 1867 and 1876, according to government statis-tics.[20] Even if the gradually diminishing number of samu-rai stipend receivers lessens the per-capita decline, it must have become practically impossible for all but a few upper samurai to sustain themselves on their receipts.

Pre-Restoration payment in rice, money value, 1867	34,621,583 yen
Payments of rice stipends in 1871, money value, 1871	22,657,948 yen
Value of the yearly interest paid on commutation bonds, 1876	11,568,000 yen

The value of the stipends for the han samurai who became prefectural samurai in 1871 amounted in that year to 15,300,000 yen, a very large sum if compared with the total government expenditure of 42,470,000 yen for the same year; [21] thus the expenditures for samurai were more than 36 percent of the budget. The government clearly had to find a solution to this fiscal problem, and it determined to enter the jobless stipend receivers into the production process.

The commutation of 1876 was paid in interest-bearing bonds with a total face value of 174 million yen, a sum about four times that of the total government revenue for one year. The system was very involved, and the rate of interest varied according to the class of samurai and the type of stipend rights. The payments themselves ranged from five to fourteen times the market value of the yearly amount of rice, while the interest was fixed at 5–7 percent.[22] This drastic decline of samurai incomes became the samurai's only reward for the support many of them had given to the Restoration movement. In addition to their economic straits, their pride was hurt by the abolition of old status privileges and of the right to carry swords. In protest some samurai carried wooden replicas of their weapons on the streets.[23] Discontented samurai became ringleaders in the peasant uprisings which plagued Japan in the first decade of Meiji. Some groups of samurai staged revolts of their own. In 1874 a large group of samurai took to arms in Saga han. They were defeated, eleven ringleaders were beheaded, and all participants were expelled from samurai rank.[24]

Other rebellions broke out in Kumamoto, Akizuki, and Hagi; finally the dissatisfied elements rallied for a last stand in the Satsuma Rebellion of 1877. Although the immediate reason for the rebellion was political (the rebels objected to the weak stand of the government in the Korean affair [25] and its excessively pro-Western policies), it was the bitterness and disappointment stemming from their economic misery and social degradation that led these samurai of southwestern Japan to defy a modern army of conscripted commoners.[26] The samurai were dealt a crushing defeat and were thus shown in realistic terms that the time of the sword and its privileges was over, once and for all. It now remained the government's task to find a way of using the samurai for constructive purposes, a way that would not only give them a living but would fit easily into their background and their peculiar mentality.

In spite of the government's ruthless suppression of samurai revolts and its liquidation of samurai privileges, the Meiji leaders were not without sympathy for their former compeers. Moreover, being samurai themselves, they were better aware than anyone else of the invaluable qualities that remained the distinctive mark of that class, such as education, social responsibility, self-respect, and devotion to duty. The Meiji leaders hoped that, once the opposition of the samurai to the inevitable changes was broken and once they had realized that the new era and the new economic conditions were here to stay, they would become the most important entrepreneurial element in the nation. The government's task was to restore the samurai to a position of leadership, this time in the economic field.

The Drafting of Samurai for Modern Enterprise

The National Banks

The commutation bonds of over 174 million yen created a grave monetary problem. Unless the bonds were absorbed quickly, they would flood the market and depreciate, thereby depriving the samurai of their last hope for economic survival and of their confidence in the government. It was felt in government circles that virtue ought to be made of necessity by turning the bonds into foundation capital for new banks. An improvement of the banking system was sorely needed. Under existing regulations, the four national banks in operation were unable to cope with the inconvertible government notes. Furthermore their number and total capital were considered insufficient for the overall needs of the gradually rallying economy. In 1876 a new banking act was passed. Its regulations on share capital and reserve requirements were designed to enable the samurai to join in the founding of new banks.[27] By the old regulations, national banks had to pay 60 percent of their cash holdings to the government. They received securities from the government in return, bearing 6 percent interest. The banks were permitted to print and circulate convertible banknotes up to the total value of these securities, but they suffered heavy losses because the notes were required to be converted at parity while they were actually depreciating rapidly. Consequently the banks virtually stopped the issue of banknotes.

The revised banking act of 1876 provided that 80 percent of the banks' capital be paid up to the government. In return the banks were to receive government bonds bearing 4 percent interest, purchased at market value. The banknote issue could be made up to the total face value of these securities.[28] Actually the commutation bonds were made the main part of the new banking capital and thus, in practice, up to 80 percent of the value of the commutation bonds invested as banking capital could circulate as paper money. By 1879 the national banks had a total capital of 40.62 million yen, of which over 29 million was in commutation bonds, the rest in currency. Against this total paid-up capital, the banks circulated 34.4 million yen in paper money.[29] Because of the favorable conditions granted the banks, they were supposed to charge less than the market rate of interest on loans — the regulations provided for 12–20 percent according to the size of the loans. But many of the new banks charged more.[30]

Along with the publication of the revised banking act of 1876 went a drive to stimulate participation of the samurai in founding new banks. The investment of bonds and cash in the establishment of banks was propagandized as a service to the country. Bankers were declared to be patriots who contributed to the building of a strong national economy.[31] Thus they were not associated with the much hated and despised money exchangers of Tokugawa days. The response to the government's drive for bank establishments surpassed all expectations. Within two years, 153 banks were founded and chartered as national banks. The Ministry of Finance stopped the rush and set a ceiling at this number in 1879. The total share capital of these national banks had risen from 2.55 million in December 1876 to 40.616 million in December 1879.[32]

From 1879 on, private banks mushroomed as the national banks had done previously. By 1883, 204 private banks were in operation, in addition to the 153 national banks.[33] Many samurai eagerly grasped the unique opportunity to invest their bonds in enterprises that received close governmental attention and were thus considered quite safe and, at the same time, gave them the distinction of being progressive patriots. Banks were founded, as the business-men would often boast, to "prevent the influx of foreign goods," to "promote enterprise," and to "promote the cause of civilization and enlightenment." Sometimes even destitute samurai became promoters of national or private banks, urging their compeers as well as commoners to con-tribute share capital. They tended to play down the risks and to emphasize the idealistic aspects in reference to the national economy.[34] Sometimes outright pressure was ap-plied. In Sendai all samurai were compelled to offer their bonds as foundation capital, and 308 samurai gathered a total of 83,865 yen in bonds and cash.[35] In 1877, a year after the publication of the revised banking act, the Min-istry of Finance sent a rescript to all local authorities cautioning against the use of compulsion: "It seems that our instructions concerning the establishment of national banks have been very well propagated among the people at large by the local authorities. . . . We cannot avoid noticing, however, that many a samurai thinks he has now by all means to compel his fellow classmen in his district to join in the foundation of companies. Thus it happens that even those who have no interest at all are forced to cooperate in the establishment of banks. The local authori-ties are herewith enjoined to prevent such bad practices." [36]

The rush of the samurai to found banks stands out in striking contrast to the attitudes of the wealthy merchant houses, which had to be forced to establish the first four national banks in 1872. Correspondingly, in this early phase the merchants also fell far behind the samurai as contributors of capital to the whole banking system. A report of the Banking Bureau in 1879–80 gives the follow-ing picture of percentage distribution of capital supply by classes for the national banks.[37]

Nobility	44.10%
Samurai	31.86
Merchants	14.85
Peasants	3.45
Artisans	0.12
Others	5.62
	100.0%

Records of individual banks indicate that even where merchants had supplied a majority of the capital, the initial drive toward foundation had come from samurai. The national banks were very successful. Until their charters expired, in 1898–99, only four banks closed and fourteen amalgamated. After 1898 a total of 122 continued as private banks, the reduction in their number being due to amalgamations or closings in 1898–99.[38] The private banks did not fare quite so well, undoubtedly because of less stringent supervision by the government; this in turn resulted in reduced public confidence. Between 1876 and 1892, a total of 410 private banks came into existence, of which 86 closed in the same period.[39]

The all-important breakthrough in the field of banking — and it was a real and lasting one — was thus achieved by the samurai in combination with the nobles, although the large amounts of capital held by the nobility tends greatly to exaggerate their share as participants. The most famous and largest of the national banks was founded by 480 nobles with 17.8 million yen of share capital, almost all in commutation bonds. As of 1881, the 147 other national banks then operating had only a total of 26 million yen. This bank enjoyed various privileges and favors from the government until 1883.[40]

The fact that the samurai had had little choice in the matter does not detract from the greatness of their contribution in the banking field. In declaring that the establishment of banks was in the interest of the country and therefore quite distinct from ordinary profit making, the government had managed to strike a note to which this class had long been accustomed to respond. Undoubtedly, at this early juncture, the arduous entrepreneurial task had to be supported by political motivations and government guidance. We can see that already a dichotomy existed in the Japanese business world. On the one hand there was "enterprise for the sake of the country" and, on the other, "business for profit." The feudal class carried its own social pride into the economy by refusing, at least outwardly, to become "merchants."

The national banks succeeded for several reasons. They inspired confidence because of government backing and were able to draw on the savings of the local population. Most of their loans were to minor local entrepreneurs and businessmen. Operation of the banks was not complicated, and the bankers received not only supervision but careful coaching and detailed instructions. Shibusawa, as president of the Dai Ichi Bank, played a major role here. He invited representatives of local banks to learn at the Dai Ichi Bank, and over twenty banks responded. Shibusawa saw to it that in times of difficulty these new banks would be supported; he also intervened for them with government officials when the inexperienced bankers misinterpreted regulations. Booklets and instructions were printed and distributed in which all operations, from banknote issue to interest-rate calculations and bookkeeping, were explained.[41]

This kind of operation was almost tailormade for the samurai, who were naturally prone to behave like officials, follow regulations, and act with a sense of public responsibility. The average director of a small or medium-sized national bank did not need much entrepreneurial vision and creativity, as Shibusawa himself once admitted. Of course, there were great entrepreneurs among Japan's bankers, but they did not, as a rule, emerge from this group that rushed into the founding of national banks. The leading bankers were far more independent men and more often than not connected with a string of industrial operations.

The chief contribution of the samurai to the success of the national banks was their willingness and ability to learn new things, qualities that were conspicuously absent in large segments of the merchant class. The samurai's willingness to start something new was of course the result of bitter necessity, but the new venture was made palatable by the appeal to patriotism. Their ability to learn hinged largely on their literacy. By 1876 Japan could no longer be called an illiterate country; perhaps 30 or even 40 percent of the population had received some schooling and could read. But the samurai were still the educated class par excellence. Between 1863 and 1871 Keio Gijuku, the college established by Fukuzawa, was attended by only 40 commoners as against 1,289 samurai.[42] Furthermore, the samurai were generally more open-minded, since their educational tradition was formal and philosophical. It is common knowledge that direct job education and practical training make the mind less flexible than a general education will. Thus the impractical outlook of the samurai actually became an asset in the face of completely new phenomena like modern banking, which had to be learned from printed material.

The Samurai Companies

Throughout the first twenty years of the Meiji era, the problem of samurai employment received priority in the government's policies. The deposed samurai class was not only an object of humanitarian concern; it constituted a real political danger. If properly directed, the samurai could eventually become a great asset to the economy. The drive to establish national banks was only one of various elements in the government's program for coping with the economic difficulties of its elite class. Roughly from the time of the Restoration on, samurai were urged to settle on small farms and reclaim land or to emigrate to Hokkaido. But by 1879 there still must have been approximately 1.5 million destitute samurai. The government planners then set out to direct the highly valued capabilities of these men toward the foundation of large-scale enterprises in company form. Iwakura Tomomi, one of the leaders of the Restoration movement and a champion of the company-foundation program,[43] expressed his expectations thus:

The samurai will be able to display a strength of character which has been groomed through the ages, and will thus enter successfully into a hundred fields of activity. Giving full sway to their mental vigor they can stand up in competition with the foreigners. In the present state of affairs there is none but the samurai who can, endowed with training in many fields, bring the enterprise of the country to a head. . . . If we take the rest of the population, excluding these high-class families, we still find much wasteland. It will take some twenty to thirty years until their strength will suffice to compete with foreigners.[44]

In 1874 the government granted a loan of forty yen per household to rebellious samurai of Saga han, after crushing their revolt. They were given this loan on the condition that they invest it in companies.[45] This precedent was followed by a larger program initiated in 1878. Loans were granted to samurai for the purpose of investment in either agriculture or manufacturing of some sort. The choice of venture was left to the imagination and skill of the individual; it also depended largely on the economic conditions of the region. But there was one invariable stipulation: the enterprise must be a joint-stock venture, with samurai as members.

This government program was not the only one. The prefectures had their own employment projects; wealthy merchants and peasants sometimes also made sizable contributions to help samurai families or to get a samurai company started. A few spinning mills, owned by groups of samurai, were established with substantial subsidies from prefectures or private individuals. Information on the prefectural subsidies and private loans is very difficult to come by. According to the original bill submitted by Ōkubo, the central government was to spend a total of 10 million yen in loans to start samurai companies; in reality only 5,256 million yen were spent over the whole period from 1879 to 1889, when the program was terminated.[46] According to a survey of Kikkawa Hidezō, 257 companies received loans from the central government between 1879 and 1885; 176 received the loans free of interest.[47] Of these companies 47 were agricultural enterprises; 78 were in raw silk or silkworm rearing; 33 could be called "modern" enterprises, with 14 of them in textiles. Again, it must be pointed out that this is only a partial list of the companies that began under central-government auspices.

If we consider that, at this early date, joint-stock enterprise was all but unknown in Japan and that modern business ventures were few, we can estimate the economic and entrepreneurial importance of this vast program. The shareholders in these companies were often numerous. Giant "all-purpose" companies tried to combine the advantages of bigness, capital and scale of operation, with the use of diversified skills and opportunities. In some instances a few thousand families would join in a single company, but they usually failed after a short time. It is not possible here to give detailed statistics on the total outcome of the program. Approaches and results varied greatly from place to place and from company to company. Usually the agricultural companies and tea-growing and silkworm-rearing establishments were relatively successful, at least for a while, but most of those entering into modern types of manufacturing fared very badly.

Generally the samurai had participated in the program out of hard necessity, to avoid starvation, and consequently many enterprises were founded upon resentment rather than enthusiasm. In Akita in 1882 a group of about 250 samurai founded a reactionary newspaper favoring the restoration of the old order. The paper went out of business for lack of popular support, and the government then granted the same samurai a loan of 20,000 yen to establish a silk-weaving company.[48] The samurai problem had become a national emergency that concerned the whole population. Many merchants or wealthy peasants felt an obligation to join the government in trying to provide a livelihood for the esteemed cream of the nation. Do-gooders of all types became founders or promoters of samurai enterprises. In the Nagasaki area [49] 17 samurai companies of various types were founded between 1881 and 1888, ranging over a wide field of activities including silkworm rearing, spinning, tea growing, cattle rearing, the manufacture of porcelain, wax, sugar, and gelatine, and iron casting. One silkworm-rearing and cattle-breeding company comprising 7,308 samurai families started with 10,000 yen of share capital, a government loan for the same amount, and a subsidy from a private source of 20,000 yen. It was a fair success for at least a decade. The records of most companies are very scanty and do not permit precise statements as to their success. One company that took up fishing, raw-silk production, and porcelain manufacturing soon collapsed, whereas another engaged in silk and sugar production, and numbering 294 shareholders, operated successfully for some time.

Shizuoka prefecture had been hit especially hard by the Meiji Restoration. Following the shogun's resignation, his direct retainers were given a threefold choice: they could become retainers of the emperor, follow the former shogun into exile to his own territory of Shizuoka,[50] or become ordinary citizens and renounce their samurai status. Some 7,000 to 8,000 samurai chose to follow their feudal lord to Shizuoka, thus increasing the stipend receivers in that territory to about 15,000 families.[51] Not unnaturally, this group was anything but enthusiastic about the new era and its programs.

In spite of the large number of samurai in Shizuoka, records show only eight companies that formed there, of which two tea-growing companies were large, one with 800 samurai members and the other with 200.[52] The larger company had started in 1869 and was organized into groups of families according to their former military regiments; the superior ranks held the managerial positions. The company was fairly successful until 1882, distributing yearly profits per family of 30 to 65 yen, an equivalent of 4–6 koku of rice. After 1882 the profits fell to an equivalent of one half to one koku.[53] On the whole, the Shizuoka enterprises in tea production, silkworm rearing, cattle breeding, and umbrella manufacturing fared worse than those in Nagasaki prefecture; perhaps Nagasaki's proximity to foreign influence and the generally progressive conditions there were partly responsible.

But there is not much point in stressing differences in

progress and entrepreneurial approach among the various regions. Many other variables were in operation simultaneously, and all combined to make the entire samurai-company plan a vast failure. After a few years most of these companies collapsed. Their capital was too thin to carry the blundering and experimental undertakings over the years of losses. With the deflation of currency initiated in 1881 by Minister of Finance Matsukata, they tumbled wholesale. The regions with the lowest per-capita loans usually showed the poorest results, a sign that scarcity of capital was an important reason for their collapse. Shimane prefecture, which had the lowest loans (0.4 yen per capita, as against 1.8 yen for Tottori and 1.5 yen for Okayama, which had the highest rates),[54] reported in 1880 that 94 percent of all its samurai bondholders had either sold their bonds for cash or had invested in company enterprises that had gone bankrupt. Three years later, Shimane prefecture reported that approximately 20 percent of all its samurai had neither employment nor savings to fall back on, and that they survived through the help of friends or relatives.[55] A survey of Osaka district in September 1881 indicated that of a total of 3,434 samurai households only 31 percent had some kind of employment.[56] An 1883 report by Hiroshima prefecture gives the following picture: only about 20–30 percent of the samurai succeeded in entering gainful employment between 1875 and 1883. In 1883 the total number of samurai households was 7,735. Of these, 1,720 had achieved economic subsistence, 4,374 scarcely had the necessities of life, 1,167 were in severe straits, and 474 were completely unable to sustain themselves.[57]

The samurai as a class did not manage to achieve a breakthrough in manufacturing, as they did in joint-stock banking. The reason was that in banking, at that time, the most important requirements were enthusiasm and strict observance of set rules — the establishment of manufacturing and trading enterprises required much more experience and imagination. The great majority of entrepreneurs of stature had more than enthusiasm; they had acquired precious practical experience and had freed themselves from the past and its traditions. Indeed, willingness to accept change may have been at the root of the different fates of the banks and the samurai companies. The banks came first and probably attracted those who were most ready to change, to accept the economic challenge. The samurai companies then were left to gather in those who "had not jumped before." The courageous volunteers who constituted the real entrepreneurial timber and had a positive attitude toward economic change were by and large already engaged elsewhere.

Within the first two decades of the Meiji era, roughly speaking, the samurai were transformed from nonproductive consumers into productive agents. Through the mechanism of commuting their consumption into bonds that were invested, actual savings were raised by almost the same amount. By the end of the Tokugawa period, the daimyo and samurai consumed most of the tax revenue, which was as high as 25–30 percent of the gross national product. Now the Meiji government was in a position to use almost all of its tax revenue for its own purposes because the interest on the daimyo and samurai bonds, which were depreciating very rapidly, became a negligible burden in a time of high inflation. The samurai could not live on bond interest and, in order to earn a living, were forced to become productive.

Perhaps, in a sense, the most important contribution of the samurai class to Japanese economic growth was, paradoxically, its abolition as a privileged and passive consumer group. In view of the quest of underdeveloped countries to raise the rate of domestic capital formation, the case of the samurai points to an interesting and probably very important possibility: the liquidation of consumer-group privileges and the transformation of the unearned incomes of such groups into savings. Even where such passive consumer groups do not exist, a similar process is feasible through the transfer of the disguised unemployed from the farms where — theoretically at least — they do not earn, but consume, into the production process of modern industry or other types of manufacturing. I need not elaborate on this possibility here because it is often mentioned in treatises on economic development.[58]

But there is something else that tends to be overlooked in discussing the theoretical possibilities of capital formation. The mechanism of social and economic transfer must also provide stimuli and incentives for the declassed or transferred groups that will break down their initial resistance and eventually make them cooperate in the program. Moreover, privileged groups of passive consumers, like the samurai in Japan, more often than not have superior qualities in terms of education and leadership capabilities, and these must not be lost to the economy by the creation of a permanent sulking resistance. The uniqueness of the Meiji experience is that the samurai were declassed by compeers who were extremely anxious to activate the best qualities of that elite class, and succeeded in doing so. Thus the samurai were able to generate a good deal of entrepreneurial dynamism and eventually provided the modern entrepreneurial elite with a new status image, based on the old vibrant "spirit of the samurai."

III

RURAL ENTREPRENEURSHIP

It is common knowledge that the burden of financing industrialization in its early stages falls heavily on the agricultural sector, unless large-scale foreign aid can be obtained. The agricultural sector must provide an initial surplus to feed the new industrial labor force and must finance by exports the required imports of capital. How did Japanese agriculture provide the necessary basis for the vigorous industrial development that started in the Meiji era? How much had agricultural productivity risen above the subsistence level during the Tokugawa period, and what were the forces that made such an achievement possible? We shall see that it was the entrepreneurial elements in the rural sector that must be given particular credit for the creation of the agricultural surplus, mainly through the reclamation of new land and the introduction of cash cropping, new farming techniques, and domestic manufacturing.

RURAL ENTREPRENEURS IN TOKUGAWA JAPAN

The Tokugawa System of Agriculture

Tokugawa agriculture rested on the nominal ownership of all land by the feudal overlord (*ryōshu*), who had the

right to levy taxes on the peasantry.[1] The amount of tax
was left to the lord's discretion and it varied from han
to han, but as a rule of thumb about four parts of the
value of the produce were collected as tax and six parts
were left to the farming peasants. The greater part of the
payment was made in kind, chiefly in rice, but another
part was paid in money, to which were added various
kinds of services, such as upkeep of roads and river em-
bankments and — along the highways — the emergency
supply of horses and messengers.

Land, according to an edict of 1643, could not be sold,
and partition of land below two cho was also prohibited.[2]
One cho produced on the average somewhere between
twelve and fourteen koku of rice, and one koku of rice
is equivalent to minimum subsistence for one person for
a year. The prohibition against partition of land was
apparently aimed at keeping a few farmers in each village above subsistence level, in order to strengthen the
village community. Peasants were exhorted to live frugally
and not to consume the surplus owed to the lords. They
were not to eat much rice but rather millet, barley, sweet
potatoes, and radishes, and they were to drink water and
not tea or sake.

The village was administered by the headman, who was
responsible to the overlord not only for the prompt deliveries of tax rice but also for general discipline. He carried a sword and had a family name, as signs of honor, and
his position was hereditary. The village was subdivided
into groups of families, usually five (*gonin gumi*); each
group had to pay the tax as a unit, though the amount was
reassessed at regular intervals of five years or more, according to the productivity of each plot. Within the village
and the *gonin gumi,* land ownership was unequally distributed. A few families were rich, owning some four to

five cho; at the other extreme were the poor peasants with no more than a quarter of a cho. The poor were forced to lend labor services to the rich and were in turn assigned some additional marginal plots to cultivate for themselves. This relationship between wealthy and poor peasants, the *oyabun–kobun* relationship, constituted another important link of social interdependence. The *oyabun* was not only the employer but also the protector and councilor of the weak *kobun*. The social control exercised by the village headman, the *gonin gumi,* and the *oyabun-kobun* relationship were all perfectly designed to keep the Tokugawa village in subordination and to suppress initiative and change.

Beginning in the second half of the eighteenth century, however, it became increasingly obvious that even a bakufu bureaucracy could not legislate against the laws of demand and supply. Village life began to change markedly. Improvements in agricultural techniques and the increased power of money destroyed the static economic and social stratification in the villages. Rural merchants and rich peasant-manufacturers gained prominence, and they did so not only by exploiting their co-villagers and reducing them to tenant position, but even more by their own entrepreneurial activity. Indeed, in the last century of the Tokugawa period, the principal entrepreneurial stirrings occurred not in the large cities but in the villages. First, however, let us examine briefly the achievements that are usually credited to rural entrepreneurship in this period. How much did agricultural productivity rise during the Tokugawa period?

We sometimes hear statements that Japan's agriculture, by the end of the Tokugawa, was close to subsistence level with no surplus for industrial investments. Some people apparently assume that Japanese agriculture "must have been" at subsistence level until the beginning of industrialization, which in turn was made possible by an unbelievable squeeze on the peasant population.

Some indicators do suggest such an interpretation — for example, the combination of almost stationary population combined with an increasing frequency of peasant uprisings. There are no precise population figures, but we may not be far from wrong in assuming the total population to have risen by no more than 10 percent over the 250 years of Tokugawa rule. Between 1721 and 1846 Japan's population is supposed to have risen by no more than 900,000, from 26 to 26.9 million, and to have fallen off during the great famines of the 1830s by 300,000.[3] We have to realize, of course, that official figures did not include unregistered people who may have constituted over 10 percent of the population. Consequently we may assume with Irene Taeuber that by 1853 Japan's total population stood at about 30 million; we must raise the earlier figures correspondingly, with the same result of a very slow population increase. The number of peasant uprisings increased steadily and accelerated in the first half of the nineteenth century.[4] We may question the accuracy of the early records and try to explain away this rising rural unrest, but it is well known that the bakufu became seriously concerned about the uprisings. Although there appear to have been, especially in the decades immediately before the Restoration, a good many political causes for the uprisings (the antibakufu forces gained extensive support among the rich peasants and rural samurai), the main cause was economic. The uprisings were directed against the exploitation of the peasants by the merchants and rural magnates.

It is theoretically possible that, in spite of rising overall productivity, the real income of the lower stratum of peasants could have declined in absolute terms. But such a postulate is not needed to explain the lack of population growth and the frequent uprisings. Even if the low-income farming population had in fact improved its absolute level of living, the introduction of new consumer goods, and the amassing of economic power by the merchants and rich peasants while many poor peasants were being reduced to tenant status, must have created widespread discontent and made the slight actual improvements appear as losses when compared to the incomes of the new village capitalists.

As for the stable population, the population rate was controlled by infanticide. Once population control becomes an accepted custom, as it did in Tokugawa Japan, it can become a habit and cannot always be assumed to be an indicator of subsistence living standards. The Tokugawa peasants in a way defied Malthusian theory; the Meiji government at times had to resort to rather drastic measures to eliminate infanticide.

There was, furthermore, a substantial rise in agricultural productivity in the Tokugawa period, and it resulted from land reclamations, land improvements, new techniques, and specialization. The total cultivated area increased constantly throughout the Tokugawa years, although it is difficult to interpret reasonably figures that suggest an increase of 300 percent, from 1.5 million cho in 1598 to almost 4.5 million cho in 1880.[5] What probably happened was that a substantial amount of cultivated land in the seventeenth and eighteenth centuries was concealed in order to avoid taxation, which was based on yield per cho of land. We know that even the first cadastral surveys of the Meiji era permitted a certain amount of concealment or undermeasurement. Another factor may have to be considered when we read of the enormous increase in cultivated land: when new land is simply added to the old, the result may be a higher set of figures than reality warranted. Sufficient cases are recorded wherein old land was abandoned by peasants because of erosion or floods, or because it was subject to a heavier tax than new land.[6]

According to a survey of the han, conducted under the auspices of the Meiji government in 1869, the total value product of all han had risen on the average from the base 100 to about 150 between 1614 and 1869, varying widely, of course, from han to han and from region to region.[7] A rise of 50 percent over 250 years cannot be considered a high growth rate, and, taking the population rise during the same interval to have been about 10 percent, it does not indicate a remarkable surplus available for industrialization. The fact of the matter is, however, that we are probably misled again by purposeful concealments: the survey was carried out by the han administrations for the central government, and it is anybody's guess how honest the administrators were when they had reason to fear that the findings might be used as a basis for tax assessment. Agricultural output is said to have risen from 18.5 million koku in 1598 to 30.56 koku in 1842.[8] This means approximately an increase of 60 percent, and it leaves out the last 25 years of the Tokugawa period when economic growth was most pronounced. So it may not be unrealistic to assume a near doubling of agricultural output in the course of the 250 years of the Tokugawa period.

Recent thinking tends toward the belief that by the end of the Tokugawa period Japanese agriculture was by no means at the subsistence level; that instead it showed every sign of a quickening growth and the capacity of supplying the initial surplus for industrialization. Wealth came into the villages through manufacturing, crop specialization, and trade. Although the distribution of income became increasingly skewed in favor of the manufacturing and commercial group, the average peasant was not completely bypassed by the rising productivity. One sign that this was so is the spread of elementary education among the peasants. By the end of the Tokugawa about 30 percent of the total population had received some elementary education. Literacy is an almost certain sign of a rise above subsistence levels.

In the following sections I shall not pursue further the question of the exact amount of potential investible surplus supplied by agriculture at the beginning of the Meiji era. The primary emphasis will be on the various factors that contributed to its emergence, particularly on the entrepreneurial elements operating in rural Japan.

Land Reclamations by Merchant Capitalists

The bakufu encouraged land reclamation, especially after the disastrous famines lasting from 1783 to 1788. A bakufu rescript dated 1790 decreed that for newly reclaimed land the tax should not be higher than 10 percent on the yield.[9] The daimyo took similar measures in their own territories. The process of reclaiming swampy river land or forests was costly, and only the wealthy capitalists, mostly merchants, could afford long gestation periods for their investments. But these investments were lucrative indeed. The new landlord was free of all burdens except the stipulated 10 percent tax. The new land was often more fertile than the old paddies, and the landlords sometimes received as much as 65–70 percent of the yield as rent, leaving the peasant only 30–35 percent.[10] This is certainly proof of high fertility because from the old land, on the average, about 40 percent of the yield was required to maintain a tenant.

The inducements to engage in land reclamation were

many. The land laborers who were employed in the reclamation project came into a tenant relationship with the
new landlord. They were provided with tools and working
capital, and were freed from the bonds of control and
interdependence that existed in the old village; instead
they became completely dependent upon the new landlords. These quasi-overlords came into opposition with
the older feudal class; yet the feudal lords welcomed them
and, at least initially, gained by their activities.

The Osaka merchants were well represented among the
new landlords. The Kagaya family of Osaka, between 1745
and 1841, reclaimed a total of 120 cho in new land by
draining the swamps between the Yamato and Kitsu
rivers.[11] The Kōnoike family carried out a major reclamation project in the vicinity of Osaka, amounting also to
120 cho.[12] The draining of swampy river land in Osaka
itself added 68 cho of paddyland to the arable area during
the second half of the seventeenth century and the first
decades of the eighteenth.[13]

A writer of the Tempō era (1830–1844) tells of vast land
reclamations which indicate the tremendous wealth of the
new landlords.[14] He laments the fact that, at a time when
retainers of feudal lords received a bare 10 koku of rice as
sustenance, merchants amassed huge profits from newly
reclaimed lands. Then he cites a few examples: In Shonai
(Tsuruoka) of Dewa province, a merchant received 140,000
koku of rice as rents from land while the officially assessed
gross total product of the same area amounted to only
150,000 koku. In Kaga province two merchants paid
80,000 koku as feudal taxes and received 160,000 koku as
rents from their reclaimed land. In Hokuriku there were
frequent instances of new landlords receiving anywhere
from 1,000 to 10,000 koku in rents from new land. In Shikoku, too, such new landlords were numerous, among them

a merchant in Iyo han who received 10,000 koku in rent in a fief totaling 10,000 koku of the gross total product. In Kyushu, he comments, the number of owners of large areas of newly reclaimed land was smaller, but many received 500 to 1,000 koku as rents, and receivers of 100 to 200 koku were very numerous. In Kyushu some feudal lords themselves undertook land reclamations. The writer goes on to explain that, wherever the feudal tax rates were high, land reclamations were few, but low tax rates and general prosperity induced new reclamations. High taxes sometimes made peasants desert their plots and emigrate to other areas.

Even if we allow for the obvious gross exaggerations of this account, the fact that merchants engaged frequently and quite successfully in the reclamation of wasteland seems to be well established. The land reclamations raised total productivity, but at the same time drove a wedge into the agricultural system. The new landlords were the first to siphon off the added surplus away from the feudal class, effectively setting a ceiling on feudal taxation. But there were other entrepreneurial, and therefore disrupting, elements on the rural scene.

The merchants from Omi region along the shores of Lake Biwa had been known as peddlers and long-distance traders, even before the Tokugawa period. They were traveling salesmen who crisscrossed the countryside, down to the last village, offering their local products, buying up new goods and selling them elsewhere. Prior to the closing of the country they had gone abroad; their ventures made them somewhat comparable to the Hanse merchants of the Baltic countries. The Omi merchants controlled the trade along Japan's coasts, sailing from the Ryukyus up to Hokkaido.

The exploration of Hokkaido made the Omi merchants

famous. At the beginning of the Tokugawa period, Hokkaido was still underdeveloped: rice was not grown and many articles of daily use were lacking. Samurai who settled in Hokkaido were assigned areas to exploit by the feudal lords, and it was here that the Omi merchants came in. They received commissions and monopoly rights in these backward areas to establish fisheries and trading services; they supplied the samurai with rice, wheat, salt, swords, and textiles. Groups of Omi merchants acquired extended rights in connection with fisheries, and they invested in fishing fleets, developed fishing villages, and started a lucrative monopoly trade in fishery products, notably herring, herring roe, and seaweed.[15]

Dried herring and dried sardines, along with nightsoil and dry leaves, became fertilizers throughout Japan. With their tradition of long-distance trade, the Omi merchants naturally became the promoters and traders of fertilizers, especially of the kinds produced from fish. The use of fertilizer increased, thanks to the activity of the Omi merchants, and contributed much to the increase in agricultural productivity. Thomas Smith mentions that in 1714 the third largest item among all of Osaka harbor's shipments was imports of fertilizer.[16] The use of fertilizer, despite its immediate economic advantages, was for many a marginal farmer the beginning of his undoing. The Omi merchant willingly gave credit at high interest and thus took the first step that would eventually lead to the acquisition of peasant land. There were frequent cases of landlords who had started as peddling merchants from Omi and had bought up large areas of land through the fertilizer trade and moneylending.

Once the Omi merchant had secured a foothold in the village through land ownership, he usually continued to combine moneylending and trade, and added to these occupations some kind of manufacturing. Special favorites of the Omi merchant-manufacturers were vegetable-oil production, the brewing of sake, and miso and soy-sauce making. The area of Hino in Omi became known as the headquarters of sake brewers and soy-sauce producers; such merchant landowners also dominated the sake brewing of the Kanto area. A survey of sake and soy-sauce manufacturing lists 59 establishments of Hino merchants, all started between 1688 and the last years of the bakufu. They were spread all over the country but centered especially in the Kanto area.[17]

A good example of an enterprising Omi merchant house is the Uchiike family in Fukushima prefecture. Between 1763 and 1848 this family had succeeded in moving from peddling to landownership and manufacturing, doing a lucrative business in sake, drygoods, oil, and silk yarn; their large farm was cultivated by hired laborers. As a sign of wealth and progress, the family collected books and employed a samurai as a teacher for its children.[18]

Cash Crops and Concentration of Landholdings

The feudal economy had originally been based on the growing of staple crops and taxes in kind, with a maximum avoidance of luxury consumption and commercialization. There had, of course, been some specialization in commercial crops all along, depending upon conditions of soil and climate. There had been sugar growing in Kyushu and the Ryukyus, cotton in Kinki, and mulberries in the highlands north of Edo. But Tokugawa policy was to discourage further specialization in favor of a maximum production of rice and grains.

Large-scale commercialization of agricultural produce became a necessity, however, with the concentration of samurai in the castle towns. Rice and the other tax commodities had to be transported to the consumer centers, and so they passed through the hands of the commissioned merchants. Part of the feudal tax had to be paid in money, and this forced the peasants to sell their farm products to the local merchant to get the tax money. In this fashion rice and other agricultural products became commercial commodities, and the natural economy increasingly gave way to a money economy.

Records from Sendai han in the 1820s show that agricultural tax deliveries in kind amounted to only 51 percent of total han income; another 21 percent were paid in money, while 28 percent were profits from han-managed enterprises. In the same han, the farmers marketed over half of their total produce left over after payment of taxes in kind, in order to pay the money tax and make their own purchases of fertilizer, clothing, and home utensils.[19]

Once the farmers became this much involved in the market economy, there was little to prevent them from taking full advantage of specialization in accordance with soil conditions and distance to the cities. In the north, rice growing became predominant. Akita han became the main exporter of rice and cereals and imported chiefly textiles. At the end of the Tokugawa period, 45 percent of Akita han's total imports were textiles, while 90.7 percent of its exports consisted of rice and other grains; of this latter sum, one third was exported from the daimyo warehouses and two thirds were shipped by merchants, who apparently had bought directly from peasants.[20] On the whole, however, the cash crops most favored were those connected with textiles, luxury items, and special foods. If the soil was favorable to cash crops, the peasants would sometimes go so far as to purchase the rice for their own use.[21]

The areas with the heaviest concentration of specialized cash crops were those close to the great consumer centers, the Kinki and the Kanto areas. Naturally cash cropping and manufacturing of the home-employment type usually went together and were concentrated in the same areas. By 1874, commercialization of agriculture was most pronounced in Kinki, followed by Shikoku and Kanto (if we take into account the size and population density of these areas — otherwise Kanto comes ahead of Shikoku), while Kyushu, Sanin, and Tohoku had the lowest percentage of agricultural commercialization. These ratings are based on the following products, which were the main items of trade: cotton and cotton textiles, silkworms and silk, tea, vegetable oil, wax, tobacco, sake, soy sauce, sugar, paper, tatami.[22] By 1877, the five Kinai provinces were producing 34.4 percent of all Japanese cotton.[23] Silkworm rearing and silk reeling were most heavily concentrated in Fukushima, Yamanashi, and Gumma prefectures. Osaka became the trading center for commercial produce: 7 percent of Japan's rice output was shipped to Osaka and 21 percent of total textiles and raw cotton were concentrated there as early as 1736.[24]

Although the degree of agricultural commercialization varied greatly according to soil conditions, climate, and, most of all, demand and the possibility of transporting the product to the consumer centers, it is probably reasonable to assume that by the time of the Restoration half or more of all agricultural products were put on the market in one form or another. This would include sales of rice to meet tax obligations in cash, as well as the sale and purchase of specialized products and converted foodstuffs like miso, sake, soy sauce, and textiles, along with ceramics and diverse household goods.

The response of the daimyo and the bakufu to this commercialization was varied. They feared the undermining of feudal agriculture and sensed that too much of their potential tax was being absorbed by merchants. But, at the same time, they urged peasants to resort to cash cropping and home employment so that they could pay higher taxes in money.

A number of daimyo with initiative began to make use of special crops and local industry by establishing their own trading monopolies. A well-known instance occurred in Satsuma han.[25] This han had been almost bankrupt at the beginning of the nineteenth century, with a total debt of 5 million ryo against a yearly han revenue of only 140,000 ryo. An energetic reform program centered on monopoly trade in sugar; sugar had been traditionally a special crop of the Ryukyu islands, which were under Satsuma jurisdiction. These islands were put on a barter-trade basis with Satsuma, delivering the raw sugar to Kagoshima. There it was refined, packed, and shipped to the Osaka market; 60 ships were built for this sugar trade. In Osaka the Satsuma sugar sold very well and provided large revenues for the han's tottering economy. By 1869 sugar accounted for 49 per cent of the total han exports; 54 per cent of its imports were textiles.[26]

Other han specialized in porcelain, lacquer, wax, paper, or silk. The peasants had to sell the products at stipulated prices to the han monopoly-trade companies. Rich peasants and local merchants were strongly opposed to these han practices and often became ringleaders in uprisings against the heavy tax burdens.

One of the side effects of agricultural commercialization was an increasing indebtedness among the marginal peasants and the eventual loss of their land to the merchants or rural usurers and rich peasants. The merchants introduced new consumer goods to the villages, and peasants became used to a rice diet, to tea and sake, to better clothing and traveling, all things that were prohibited in the frequent rulings issued by the bakufu and daimyo. Village life became subject to disruptive external influences. The old *oyabun–kobun* relationship and cooperation within the *gonin gumi* gave way to individual ambition and competition. The strong ones could now move ahead of the others. The idea of an immutable rural status quo disappeared; land that had been considered unsalable was sold, and no amount of bakufu prohibition could change this.

From the middle of the Tokugawa period, the number of tenants increased: the wealthy peasants amassed more land, and the marginal peasants became landless laborers or tenants. Landowners of the new type came mainly from the ranks of village samurai, village headmen, merchants, and rural manufacturers. By the 1830s, of the landowners with 50 or more cho of land in the Kinki area, 48 percent were merchants and 24 percent village samurai and village headmen; in Tohoku, 30 percent were merchants and 19 percent samurai and village headmen. In Kanto and Kyushu, the latter group, with 65 percent and 35 percent, was ahead of the merchants, who represented only 13 percent and 18 percent of the rich landowners.[27] In the Kinki region, with its heavy concentration of merchant capital and cotton growing, landownership became particularly skewed. In some places at the end of the Tokugawa period, landless peasants comprised as much as 70 percent of the total village population.[28] The Hirano area, close to Osaka, was most conspicuous for cotton growing and had numerous cotton merchants; by the mid-eighteenth century the merchant-landlords had as many as 2,000 tenant farmers under their control, and 8.2 percent of the population owned 46 percent of the cultivated area.[29]

I shall not follow up the social implications of this concentration of land ownership or comment on the role of the rich peasants and landlords in the Restoration movement. From the entrepreneurial vantage point, the most important function of the rural merchants, usurers, and rich peasants was their engagement in manufacturing.

The Putting-Out Masters and Rural Manufacturers

The men who became landlords through trading, usury, and cash cropping were often very imaginative and enterprising; not bound by tradition, they tried new ways of making money and of investing their capital. Cash crops usually provided an immediate opportunity for investment in some type of manufacturing, as by-employment for the tenant farmers or even as full-time employment for landless laborers. The field of activity was wide and varied according to local conditions and the availability of capital. Investments in such activities as sake brewing, usually combined with miso and soy-sauce making, required large capital, while cotton and silk spinning could be entered into with small initial investments. The sake brewers frequently had their tenants help them during the agricultural off-seasons of winter and early spring. Sake brewing was somewhat restricted by a bakufu license system, but the Hino merchants made sake brewing their favorite investment. The rural manufacturers in the field of silk and cotton textiles provided the tenants and landless laborers with raw materials and some working capital; they also bought looms and rented them out.

The two most famous centers of "putting-out," or domestic, manufacturing were the Kinki area (for cotton textiles) and Fukushima (for silk). In the first decades of the nineteenth century, the Fukushima silk industry had become nationally famous and the silk market drew buyers from far away. A record of 1818 mentions that several thousand producers sold their silk yarns and silk cloth there, worth 15,000 to 16,000 ryo.[30] In the Fukushima area specialization was carried down to the village level, some villages concentrating mainly on silkworm rearing, others on reeling, and still others on weaving.

On the whole, rural putting-out manufacturing did not reach the factory-production stage. There were a few exceptions: spinners in some cases were assembled in one place, and there were other types of large-scale and factory manufacturing that occurred under han management prior to the Restoration. But most of the putting-out masters remained farm landlords, becoming merchants and usurers at the same time.

Satō Gentabei of Kakeda village in Fukushima was a typical highly successful rich peasant, manufacturer, and trader. Records of 1727 from the Satō family indicate that he produced and traded sake in large quantities, and did a lucrative business in yarns, tea, rice, and soybeans. In a single day the ledger shows 279 koku of sake produced; another day records 356 koku of sake sold for over 591 ryo, and silk yarn sold to Fukushima for 184 ryo — yarn that had been spun by people he employed.[31] In this fashion the rich became richer and the poor villagers became ever more dependent upon these village capitalists. The case of the Satō family is of course an extreme one, but lesser capitalists of a similar type were to be found in almost every village. Sometimes a poor farmer could manage to climb the ladder to success, starting with some extra employment or moneylending on a small scale and, with luck and skill, becoming a rural entrepreneur. Smith mentions such a case — a landless peasant in Mino province who had started out in the Meiwa era (1764–1771) trading cotton, rice, and fertilizer and by 1819 had become a landowner of 190 koku, scattered over 15 villages.[32]

Putting-out manufacturing was a mixed blessing to the rural population. It made the majority of the villagers de-

pendent upon a few magnates, but at the same time it did
provide additional income and employment for wives and
daughters. Peasants and local authorities therefore often
welcomed new home-employment opportunities which
helped to alleviate economic pressures. An application of
four villagers in Settsu to be permitted to start weaving
was endorsed by the village headman and the leader of
the *gonin gumi*. Incidentally, of these four only one was
a landless peasant; the other three owned their land, one
earning 33 koku and the other 20 koku, the third an unknown amount. These men argued that it was impossible
to make a living by farming alone.[33] But with home employment even small tenant peasants and landless laborers
were often not badly off, and their wage rates rose with
the further spread of home employment and rural manufacturing.

As a consequence of the attractions of home employment,
rural wage workers became scarce. In the Tempō era
(1830–1844) there were complaints that domestics were
difficult to find because the girls were employed in spinning and weaving.[34] Because of rising wage rates it became
profitable to rent out land instead of operating large units
with hired help,[35] a practice that increasingly broke down
the large household units in the villages. The tenants, in
turn, cut loose from the large farming units and unable
to live on agriculture alone, were forced to seek extra
employment.

From various sides, then, the solidarity and cooperation
within the village were undermined, and the establishment
of small independent working units opened the way for
enterprising individuals. Smith cites a village in Shinshu
in which the size of the average family declined from 3.3
couples to 1.2 couples and from 12.3 members to 3.8
members between 1755 and 1830. The total number of
families in the village rose from 30 to 83 during the same

period.[36] This means, incidentally, a drop in population by about 15 percent. Small family units certainly helped greatly to bring mobility as well as progressive new attitudes to rural Japan. The commercialization of agriculture and putting-out manufacturing had a leavening influence on rural life and prepared the way for the Restoration and the success of the Meiji government's industrialization and modernization efforts.

Rural putting-out manufacturing prior to the Restoration, and the beginnings of factory work, offered a training ground for Japan's industrial labor force. Farmers were getting used to having their daughters work for wages at spinning and weaving: the only change that came later was that the daughters went to the city to do the same work in factories, sending their wages home to support the family. The first workers in Japan's industries did not sever all ties to the village, but the way had been prepared when the villagers were reduced to tenant position and were forced to work for wages on the side. The first steps toward severing the strong bond to the soil was one of the secondary effects of rural entrepreneurship during the Tokugawa period.

During the later part of the Tokugawa period, the most enterprising elements in Japan were to be found in the villages, not in the cities. In the villages the shackles of tradition were thrown off and a liberal and "bourgeois" ideology emerged among the new landlords, rich peasants, and putting-out masters. The guilds that hampered progress in the cities had no significance in the villages, and economic conditions succeeded in changing village attitudes. The rich peasants and putting-out masters took pride in displaying their break with the old restrictions that had been imposed on peasant life. They indulged in luxury consumption and took on political and literary interests. Social critics during the last decades of the Tokugawa frequently complained that rich peasants indulged in literary pursuits that were quite unsuited to their status. They paid more attention to collecting books and taking lessons from samurai tutors than to tilling their lands. They purchased samurai titles, traveled about the country, and took part in politics. Being close to the villagers, many of the rich peasants promoted general education. Many of the village schools were built and financed by landowners and putting-out masters. A survey of Fukushima area, which had many prosperous silk spinners and weavers, shows that at the end of the Tokugawa period 37 percent of all its village schools (*terakoya*) were sponsored by rich farmers and another 15 percent by village headmen.[37]

Of the leading entrepreneurs in the early Meiji era who were sons of rich peasants, landlords, or putting-out masters, most had come into contact with Western ideas and had participated actively in political life while still on the village farm. Shibusawa Eiichi, the greatest of all Meiji entrepreneurs, was a prime example. He was interested in literary pursuits and wanted to become a samurai. His father was a rich farmer, merchant, and moneylender in the village. Shibusawa received a literary education as well as practical business experience. His deep antagonism to the feudal system became a decisive factor in his later career.[38] Hara Rokurō, another famous Meiji entrepreneur, had a similar background as the son of a rich peasant and putting-out master. His father owned a farm of 67 koku and operated a silk-reeling factory prior to the Restoration; the tenants delivered the cocoons to this mill where their wives and daughters did the reeling. The Hara family, hereditary village headmen, was known for its broadmindedness and progressiveness and its lavish treatment of guests.[39]

In sum, we find that all the requirements for becoming modern industrialists existed among the rural entrepreneurs before the Restoration. Those who combined agriculture, trade, brokerage, and manufacturing succeeded in accumulating relatively large capital resources. They had basic experience in putting-out manufacturing and at times even in factory management. They were progressive and vitally interested in political and social changes that would allow greater scope to their entrepreneurial interests. The question that arises immediately, then, is whether these landlords, rich peasants, and merchant-manufacturers constituted the chief element among Japan's modern entrepreneurs — that is, whether there was a straight line of continuity from village manufacturing to city industry.

In the following section I shall examine rural entrepreneurship after the Restoration, in pursuit of an answer to this question of continuity. At this point it may be stated that, on the whole and with some qualifications there was no such evolution. Three basic factors were responsible for the failure of rural manufacturing to move in a continuous direction toward modern industrial enterprise. The first is that the gap of technological backwardness was too great for the rural manufacturers to overcome. The second factor is that their very success in rural areas prevented them from making a break with the country, and migration to the cities became an almost necessary condition for successful entrepreneurship in modern industry after the Restoration. The final factor is the lack of government promotion of rural industries. Government coaching and subsidies were concentrated on a small elite in a narrowly defined sector; the rural manufacturers did not belong to this elite, and their own capital was not sufficient for successful large-scale ventures of the modern type. After a while they found it more profitable to turn from manufacturing and to go back more or less exclusively to farming. The extent to which these three arguments hold will become clear as we proceed.

THE RURAL MANUFACTURERS AFTER THE RESTORATION

The reader may have been somewhat annoyed at the casual treatment given here to the various rural entrepreneurial activities during the Tokugawa period. I have cheerfully lumped together merchants, pawnbrokers, landowners, rich peasants, Omi merchants, and putting-out masters. They differed widely in their activities, of course, but more often than not they were one and the same person. On the whole, a division of labor had not taken place. In the field of rural manufacturing, too, it is possible to give the same treatment to textiles as to oil extraction and sake brewing, to sugar refining as to paper production. All these products faced a uniform market, increased as demand did, and were neither threatened by imports nor promoted by export possibilities.

This uniform situation changed after the opening of the ports. Foreign trade became a major, if not the most important, determinant of the further development of rural industry. Some were threatened by imports and had to struggle for their existence; others received a strong boost through exports and grew by leaps and bounds; still others remained unaffected until internal competition from modern industry made itself felt in the late 1890s. Since foreign trade strongly influenced the course of Japanese rural manufacturing, let us examine separately the development of these three different groups of rural industries.

Silk Reeling

It is sometimes maintained that Japan owed her continued independence, her avoidance of reduction to colonial status, to the poverty of her natural resources. This may have been one reason, though probably not a very important one. But the lack of natural resources would certainly have become a severe handicap to industrialization if Japan's agriculture had not provided an exportable surplus for financing capital-good imports. Most underdeveloped countries of today export primary products in which they have a comparative advantage owing to climatic conditions and natural resources. Japan had neither of these advantages over the Western countries.

There were two commodities that offered great promise for trade: tea and silk. Both had a long tradition in Japan and had been highly developed through rural entrepreneurship. Tea and raw silk were the chief export items that went to pay for the bulk of Japanese imports in the first fifteen years of the Meiji, and even later they occupied commanding places in the export lists, along with rice, copper, coal, camphor, and silk cloth. The main export commodities are shown below (five-year averages, units in million yen).

Years	Raw silk	Tea	Rice	Total exports
1868–1872	8.38	3.82	0	15.44
1873–1877	9.42	5.76	0.78	21.32
1878–1882	11.40	6.64	1.44	29.62
1883–1887	15.40	6.82	1.92	42.36
1888–1892	26.44	6.62	5.30	70.36
1893–1897	39.98	7.74	6.38	120.52
1898–1902	58.18	9.02	6.70	216.30
1903–1907	72.50	12.14	4.04	311.56

Computed from *Dai Nihon gaikoku bōeki* (The foreign trade of great Japan), ed. Nōshōmushō shōmukyoku (The Ministry of Agriculture and Trade, Department of Trade; Tokyo, 1911), pp. 3, 7, 10.

The Japanese raw-silk export boom had actually started with the export of silkworm eggs. They were in high demand after the opening of the ports, because of a silkworm disease that had crippled French sericulture around 1860. The opening of the Suez Canal in 1869 also aided Japan, since the export trade in silkworm eggs catered to the European market. But a few years later the silkworm disease in Europe was eradicated, and the new breed imported from Japan had restocked the European supply. Silkworm-egg exports began to drop sharply after 1868. From 3.7 million yen in that year, their export value fell to 347,000 in 1877 and to almost nothing by 1887, with not quite 3,000 yen.[40]

Japanese exporters had to switch to raw silk and compete on the European market with quality yarns. This raised new problems in silk reeling. The traditional hand reeling that had been practiced under the putting-out masters produced rough and uneven yarns; mechanization of the reeling process was called for. The House of Ono was among the first to initiate factory reeling using imported machinery; three mechanical mills had been built by 1873.[41] Ono invested heavily in raw-silk production, especially in its Tsukiji reeling mill, which became the immediate reason for the house's bankruptcy in 1874.[42] The government itself established two model mills, one in 1874 (Kankōryō) and the other in 1875 (Tomioka). All of these pioneering mills were either Italian- or French-oriented in machinery, management, and scale. Each of these grand beginnings ended in failure because the Japanese were not used to large-scale operations of this kind. The successful mechanization of silk reeling was effected through another approach — imported machinery was used, but on a small scale and adapted to rural conditions.

The success stories in raw silk are to be found among

the rural capitalists, the sake brewers and merchants and landlords who had some experience in the employment of rural hands. Two of the first mechanical reeling mills were established in 1869 by two sake brewers in Fukushima prefecture (at that time still Shirakawa han); they were well aware of the silk-export opportunities and had sufficient capital from their trading and brewing to purchase machinery and build reeling factories.[43] The man who had the greatest success in silk reeling was Katakura Kentarō. He was a landowner with literary interests who kept in close touch with events in Tokyo. He started a silk-reeling establishment on his farm, and after the collapse of the House of Ono he bought part of its machinery, sold his farm, and became exclusively a silk spinner. By 1894 his mill had a larger output than the government-built Tomioka mill. This progressive entrepreneur sent his son to the United States to study modern reeling techniques, thus assuring the further progress of his mill.[44]

Mechanical reeling did not take the lead over hand reeling, however, until after 1895, and even then the scale of operation was usually small. It is interesting that the degree of mechanization was by no means uniform in all areas of raw-silk production. Nagano prefecture was the most mechanized, while Gumma prefecture remained largely at the hand-reeling level. A survey of 1879 showed Nagano to be far in the lead with 358 mechanized mills, each with at least 10 employees; Gifu prefecture had 143, Yamanashi 80, and Gumma only 11. But generally the operation was a small one; the capital of most mills remained under 300 yen, and the mills did not operate for more than half a year on the average in the agricultural slack periods.[45]

Essentially, then, raw-silk production retained the character of rural small-scale manufacturing, financed by the former putting-out masters and silk spinners. This was a straight line of continuity. The sudden leaps into large-scale operation attempted by the government and by the house of Ono were not crowned with success; the rural entrepreneurs preferred a slower step-by-step advance. The large, fully mechanized reeling mills did not come until the second decade of the twentieth century.

One of the important groups to jump on the bandwagon of the silk-yarn export boom was the samurai. Many of them had spun silk earlier, before they were deprived of their status. When the government started to encourage the establishment of businesses by samurai, many samurai companies took up silkworm rearing or silk reeling, in almost all cases by hand. Of the fifteen samurai companies that started in Nagasaki prefecture between 1881 and 1888, eight were in silkworm rearing or silk reeling.[46] In Akita a large company of fifteen hundred samurai families engaged in raw-silk production.[47] Silk reeling was practiced in almost all parts of the country, and a large contingent of these new producers were samurai.

In the first decade after the Restoration when mechanization was still in its infancy, Gumma had by far the largest output of all the prefectures. It had an old tradition of silk manufacturing and was close to the export center of Yokohama. The silk-export boom brought prosperity to the villages, and rich farmers, merchants, and other moneyed men took up silk reeling on a putting-out basis or in small factory-like establishments. A collection of two hundred biographical sketches of prominent men in the Gumma silk industry during the Meiji era provides interesting information on the methods used and the general trends displayed by these rural entrepreneurs.[48]

The Gumma farmers enlarged the mulberry-growing area, organized local unions for the promotion of sericulture, and had their own marketing boards, which maintained close contacts with Yokohama. The well-to-do employers frequently went to Yokohama, not only to arrange their export deals but to gather the latest information and purchase machinery to raise standards of quality. Some sent their sons abroad to study the silk industry. Local training schools were established to teach people better reeling techniques and to raise the general level of education. The skyrocketing price of raw silk (it quadrupled between 1859 and 1867) brought a general air of prosperity and progress to the villages of Gumma prefecture.

But one thing is noteworthy: with only a few exceptions, these successful men in silk production and export did not consider moving to the city. The village enterprise, after all, had brought them prosperity and was the basis of their success. It was a direct and rather simple continuation of what they had done before, with the addition of a few new machines. They were not completely bypassed by the modernizing influence coming from Yokohama and even more from Tokyo, but they did not encounter the full impact of Western technology. Raw-silk production, even where it became mechanized, remained halfway traditional; and because profits were assured even with relative inefficiency, these rural putting-out masters were not forced by economic necessity to become modern industrialists, at least not for a few more decades. Silk production did not provide the avenue toward Western large-scale industry, and we find almost no successful silk reelers among the great entrepreneurs of the Meiji era.

Cotton Spinning

One of the great worries of the Meiji government was the balance-of-payments problem. Government officials did everything possible to institute a new era of progress and tried to demonstrate the advantages of Western technology. But as a side effect of their efforts there developed an ever-rising demand for Western imports, notably cotton yarns and cotton cloth, which constituted as much as 30–40 percent of Japan's total imports in the first Meiji decade. Inevitably, this had an adverse effect on Japanese cotton growers and spinners. In some rural areas people began to riot and demonstrate against the cotton imports, and campaigns were launched against all Western goods that were competing against the established rural manufactures. It was claimed that these imports would ruin rural Japan and with it the whole national economy. Calico cloth, lamps, railways, even the solar calendar and Western-style haircuts, became targets of criticism.[49] The government was probably little impressed by the rural riots and protest meetings, but the balance-of-payments problem caused serious concern, and some effective measures were called for.

The government established two model spinning mills and bought machinery for ten mills which it sold at discount rates to prospective founders. In order to stimulate interest in mechanical cotton spinning among the cotton merchants and putting-out masters, the government launched a propaganda drive. A series of exhibitions on cotton spinning was staged, and on these and similar occasions the speakers hammered away at the point that many more mills must be established to save Japan from the menace of imported yarns. Defense against this threat was presented as being rather simple, as though the application of Western technology to spinning would assure success and high profits.

Those who ventured first into the founding of spinning mills, those of the so-called two-thousand-spindles era, were typically men who readily responded to the government's appeals and who were already imbued with a faith in modern technology. Among the twenty founders of mills prior to 1884 — the year that marked the transition to the second stage of large-scale, profitable mills — ten were samurai and ten were merchants or peasants. The samurai were mostly officials of one kind or another, to whom a concern with the "menace from imports" came naturally and who could rely on public funds or pressure moneyed men into contributing capital.

The mill founders who were either merchants or rich peasants, most of them connected with the cotton trade, showed traits and motivations surprisingly similar to those of the samurai-officials. They belonged to the progressively modern wing, had close connections with government officials, and were quite conscious of being among the avantgarde of their time. But the vast majority of cotton merchants and putting-out spinners were still cautious and did not invest in the new mills; they were too rational, in the profit-maximization sense. They realized apparently that, in spite of some monetary and a great deal of moral support from the government, these mills would not be able to compete effectively with the imported yarns. Indeed, until after 1885 the small-scale cotton mills were barely managing to survive; profit rates were on the average not higher than 3–4 percent, but some mills stayed in the red for years. So even the fervor of the enthusiasts was in danger of cooling down in the struggle for survival. Naturally, in the years of pioneering, it was the progressive, politically inspired idealists who dominated the field.

Kashima Manpei, the first cotton merchant to switch to mechanical spinning, is typical of the progressive pioneering group. He had urged the bakufu to introduce mechanical spinning as a solution to the high prices of cotton goods, and he then established, with capital contributions from a few of his fellow merchants and against formidable odds, the first private spinning mill in Japan, completed in 1872. Later Kashima insisted on having his spinning machines produced in Japan according to his own designs, in order to make Japanese cotton spinning "independent of imported machinery," although the machines made in Japan cost him much more than the imported ones.[50] The pioneers in cotton spinning, be they samurai or merchants, were all interested in innovations, and once they had ventured into the area of the untried, they fanned out over a broad range, promoting modern methods and technology. There was, for instance, Kurihara Nobuchika, the founder of Ishikawa Spinning Mill (established in 1882), the son of a broker and scholar. He had originally shown little interest in business but was a man of public affairs with a great esteem for the emperor. Once he started to innovate, he did not stick to one field. He promoted agriculture and trade in various ways and founded a bank, in addition to the spinning mill.[51]

Men of this kind were drawn into entrepreneurship partly through politics, through their close contacts with officials and with the new tide of events. If their start was politically inspired, this does not mean that they were entirely uninterested in maximizing their own profits. The point is that from the beginning they were far removed from the conservatism that still prevailed among the majority of the cotton capitalists of the Kinki area, the center of cotton growing and trade. It is said that the immediate reason for the founding of the Kuwahara Mill in 1882 was a strong appeal by Matsukata, who urged the building of spinning mills to provide competition against imports. A rural manufacturer and vegetable-oil producer, Kaneda Ichihei, responded by deciding there and then to build a mill with his capital.[52] The more hesitant men of the cotton trade and the rural putting-out masters stayed away from mechanical cotton spinning, by and large, until after the breakthrough achieved in this field by the Osaka Spinning Mill (1883). Shibusawa Eiichi had founded this large-scale mill after careful study of the technological problems involved; it had ample capital resources, the latest machinery, and an expert technician, none of which had been available to the other faltering mills. In 1884, the second year of its operation, the mill paid out an 18 percent dividend.

By this time the cotton merchants had come into severe economic straits. The imports of calicoes and yarns, as well as the competition from the mechanical mills, caused a serious depression in the trade: cotton growers and hand spinners found themselves hard hit and had to seek a new economic basis. With a profitable avenue of investment opened up by the breakthrough of the Osaka Mill and under ever-growing pressure for change, the conservative cotton merchants finally moved into mechanical spinning. They still had large capital resources to invest and needed neither government help nor political incentives.

Between 1886 and 1894, thirty-three new mills were founded, most of them large. Of these, ten were located in the vicinity of Osaka, the center of the cotton trade; by 1913 the Osaka area had nineteen spinning mills. Okayama came next, with nine.[53] The representative founders of this period were wealthy rural capitalists or merchants from Osaka. When five Omi merchants applied for permission to build the Kanakin Mill (1888), the government investigated their financial position in order to assure stability for the venture. It became apparent that one of them had assets totaling 9 million yen, three 500,000 yen apiece, and the last 100,000 yen.[54] Such men had kept back their capital until a sure investment project turned up. Pioneering in untried areas with new technology was not to their liking. As one of them, the founder of Kurashiki Mill (1886) put it, his theory was not to strive for the first place but to stay in the second or third, because that was more profitable.[55]

Among the mills founded in the late 1880s and the 1890s, some had too little capital and failed. The prolonged depression in cotton trade and spinning had impoverished many merchants and putting-out spinners, and founding a mill became their last hope. The Hirano Mill was a case in point. The eleven founders could muster just enough capital to buy the site and build a wall around it with their combined 25,000 yen. An Osaka financier rescued this venture with a large loan, so that the mill was completed and eventually became a success.[56]

Hand spinning was practically extinct by 1895. Hand-loom weaving, however, continued for some time longer, although here too the depression became severe. We find a few cases where spinning mills were established for the purpose of supplying cheaper yarns to local weavers and thus alleviating their plight. The Kurume Mill in northern Kyushu started this way. The Kurume area had been nationally famous for its rough cotton cloth. The weavers suffered because the imported yarns were not suitable for this cloth, and hand spinning had become disorganized. Some wealthy putting-out weavers and merchants established a mill in 1889 for spinning the required yarns.[57] The development of handloom weaving and its eventual decline need not be traced any further, but it is probably not wrong to assume that the phases of its changeover into factory weaving were similar to those of cotton spinning.

Silk reeling and cotton spinning were the first industries in Japan to achieve substantial success, but for different reasons and through different approaches. Silk reeling remained rural and small-scale, changed only in part by the introduction of some Western machinery. It was carried out chiefly by the rural capitalists by way of a continuous development from putting-out home employment. There was no revolution and no crisis, but a gradual innovational process. This type of development was aided by the export boom, and its basis continued to be inherited local skills. The initial capital requirements were not too large for the individual rural capitalists; there was no need for joint capital.

Cotton spinning emerged as a modern, efficient industry through the crisis of import competition. Ultimately it had the advantage of cheap labor, but in the short run the technological problems and the necessity for joint-stock enterprise, because of large capital requirements, made this type of investment unattractive to rural capitalists. The pioneering problems therefore had to be solved by men of a different kind, those who had political connections and a strong faith in technology. Such men were found chiefly among samurai administrators and a small group of putting-out masters and merchants who had come far in absorbing Western influence and the new Meiji outlook.

Traditional Rural Industries

Despite the large imports of foreign cloth, Japanese daily life and general consumption patterns were little touched by the Western craze. The effect of innovations like haircuts, beef eating, umbrellas, and many of the other signs of "civilization" of the day was marginal and largely confined to the cities. Japanese home life went on as it had for centuries. People built their houses as they had before, of wood with almost no furniture and no heating except for the traditional hibachi or the kotatsu. They kept the getas as their footgear and kimonos as their favorite garments. Eating habits proved to be most resistant to change. Beef, milk, butter, and bread, not to speak of beer and whiskey, had to wait until the next big Western "boom," after 1945, to become popular. The dogged adherence to traditional living and consumption patterns became an economic blessing to Japan. It prevented unnecessary capital outflows and the erosion of the economy by the so-called demonstration effect, the great problem for present-day underdeveloped countries.

Foremost among the traditional manufactured products that were not affected by foreign trade were sake, miso, and soy sauce. As general consumption levels began to rise, these foodstuffs enjoyed a period of prosperity. Sake, miso, and soy sauce were often manufactured by the same producers — merchants or rich peasants. They occupied the top position among all manufactured goods. According to a survey of all prefectures carried out in 1874, the value of the total sake production was 18.6 million yen; next in value came the weaving sector, with 17.1 million yen. All textiles combined, including raw silk, were worth 31 million yen, as against 30.1 million for sake, miso, and soy sauce alone.[58]

Since the three foodstuffs were articles of daily use (sake consumption had long since spread to the peasant level in spite of the bakufu's efforts to the contrary), their production was not concentrated in particular areas. Aichi prefecture led in sake and Gumma prefecture in miso production, though the degree of concentration in these areas was not too pronounced. In almost every village, one rich farmer had a brewery. Sake production had been restricted prior to the Restoration by a license system; when this system was abolished, new breweries sprang up everywhere. The number of Omi merchants from Hino area who operated breweries and produced soy sauce almost tripled between 1868 and 1906, the establishments going from 59 to about 150.[59]

The location of the sake breweries moved from the countryside over the next few decades, and the scale seems to have increased with rising demand. The sake brewers in the 1880s still typically combined trading, land-ownership, and moneylending. Specialization in large-scale sake brewing and miso and soy-sauce production in modern factories came gradually. By 1895 more than half of 137 surveyed sake breweries and miso and soy-sauce factories were located in cities; only 60 were rural establishments. Of the 137, 44 had over 10,000 yen and 60 over 20,000 yen of invested capital.[60] The gradual movement of the brewery industry toward the cities marked the beginning of the final stage of traditional rural manufacturing. The landowners, merchants, and putting-out masters began to specialize; some finally became industrialists, but most of them returned to agriculture and became landlords.

Vegetable-oil production had been another of the more important rural industries of the Tokugawa period. It did not remain entirely unaffected by imports. The introduction of petroleum lamps was a serious blow to vegetable-oil producers, who had been the principal suppliers of oil for the old-fashioned lamps. Prices of vegetable-oil declined and so did oil production. This process of decline, however, was slowed down by two new factors: the introduction of the hydraulic press, which greatly increased efficiency in extracting oil, and the use of vegetable oil as a machine lubricant. Since the new demand came mainly from the industries in the cities, oil production, whatever remained of it, also began to move there.[61]

Sugar production which had played a large role in the economic recovery of Satsuma, and had been produced in three varieties as black, red, and white sugar, suffered a similar decline. Sugar-cane growing, which had been concentrated in Kagoshima prefecture and also in parts of Shikoku and Shizuoka, vanished with the coming of imported refined sugar.

Import and export conditions, and the patterns of Japanese consumption, were not the sole determinants of the course followed by rural manufacturing after the Restoration. Another, and highly important, factor was the changing situation in agriculture itself. After the Restoration it became very profitable to go back to primary-food production.

The Landlords' Return to Agriculture

The return to primary-food production by those putting-out masters who had not become cotton spinners or raw-silk producers was induced by two factors: the steep rise of primary food prices and the land-tax reform. Both together greatly encouraged the abandonment of traditional industries that had once been very profitable but were now increasingly difficult to manage.

The prices of staple foods soared in the post-Restoration years and were highest of all for basic foodstuffs, according to the Tokyo commodity-price index. The group of five commodities consisting of rice, barley, wheat, soybeans, and red beans moved from its base 100 in 1873 to 172 in 1893, with a peak of 192 reached in 1890. The next highest group, consisting of salt, soy sauce, miso, and fuel, moved during the same period from 100 to 154. On the other hand, lumber, coal, raw and refined copper, and iron declined from 100 to 85.[62] It is evident, then, that the production of rice and other grains became more attractive than the once lucrative production of miso and soy sauce.

As an inducement to a return to exclusive primary-food production, the land-tax reform of 1873 was even more important than the favorable price movements of agri-cultural products. This most important reform has been discussed frequently in Western literature and will be presented here only in bare outline form.

The three most important features of the land-tax law of 1873 were: (1) The tax was to be determined by the market value of the land, not by its yield, as had been the rule during the feudal era. In 1873 the tax level was set at 3 percent of the market value; this was lowered to 2.5 percent in 1877. (2) All taxes were to be paid to the central government, and in money, not in kind. (3) The owners and not the cultivators were taxed. The sale of land had already become legal in 1872. But this did not really constitute a practical change because the prohibition against land sale had long since lost its effectiveness.

In effect, about 30 percent of the gross agricultural produce was taxed away under the new land tax. This was no real change from the prior feudal rates. The nominal rates of the feudal tax (50 percent or even 60 percent) had been lowered in the course of the Tokugawa period through increases in productivity with which the upward revisions of the yield surveys had not caught up. Further-more, the feudal tax had been substantially lower on reclaimed land. The initial 30 percent tax rate very soon became lighter because of the revision of the assessment from 3 percent to 2.5 percent of the market value of the land; but even more important, the inflationary price spiral reduced the real burden to as low a rate as 15.5 per-cent of the yield by 1888–1892. Nevertheless, agriculture had to bear the main tax load; the rest of the economy — that is, the secondary and teriary sectors — had tax rates on the average of only about 2.3 percent.[63]

In addition, in the wake of the land-tax reform, about half of all forests and wasteland became state property.[64]

This was a heavy blow to many marginal farmers who had supplied themselves with fertilizer and firewood from the common forests and wastelands.

Although the land-tax reform lowered the actual tax burden in comparison with the feudal rates, it must still be called high in absolute terms. If approximately 20 percent of the gross produce of agriculture could immediately become government revenue, this throws light on the solution sought by the Meiji government to its central problem of capital formation. The primary solution lay not in heavier burdens on agriculture and not in raising additional sources of income, but in channeling the samurai into productive processes. The savings of agriculture which had previously been consumed by that class were now made available for industrialization. Indeed, thus conceived, the cost of industrialization in a sense fell most heavily upon the abolished feudal class.

The government succeeded in financing its armament and industrialization program almost completely from land-tax revenues. Except for two major debt issues — the commutation bonds of 1876, with 173.9 million yen, and the adjustment debt to liquidate inflation and the inconvertible notes in 1886, with 175 million yen — no major borrowings were necessary, either internally or externally. The land tax provided 85.6 percent of all government revenues in 1888–1892, although in this same period agriculture produced only 50 percent of the national income. Business taxes furnished a bare 1.6 percent, income tax gave 2.4 percent, and 10.4 percent was provided by customs duties.[65]

In spite of the fact that agriculture financed industrialization, a considerable surplus over and above the tax was still left to the cultivator, if he happened to own his land. The sustenance of the cultivator and his family required about 40 percent of the yield; if we add approximately 20 percent or even less for the tax, a surplus of 40 percent remained. The landowners and rural capitalists saw in this exploitable surplus their great opportunity. Around 1887 the rents charged the tenants averaged, for the whole country, 58 percent of the yield for paddy land and 56 percent for dry lands.[66] The difference between the 58 percent or 56 percent and the land tax was the profit rate for the landowner.

The stimulus toward landownership is quite clear from these figures. The question that remains is why peasant proprietors lost land if the conditions for owners were so favorable. The answer is doubtless complicated, but one reason is certainly the erratic price movements of agricultural commodities and the fluctuations in the income level of the farmers. The price of rice fluctuated in wide arcs; for example, it rose from 5.82 yen per koku in 1878 to 10.07 yen in 1880 and fell again to 4.62 yen in 1883.[67] And it was not only the price of rice that was affected — one can argue that low rice prices were caused by bumper crops and that sales volume at least partly compensated for declining prices. Total agricultural income followed the same jerky movement: the gross value of agricultural produce rose from 254 million yen in 1878 to 534 million in 1880 and fell to 253 million in 1884.[68] These examples should suffice to show that, despite favorable average conditions for proprietor-peasants, the unwary and marginal ones could easily be thrown into debt and lose their land. It is easy to get used to higher levels of living in a series of two or three good years and then resort to borrowing in a year of sudden income loss. Those who did not have sufficient capital reserves, the marginal owner-farmers, were always in danger of being reduced to tenancy.

For the whole country, the percentage of tenant land continued to rise after the Restoration: from 31.1 percent in 1873, it rose to 36.8 percent in 1883, 40 percent in 1893, and 44.5 percent in 1903.[69] Landholdings were largest in the northern sections of Japan, notably the Niigata and Akita areas, which were the chief rice-producing regions. In the Kinki area the merchant-landlords succeeded at times in reducing almost entire villages to tenant status.

The village of Kuga near Kyoto illustrates this general trend. The percentage of large holdings increased steadily at the expense of the middle-sized farms, while the percentage of small farms stayed about the same. This indicates, of course, a sliding down the scale from middle-sized to small, and the exodus of the small farmers into tenancy. The number of landowners with over ten cho of land more than tripled, rising from 0.9 percent to 2.9 percent between 1875 and 1905, while the medium farmers of one to two cho declined from 14.1 percent to 7.8 percent in the same period.[70] A rich vegetable-oil producer and merchant in this village lent money at 10 percent interest to other growers, and demanded in addition that they sell their vegetables to him at 10 percent below the market price.[71] In this fashion, rural moneylenders and manufacturer-merchants used the economic weakness of small farmers to reduce them to tenant position. In the same village the rural capitalists had succeeded by 1893 in enlarging their landholdings to 82 percent of all village land.[72]

The movement of rural manufacturers and merchants into landlordism has elicited much criticism and comment from Japanese economic historians. Depending upon the writer's particular school of thought, both praise and blame are accorded these "parasitic" landlords.[73] My concern is not whether these landlords were good or bad, whether they were bourgeois or feudal. The important fact here is that the new landlordism constituted the terminus of

Tokugawa rural entrepreneurship, insofar as it had not moved into modern industry via raw silk or cotton spinning.

But the contribution of the new Meiji landlords to the astonishing increases in agricultural output throughout the Meiji era was by no means insignificant. These men occupied something like a middle position between the Prussian Junkers, who managed their own demesnes, employing land laborers, and the Western European absentee landlords, who left farming entirely to their tenants. In Japan rents were fixed neither by long tradition nor by law; therefore the landlord could raise rents if he succeeded in increasing the productivity of the land. Because the landlords did this, they contributed to agricultural progress. They tried out new seeds and techniques, regulated rivers and constructed dams to prevent natural calamities, in order to assure stable rent payments.[74] The use of fertilizer rose steeply owing to their initiative. Fertilizer use rose from its base 100 in the 1878–1882 period to 171 in 1888–1892 and eventually to a staggering 3,997 in 1913–1917.[75] During the same periods, the production of rice rose from 100 to 130 and then 185.[76]

All this time, however, Japanese agriculture remained labor-intensive and small-scale. Industry did not grow fast enough to absorb a large percentage of the rural population. Initially the jobless samurai were the main constituent of the industrial labor force; then population soon began to grow and to add to the labor supply. But owing to the steep rise of agricultural prices and the slowness with which the rural population migrated to the cities, land rents stayed high and provided a constant inducement to invest in further improvements. The rural labor force remained at approximately 15.5 million until the 1890s, when it began to decline gently.[77] The real income in agriculture continued to rise, although much more slowly than in industry.

The avoidance of a mass exodus from the villages into the cities was a characteristic of Japan's economic development. The landlords did not resort to extensive capital-using agriculture, but improved rice planting to yield higher productivity. Certainly this was important, since it made Japan a pioneer in high-grade rice cultivation, enabling the nation to achieve productivities several times greater than those of other Asian rice-growing areas. Today in some Southeast Asian countries, with their dense rural populations and still primitive rice-growing techniques, a more intensive agricultural effort may also be necessary and prove to be most advantageous, along with gradual industrialization.[78]

IV

THE INITIATIVE
FROM THE CENTER

The economic development and industrialization of Meiji Japan was a complex process resulting from the interaction of diverse forces, political, social, and economic; to dwell exclusively on economic variables invites serious misrepresentation of the entire process. A similar caution is necessary when we deal with the government and the private sector of the economy, for they were closely connected. Consequently, although my primary concern is with the emergence of entrepreneurs, and hence with the private sector, the paramount role of the government's initiative in the formation of a new entrepreneurial elite must be given due attention.

The word "government" will be used here in a broad sense. This is why I prefer to speak of the initiative from the center rather than of the role of government investments. Government investments were important, but not so much as one may be tempted to think. Probably a more far-reaching effect upon the whole course of Japan's modern industrialization came from the successful establishment and fostering of a new way of thinking. Initially the crucial task of the Meiji officials was to inculcate an unbending will to progress, to rouse the nation out of its long sleep and rally it behind the great program of advance. In a sense the Meiji government became for the people a symbol of what has been called the "post-Newtonian mentality." In communicating this newborn faith in modern technology and industrialization first to an entrepreneurial elite and then to the whole population, the Meiji officials performed brilliantly.

Alexander Gerschenkron stresses two important conditions that stimulate economic development in backward, tradition-bound countries.[1] One is the growth of internal tensions and dissatisfactions; some group or groups in the society come under economic pressure or rise economically while not receiving corresponding social recognition. If then the roadblocks that stood in the way of change are removed by external or internal events, a snowball reaction may set in and lead eventually to dynamic economic growth. My first three chapters have sufficiently indicated the rise of internal tensions in Tokugawa society, resulting from the economic plight of the samurai and the accumulation of wealth in the hands of city merchants and rural capitalists. The underlying discontents could not be mobilized as creative forces for change so long as the bakufu retained its iron grip on the country. When, after the opening of the ports, the bakufu rule started to show signs of weakness, general unrest and uprisings followed. Undoubtedly this gradual growth of tensions and discontent contributed much to the ease with which the Meiji government was able to initiate its new course.

But Gerschenkron mentions a second condition that is fundamental to the speed with which industrialization will take place. This is the amount of technological experience that the backward country can borrow from the advanced countries. The sudden realization of the vast gap of backwardness that separates the underdeveloped country from the industrialized nations can produce a psychological shock, as well as opportunities for cutting corners and for skipping intermediate stages. This shock can awaken a sluggish people to feverish activity and a firm determination to catch up as quickly as possible.

Like the castle community in the Sleeping Beauty tale, Japan not only awoke, but it came suddenly to realize how much the world had changed during its long sleep. This experience stunned the best men of the nation and propelled them to move at top speed in order to close the gap. Of course, there is always the possibility of a passive reaction, of adopting the bonanzas of modern industry by importing consumer goods from the West. In this fashion the contact with the West would have eroded the Japanese economy: the rich would have benefited, and the country as a whole would have remained backward and weak, subject to the exploitation of foreign interests.

It was at this crucial junction that the Meiji government demonstrated its strength and leadership. It made the best of the shock effect by harnessing all of the national virtues toward the great single goal of accepting the challenge and overtaking the most advanced Western countries. Natural ambition and national fervor, feudal virtues, and religion were appealed to and guided through conscious policies toward this one goal. Clearly, the establishment of a mentality of progress, and of a determination to compete rather than to accept passively, is of the greatest significance in the course of Japan's economic development. Therefore, despite the elusive character of this process, it will be discussed briefly in the following section. I shall then turn to the other problems associated with government initiative: the transfer of modern technology and government investments.

THE BUMMEI KAIKA

The rather sudden about-face of Japanese patriots, from deadly hostility toward the barbarians from the West to boundless admiration and acceptance of almost everything and anything Western, may seem like a total capitulation of the "Chrysanthemum and the Sword" before the steam engine and the cannon. But Japan exchanged the sword for guns and steam engines in order to preserve her most important treasure, the Chrysanthemum, that is, her national identity and self-respect. The shock of the realization of their national weakness did not make the Japanese subservient to the West but, in judo fashion, made them turn the best of that foreign strength to their own advantage.

At the very outset of the Meiji era, the emperor proclaimed a new era of "seeking knowledge from the whole world." Now was to come a glorious time of progress and civilization. *Bummei kaika* (civilization and enlightenment) became a catchword of the early years after the Restoration. In it was reflected not only an admiration of Western civilization, but the proud determination of the island nation to become equal to the West in every respect. The story of the drastic change from "hate the barbarians" to the *bummei kaika* mentality has often been told.[2] I shall concentrate here mainly on two aspects of that story. First we shall see that this apparently sudden shift in attitudes was not a freak of Japanese psychology but had its roots in a long development, and, second, we shall look at the economic consequences of the *bummei kaika* ideology.

When for the first time the West met the East on Japanese soil in the sixteenth century, the result was mutual admiration. The Japanese were awed by Western ships and culture and science, and the missionaries and merchants from the West became captivated by the natural grace and nobility of the people and their customs.[3] The course of Japanese history might have been very different if that early romance between the West and Japan had been given time to mature, and if Japan had adopted Western culture and Christianity as she had earlier accepted the Chinese influence.

For reasons that will not be elaborated upon here, this early romance deteriorated, step by step, until the country was closed completely to the West. First the European ships were limited to Hirado and Nagasaki in 1616; in 1641 all Western ships were banned except those of the Dutch. The latter were permitted to keep a trading post on Dejima, a tiny island connected with Nagasaki by a bridge. In one of the bloodiest persecutions history has known, Christianity was almost completely eradicated.[4] Information about the West was severely limited, but it did trickle into Japan through Dutch books, which were eagerly studied by the so-called Dutch scholars (*rangakusha*). All books that so much as mentioned the "wicked religion" were banned by the bakufu which made heroic efforts to build a self-contained, stable, and contented country. Any potential source of dissatisfaction and any wish for change were to be killed in the bud. Dutch learning was controlled; during most of the seventeenth and eighteenth centuries it remained limited to such practical matters as medicine and astronomy and was engaged in by the interpreters for the Dutch in Nagasaki and other lower samurai and commoners.

Dutch learning came to assume much greater importance in the field of science, and it was chiefly for this that the bakufu came to promote it by the beginning of the nineteenth century. The bakufu established a translation bureau in 1811, and in 1856 it opened a full-fledged school of Western learning, the Bansho shirabesho (place to study barbarian books), in Edo.[5] The bakufu's lead was followed by a number of daimyo, notably Mito but also Saga, Satsuma, Tosa, and a few others. During the first half of the nineteenth century, Dutch learning became increasingly a subject of political controversy. After Britain's victory over China in the Opium War, the Japanese wakened to the fact of Western military superiority and its potential threat to national independence. The bakufu and the han administrators fully aware of the inadequate state of the national defenses, established schools for military science and experimented with Western weapons.

Who were the scholars that carried on Dutch or, as it was later called, Western learning? They were more often than not Confucian philosophers with rigid ideas about the function of the state and the position of the individual in society, and with an unbounded belief in the superiority of Japan over the West. Western studies did not shake this basic belief but instead gave it a strongly patriotic force. No matter what their conclusions and policy recommendations were, these men thought in national rather than in individual and private terms. Even scholars like Fukuzawa Yukichi, who managed to stay out of political controversies and concentrated on the philosophical and scientific, rather than the military and political, aspects of Western studies, thought that national greatness, prosperity, and independence must be the ultimate end of Western studies.

It has been stressed that, although the Weltanschauungs underlying Confucianism and Western science are very different, Japanese scholars managed a synthesis of their own. Western learning was limited to practical aspects, while ethics and social philosophy remained thoroughly

Confucian and thus feudal. If anything, the acquaintance with Western technological superiority tended to bolster national pride in Japanese ethical superiority; all that Western learning could contribute was the means and weapons with which to keep the Western barbarians from the sacred soil of the nation of the gods.

But while Western learning thus fanned the fires of patriotism, it also caused clashes of opinion with respect to means. How far was Japan to go in using Western methods? The bakufu, with its insistence on the status quo, became extremely nervous whenever some scholar advocated social or economic change according to Western models. It then clamped down relentlessly on such "traitors." [6] On the other hand, when the bakufu was forced to open Japan to foreign trade, these scholar-patriots wrote and spoke against the bakufu and called its officials traitors. Yoshida Shōin was the outstanding example of this type of patriot; he became a leader of the *sonnō jōi* movement (revere the emperor, expel the barbarians) which at once fought against the bakufu because it had admitted foreigners to Japan and vowed to expel the Western powers from Japan. His great teacher, Sakuma Shōzan, had been much more judicious and moderate. [7] But Yoshida was a revolutionary, an indication that philosophers were tending increasingly to become embroiled in politics and that the study of Western science would become a vehicle for revolutionary tensions. Yoshida tried to smuggle himself onto Commodore Perry's flagship to be taken to America, but all the time he was full of hatred for foreigners and urged the samurai to study Western military science in order to drive out the barbarians. [8] Through his celebrated writings and the teaching at his private school in Choshu han, Yoshida exerted a great influence on the men who were to form the Meiji leadership. Among the most famous of his disciples were Itō Hirobumi,[9] Yamagata Aritomo,[10] Shinagawa Yajirō,[11] and the previously mentioned Inoue Kaoru.

The *sonnō jōi* movement was, of course, nothing but the Restoration movement. But while the slogan remained, many of its leaders changed their minds abruptly with respect to the *jōi*. A single experience was sometimes sufficient to convince them once and for all that Japan lacked the means to expel the Western powers —something the bakufu had realized before — and that it was not in her interest to do so. By the time the Restoration was achieved and the bakufu replaced by the *sonnō jōi* leaders, the *jōi* had changed beyond recognition. One of the first measures of the new Meiji government was to throw the country wide open to Western influence. Yet the basic goal remained constant in spite of the sharp change: Japan had to come onto an even keel with the Western powers, had to gain respectability, *and thus* would she retain her independence and integrity and demonstrate her ethical superiority. This theme recurs frequently in the speeches and writings of the Meiji period and was publicized time and again by the leading entrepreneurs as the ultimate rationale for their private empire building.

In order to achieve this new type of *jōi* — that is, the equality of Japan with the West — the *sonnō* became a primary force. The emperor moved from his centuries-long obscurity in Kyoto into the seat of attention and actual power; he came to Edo, which was renamed Tokyo ("eastern capital"). The nation itself became rejuvenated with the young emperor, and it looked with religious faith to the throne for guidance in a time of apparent contradiction and hectic change. From the imperial throne came the word, clear and strong, dispelling any doubt about the new direction. In the Charter Oath of the Five Articles, the emperor proclaimed in April 1868: "All absurd usages shall be abandoned; justice and righteousness shall regulate all actions. Knowledge shall be sought for all over the world and thus be [sic] strengthened the foundation of the Imperial Polity. In this way Japan break [sic] the shell of national isolation and tread the road of national reopening." [12]

The importance of the emperor as the symbol of national unity and purpose in the Meiji period cannot be overstated. The original Japanese Shinto faith, in which the emperor occupies the central place, was restored as the national religion in 1868, separated from its long amalgamation with Buddhism. The measure was followed by a wave of violence and vandalism against Buddhist monks and temples.[13] Although the establishment of Shintoism as a state religion met with only qualified success, the people as a whole, and government officials, became imbued with a strong faith in the descendant of the Sun Goddess, and they responded to his call with unquestioning loyalty. At times the very name of the emperor would break down resistance to the industrialization and modernization efforts. This is well illustrated by an episode connected with the building of the railways. Ōkuma Shigenobu [14] and his planning group were strongly opposed by conservatives who could not be swayed by rational arguments in favor of the building program. At this point Ōki Tamihira, the governor of Tokyo and later Minister of Railways, played his trump card by saying that the emperor would henceforth have to make occasional trips to Kyoto. Who would dare impose upon him the hardships of traditional travel if railways could make possible speedy and comfortable transportation? This argument is said to have silenced the opponents.[15]

From the very beginning the *bummei kaika* was associated with the purpose of national greatness and had its strongest symbol in the imperial throne. This strategic combination of the most progressive ideology and the oldest national faith and self-respect not only preserved the Chrysanthemum at a time when the Sword had become outdated, but it frustrated the dissatisfied conservatives and prevented them from effectively splitting the country into two opposing factions. The people as a whole were willing to follow into the new era of progress.

Meiji officials and the men close to them expended great efforts to popularize the new era.[16] In 1873 a group of intellectuals founded an association, the Meirokusha (sixth-year-of-Meiji association) with the purpose of studying and propagating Western civilization. Most of the prominent members of the Meirokusha were members of the government or were closely associated with them.[17] The publications of the association were on such topics as modern education, business methods, democracy, equality of classes, and modern dress. Fukuzawa Yukichi, a prominent Meirokusha member, played a key role in the *bummei kaika* efforts through his prolific writings on Western conditions. These concerted efforts to establish progressive thinking among the mass of the people ranged from learned treatises and public discussions, to magnificent Western-style mansions for government officials, all the way down to songs for children. In 1878 a play song was composed for children which made them "count the bounces of the ball reciting the names of ten objects deemed to be most worthy of adoption — namely, gas lamps, steam engines, horse carriages, cameras, telegrams, lightning conductors, newspapers, schools, letterpost, steam boats."[18]

As much as the Meiji officials were preoccupied with economic and military problems, they were certainly not completely convinced that the building of an "infrastructure" by direct investments would suffice to set the process of modernization in motion. They apparently felt that economic development depended as much on cultural and ideological as on material premises, and that capital supply and investment programs could by themselves achieve little unless the changes were accepted and a dynamic will for development was born out of them. One might think that the government ought to have had worries larger than the popularizing of Western haircuts and dress, but it seems to have understood well the value of symbols, and these seemingly little things did serve as effective symbols of the new era.

It would appear that even measures of vast economic consequence were governed by cultural and ideological considerations. A case in point was the drive against infanticide, which had become such a deep-rooted habit during the Tokugawa period. Official pamphlets and decrees, it is said, stressed primarily the immorality of infanticide and its contradiction to the *bummei kaika*. Infanticide would put Japan to shame in the eyes of the world. Severe punishments were decreed for abortions; investigation offices were established; midwives and pregnant women were registered; societies were established to rear foundlings; and monetary rewards were given for births and for raising a third and fourth child.[19] At the time of the Meiji Restoration, the officials had no need to worry about a short labor supply. On the contrary, the government's biggest problem was how to employ the many jobless samurai; Malthusian thinking ought, on purely economic grounds, to have suggested rather a further encouragement of infanticide. But the government sensed that economic development depended a good deal upon the healthy vitality of the population rather than on the limitation of numbers that is born of a defeatist distrust in the future.

Among the variety of measures adopted to break down

traditionalism and to establish new and vigorous attitudes as a basis for development, two need special mention. One was the travel program and the other the introduction of compulsory education.

If merely reading about conditions in the West had been able to inspire many Japanese scholars and patriots, travel to a Western country would certainly be a complete eye-opener in revealing the gap of backwardness that separated Japan from the advanced countries. The traveler would then return to Japan as a champion of all-out modernization. Government officials who had seen the functioning of modern industry at first hand wanted others to share the same experience, and so they promoted foreign travel. Godai Tomoatsu of Satsuma han had sailed to England prior to the Restoration, and he had been so much impressed that he urged his daimyo to send others to Europe. Of those Satsuma samurai who were sent later, some became important government officials.[20] Itō Hirobumi and Inoue Kaoru of Choshu han had completely changed their political outlook during their stay in England and, after their return, fought the violent antiforeignism in Choshu at the risk of their lives.[21]

Itō considered foreign travel so important that in 1870 he originated a broad travel program. Generous subsidies were provided for studying in foreign countries and were granted to commoners as well as samurai.[22] Japanese students by the score sailed to the West in subsequent years and swarmed through European and American universities and factories. By 1872 the number of Japanese students abroad had reached 380.[23] Government officials also made frequent visits to the West. In 1871 almost the entire Meiji government sailed abroad under the leadership of Iwakura Tomomi, covering all of the important European countries as well as the United States. Their explicit purpose was to study "the laws and regulations concerning fiscal matters, taxation, public debt, paper money, public and private stock exchanges; also the establishment of insurance companies for fire, maritime disaster, and theft; furthermore the types of companies in trade and manufacturing, companies for steam engines, electric cables, and postal service. They ought further to study the establishment of gold and silver mints, various kinds of factories, and finally the laws and regulations covering those factories, and the real and apparent overall conditions. The objective of all this is to see how all these things can be applied and implemented in our own country." [24]

While government officials and students constituted the majority of the pilgrims to the West, progressive businessmen also joined in. The head clerk of Mitsui, who was close to the government, sent five of the Mitsui sons to study in the United States as early as 1872.[25] Sons of successful silk reelers and cotton spinners also crossed the ocean in order to learn. Some of the most influential entrepreneurs, like Shibusawa, Hara, and Ōkura, were decisively influenced in the conduct of their careers while in the West. The most efficient way to cure an obstinate conservative was to send him to the West. Kuroda Kiyotaka, the president of the House of Councilors, had been a leading opponent of Ōkuma's railway program. He denounced Ōkuma as an enemy of the state who would end by selling out his country to the foreigners. After his return from a journey to the West, he apologized publicly to Ōkuma and asked to be permitted to serve him loyally in the important task of building the nation's railway system.[26]

In spite of the heavy stress put on firsthand experience by travel abroad, most people could be influenced only by education in schools. The Meiji government moved quickly to establish a system of general compulsory education in 1872. The Japanese people at that time could by no means be called illiterate. Not only the samurai and most of the merchants, but even large segments of the peasantry were receiving some schooling. Some elementary instruction in han schools and *terakoya* (temple schools) and other private schools may have been given to as much as 30 to 40 percent of the young people. For most it did not go far beyond the fundamentals of reading, writing, and arithmetic; but many others received some instruction in Confucian ethics. The decisive turn in the Meiji education program was the reorientation of the goals of learning. Compulsory education was not only to assure that people learned how to read, write, and count; education was to be a chief instrument in spreading the *bummei kaika* ideology.

The Ministry of Education had the textbooks compiled exclusively after Western models; they were based largely on the teaching experiences of Fukuzawa Yukichi, who had been teaching Western subjects according to modern methods since 1864. Progress in implementing compulsory education was comparatively rapid. At the start, in 1873, a bare 4.24 percent of the eligible children attended. The others either continued to attend the *terakoya* or were left out for other reasons, such as lack of teachers and schoolrooms. By 1891 half of all eligible children were already receiving an elementary education, and in 1906 the figure was 95 percent.[27]

These few remarks on the progress of general education may suffice to indicate the determination of the government to spread a new outlook among the people. Next I shall turn to the more specific problem of technical education and the transfer of Western technology to Japan. This task could not be accomplished by the government alone, but required a combination of government and private initiative. Yet even here the impetus came very much from the center.

THE TRANSFER OF TECHNOLOGY

The Government's Efforts

The Industrial Revolution in England spanned a long period during which one step could be taken at a time. A gradual rise in the level of technical knowledge and experience prepared the way for the next step forward. It is true, of course, that inventions and innovations came in rapid succession at the end of the eighteenth century: the great breakthroughs by Crompton and Arkwright in cotton spinning and by Cartwright in weaving, Watt's fundamental improvement of the steam engine, and Wedgewood's innovations in pottery all came within twenty years. But the men responsible for these inventions, as well as those who put them to industrial use, could build upon knowledge and experience gained in previous stages of technology. It was therefore possible for inventors and innovators with little book learning to be wizards in practical matters. The general level of technical understanding was also high in other European countries and the United States. Moreover, the transfer of technology from England to the rest of the West was greatly eased through the bond of a common civilization and the relative unimportance of language barriers.

For Japan things were different. She had to absorb a technology coming from a completely alien culture; it had to be transmitted in Western languages that of themselves posed a formidable barrier; finally, it came at a very advanced stage to an unprepared people. The Japanese governmental officials who were so much awed by the marvels of European and American factories were not expert technicians. But they realized that there were few others in Japan who knew more than they. They understood, then, that their ambitious program of industrialization hinged decisively on effective technical training and on the formation of a native elite of technicians and scientists.

Foreign technology had not, of course, been completely unknown even in Tokugawa Japan. A considerable number of samurai had studied technical treatises and had made experiments in physics and chemistry in the 1840s and 1850s. They were even able to construct weapons and furnaces by following carefully the descriptions found in Dutch or English books. The building of Japan's first reverberatory furnace is a case in point. The daimyo of Saga han decided to have a furnace built to make cannons and put seven "experts" in charge of the project. A student of Dutch was to translate passages from Dutch books pertaining to reverberatory furnaces; another student of Western science was to give advice on the overall plan; a mathematician was to draw up the blueprint; and the other four experts, in metallurgy, gunnery, sword making, and administration, were given charge of the construction work itself.[28] These "seven wise men of Saga han," as they were called by the people, eventually succeeded, after repeated failures and immense difficulties.

The bakufu in its last years followed a more rational course by employing foreign experts; and the Meiji government did everything possible to enlist the help of Western technicians and teachers. It did not intend to rely on book knowledge alone or to waste time and resources on experiments of the Saga type. In almost all major government projects, foreign experts were given the double task of technical supervision and on-the-spot training of Japanese engineers. The Ministry of Industry, which was established in 1870 and was one of the most important branches of the Meiji government, sponsored this technical program. Between 1870 and 1885 the ministry employed over 500 foreign engineers and technical instructors; of these 393 were British, 71 French, 19 German, and 9 American.[29] This indicates, incidentally, Japan's heavy reliance on British industry in the early phase. Railway building received the largest contingent of foreigners (256), followed by machine shops with 81 and mining with 78.[30] The total expenditure for all foreign experts is not known; but the cost of 130 foreign technicians and instructors at the Technical University in Tokyo in the year 1879 was 341,000 yen, more than half of the ministry's 518,600-yen budget in that year.[31]

As important as foreign instructors and engineers were, their cost was felt to be disproportionately high. Their salaries, which were far above those of the highest-paid officials, hurt not only the government's finances but the feelings of the people.[32] The most important function of the foreigners, therefore, was to make themselves superfluous as quickly as possible. The government expended all efforts to build up native technical personnel and to promote technical education in order to dispense with direct foreign technical assistance. Technical education was introduced at the university and middle-school levels, and it covered a broad range of theoretical science and practical instruction in agriculture, trade, banking, and, above all, industrial technology.

Three agricultural schools were established by the government. The first was started in 1872 as an experimental station in Shinjuku. There foreign seeds were introduced and farming tools were modeled and manufactured. Another school was established in 1874 in Shiba, Tokyo, with an American, Horace, Capron, as instructor. He brought from America many sample seeds and tools and advised on new types of crops and on animal husbandry. From the whole of Japan students were called to this school, which was intended to pioneer the agricultural development of Hokkaido. In 1875 the school was transferred to Sapporo and became the forerunner of the University of Hokkaido. A third agricultural school was opened in 1876 in Kyoto.[33] Prior to 1880, thirty-four foreign experts on agriculture were employed by the government, and many Japanese were sent abroad to study.[34] The benefits of their studies and experiments were spread among the peasant population by information bulletins, seed-exchange societies, and discussion clubs in the villages. From 1874 on, in many rural districts farmers' organizations were set up for the purpose of disseminating technical information, better seeds, and improved cultivating methods. "Veteran farmers" traveled far and wide to teach other farmers. In Fukuoka prefecture, a private school of farming was established in 1883 which systematically sent its staff members and graduates on rural lecture tours.

Commercial and financial training also received the attention of the central government, because it had realized how inadequate the methods of the Osaka merchants were in dealing with foreign companies. In 1874 the Ministry of Finance established its own school with a four-year course in banking, finance, and bookkeeping. This school continued until 1893 and graduated six hundred students. In 1875 the Minister of Education, Mori Arinori, established a business school of the American type; in 1881 it had nine foreign instructors on its teaching staff. By 1883 Japan had seven commercial colleges, all but one of which were either private or prefectural.[35] Commercial training was promoted more by private entrepreneurs than by the central government, probably because the officials felt that trade was really not difficult to learn and that instruction in it could be left in private hands.

The training of engineers received top priority within the government's program of special education. Two technical schools at the university level were sponsored by the government. One of them, the Kōgakuryō, was established in 1871 with departments in civil engineering, machinery, construction, telegraphy, chemistry, finance, and mining. It had a six-year curriculum. In 1877 the name of the school was changed to Kōbu Daigakkō, and it eventually became the engineering department of the Imperial University. The other school was a continuation of the technical school (Kaiseikan) of the bakufu; it was established as an engineering school in 1873 with two departments, industry and mining, and a curriculum lasting six years.[36] The Ministry of Industry also had special training programs connected with certain of its offices, such as the telegraph office and the lighthouse office.

The top-level training of engineers was to be supplemented by a broad program of technical instruction on the secondary-school level. Middle schools specializing in foreign arts, industry, and mining were to be established, and each of these was to have foreign instructors. This ambitious training program did not materialize, however, because it was too far ahead of demand. The first middle school under the plan was started in Tokyo in 1874 with a four-year curriculum. Fifty-one students applied, and the staff included a German instructor. But in the following years applications dropped so low that the school had to be closed in 1877. A few other schools of the same type fared no better. The system was changed in favor of a practical apprentice training along narrowly defined technological lines. Such a school was the Tokyo *shokkō gakkō,* founded in 1881, in which engineering assistants and foremen were trained for jobs.[37]

In view of the high cost of foreign instructors and the strained finances of the Meiji government, these efforts to establish a system of technical education were certainly remarkable. We do not know the exact number of foreign instructors involved in this process of training Japanese engineers and middle-school students. There were quite a few private schools in which foreigners taught, and these are apparently not included in official government lists. The lists give the names of 151 foreign instructors employed by the government prior to 1900, but this does not include engineers, who often were also engaged in training and teaching on the spot. It is interesting that while British engineers outnumbered those of other nationalities, among the instructors in all fields, including mathematics, medicine, and the natural sciences, the Germans led with 60, followed by 39 Americans, 28 Britons, 20 Dutch, and 4 French.[38] And yet the educational system as a whole had been set up mainly on the French model.

In its effort to seek knowledge from the whole world, the government was the chief employer of foreign teachers, engineers, and other experts. Besides teaching, the foreigners served as technicians, particularly in railway building and other great government enterprises. The private enterprises were by far less well supplied with foreign experts, obviously because of the high salaries. Commercial shipping stands out as an exception in the private sector with many foreigners among the navigation officers. But in this field there was little choice, since few Japanese had any experience with modern ships and safety had to come first. Furthermore, commercial shipping was almost a complete monopoly of the Mitsubishi Company, which received enormous subsidies from the government and thus had the resources to pay handsome salaries to its foreign officers. In 1874 there were only 4 Japanese among 74 captains and navigation and technical officers. The Japanese learned fast, and by 1893 with a greatly increased fleet of ships there were 3,878 Japanese shipping officers and 722 foreigners.[39]

Entrepreneurs and the Problem of Technology

The government went to enormous pains to employ many foreigners in privileged positions, but there often seems to have been public resentment against foreign engineers. One complaint was that they received high salaries while apparently doing little work. Further, the presence of foreign experts was too strong a reminder of Japanese technical backwardness, and this reminder was hard to swallow at the time of the *bummei kaika* boom. Public antagonism toward the privileged foreign engineers was well illustrated in the construction of the Kyoto-Otsu railway line: Inoue Masaru, a British-trained engineer and chief of the railway-construction program, had by that time acquired sufficient experience to supervise the construction of the whole line except for necessary tunnels and bridges, for which foreigners were still employed.[40] This Japanese engineering achievement was given much publicity. The *Tokyo akebono shinbun* wrote on November 12, 1879, that the Kyoto-Otsu line had been advanced 78 miles in one year without foreign help and at only half the usual cost, although its course ran through mountains and rivers. No problem should henceforth be beyond the capabilities of Japanese engineers. The foreigners only wasted time and money because of their language problems and their inexperience with Japanese conditions. It ought to be possible from now on to dispense entirely with their services.[41]

Opinions may differ as to just when and to what extent

the Japanese should have sought to eliminate all direct foreign services. A certain amount of blundering by new and inexperienced native engineers, and the cost of malfunctionings and breakdowns, had to be weighed against the advantages of low salaries and the acquisition of early independence and self-assurance. But in those sectors of private industry where the government had shown less interest than in railway building and shipping, the attempt at independence from foreign help undoubtedly came too early. In many cases foreign expert advice was dispensed with completely or much too soon with disastrous consequences.

Cotton spinning in its early phase suffered particularly from a lack of expert engineers. At the Kagoshima Spinning Mill, the first on Japanese soil, British engineers were employed for one year; after that the samurai administrators took over, with considerable bungling and resultant prolonged losses. The mills that were established afterward relied almost completely on native personnel. Many of the enthusiastic founders of the two thousand-spindle mills in the pioneering period before 1885 considered themselves experts if they had read a book on cotton spinning and had visited an operating mill. In some mills no engineer was available even to set up the machinery, and it had to be done by trial and error. Experts of sorts went from one mill to another, serving as engineers in two or even three mills at the same time.[42] The greater the enthusiasm and the louder the patriotic slogans that accompanied the founding of these mills, the smaller was the amount of practical knowledge, as a rule. It was thought that the new technology would by itself perform miracles.

It was Shibusawa himself who eventually broke the technological impasse in cotton spinning. He not only gathered capital for a large-scale mill but saw to it that the engineering problem was solved. He advised Yamabe Takeo, who was studying engineering in London, to receive practical training at the best English mills. Yamabe came back in 1883 and took over the technical management of the new Osaka Spinning Mill. He thus achieved the engineering breakthrough in cotton spinning and remained the expert in that field for many years.[43]

Other industries repeated these experiences. Paper manufacturing was plagued for years with technical difficulties and apparently had no foreign engineers in charge. Again Shibusawa broke the spell. He sent his nephew Ōkawa abroad to study paper manufacturing, and after his return Ōkawa became the great expert in paper manufacturing, as Yamabe had in cotton spinning.[44] In cement, glass, fertilizer manufacturing, and electricity, the picture of technological incompetence was quite similar, as were the losses for long periods.

Even Shibusawa, who usually planned very effectively, could be trapped by the technological problem. For instance, he had built a fertilizer factory on the advice of a Japanese engineer; but this expert left shortly, sailing abroad before the production began. Shibusawa was then left to his own devices, with no other expert available. He did not know enough either about the technology of production or about the use of the fertilizer. When the product was finally produced after a few years of wasteful experimenting, the peasants were given no instructions on its use and often achieved negative results. It took another few years to overcome this practical market problem.[45]

The next chapter will furnish more examples of technical difficulties in the sector of private industry. Usually, the few large industrial *zaibatsu* (lit., "financial clique," used for the giant trusts combining industry, trade, and banking) were able to overcome the technology problem either by enlisting foreign expert help or by their ability to hold out over the period of initial difficulty. But many of the lesser enterprises stumbled over the hurdle of technology. To the entrepreneurs with small capital resources, the salaries of foreign engineers appeared forbiddingly high, and they tried to save by following the brave example of the "seven wise men of Saga han." In this fashion the little knowledge picked up from a book or during a hurried visit abroad became a dangerous thing. It created an unwarranted enthusiasm and encouraged bold ventures without a thorough weighing of the practical difficulties involved. In the atmosphere of the *bummei kaika* and the government's strong encouragement and propaganda for modern industry, this hasty approach to new ventures is understandable. For the general success of the initial spurt toward modern industry, it was probably not altogether bad. True, the men who incurred the losses had to pay heavily for their bungling, at times being forced into bankruptcy. But other men picked up the pieces and somehow carried on the work. The boldness of approach and the overconfidence in Western technology greatly helped to break the initial timidity within the private sector. A more rational weighing of the detailed problems might have made for more caution and fewer losses, but might also have reduced the urge to invest at a time when it was most needed.

A certain bookish approach to practical engineering problems characterized the pioneering period of Japanese private industry. The entrepreneurs seemed to view independence of foreign help as an absolute ideal, as had the early samurai administrators of the progressive han. At a later stage of development, in the 1890s, the graduates from the universities, notably Keio and Waseda, moved into top managerial positions; they, too, stressed book learning as a prerequisite for industrial success. From the very outset, then, Japanese entrepreneurship noticeably underestimated practical training. This trend seems to be continuing even today.

This difference in approach between Japan and the Western, especially European, countries was decried by men who were in a position to make comparisons. Hara Rokurō, one of the top bankers and promoters of Meiji industry, complained about the neglect of technological training and the heavy stress on school records. According to him, many industrial failures in the Meiji era were caused by this onesided approach.[46] Industrialization had come to Europe as a gradual process with a continuous carryover of skills and experiences from the handicraft stages. There was no such carryover in Japan, but rather a sharp break with traditional craftsmanship. The entrepreneurial group did need better education more than handicraft training, since the transmission of technology came through books and through travel to countries with different languages. The entrepreneurs looked on their high level of general education as a distinctive mark of status. This stress on education was probably unavoidable in view of historical conditions, but it did leave a lasting imprint on Japanese industry. If European technology excelled in its precision and reliability, it was largely because of the continuity from handicraft traditions, whereby the reputation of the master was at stake in every piece that left his shop. In Japan the tendency until recently has been to imitate foreign samples or blueprints, and pride was taken in the closeness of the imitation, rather than in originality or craftsmanship.

In the classic time of the great Meiji entrepreneurs, achievement had consisted in close adherence to Western models. If a Japanese technician could do just that, he would not only save money but would successfully "expel" foreign engineers by making them superfluous. Imitation was of course necessary, and it does not detract from Japan's total achievement of absorbing an alien technology with truly remarkable speed. But we can recognize in the copying and in the attempted early independence from foreign engineers a strong ambition to be equal to the West; in a way it was the *sonnō jōi* attitude in a new shape. Entrepreneurs repeatedly mentioned this *jōi* motive as important for their industrial ventures and technical experimentation. Asabuki Eiji, a prominent Mitsubishi manager, expressed this idea at the opening ceremony of Mitsui Bussan in 1880, saying that he had been a fanatic *jōi* partisan until about ten years before. Expulsion of the foreigners still remained his ideal, but the means had changed. Now the expulsion had to be accomplished by peaceful competition, not by force of arms.[47]

THE TRANSPORTATION SYSTEM

The Railways

The construction of an efficient transportation system, particularly of a railway network, constitutes the classic case for government investment, or at least for government subsidy and planning. Railways are essential for successful industrialization, to open up the country and to create a unified national market. But the long gestation periods involved, and the large initial capital outlays required for railway construction, do not make it very attractive for private capital in the initial stage.

In Europe, all countries except Britain witnessed active government planning and investment in railway construction. The first instance was Belgium, which as a young state started its industrialization period with the building

of a well-planned railway network, financed entirely by
the government. In Germany, too, the industrial revolution gathered speed only after the full layout of a railway
system. The German states — mainly the southern states
— had either invested directly or, as in the case of Prussia,
had at least planned and coordinated private investments.
In Russia railway building had initially been left entirely
to private initiative, but, as soon as the government started
its industrialization drive under Witte in the 1890s, the
government took over the construction of important trunk
lines and supervised the building and operation of the
others.

The Meiji government did not follow Belgium's example
by establishing a state monopoly on railways; it intended
to follow more closely the example of Prussia, by way of
a mixed approach of direct investments and subsidies plus
overall planning and control of private lines. Private capital was urged to participate in the building program, but
the initiative came entirely from the government. General
interest was completely lacking in the beginning, for the
simple reason that very few people with capital resources
had seen the railways in operation abroad; the attitude
toward railway construction was hostile rather than
friendly.

The officials who promoted the railway-construction program knew its importance for the economy. They realized that Japan, perhaps even more than the European
countries, needed an efficient means of land transportation.
The country had been unified politically by the abolition
of the han and the establishment of prefectural administration. But the division of Japan into many han had never
been an effective barrier to internal trade, as had been, for
example, the division of Germany into many small prin-
cipalities, each with its own tariff sovereignty. In Germany

the abolition of those tariffs and the establishment of the Zollverein in 1834 had been a crucial step toward the formation of a unified market area. In Japan the han had never had a tariff monopoly, and the checking stations along the highways had been established by the bakufu for the sake of political security and not to interfere with trade. A much greater obstacle was Japan's natural trade barriers, consisting of mountains and rivers that made overland travel extremely arduous. Bulk goods had to be transported by ship or carried by men. Travelers went on foot or were carried along the highways; but the mountains and the many unbridged rivers, impassable during heavy rains or floods, made traveling a mixed pleasure.[48]

In the debates over the railway-construction program, one of the main arguments in favor of the rapid layout of a railway net was that the country could thus become economically united. The other arguments frequently advanced were that railways could develop the backward areas of the country and that railway transportation would serve both the convenience of the people and the military needs of the nation.[49]

From the very beginning, the officials realized that the financing of a broad construction program would far exceed the means of the government alone. Some advocated floating a large foreign railway loan, but eventually it was decided to let private Japanese capital participate. Mitsui was asked to raise capital for a company to construct a railway line between Osaka and Kyoto, while the government started its own line connecting Tokyo with Yokohama. Since the construction cost of the proposed Osaka-Kyoto line was estimated at 700,000 yen, at least that much capital subscription was required for the private company. The government was willing to guarantee a 7 percent dividend rate on invested capital while sharing half of

the profits exceeding 7 percent. As an additional inducement to would-be investors, the government stressed the
great honor of cooperating with the government in this
national endeavor. In spite of considerable effort on the
part of Mitsui, however, the company did not materialize
for lack of subscribers.[50] For the time being, the government remained alone in the field and went ahead with the
construction of its Tokyo-Yokohama line.

The Tokyo-Yokohama line was completed and opened
to traffic in 1872, with 18 miles laid out. Total construction cost had been estimated at about 800,000 yen, plus
the cost of locomotives and cars, which amounted to another 150,000 yen. This railway was a complete success
from the start. It carried from 1872 to 1886 a yearly average of 1.5 million passengers and averaged annual profits of
234,000 yen; in 1886 profits were as high as 333,771 yen.[51]
With a profit rate of about 20 percent on its capital investment, the government felt greatly encouraged and the
opposition was silenced. Two years later the government
began to operate 20 miles of a line between Kyoto and
Kobe, and it completed the 47 miles between the two
cities in 1877. Traffic density on that line even topped
that of the Tokyo-Yokohama line, with 1.8 million passengers per year until 1886, with annual profits averaging
319,981 yen for the same period.[52] This already marks a
considerable drop in the profit rate, from about 20 to some
10 percent. Still, prospects were good for further exten-
sions of the railway network by the government.

In the years from 1870 to 1874, the government had its
heyday of railway construction: total outlays for the program in these five years constituted 33 percent of total
government investments. But in 1875 this suddenly
stopped, and government funds were diverted from railway construction to a military buildup, in connection with

the chastisement of Taiwan and the threatening conflict with China. Railway outlays dropped from 30.2 percent of government investments in 1874 to 7.1 percent in 1875 and were kept at an average of 4 percent between 1875 and 1882.[53]

If the railway program was not to bog down at this early stage, private capital had to come in. Fortunately, the immediate success of the two government lines that had been completed dispelled many of the previous misgivings. With a good deal of persuasion, especially from Iwakura Tomomi, a group of nobles joined together in the establishment of the first private railway company, in order to construct a line between Tokyo and Aomori. This Nippon Railway Company received tax exemption on all land that was needed, plus a guarantee of 8 percent dividends for ten years, starting from the time of commencement of traffic. Furthermore, the government itself took charge of the construction work; the shareholders had only to contribute their capital. The government never had to supplement the dividend rate; from the very start the Tokyo-Aomori line was a sound success. By 1885 the Nippon Railway Company had grown into the largest joint-stock company in Japan, with a total of 20 million yen capital. Iwasaki's Nippon Yusen Company came next, with 11 million yen.[54]

The private railway boom was on, but the success of the Nippon Railway Company was not repeated. On the contrary, profit rates began to drop sharply for the subsequent lines. After 1880 the government again increased somewhat its own outlays on railway building, but the mileage of private companies grew much faster. By 1892 Japan had laid out a total of 1,870 miles of railways, of which only 550 miles were government-owned; the other 1,320 miles had been built and were operated by private companies. The government lines had cost 35.4 million yen and in 1892 netted some 2.4 million yen in profits. The cost of constructing the 1,320 miles of private lines had been 47.5 million yen, which means that the government lines had cost almost twice as much as the private ones. But profits rates for the private lines (2.7 million yen in 1892) were even lower than those on the government lines.[55]

In the years 1883 to 1892 private companies received government subsidies in various forms, notably tax exemptions. The government's direct investments in railway construction picked up in the 1890s, averaging in that decade 8.1 percent of total government investments, and in the first decade of the new century the figure rose to 18.8 percent.[56] At the same time, private lines were bought up by the government in a program to nationalize the railway network. But it is of great significance that at the point when the government was harrassed financially, private capital had taken up the task and, in spite of mounting difficulties owing to low profit rates, had continued to expand the country's railways.

Shipping

As a country of islands, Japan naturally was dependent on shipping as a means of transportation, quite irrespective of her foreign trade. Until the coming of the railways, bulky cargo could not easily be carried overland since vehicles could not be used on the bad roads. Prior to the closing of the country, shipping must have been fairly well developed, with large ships used for foreign trade, as the records on the Omi merchants suggest. But in 1636 the bakufu prohibited the construction of ships exceeding eighty gross tons (five hundred koku), and this prohibition was officially maintained until Japan's seclusion was ended.

But after 1853, and even before then, the bakufu and the daimyo of the major han that faced the Pacific Ocean moved energetically to build or purchase large modern ships, in view of the military danger from foreign vessels.

Modern shipping in Japan was thus from the beginning strongly stimulated by military considerations. The defense of the country dictated the creation of a modern fleet, and to a large extent this military approach continued to characterize the shipping and shipbuilding efforts in the first decades of the Meiji period. Large sums were expended by the daimyo and the bakufu for modern ships, cannons, and coastal-defense installations. And in order to acquire the needed capital for this program, the large southwestern han began their well-known reform programs, which eventually put them ahead of the rest of Japan economically and militarily and enabled them to overthrow the bakufu.[57]

Satsuma, Choshu, Mito, Saga, and Tosa had their own military and economic reform programs in which naval construction, or the purchase of modern ships, was one of the most important items. The economic reform program of Tosa han was closely linked to the objective of building a strong naval-defense force. A large economic-planning and administration center contained departments of fishing, mining, medicine, translation, finance, and production encouragement. Connected with the center were a naval and a merchant-marine school. A han monopoly trading company with branch offices in Osaka and Nagasaki provided the main financial backing for the purchases of arms and ships. Iwasaki Yatarō was chief of the Nagasaki branch, which handled the foreign imports and exports. Within one year, 1866–67, the company purchased ships, guns, and machinery from abroad worth 426,851 ryo, and it ran a deficit of 100,000 ryo.[58] Because of the heavy deficit operations, the company came under fire from han officials and was then turned over to Iwasaki as a private enterprise; in this way it became the nucleus of Mitsubishi, Japan's most powerful shipping company.

The double objective of *fukoku kyōhei* (wealthy nation, strong army), had been stressed in the han reform programs, and during the last years of the Tokugawa and the early Meiji it was largely biased in favor of the military objective — the *fukoku* was made subservient to the *kyōhei*. Spinning mills were founded, mines modernized, and reverberatory furnaces built for the sake of defense, to build cannons and to acquire modern ships.

By 1868 Japan had 138 modern ships, of which 44 were owned by the bakufu and 94 by various han; the total capacity was 150,000 tons. Most of the ships had been purchased; only one steamer and twenty sailing vessels had been constructed in Japan.[59] Of the four shipyards inherited by the Meiji government, one, the Ishikawajima yard, had been built in 1856 and operated since then by Mito han; in it the first Western-style ship, the *Asahi Maru,* had been constructed. This yard was soon abandoned by the Meiji government, and its machinery was transferred to the Tsukiji machine shop. In 1876 a private entrepreneur, Hirano Tomiji, took over the dilapidated shipyard and struggled for many years before he finally made it a success in the late 1880s. Two other yards, one established in Nagasaki in 1861 and the other in Kobe in 1864, were small and could only handle repair work on larger ships; they remained small and inefficient under government management, until they were transferred to private entrepreneurs in 1884 and 1886.

It was on the Yokosuka shipyard that both the bakufu and the Meiji government concentrated their efforts in modern shipbuilding. Yokosuka had been modeled after the Toulon shipyard and was two thirds of its size. It had been planned under the aegis of the French consul, and its staff included French engineers. Connected with the Yokosuka yard was an iron-construction plant in Yokohama. Within four years the bakufu had invested in Yokosuka over 4 million yen. The Meiji government expanded its facilities further and turned it over to the navy for the construction of military vessels. In view of the great military importance of shipping it is somewhat surprising that the Meiji government did not invest more heavily in shipbuilding from the very start. Shipbuilding, in the first decade of the Meiji era, had to take a back seat to railway construction.

The Meiji policies in the first years were dominated by the goal of economic reconstruction, particularly between 1871 and 1874. But beginning with 1874 military build-up received more attention because of the Taiwan expedition, growing hostility toward Korea, and internal unrest that reached its climax in the Satsuma Rebellion of 1877. As soon as military needs dictated a change of policy, the priority in outlays on the transportation system turned from railways to shipping.

Between 1868 and 1874, total government investments in railway construction (which had actually started only in 1870) amounted to 8.71 million yen, while investments in shipbuilding and the purchase of ships, both merchant and naval, ran only to 1.57 million yen. But between 1875 and 1879, expenditures for railway construction dropped to 1.44 million yen, and government outlays for the construction of naval vessels rose to 5.95 million yen. Merchant shipping also received top priority in these years in spite of the low figure of 103,300 yen of direct government investments in that field.[60] The fact is that commercial shipping was a private monopoly enterprise of

Iwasaki; it received huge indirect subsidies and privileges that are not included in these government figures.

The turn from purely economic considerations, with railways occupying a central place, to military investments, closely connected with shipping, is highlighted by a comparison of the percentages of total government investments: from 1870 to 1882 railways sank from 33 to 4 percent and military investments rose from 2 to 40 percent of government investment outlays.[61] Thus it is quite obvious that shipping maintained its military focus, while railways kept their primarily economic significance.[62] The build-up of a strong naval force became quite naturally a very important, but also costly, concern of the government. Naval construction took 60 percent of all military investments between 1875 and 1893; in 1894, on the eve of the conflict with China, naval-construction costs rose almost ten times over the average of the 1875–1893 period.[63]

Iwasaki's merchant fleet also retained a strongly military character, as did Iwasaki himself. The Tosa samurai regarded his work as a fight for Japan's equality with the Western countries on the high seas, true to the tradition of *fukoku kyōhei*. During the Taiwan expedition and the Satsuma Rebellion, Iwasaki's shipping company was of strategic importance in transporting troops to the battlefields. It was therefore in the economic and military interest of the country that the government should accord heavy subsidies to Iwasaki. A few examples of the types and sizes of these subsidies to the champion of Japanese shipping will show the intense concern of the Meiji government for commercial shipping, something that is easily lost sight of in the statistical figures on the government's direct investments.

In 1874 the government bought 13 ships abroad worth $1.56 million (over 2 million yen at the prevailing exchange rate) and handed them over to Mitsubishi, together with 18 other ships that had been inherited from the bakufu. During the Satsuma Rebellion 10 more large steamers were purchased for $700,000 and turned over to Mitsubishi with additional large subsidies for their operation. By the end of 1878 the total of subsidies for the operation of this shipping company had reached 2.7 million yen. Sixty percent of the budget of the Ministry of Trade and Agriculture for 1881 consisted of subsidies to Mitsubishi.[64] Finally, the government turned the Nagasaki shipyard over to Iwasaki at a bargain price; Iwasaki transformed the small inefficient yard, through huge investments in new equipment, into one of the most modern shipyards in the Far East.

By 1880 the shipping company of Iwasaki operated a stately fleet of 56 modern ships, of which 37 were steamers.[65] We shall see in Chapter Six that Iwasaki's ruthless practices made him enemies inside and outside the government. A powerful rival shipping company was set up in 1882 with large government support. Both Mitsubishi and the rival Kyōdō Unyu Company were almost ruined by the ensuing cutthroat competition and came close to collapse in 1885. But after their amalgamation into one company under Iwasaki's control, progress in shipping was rapid. In 1895 Japan had, all told, a total shipping capacity of 350,000 tons, with 701 ships, of which 528 were steamers. By the end of the Meiji era, in 1912, Japan ranked sixth in the world in total shipping capacity and could boast of 1.635 million tons. This put her close on the heels of France, with 1.638 million, and far ahead of Italy, with only 1.1 million tons.[66]

The building of Japanese transportation, both railways and shipping, had resulted from a close cooperation between the government in the form of direct investments, subsidies, and general encouragement to would-be investors, and private industry. But while the railways were more closely connected with purely economic considerations, shipping, true to the tradition of the southwestern han, retained a distinctly military coloring. This was so not only because of the government's heavy investments in naval construction, but also because of the role that commercial shipping played in military engagements and in Japan's struggle with the West on the high seas. It was both typical and providential that a militant Tosa samurai became the leading exponent of Japanese commercial shipping.

OTHER GOVERNMENT ENTERPRISES

From the viewpoint of classical international-trade theory, Japan ought to have specialized from the start in labor-using industries because of her scarcity of capital and her abundant labor resources. The capital accumulated during the Tokugawa period by the city merchants and rural putting-out masters had in part been dissipated in the turbulent years of change, and it could certainly not be considered as adequate to finance a large-scale capital-using investment program. The surplus rural population and the many jobless samurai could supply abundant labor for highly labor-intensive industrial employment.

But the Meiji government did not follow the classical prescription of specializing according to relative factor endowments. It did not accord top priority to light industries, but from the very beginning invested primarily in heavy, capital-using enterprises. The construction of a railway network and a modern shipping system was very costly, but the two areas were highly important as suppliers of overhead capital for the ensuing development program. The government also invested a good deal in mining and chemical factories, while textiles were soon left, after some initial help and guidance, to the initiative of private capital.

The stress on capital-intensive investments on the part of the government was wise development policy, in spite of the extreme scarcity of capital. This is not only true for railways and shipping, since the establishment of an efficient transportation system is a prerequisite for industrialization; the statement also applies to the capital-using manufacturing and mining enterprises. For one thing, the latest Western machinery and production methods made it quite clear to the Japanese that they could no longer rely on their own past experience and that trial and error would not do. Whenever trial-and-error methods were used, they usually failed badly. This forced them to adopt and master the new advanced technology.

Another, and in my view extremely important, aspect of this concentration on heavy industry has to do with the self-confidence of the Japanese people. Modern enterprises were eloquent symbols of the new era, of progress and national achievement. They helped to harness for industrialization at least part of the strong patriotic emotions so characteristic of the Meiji era. It was in the government enterprises that, with the aid of foreign technicians, the most staggering technological problems could be and were overcome; these large endeavors became monuments of the nation's progress. It is true that there was much waste of capital involved in the prolonged losses and inefficiencies of the first factories and mines, but this was compensated for by these other, indirect, effects. For a nucleus was formed from which the most enterprising men of the period could make a start into modern industrial ventures.

The Meiji officials were by no means unanimously in

favor of government involvement in industrial investments. Some had been opposed from the beginning to
any type of government intervention, while others insisted
that the government ought to assume full responsibility
for building the nation's industries. Until 1878 economic
policy was by and large determined by the Minister of the
Interior and strongman Ōkubo who, together with Ōkuma,
the Minister of Finance, went as far as possible in com-
mitting the government. They were of the opinion that
the private sector was still too immature and that the
government ought to occupy the central position in economic life. The government investments that coincided
with the costly liquidation of the feudal system and the
samurai-employment program caused strong inflationary
pressures. Ōkubo was assassinated in 1878, and Ōkuma
resigned as Minister of Finance in 1881, making room for
the other economic policy group, represented by Matsukata, the new minister.[67]

Matsukata's policies represented a significant step toward
laissez faire and private enterprise and a transition from
direct government investment in industry. But the blessing to the private sector came in a harsh disguise indeed:
in 1881 Matsukata initiated a long-overdue deflation policy which for a few years played havoc with private industry. The large amounts of government paper money
had caused not only rapid price inflation but also a dangerous balance-of-payments deficit. Matsukata curtailed government expenditures drastically and initiated the sale of
government enterprises, which were one of the main
drains on the treasury. The Bank of Japan was established
in 1882 to regulate the money supply, and a large amount
of paper money was withdrawn from circulation in order
to achieve convertibility at par of paper money against
specie.

By the end of the deflation period in 1884, a positive

balance of payments had been achieved. But the typhoon of deflation had also left in its wake the wreckage of numerous trading and industrial enterprises; many of them had started under the favorable conditions of inflation and were unsound to begin with. After 1884 private industry made a new start. Solid monetary conditions had been established; the government enterprises which had been sold out at bargain prices, as well as many of the wrecked enterprises, had been cemented into this new foundation. It was a heavy but perhaps necessary price to pay during a transitional period.

It is not necessary to go into the details of the government enterprises, which have been well described and analyzed elsewhere.[68] In absolute terms, these investments were not overwhelming and should not be exaggerated. Mining was the main field of concentration. The government operated nine modern mines, chief among them the Takashima and Miike coal mines, the two most profitable mines in Japan. But the government also paid a heavy penalty for inefficiencies and technical incompetence: for example, a total of 2.5 million yen was invested in the Kamaishi iron mines; smelting was finally started there in 1880, but the smelting operations lasted no longer than 198 days. Owing to a combination of disasters and technical difficulties, the project was abandoned. The mines with all the installed machines lay unused for a few years, until finally Tanaka Chōbei, a private entrepreneur, was persuaded to continue the work.[69]

Besides the already mentioned Yokosuka shipyard, and two arsenals in Tokyo and Osaka, the government operated a large-scale construction plant in Akabane. From that plant came most of the durable equipment and machinery that was produced in Japan: steam engines, boilers, machinery for cotton spinning and silk reeling. In 1881 the ma-

chine shop employed 537 workers, a large-scale operation
for the time. Akabane served also as a training center for
the engineering department of the Ministry of Industry.[70]

There were also the chemical factories: Fukagawa cement, Fukagawa white bricks, and Shinagawa glass. Finally,
in the field of textiles the government briefly operated two
cotton-spinning mills, the large-scale Tomioka filature, a
mechanical thread-plying mill, and a weaving factory.
None of the government textile factories was economically
successful; they operated at losses or very low profits prior
to 1884 while under government management, and they
were the first to be sold.[71]

If measured solely in terms of profit rates, the government factories were complete failures and a constant drain
on the state finances. This was one of the main reasons
why they were sold out as part of Matsukata's deflation and
retrenchment program. Between 1868 and 1884 the total
investments in these enterprises amounted to something
over 32 million yen, while total profits for the entire
seventeen-year period were no more than 17.173 million
yen.[72] When these model factories and mines came up for
sale, it was sometimes very difficult to find purchasers, in
spite of the giveaway prices that were asked. The sale of
the government factories, shipyards, and mines represented
of course a substantial subsidy to private industry. But
without it, private enterprise would have had little chance
even to start in these fields, since the government had
failed to demonstrate the one most important thing, the
possibility of making profits. With so much done by the
government in technical experiments and machinery investments, the purchasers of the enterprises, with some
additional investments, could overcome the critical stage
rather quickly and make these factories and mines the
foundations of their own industrial empires.

Two rather extreme examples may suffice as illustrations of the favorable rates of the sales. The Shinagawa Glass Factory was sold for 79,950 yen to be paid in installments over a period of fifty-five years, beginning ten years after the sale. Total government investments in that factory had been 350,000 yen. The Ani Copper Mine had cost the government 1.6 million yen in investments and was sold for 250,000 yen, of which 10,000 yen were paid immediately and the rest spread over twenty-four years, starting five years after the sale.[73]

It would be interesting to know the relative position of government enterprises within the whole of the economy and of the modern industrial sector. But private modern enterprise was not well surveyed at that time. The data on manufacturing that do exist lump together the traditional and the modern sectors; and even within the modern sector most establishments were still small-scale. Within the totals of output figures, the model factories do not occupy a prominent place. Figures on factory employment indicate a rather steady ratio of 10 to 1 between the private and the government sectors throughout the 1880s and 1890s.[74] But if we concentrate attention on mining and heavy and chemical industries, the government enterprises are seen to be highly significant, because of their scale of operation and their advanced technology. Whether intended or not, Ōkubo's early insistence on government leadership and dominance in modern industry paid handsome dividends to the private sector after 1884.

INDIRECT SUBSIDIES TO PRIVATE INDUSTRY

It has been indicated that the sale of government enterprises to private entrepreneurs marked a turn in the direction of laissez faire. The direction was clear, but nobody at the time within the government thought that the private sector could altogether dispense with help from the center. The sales in themselves were a form of subsidy; other encouragements and subsidies followed, some of them planned, some of them unwittingly extended to the emerging leaders of modern Japanese industry.

I shall not go into detail on the varieties of direct and indirect subsidies and of monopoly rights granted to industrialists. Instead, I shall concentrate on one aspect that was of considerable importance: the way in which the government subsidized private industry by becoming its chief customer. The Japanese market could easily absorb the traditional products, and it was also open to cotton textiles, if the cotton industry could overcome foreign competition. But the situation was altogether different with regard to electrical industries and to chemicals, such as cement, bricks, paper, glass, and leather. There the private entrepreneurs faced their greatest difficulty. People were hesitant to buy the things they did not know, and their demand was usually much too small for large-scale production. Government orders saved many enterprises from bankruptcy in the critical years prior to about 1895. This was the case with leather manufacturing, where the main demand came from the army; with paper manufacturing, where government offices bought large amounts; and also with cement and bricks. The woolen industry depended almost entirely on the military demand for uniforms and blankets.

Asano Sōichirō, who had purchased the government cement factory, succeeded in increasing the efficiency of production and solved some technical problems magnificently. But this would not have saved him from bankruptcy if government orders had not come in to solve his market problem. The government bought up most of

Asano's cement for its railway program, and for the building of the Imperial Palace and the Ueno Museum.[75]

The Meiji government seems to have followed the bakufu's tradition of doing its business with monopoly contractors. There was no competitive public bidding, and consequently business with the government invariably became a source of handsome profits for the suppliers. This method could and sometimes did support inefficiency, but the general impression is that the officials did not mind monopoly profits, so long as it was certain that these profits would be reinvested in modern enterprises. The chief government suppliers were usually also the most daring entrepreneurs.

During the Satsuma Rebellion, all army provisions were supplied by Mitsui Bussan (Mitsui Trading Co.), and the Ōkura and Fujita companies. Mitsui Bussan received 60 percent of total contracts, and the other two 20 percent each. Mitsui, which started its operations in 1878 with 100,000 yen in capital, earned a net profit of 500,000 yen in that one year. Ōkura and Fujita made similar gains. Mitsubishi, which was in charge of all troop transports, netted in that year over 1.2 million yen.[76] But these same companies were in the forefront of Meiji industry, and the huge profits were used to expand their enterprises, which grew eventually into the zaibatsu.

Light and labor-using industries, in contrast with the capital-intensive industries, received more verbal than financial encouragement. Direct help for cotton spinning and silk reeling was confined to the years prior to 1884, and even then was not too large in absolute terms. The government apparently made the correct forecast that textiles would take care of themselves if sufficiently encouraged by a promotion program. Capital requirements were relatively small even in cotton spinning during the two-thousand-spindle-mill era (something like 50,000 yen per mill on the average), and for silk reeling the figures were much lower. The field of textiles was also under direct stimulus from foreign competition and, with proper handling, could be stimulated to respond to the challenge. The government's promotion program consisted consequently in spreading technical knowledge and in drumming up patriotic sentiments against the importation of cotton yarns.

Fairs and exhibitions served this purpose. The first fair for the promotion of exports and of import-competing cotton spinning was held in Kyoto in 1872 and attracted over 31,000 Japanese and 770 foreign visitors. After this encouraging start, the fair was repeated annually until 1888. Local fairs and exhibitions across the country had the same purpose. By 1887 the number of local fairs had reached 317, with over 2 million visitors.[77] One point that always received strong emphasis in the speeches and writtings on these occasions was the need to expand and improve the production of raw silk and to build mills. A report from an exhibition held in Osaka in 1880 stated that Japan was producing no more than 3 percent of its total cotton-yarn consumption in its mechanical mills. Another 241 mills would have to be built in order to stop the importation of foreign yarns.[78]

We have seen in Chapter Three that this general encouragement of the textile industry, both silk reeling and mechanical cotton spinning, had its positive effects. In spite of the heavy competition from the imports and the continued losses prior to 1885, the cotton-spinning industry weathered the difficulties and eventually became Japan's number-one industry and her first industry to move into the world market. Thus the sector that had received comparatively little direct help in fact grew fastest and became the mainstay of Japan's modern industry. The pioneering problems in cotton spinning were overcome with great speed because of the positive response to the general encouragement offered by the government. Later, Japan's natural advantages in the area made themselves felt: the availability of cheap labor, a ready home market, a comparatively simple and labor-using technology, and the readiness of the cotton merchants and cotton spinners to invest in a field that was close to their former business. Where these advantages were not present, as in the chemical and heavy industries, continued indirect support by the government was a practical necessity.

JAPANESE INDUSTRY IN THE MID-MEIJI YEARS

Before turning our attention to the private sector and its entrepreneurs, we may take a brief glance at the state of Japanese industry relative to the whole economy in the late 1880s and early 1890s. It is important to keep in mind that my period of investigation, 1868–1895, marks the very beginnings of industrialization. But the pioneering phase during the eighties and early nineties is of particular interest because during this time many of the most crucial problems were solved and obstacles to industrial growth removed. Notably this came about through the energetic initiative from the center and the efforts of a small entrepreneurial elite.

During this period the primary sector, in particular agriculture, retained its strongly dominant position in quantitative terms of output and employment. But its relative position began to decline noticeably, which in itself is a sure sign of industrial growth.

Field	Production	1878–82	1893–97
Employment	Primary	82.3%	73.1%
	Secondary	5.6%	10.4%
Real income	Primary	64.0%	51.0%
(percent)	Secondary	10.0%	18.0%
Real income	Primary	909	1,467
(totals in	Secondary	147	528
million yen)			

Adapted from Ohkawa Kazushi et al., *The Growth Rate of the Japanese Economy since 1878* (Tokyo, 1937), p. 17, 27.

The decline of employment in primary production was accounted for mainly by the increase of total employment in the secondary sector; there was actually very little decrease in total agricultural employment. Agriculture remained highly labor-intensive and small-scale, but all the time its productivity kept rising per capita. Over the fifteen-year span, as indicated in the table above, it achieved a productivity increase of 4 percent per annum, mainly owing to better seeds and techniques and the increased use of fertilizer. But if brought into relation to the secondary sector, incomes fell by 20 percent in the primary sector while employment totals diminished by only 11 percent. In secondary production during these fifteen years, there was a threefold increase in total real income produced; this indicates the magnitude of relative industrial growth. The secondary sector in the above table does, however, include domestic manufacturing, and this obscures the evidence concerning industrial growth. Although both the domestic and the industrial sectors were moving upward, their rates of growth were different.

A comparison between the secondary and the tertiary sectors would not serve my purpose of illustrating the speed of industrialization and modernization, because both sectors presented a mixture of traditional and modern establishments. I take instead, as another indicator of the modernization process, the authorized joint-stock capital of all limited companies. We may safely assume that shifts toward the company form of enterprise and increases in totals of joint-stock capital in any field reflect rather closely the growth of that particular sector as well as its modernization.

	Authorized joint-stock capital			
	End of 1883		End of 1893	
Field	Totals (thousand yen)	Percent	Totals (thousand yen)	Percent
Agriculture	1,053	0.76	2,542	0.85
Trading	35,904	25.80	57,616	19.33
Manufacturing	14,725	10.59	68,259	22.91
Railways	12,080	8.68	57,945	19.45
Banking	75,375	54.17	111,635	37.46
Totals	139,137	100.00	297,997	100.00

S. Uyehara, *The Industry and Trade of Japan*, rev. ed. (London, 1936), p. 271. Percentages computed.

Agriculture played a negligible role as an investment possibility for joint-stock capital. But of the four other fields in the table, banking and trading were far in the lead in 1884, the point at which the government was preparing to sell its own enterprises and to promote private industry by direct and indirect subsidies. We have seen in Chapter Two that modern banking had achieved a breakthrough after 1876, with many samurai becoming founders of national banks. Banking capital, though still growing absolutely and still occupying first place, had within ten years fallen from 54.17 percent to 37.46 percent of total joint-stock capital. Manufacturing and railways had by that time already overtaken trading, which ten years earlier had had three times as much joint-stock capital as railways, and more than twice as much as manufacturing. Only railways showed gains similar to those of manufacturing, moving from 8.68 percent of the total in 1883 to 19.45 percent in 1893, and in absolute terms increasing five-fold. This sharp increase in manufacturing and railways, each to outstrip even trading capital, is an eloquent sign of the dynamic growth of modern industry in Japan in the decade that began with the liquidation of government enterprises and ended just before the Sino-Japanese War.

Within the field of manufacturing, the trend was increasingly toward factory production. But prior to the turn of the century, domestic and factory manufacturing grew side by side in absolute terms. During the period from 1878 to 1895, the gross-value product of domestic manufacturing rose from 37 to 199 million yen, and factory production registered during the same time a rise from 40 to 323 million yen; [79] while factory production increased 8 times, domestic production nevertheless registered an increase of 5.4 times. These average figures of domestic and factory gross-value products do not, however, reveal the very erratic movements that took place in domestic manufacturing — movements that not only caused hardship but helped to hasten the eventual decline of domestic manufacturing in absolute terms. From a 79-million-yen gross-value product in 1885, domestic manufacturing rose suddenly to 114 million in the next year, and then fell from 196 million yen in 1888 to a calamitous 71 million yen two years later.[80]

Employment figures within the secondary sector indicate a wide discrepancy in productivity per worker between traditional domestic manufacturing and modern factory industry. During the 1893–1897 period the total employment in the secondary sector registered an average of 2.468 million workers, but only 418,140 were factory employees, and of these 60 percent were women.[81] This last fact, incidentally, reflects the heavy preponderance of textiles within the modern industrial sector. But while around 1895 the labor force in factories constituted only one sixth of total secondary employment, the total gross-value product of factory industry had by that time already surpassed that of dometsic manufacturing with 323 versus 199 million yen, as shown above. The low productivity per worker in domestic manufacturing, which was often nothing but a by-employment for tenant farmers, was the main cause of the inevitable decline after the turn of the century.

In 1884, at the beginning of the decade of energetic growth, Japanese industry still showed predominantly rural characteristics. Not only because of the domestic manufacturing sector, but because factories also were frequently rural, especially in the fields of textiles, ceramics, food processing, and iron. A survey of factory production in 1884, which comprises a total of 1,981 establishments employing 5 or more workers, gives the following picture: of chemical industries like paper, matches, and cement, 56 percent were located in cities, 26.4 percent were rural, locations of the rest were unspecified.[82] Shipbuilding and weaving were also typically city industries. Machinery construction was a "city" industry to the extent of 47.4 percent of its total; only 15.8 percent was rural, and the location of 36.8 percent was unspecified. On the other hand, food-processing industries, ceramics, and iron casting and refining, as well as silk reeling, remained typically rural industries.

In 1884 the division between city and rural factories corresponded closely to a grouping by size.[83] The typically large establishments tended to be city-located. In terms of workers employed, the largest factories were found in the chemical industry, followed by machine and machine-tool plants and then by textiles. In the chemical industry 31.9 percent of all establishments employed 50 or more workers, machine and machine-tool factories followed with 23.6 percent, and textiles with 9.7 percent.

If we were to take cotton spinning alone, it would perhaps rank even above the chemical industries in the size of its establishments; the large number of silk-reeling factories that the survey includes in the textile group overshadows the spinning mills and unduly pulls down the arithmetical average of the size of all textile establishments. Of all 1,981 factories in the survey, no less than 1,043 belonged to silk reeling, and of these 69.5 percent had less than 20 workers per factory. We see here also that in the mid-1880s, when factory production was emerging, it was still dominated by silk reeling, with typically small-scale operations. At this time, textiles — and this means mainly silk reeling — accounted for over 60 percent of all factories, followed by the traditional ceramics and food-processing industries with 21.3 percent.

In textiles Japan achieved her first industrial success. Silk spinning had been stimulated by early export opportunities and cotton spinning by competition from imports. But, apart from textiles, other modern large-scale industries began to multiply and to make vigorous inroads into traditional putting-out manufacturing. This movement was supported by direct and indirect government subsidies and by the building of a broad transportation system. The government's efforts in stimulating and subsidizing the nascent modern industrial sector were crowned with remarkable success.

V

THE SPIRIT OF ENTERPRISE
IN THE PRIVATE SECTOR

The Meiji Restoration brought about a new evaluation
of the government and its role in the life of the nation.
During the feudal era, the bakufu officials were feared but
hardly admired, and few talented and ambitious men were
attracted into official service. The Restoration carried the
government from the margin of attention into the center
of everyone's interest. Everything that was great and exciting in these years, the restoration of the emperor, the
unification of the country, the abolition of feudal privileges, the beginnings of modern industry, all had been
wrought by the Meiji officials. The light radiated again
from the imperial precincts, and those who wanted to stay
in the light had to move to the center and become officials,
or at least associate with them. By way of contrast, the rest
of the population appeared to be all the more backward.
There is small wonder that the officials were idolized and
the common man counted for little at this time. This
kanson minpi attitude (awe for the official, contempt for
the crowd) was but the other side of the coin of the astound-
ing Meiji achievements.

Few people expected any initiative or contributions to

progress from the private business sector, which still seemed
so backward and which had disappointed hopes so often
during the first Meiji years. The great industrial enterprises, the large and centrally located factories, had been
established by officials; now the private sector was expected
to accept guidance gratefully and humbly. Indeed, the
bowed head and passive obedience to government officials
had been the chief traits of the *shōnin* all through the
Tokugawa period. The populace had no other image of
a businessman than the one represented by the former
merchant class, and that class, during the first decade of
the Meiji era, was not only leaning nostalgically backward, but had become disorganized, unreliable, and prone
to pursue profits in total disregard of the public interest.

In the early years of the Meiji, two new types of businessmen emerged in the private sector: the *seishō* (political
merchants), who rode on the crest of government favors
and used every opportunity to amass fortunes for themselves, glorying meanwhile in official titles and patriotic
slogans; and the many second-rate businessmen or industrialists who had neither experience nor capital but only
enthusiasm. We find the latter chiefly among the founders
of national banks and also in cotton spinning in its first
period. But neither of these two types could be counted
upon to build a viable and independent sector of the
modern economy. The private sector needed a progressive
business group that would develop its own initiative with
less reliance upon government coaching and government
subsidies.

The Entrepreneur, A New Status

In the last decades of the Tokugawa period, the merchants had, through the back door of daimyo lending,

purchase of samurai titles, and land reclamations, managed to break down at least part of the social prejudice against their lowly status. The Meiji Restoration had practically wiped out those gains. Business needed a complete rehabilitation of its status if it was to succeed in the establishment of a strong private sector. The public as well as would-be entrepreneurs had to be impressed with the fact that modern business was not only beneficial to the country, but was as vital as the work of the Meiji government itself. Only by restoring the social status of private business, or rather by establishing it for the first time, could a healthy growth of private industry be guaranteed.

The need to create a new image of business, and to make the businessman confident of his own worth, was clearly perceived, and the task was taken on by a small group inside and outside of the business sector. A conspicuous contribution to the eventual rehabilitation of business pursuits and the creation of new status for the entrepreneur was made by two men: Fukuzawa and Shibusawa, the one an educator, the other an entrepreneur.

Fukuzawa Yukichi (1835–1905), the founder of Japan's first modern college, the Keiō Gijuku, had been for a few years following the Restoration closely associated with the government: he was a close friend of Ōkuma Shigenobu, one of the leading government officials. He had been one of the brain trust that promoted the *bummei kaika* and had been chiefly responsible for shaping the new educational policy; the graduates of his school entered government service. But when Ōkuma was ousted from the government in 1881, Fukuzawa also severed his ties to the regime and became one of the most outspoken enemies of government control over economic and cultural life. Although he had stressed modern business rationality in the education of his students, he now steered his graduates

almost exclusively into the private business sector. Thus
Fukuzawa's Keiō Gijuku and the Imperial University
came to deviate widely in their educational policies: the
former represented Western liberal thought and stressed
individualism, in the tradition of John Stuart Mill; the
latter was a state institution, working for the state, edu-
cating officials, and maintaining more of the feudal Confucian mentality.

Mori Arinori,[1] the Minister of Education, shared with
Fukuzawa an admiration for Western ideas and methods,
but he wanted college education to serve primarily the purposes of bureaucracy. Officials, not businessmen, were to
be educated in the state universities, in pursuit not of the
English but of the Prussian example.[2] Fukuzawa often gave
expression to his aversion to the prevailing *kanson minpi*
mentality and insisted that his graduates ought to stand
on their own feet and spurn government connections. The
prevailing bureaucratism became an object of his scorn,
as the following shows: "The schools are officially licensed,
sermons and moral preachings are licensed, cattle raising,
sericulture, and indeed, eight out of every ten enterprises
are connected with the government . . . the flattering of
the official, the awe and idolization of the official, is ugly
and unbearable." [3]

The Keiō students were trained for private enterprise,
while the graduates of the Imperial University regarded
private business as degrading. When Shibusawa on one
occasion asked a few graduates of the Imperial University
to join the Tokyo Gas Company, they answered typically
that they did not intend to "descend to the level of the
common people." [4] Fukuzawa taught his students to respect business pursuits, and he himself presented an example: he insisted that he taught "for money" and demanded that the tuition fees be paid into his hands, some-

thing unheard of for a samurai-teacher. By tradition, teaching was an honorable occupation and teachers were given presents, wrapped in special paper.[5] Since almost all of Fukuzawa's students were samurai, he had to fight their deep-rooted contempt for business.

A frequently recurring theme in his writings was the stress on a new business rationality. His "merchants of the *bummei kaika*" were to take pride in their occupation if it was "for profit and for Japan." In his opinion, only educated and independent businessmen could build up the economy of the country. Fukuzawa insisted on education as a prerequisite for modern business because without learning a merchant could neither understand the problems inherent in the new business activities nor find social respectability.[6] Fukuzawa urged his students to enter business and not the government because, at a time when everybody was rushing into administrative positions, pioneers were needed in industry and trade.

Fukuzawa's influence was by no means confined to his Keiō Gijuku; it reached the entire population through his numerous writings. His most successful book was *Gakumon no susume* (An exhortation to learning), which in the five years between 1872 and 1876 reached the record sale of 3.4 million copies in 17 editions. In this book Fukuzawa forcefully propounded a new pragmatism and assailed the traditional views on learning, business, and status. Learning was to be emancipated from its theoretical bias and put into the service of daily life, notably of business; it was to open the way to social and economic success. Self-respect ought not to depend on status but on learning and business achievement. Other of his books contained similar views. In *Seiyō jijō* (Conditions in the West) he described life in Western societies, with its stress on the respectability and rationality of business. At a time when newspapers and books were still scarce, Fukuzawa's books with their many editions must have exercised a tremendous influence on the public mind. By 1897 the total sales of his books and pamphlets had reached about 10 million.[7]

The immediate effects of Fukuzawa's pragmatic approach were, of course, most evident in the Keiō Gijuku. The school became the chief supplier of the leading Meiji business managers and entrepreneurs. The Mitsubishi and Mitsui zaibatsu in particular drew heavily on Fukuzawa's graduates to fill top positions in their enterprises. Fukuzawa's connections with Mitsubishi were particularly close, and people used to say the Mitsubishi Company was run by Iwasaki's money and Fukuzawa's men.[8]

Shibusawa Eiichi (1840–1931), perhaps the outstanding entrepreneur of Japanese modern history, through his knowledge and moral leadership most decisively influenced the course of private industry in the crucial stage of its development.[9] Like Fukuzawa, Shibusawa insisted upon joint-stock enterprises and upon independence from the government. He himself resigned his respected position in the Ministry of Finance in order to work as a leader in establishing a viable private sector.

The son of a rich farmer in Musashino province, Shibusawa acquired some early experience in business dealings, but had leisure enough to become an ardent *sonnō jōi* partisan; he even entered into a plan with a few others to overthrow the bakufu. After the failure of this scheme he entered the service of the Tokugawa and gained the confidence of the last shogun. He was chosen to accompany the shogun's younger brother, as his financial manager, to the World Exhibition in Paris in 1867. In France Shibusawa absorbed his new experiences with intelligence and zeal. Three things in particular made a lasting impression on him. First, he saw the ease and liberty with which businessmen moved in the highest social circles and were accepted as equals. Second, he realized that large industrial ventures and other vast projects could only be realized on the basis of joint-stock operations. Finally, he was introduced by a friend, the banker Flury-Herald, to the technicalities of the modern banking system.

After his return to Japan in 1869, Shibusawa was called by Ōkuma to serve in the Ministry of Finance; he accepted on condition that he might resign at any time to work as a private businessman. During his four years in the Ministry of Finance, Shibusawa is said to have been the man chiefly responsible for the tax reform and the monetary reorganization. Although at the age of thirty-four he had become second in command in the Ministry of Finance, he resigned his post in 1873.

Shibusawa had not yet left the ministry when he was elected general superintendent of the newly established First National Bank (later the Dai Ichi), a joint enterprise with capital mainly from Mitsui and Ono. In 1875, after the downfall of Ono, he was unanimously elected president of the bank, which became the headquarters from which he coordinated and directed many of the newly emerging business and industrial enterprises. Shibusawa had not only spurned a career in the Ministry of Finance. He also refused extremely tempting offers from the private sector: Minomura Rizaemon wanted him as his own successor as manager of the entire Mitsui combine, the largest enterprise in Japan; and Iwasaki invited him to become a partner in the powerful Mitsubishi zaibatsu. Shibusawa firmly declined both offers in order to remain free for the work of promoting modern industry in general.

One of Shibusawa's chief concerns was the spread of the joint-stock form of enterprise. The traditional merchants shunned the pooling of capital for a common purpose, and the new strongmen of industry and finance, such as Iwasaki, sought their own aggrandizement and built up private empires. Shibusawa was strongly opposed to both types; he chided the old-fashioned merchants, and he fought Iwasaki's dictatorial monopoly tooth and nail by organizing a powerful rival shipping company. For Shibusawa the common good, the progress of the country's economy, was more important than personal gain and power, and he demonstrated this unselfish attitude time and again in organizing new joint enterprises from which he could expect little or no gain. He felt that the company form of enterprise was necessary not only in order to gather sufficient capital for large-scale ventures, but also because the capital owners were still too uneducated and immature for modern business management. The company form of enterprise made it possible to entrust direction and management to capable and progressive men, whether or not they had capital of their own. Shibusawa himself had become president of the Dai Ichi Bank because of his capabilities alone, and he in turn chose the managers for his own numerous enterprises on the same basis.

Shibusawa, like Fukuzawa, was most emphatic about the need for education in the conduct of large-scale enterprises, and in this he wanted his businessmen to be radically different from the Tokugawa merchants. According to Shibusawa, a modern businessman had to be able to evaluate trends and to understand the consequences of his plans and actions, for his own enterprise and also for the whole country; this could only be accomplished by means of a thorough education. He was so insistent upon learning as a prerequisite for his type of entrepreneur that he refused assistance and cooperation to those who failed to qualify. Suzuki Tōsaburō, the pioneer in sugar refining, recalled with bitterness that he had been refused a loan by Shibusawa on grounds of insufficient education.[10]

In 1874 Shibusawa, together with Mori Arinori, planned

the establishment of the first business school in Japan,
which developed into Hitotsubashi University. Under his
presidency, the Jitsugyō no Nihonsha (Japanese association of enterprise) published a periodical to bring business knowledge and ideas to those who could not attend
a school. As president of the Tokyo Chamber of Commerce and of the Bankers' Association, both of which he
founded in 1878, he exercised his leadership to form the
new business attitudes. The ever-recurring theme in his
many speeches was the necessity for the modern entrepreneur to be different from the old merchant in terms of
education, standards of honesty, and dedication to the
public good, while at the same time maintaining his independence from the government.[11]

Shibusawa was not content to be the recognized leader
in the top echelons of the Meiji industrial, banking, and
business communities. He also wanted to extend his influence over the younger generation. In his own house he
gathered a group of business students who became known
by the name Ryūmonsha (lit., "dragon door club"). They
published a periodical, the *Ryūmon zasshi* (Ryūmon periodical), one of the first in Japan to be dedicated to economic matters. In it were propagated the basic tenets of
Shibusawa's business ideology, which was essentially the
same as Fukuzawa's. In one article Shibusawa was compared to the famous warlord of the eleventh century,
Minamoto Yoshiie.[12] "Just as the samurai gathered behind
Minamoto to follow him into the battle of war, so now the
younger generation gathers around Shibusawa to follow
him into the battle of enterprise, as merchants of the
modern kind." [13]

Shibusawa's leadership in raising educational standards,
and consequently the efficiency and the self-respect of the
new business community, was imitated by many of the

pioneering entrepreneurs of his time. Among the fifty entrepreneurs selected for discussion in Chapter Seven, nine built schools at their own expense. Godai Tomoatsu established a private school in Osaka for the education of the children of merchants in order to break down their conservative business attitudes. The first three subjects taught there were accounting, economics, and arithmetic. The rapidly increasing number of students made enlargement of the school necessary within a few years.[14] Iwasaki, who was probably the most successful of all Meiji entrepreneurs, acted differently from Shibusawa in many ways, especially insofar as government connections and political machinations were concerned, but he agreed with him completely with respect to a thorough education. And Toyokawa Ryōhei, himself a Keiō man, made his most valuable contribution to Iwasaki's Mitsubishi company by scouting for talented college graduates and bringing them into that zaibatsu.[15]

Independence from the government and freedom from bureaucratism were very difficult to achieve in reality. As much as Fukuzawa insisted that private enterprise should be built "for profit and for the sake of Japan," the first thirty years posed such tremendous problems in terms of technology, organization, and, especially, capital supply that the ideal so much admired in Britain and the United States was almost unattainable. Shibusawa, however, took energetic steps in the direction of independence. He frequently scored the group of political merchants who made hay from government contracts and boasted of their titles and privileges, and he asserted that his basic motive in giving up his own government post was his desire to fill the vacuum of leadership in private enterprise.

Godai Tomoatsu also exchanged a government post for an entrepreneurial career in Osaka, although in his case political opposition was behind the move. He later received large favors from the Meiji government. Yet when he handed in his resignation, he told his friend Ōkubo: "There is no lack of able men in the imperial government; therefore I may now resign and descend to the level of the common people. I intend to promote henceforth the general state of business and industry, and to work for the prosperity of the people's enterprise. In this way I shall also be contributing to the prosperity and strength of the country and the nation." [16] This statement at least reveals the sorely felt need to boost private initiative, even if actions would not or could not always be in step with such pronouncements. For the time being, the private entrepreneur was not only a scarce commodity, but he enjoyed neither adequate capital backing nor social prestige. As Shibusawa once put it, he was like the tools in the kitchen, very useful but earning little attention as compared to the showpieces in the living room — meaning the officials.[17]

At the bottom of the widespread contempt for private business was the persistence of popular opinion concerning low business ethics and standards of honesty. The disorder in the business world since the opening of the ports aggravated the situation and brought the merchants' reputation to an all-time low. Shibusawa and his associates had to prove to the public that they were totally different from the speculators in the port cities or the monopoly traders of old. In order to stress this difference, Shibusawa went so far as to coin a new word for his type of businessman: the name *shōnin* (merchant) was to be replaced by *jitsugyōka* (entrepreneur, lit., "a man who undertakes a real task"). He defined a *jitsugyōka* as "someone who works with honesty for the establishment of industry." [18] In his mind honesty and industrial enterprise were linked. When

he once heard a graduate of the Imperial University remark at a banquet that in business matters "a lie must
sometimes also be considered as a way," he scolded the
man in public and insisted that a businessman should go
so far as to "vow to the Gods and to Buddha never to tell
a lie." [19] Other men followed Shibusawa's lead in fighting
for the honor of the businessman. Ōtani Kahei, a tea exporter of Yokohama, is probably best known for his untiring efforts to stamp out cheating and unreliability
within the trade association.

Indeed, Shibusawa did succeed in creating a new self-
respect among the entrepreneurs of the Meiji period; they
used the new word *jitsugyōka* with pride and eventually
came to be highly respected by the people. A large part of
his achievement must undoubtedly be attributed to the
bummei kaika mentality and to effective support by the
government. But the leadership of Fukuzawa and Shibusawa and of a few similarly minded men was most crucial
to the formation of the new status for private entrepreneurs.

As much as Shibusawa planned and founded new industrial undertakings, as generously as he encouraged and
supported the closely knit group of pioneering Meiji entrepreneurs in any work that would promote industrial
progress, he seemed little interested in building an industrial and financial empire of his own. Although he could
unquestionably have become a zaibatsu builder much like
Iwasaki, Ōkura, or Yasuda, he did not strive for this type
of power. The man who was connected with over six
hundred enterprises by way of presidential or advisory
positions often left control to others as soon as the enterprise was firmly established. Although he was president
of the Dai Ichi Bank from 1875 to his retirement in 1916,
his family owned no more than 4 percent of the bank's

stock by 1926.[20] Shibusawa was a man of cooperation; he wanted to serve the common cause, the cause of the country and of the business world.

Shibusawa's dedication was molded by his Confucian background. He used to carry the Analects of Confucius in his pocket and knew large parts of it by heart, quoting Confucius frequently in his speeches. In his Confucian outlook he differed from Fukuzawa whose thinking was molded by the English liberal school. Confucian ethics during the Tokugawa period had been an instrument to preserve the status quo. Shibusawa set out, in his own words, "to manage business enterprise using the Analects of Confucius." [21] It may be that it was precisely this fusion of the best of Japanese tradition with the most progressive ideas and methods of the West that gave Shibusawa his influence on the Japanese business world. But in a sense Shibusawa was a cross between a businessman and a government official. He never tired of proclaiming the need for self-respect in business for profit, but he acted half of the time like a Meiji government official, worrying and working on problems of economic and educational policy, of domestic and international politics. His thousands of speeches and addresses do not sound at all like those of a private businessman.

Perhaps Shibusawa's influence during his lifetime, and the great admiration he is accorded in Japan even today, can be explained by the fact that he was a transitional type, a businessman who was both a samurai and a Meiji official. This was an image that the samurai could imitate without lowering their idea of personal status. Shibusawa alone, of course, could not effect a change in the traditional valuation of business activity. Others donned the same robe of respectability and voiced the same kind of phrases; there is no need to investigate the sincerity of all these patriotic claims. They were intended for public consumption. When a class image is in the process of being transformed, one must not look too closely at actual performance; the image, once made creditable, can stand a good many factual discrepancies and contradictions.

In other countries, Germany for example, entrepreneurs also found it necessary to paint a new class image by claiming that they were working for the sake of the country. Some symbolic action or success itself in modern enterprise may then suffice to justify the claim of selfless dedication vis-à-vis the public. In this context, the situation in Russia in the second half of the nineteenth century deserves notice. The bourgeoisie, which was thriving at the expense of other groups, was despised and labeled base, greedy, and vulgar by the gentry, the intelligentsia and the peasants alike. Thus far the Russian situation can be seen as parallel to that of Tokugawa Japan. But in Russia the rehabilitation of the image of the merchant came very late, under the influence of the Marxian intellectuals, and even then the transformation was not complete. Entrepreneurial activity remained handicaped in Russia under the burden of the low esteem in which the business class was held.[22] In Japan entrepreneurial activity was stimulated by an early achievement of social respectability.

THE LOW PROFIT RATES

Even a *jitsugyōka* in Meiji Japan was in business primarily for money. The profit he earned was the yardstick of his success. One might take exception to the idea that money is the ultimate goal in all business activity. Most people, in Japan or elsewhere, are probably motivated ultimately by a desire for prestige, power, or success as such; but if they are in business, the achievement of the ultimate goal will depend on and be measured by the monetary returns they can earn. A man may operate a shop or a factory for charity and give away all his profits, but if he fails to earn them in the first place he is probably a bad businessman.

It is understood that entrepreneurial activity, especially in a pioneering period such as the industrialization of Meiji Japan, is beset with risks and uncertainties. But a rationally calculating entrepreneur has cognizance of the chances involved and does not let himself be carried away by undue optimism, like a gambler. Therefore, on the average and in the long run, we expect entrepreneurs as a group actually to earn the going rates for routine business activity, plus an extra reward for their innovations. In Schumpeter's view, the innovator is the one agent in the economy who earns profits in the strict sense; the returns on capital in the noninnovating enterprises occur as interest, rents, and wages. We should therefore expect the *jitsugyōka* of modern Japanese industry to have been rewarded for their risk-taking efforts by high profit rates, certainly higher than those in the traditional business sectors. A persistence of low profit rates in the private sector of modern industry, on the other hand, would present us with a problem in assigning motives to these entrepreneurs.

In order to answer the question of entrepreneurial motivation, it is important to ascertain comparative returns in the various sectors of the Japanese economy during the time when modern private industry was struggling for its existence and when it was making its first efforts toward independence of the government. Returns within the government enterprises pose no problem, since the government is not supposed to be in business for profit. But it is extremely difficult to draw the dividing line between government and nongovernment operations because of the extent to which large-scale modern enterprise was tied to the government by direct and indirect subsidies. We need to know the rates of return on private capital only, and on private capital that was invested by free choice. Clearly, alternative investment opportunities do not enter into the decision process if they are not open to a particular entrepreneur, either because of lack of knowledge or because of outside interference. It can be seen that to find and use comparative profit rates in various investment sectors as indicators of entrepreneurial motivation encounters a host of snags.

As a first step I shall try to establish the comparative rates of return on as broad a basis as possible, taking first the going interest rates and profits on nonindustrial investments in the 1880s. Then I shall investigate profit rates in private industry, with particular attention to those sectors and those specific cases where government initiative and subsidies were small or completely absent. Because there are no general statistics, it will be necessary to try the patience of the reader by detailing many individual cases. But from these descriptions he may glean a partial answer to the motivation problem and thus be compensated for the lack of succinctness in what is basically a matter of statistics.

The Alternatives to Industrial Investments

Interest rates during the mid 1880s must serve as a basis for our comparison of rates of return on capital. Anyone who invests his money into some enterprise can, as an alternative, either lend out his money or at least put it into a bank for safekeeping. Rates charged by banks on loans during the period from 1875 to 1884 averaged 15.09 percent, with the lowest at 10.80 percent in 1883. Interest rates on time deposits varied around 4–5 percent.[23] Of prime importance, of course, are the rates charged on bank loans. We have to assume theoretically that an entrepreneur borrows capital and pays interest on it, his profit being the difference between the interest on his loan and the total net return. If he uses his own capital, he forgoes the opportunity of lending it out against interest. Therefore profit rates in industry should be above the rates charged on bank loans. The rates on time deposits paid by banks are the absolute floor; a man who has money can at least put it into the bank.

Banking profits constitute another important item of comparison because we may assume that an investor in an industrial enterprise could as an alternative buy stock in a bank or perhaps establish a bank of his own. The profit rates of national banks during the 1876–1894 period averaged 16.29 percent on paid-up capital, ranging from 19.32 percent in 1876 down to 13.59 percent in 1886.[24] A statistical survey of all Japanese banks shows approximately the same picture for the same period, with only two years, 1877 and 1878, under 14 percent, and an average of 15.6 percent.[25] Surveys of Tokyo banks in 1881 and 1883, with 25 (leaving out 2 with over 100 percent profits) and 31 banks reporting, similarly showed averages of 19.80 percent and 12.10 percent on paid-up capital.[26] These figures should suffice to indicate that the banks were making somewhat higher profits than the going rates charged on loans. The general figures, of course, obscure the variations of individual banks, but we have seen earlier that few banks closed during this period and that the overall picture in banking was one of stability.

Trading enterprises are not as easy to handle as banks because, for one thing, they differ widely in character and type of operation and, for another, statistical evidence for these years is not easy to find. In fact I could find nothing that may represent a general picture of profits in trading, except for two surveys from Tokyo for the years 1881 and 1883. They have many deficiencies; we do not know how the profits were calculated or how such things as stocks, depreciation, and good will were handled. But it seemed desirable to take figures for as early a time in the 1880s as possible because my argument is based on the opportunity-cost principle. The entrepreneur who invested in industry, say during 1885 or 1888, had to base his calculations on returns in trading in the preceding years because investment there could be considered an alternative possibility. So statistics from after 1890, even if more reliable, would not do for my purposes.

In 1881, 22 trading establishments reported their total profit and loss figures.[27] The average profit rate was 14.4 percent, with the highest at 96.1 percent and the lowest at 0.3 percent. The average capital invested in these businesses was 48,305 yen, with the highest at 600,000 yen and the lowest at 313 yen. Eleven businesses had over 10,000 yen capital and averaged 10.6 percent profits, less than the overall average. It is anybody's guess whether and by how much these rates would have to be revised upward or downward if they were made to correspond to modern bookkeeping rules.

The 1883 survey presents profit rates of 24 establishments of the same type as in the 1881 survey.[28] If again we leave out two nonrepresentative businesses with over 100 percent profits, the other 22 have an average profit rate of 15.2 percent. Their breakdown according to capital shows that 6 businesses with under 10,000 yen capital averaged 18.6 percent; another 8 with capital between 10,000 and 49,999 yen earned 11.1 percent; and the last 8, with 50,000 yen capital or more, averaged 16.7 percent in profits.

Transportation enterprises are listed in the 1883 survey with 9 establishments; their profit rates reach the average of 11.2 percent with only one enterprise left out as non-representative. Two of those included, however, the Nippon Railway Company and the Kyōdō Unyu Company, each with over one million yen capital, had as low profits for that year as 3.4 percent and 1.3 percent, respectively. It is here for the first time that we encounter the phenomenon of very low profit rates in large-scale modern enterprises; more will be said about this later.

Manufacturing companies listed in the same two surveys from Tokyo include a large variety of types, with both old and new technologies. Furthermore there are no clues as to the structure of capital and ratios between total paid-up capital and fixed investments, and no way of determining how depreciation was handled. Direct or indirect government subsidies (cheap sales, special procurements, and such) may also be involved to make simple profit and loss statements all but valueless. To make matters worse, we must remember once more that the years 1881 and 1883 marked the beginning and the worst period of the Matsukata deflation. This deflation, though necessary and on the whole salutary in its effects, was the worst storm that the young Meiji industries had to weather.

Yet when all this has been said, there simply are no other data. Consequently I shall use these as very rough indicators of general direction rather than as exact statistics. Because of the importance of finding indications of profit trends in manufacturing, particularly of the modern type, as compared with alternative return possibilities, I shall then probe further into various industries and individual enterprises.

The Tokyo survey of 1881 lists a total of 90 manufacturing establishments.[29] If we leave out again those with profit rates of over 100 percent and less than 1 percent as non-representative, the remaining 84 averaged 18.8 percent in net returns on paid-up capital. The breakdown according to capital reads as follows: 28 firms with 10,000 yen and more capital averaged 14.3; 43 firms with capital between 1,000 and 9,999 yen averaged 17.1 percent; and 17 firms with under 1,000 yen capital averaged 21.6. We notice here a marked tendency for the smaller establishments to have higher profits than the larger ones.

The 1883 survey mirrors the severe effects of the Matsukata deflation: of the 80 reporting firms, 14 operated at a loss, while 19 showed profit rates exceeding 100 percent. If we lump all of them together and average the profit rates, we get 51.9 percent, obviously a meaningless figure. We would expect to find a lower-than-normal average, of course. Could it be that the superprofits in some cases were nothing but returns on sellouts prior to liquidation? I must leave the explanation to the imagination of the reader. It is perhaps worthy of note that of the 20 weaving establishments, all rather small-scale with on the average not more than 2,500 yen capital, half operated at a loss and the other half earned superprofits that pulled their combined average profits up to 52 percent. The years 1883 and 1884 saw the ruin of many such small-scale enterprises.

Taken as they stand, the two surveys indicate something about the general conditions of the traditional, rather small-scale manufacturing enterprises. The year 1881 provides us with a meaningful and not unexpected set of profit rates; the year 1883 has too many erratic data and the average is meaningless. With due reservations about the significance of these figures on capital returns in the 1880s, the picture in summary looks as follows:

Interest rates, 1875–1884	15.09%
Profit rates of banks	
National banks, 1876–1894	16.29%
All banks, 1876–1894	15.60%
Tokyo banks, 1881	19.8%
Tokyo banks, 1883	12.1%
Profit rates of trading enterprises	
Tokyo, 1881	14.4%
Tokyo, 1883	15.2%
Profit rates of transportation enterprises	
Tokyo, 1883	11.2%
Profit rates of manufacturing enterprises	
Tokyo, 1881	18.8%
(Tokyo, 1883	51.9%)

In spite of the weakness of the Tokyo survey data, we can probably assume with a high degree of confidence that the prevailing rates of return in all the well-established lines of business stayed at an average of 10 percent or higher. With this much ascertained, let us now take a close look at the modern large-scale enterprises that should be considered as alternative investment opportunities for private capital.

Profit Rates in Industrial Enterprises

The railways are here included in my "industry" concept; cotton spinning and railways were the beneficiaries of a private-investment boom. The initial public aversion and even hostility to railway building rapidly changed to great enthusiasm after the completion of the first government lines and the private Tokyo-Aomori line. The Tokyo-Aomori line was founded in 1881, and two years later dividends of 10 percent were paid to stockholders. Probably as a consequence of this success, no fewer than ten railway companies had been founded by 1887, with 42 million yen in paid-up capital and 1,000 miles of lines laid.[30] The steepest growth occurred in the years between 1887 and

1890, as indicated by the increase of capital in the regional railway companies, from 12,130 million to 52,390 million yen. In 1887 a Private Railway Regulation Act was passed which set up standards for the foundation and operation of private companies. Among the outstanding entrepreneurs of the early Meiji era, we find many who founded or actively stimulated the founding of several such railway companies.

If the first railway company was a success, how did the others fare in terms of profit rates? This question can easily be answered from statistics on capital, fixed investments, and returns on capital, as well as on fixed investments, over the period from 1883 to 1893.

Year	Paid-up capital (million yen)	Fixed invest- ments (million yen)	Profits on fixed invest- ments	Profits on paid-up capital (computed)
1883	5,966	905	21.00%	3.18%
1884	11,830	2,062	12.80%	2.24%
1885	11,830	3,106	10.20%	2.68%
1886	12,080	5,493	8.90%	4.03%
1887	12,130	6,703	11.80%	6.51%
1888	31,870	11,834	9.50%	3.53%
1889	45,390	20,366	7.00%	3.14%
1890	52,390	33,816	4.80%	3.11%
1891	52,960	44,062	4.80%	4.00%
1892	56,235	47,508	5.60%	4.73%
1893	63,145	52,050	6.70%	5.49%

Nihon keizai tōkei sōkan (Survey of Japanese economic statistics), ed. Asahi shinbunsha (Asahi Newspaper Co.; Tokyo, 1930), p. 820.

The table indicates that these private regional railways averaged, over 11 years, a bare 7.65 percent on their fixed investments and 3.88 percent on the paid-up capital. With the increasing ratio of fixed investments to paid-up capital —that is, with the extension of the mileage — these two rates moved closer together, to around 5 percent. The government-operated lines did not fare much better. Their returns on fixed investments moved gradually upward, from 3.90 percent in 1886 to as high as 10.40 percent in 1896, the average over these 11 years being 7.32 percent.[31]

With such poor results in the railway companies over at least one decade, we cannot very well attribute the investment fever solely to the effect of the 10 percent dividend rate of the Tokyo-Aomori Railroad. Even the most ardent optimists would soon have learned better. There must have been strong noneconomic stimuli in operation which supported a dogged optimism in the face of prolonged low returns.

It cannot be claimed that the investors, if they were samurai, remained unaware of the opportunity-cost principle. We have an interesting example of samurai calculation in the case of the Maruya Company, now known as Maruzen, which was established in 1869. The samurai founders first made a thorough inquiry into the going profit rates in Tokyo and then decided that their trading establishment must yield at least 15 percent; they set up a very interesting and elaborate system of rewards and punishments for workers and managers to assure that they would actually receive their 15 percent dividend payments.[32] Undoubtedly the men who rushed into railways had the same opportunity to investigate the returns of existing companies and to find out that returns were on the whole very low. Nor were the railways the only instance of this apparently irrational enthusiasm for modern industry, as we shall see.

The full impact of foreign competition was felt in the import-competing industries; they were not shielded by any protective tariffs to speak of and had to grapple internally with the two basic problems of technology and lack of demand. Lack of demand may sound paradoxical at a time of large imports, but the market for imported goods was not automatically ready to absorb the competing products "made in Japan," which were often of poorer quality. It was felt all the more that import-competing industries had to be given special attention and that their promotion was a national task of great urgency. While by their very nature the import-competing industries were mainly modern enterprises, we may expect to find here also both prolonged low returns on capital and a marked display of motives other than that of private profit maximization.

The following table lists the most important import-competing industries and indicates their position toward the end of our period of investigation, in 1892.

Industry	Number of companies	Paid-up capital (1,000 yen)	Number of employees	Power (horsepower)
Textiles	47	11,224	29,103	8,334
Paper	37	1,575	2,744	2,466
Shipbuilding	13	522	3,072	1,023
Machines	18	45	1,041	206
Cement	14	775	919	694
Bricks	39	538	2,122	145
Glass	19	192	555	8
Matches	73	452	15,264	32
Soap	16	97	337	6
Electrical equipment	12	1,710	135	1,021
Type printing	95	556	4,299	28
Total	383	17,686	59,591	13,983

Takahashi Kamekichi, *Meiji Taishō sangyō hattatsu shi* (The history of manufacturing during the Meiji and Taishō eras; Tokyo, 1929), p. 240.

I again call attention to the fact that the Matsukata deflation from 1881 to 1884 had a shattering impact on the young industries. The impact of the deflation is reflected

in the fall of interest rates from 14.05 percent in 1881 to
9.10 percent in 1886; between 1882 and 1887, about 7
million yen of export surplus was accumulated annually;
the general price index fell from 162 in 1881 to 110 in
1884.[33] By 1885, the inconvertible government notes had
been absorbed, and the ensuing years marked the establishment of numerous companies in cotton spinning and
in a number of other import-competing industries. The
losses incurred during the Matsukata deflation must be
attributed largely to the extraordinary external conditions
and cannot be of much use to us in substantiating the
case for noneconomic motivations. It is the whole picture
over this period, with external disturbances and internal
difficulties taken together, that will serve as an illustration of the odds that faced the entrepreneurs.

Cotton spinning, which had been so much stressed and
promoted as being in the national interest, was severely
hit by the deflation. The president of the Ichikawa Mill
said in a speech that during the years of the depression
many mills had to sell almost at raw-material cost; prices
dropped by 20–30 percent and stocks of unsold yarns
piled up.[34] The mills, which had all been enthusiastically
established with strong government encouragement, were
in severe trouble by 1883–84.

The Hiroshima Spinning Mill had been built by the
government as a model enterprise, for 49,000 yen, and was
sold to 5,860 samurai shareholders for 12,000 yen. After
seventeen months of operation under the samurai, in 1883
a total operating deficit of 23,000 yen had been reached.
The government then placed the mill under prefectural
supervision, and regular reports had to be filed with the
Ministry of Agriculture and Trade. From 1884 on, operating losses were avoided, but a considerable debt load remained for a number of years.[35]

One author gives figures of total profits and losses for twelve mills, covering sporadically the period from 1882 to 1888.[36] If we take the initial capital investments and calculate an average from twenty-six profit-and-loss statements on these twelve mills, we arrive at a 6.17 percent profit per mill; this figure should, if anything, be revised downward because of additional unspecified capital investments that were made after the foundation of the mills. Another author gives 6 percent as the average dividend rate for cotton spinning in 1883.[37] This dividend rate reflects closely the profit rates, since in that year only 2,000 yen of undistributed profits were retained against 280,000 yen capital in that industry.

The depressed state of mechanical cotton spinning caused concern in official circles. At a time when cotton cloth and cotton yarns made up some 30 percent of total imports, the success and expansion of spinning was of vital importance to the national economy. But verbal encouragement would fail to find a response unless the underlying problems were solved. The large capital suppliers still avoided investments in cotton spinning.

Capital scarcity and technical difficulties were the basic reasons for the failure of the two-thousand-spindle mills. The ratio of overhead to productive capacity was much too high, and low labor efficiency and underutilization of machinery because of exclusively day-time operation added to the problem. The use of water power necessitated stoppages when the rivers were flooded or dried up. A dire lack of trained technicians caused breakdowns and rapid depreciation of costly machinery. And on top of all this came the poor quality of the Japanese yarns, which were no match for the imported quality yarns.

Shibusawa, who as president of the Dai Ichi Bank was well aware of the foreign-exchange problem, decided to make a supreme effort to break the impasse in cotton spinning. He succeeded in interesting a few top entrepreneurs and a number of nobles in founding a large spinning mill. In 1883 the Osaka Mill was established by this group with 280,000 yen capital; the mills then in existence usually had no more than 30,000–70,000 yen. Under the expert technician and manager Yamabe Takeo, a Keiō graduate, the mill became a resounding success. Yamabe used steam power and introduced night-shift work for this 10,500-spindle mill; in the year after operations started, 18 percent in dividends were already being paid. In 1886 the mill was enlarged to 31,000 spindles, and in 1887 the dividend rate was up to 30 percent.[38]

The phenomenal success of the Osaka Mill broke the caution and timidity of the wealthy Osaka men, especially of the cotton merchants. Between 1886 and 1894, 33 new mills were established: the average capacity per mill rose to 10,000 spindles and the profit rates now compared favorably with those in traditional investment industries.[39] Most of the founders and capital suppliers in this period were rich merchants; they needed no patriotic enthusiasm and did not claim to work "for the national economy" or to "stop the imports." They invested for profits and received them.

Paper manufacturing received almost no help from the government. The first mill on Japanese soil was built by the economic reformer of Tosa han, Gotō Shōjirō. When paper production encountered many unforeseen difficulties, the mill was sold to its engineer in 1876. He in turn sold it after a short time to Sumitomo, and it was shortly sold again. It changed hands so often because it could not be made into a profitable enterprise; losses alternated with very low returns.[40] The daimyo of Hiroshima also had a paper mill built, which piled up losses for three years and sold no paper. It was only when the government ordered paper for title deeds from this mill that final ruin was avoided: nevertheless, low returns continued for several more years.[41]

The Ōji Paper Mill, founded in 1875 by Shibusawa with capital mainly from Mitsui and Shimada, was the largest and most famous paper mill of the early Meiji era. Shibusawa established it because of his belief that paper and printing were prerequisites for the progress of learning and of civilization in general. He regretted the amount of attention being paid to armaments and heavy industries.[42] After five years the mill was considered quite successful, achieving a profit rate of 10 percent. But the young apprentice Ōkawa, Shibusawa's nephew, wrote a memorandum to his uncle explaining that a 10 percent rate could by no means be regarded as satisfactory when, at the same time, the interest rate charged by banks was as high as 12–13 percent. Considering the risks and the initial waiting period involved, the profits should rise to at least 20 percent. Ōkawa, under the influence of the English economists, was thinking in terms of economic rationality. His memorandum contained the sentence: "The famous economist Smith determines the average rate of profits on capital from the general rate of interest." [43] Ōkawa was sent abroad to study paper production and after his return eventually made the Ōji Paper Mill a great success. All told, by 1878 Japan had four paper mills, and their number did not rise above five until 1889, although the quantity and quality of the paper produced did improve throughout the whole period.

The pioneering attitudes and the courage that the entrepreneurs displayed in founding of modern industrial enterprises at this time are brought out by the example of Sakuma Sadaichi. He had gone to great pains to build a printing establishment and then, when he was ordered to do a book with cardboard covers, he decided not to import the cardboard but to set up a factory to produce it. He succeeded in his drive to raise 170,000 yen share capital and established a cardboard factory in 1885, but it operated so inefficiently that the shares very soon fell from 50 yen to 6 yen. Sakuma handed control of the enterprise over to the "industrial troubleshooter," Asano Sōichirō. Still, the enterprise remained in the red for eleven years.[44] Depressed conditions in paper manufacturing were mainly traceable to technical difficulties, which resulted in poor quality and high prices, and to lack of general market demand. Shibusawa and Sakuma Sadaicha seem to have had some definite ideas about the necessity for paper and cardboard manufacturing, assigning the factor of profitability to second place.

Cement production was started by the government in its Fukagawa works in 1874. In 1884 the enterprise was first rented and later sold to Asano. At the time when Asano was to take over, the prospects were so bleak that Shibusawa felt it necessary to warn him and to suggest that he might better invest in cotton spinning. Asano is on record as having replied that the raw material for cotton spinning had to be imported in part from China, while all raw materials for cement production were available at no cost in Japan.[45] Asano succeeded, owing to the combination of his own entrepreneurial genius, the technical skill of his engineer, Utsunomiya Saburō,[46] and the large government orders he received. Profit figures, however, are not available from the company records.

By 1890 a total of ten cement mills were in existence in Japan, with total capital of over one million yen. The records stress the fact that profit rates were very low in almost all of these establishments.[47] The Aichi Cement

Mill, for example, constructed four furnaces in 1887, bought two fret machines, and was to set out on a large scale, but remained in the red for some years and was then sold.[48] Onoda Cement, which was the most successful of all after Asano Cement, reported its first real success in 1890, ten years after its establishment, when it could distribute 10 percent in dividends. Before that year, the rate of dividend payments was considerably lower, and in some years no dividends were paid, owing to operating losses.[49] Dividends, of course, do not necessarily reflect profit rates, but in those years they were usually quoted to describe the profitability of an enterprise. In cement production the basic problems were the same as in paper manufacturing — namely, technical difficulties that resulted in high unit costs in spite of low wage levels and the lack of market demand. But the optimism and courage of the entrepreneurs were undaunted because they were struck with the idea of producing cement from "dirt at home" and thus preventing the outflow of gold to pay for imported cement.

Glass manufacturing, like cement production, had been started by the central government. The Shinagawa glass factory was established in 1876, but it was run by the Ministry of Industry at continued losses that totaled 15,000 yen.[50] In 1884 Nishimura Katsuzō, a very patriotic and dogged entrepreneur, rented the glass factory from the ministry jointly with a partner. He lost 13,000 yen in that one year, and his partner wanted no more of it. Nishimura bought the factory in 1885 for 79,950 yen, to be paid in installments over fifty-five years with payments starting in 1890. He lost no time in trying to modernize the plant; he made a trip to Europe to study production techniques and introduced a few improvements. In 1888 he joined with Shibusawa Eiichi and Masuda Takashi and made the enterprise a joint-stock company, with 150,000 yen capital. But the factory remained uncompetitive; [51] it was closed in 1892 because of continued losses. In 1887 another glass factory was built, by the Iwaki Glass Company with Shibusawa, Asano, and Masuda as its main shareholders. Shibusawa pushed the plan because he was worried about the rising imports of glass. This company lasted only three years and had to labor under the same difficulties as the Nishimura Company.[52]

Iron mining must also be regarded as an import-competing industry because a considerable amount of iron and steel were imported into Japan. The government decided to modernize and enlarge some of the existing small-scale iron mines in the Kamaishi area. In 1874 the government investments in these mines began; among other things, machines were imported and a ship for the transportation of pig iron was procured. Smelting did not start until 1880 but by that time a total of 2.5 million yen had been used up. Technical difficulties, insufficient supply of charcoal, and destruction of buildings by fire caused a stoppage of work after only 196 days of actual operation. The total pig iron produced during government management was worth 175,126 yen.[53]

This truly spectacular failure of one of the largest government investments turned even the most optimistic officials against any further government commitment in iron mining. It was argued that Japan should continue importing iron from abroad because mining still presented too many difficulties to Japanese technology, and Japanese iron ore was too poor in quality to warrant large investments.[54] The Kamaishi mines were for sale, but nobody was interested in purchasing them. Tanaka Chōbei, a political merchant, bought initially only the residue of iron ore that had already been mined. In this deal he lost

30,000 yen.[55] But Tanaka was convinced by his head clerk, Yokoyama Hisatarō, to purchase the mines and all the equipment and to continue the work of the government. Yokoyama's arguments are interesting and reflect not only his own attitudes but also those of many entrepreneurs of the period.

Yokoyama argued that a few million yen in government investments and eight years of effort must not be permitted to go to waste. Somebody must continue the operation of the mines or all the machines would rot and enormous amounts of ore would be lost to Japan. He further stressed that a defeat at this stage would discourage for a long time any further attempts in iron mining. His final argument was that the government would certainly not fail to lend assistance to someone who undertook to continue its own frustrated efforts.[56] His confidence in government assistance follows from his first two arguments: if an entrepreneur acted with a view to general economic necessity he could rightly expect official assistance; public and private enterprises were not strictly separated, but were viewed as integral parts of one great effort in Meiji Japan.

The import-competing industries reviewed here owed their staggering difficulties both to competition from imports and to internal technical problems. But the persistence of low returns over long periods was not unusual in other modern enterprises; there, too, it took courage and perseverance to carry on to final success. For instance, the famous Tomioka filature, which was sold by the government for 130,000 yen after five years of operation, totaled in the next five years losses of 159,800 yen.[57] The shipyards fared quite similarly. The pioneers in leather-good manufacturing and sugar refining also had to overcome long periods of losses and low returns. It is significant that these were all ventures with large capital investments, usually over 100,000 yen, as contrasted to the average capital of the Tokyo manufacturing firms, in 1881, of 13,790 yen.

This survey of import-competing industries and other modern enterprises has often lacked exact figures, because they are not available. But the descriptive approach thus necessitated should also have conveyed an impression of the prevailing attitudes, above all of the stubborn determination, of the first entrepreneurs. Persistence and continued pioneering in spite of low returns over long periods is one of the characteristics of all the leading Meiji entrepreneurs. I may add here two more cases in which this typical trait was displayed by Shibusawa.

A brick factory was founded by Shibusawa and Masuda, with 200,000 yen in capital.[58] Unexpectedly, various technical troubles developed and the anticipated government demand did not materialize. Consequently the brick factory operated for five years at a loss. The stockholders insisted that the project be abandoned, but Shibusawa remained adamant and himself invested more capital in it. Only after the Sino-Japanese War, ten years after the start of the factory, were satisfactory dividends of 10 percent paid.

The Tokyo Gas Company was started by a government official in 1871, but was managed so poorly that Shibusawa was asked to take charge of it.[59] By 1876 a total of 171,536 yen had been invested, with the total receipts during the five years amounting to only 6,310 yen. It took the Tokyo Gas Company thirteen years to achieve the first small gains. Again, lack of demand was the most important difficulty: people did not trust the new lighting system. Shibusawa distributed pamphlets on the use of gas light and gave parties for shopkeepers, but he was still unable to change the prevailing attitudes. After a while even the city council voted to abolish the enterprise, and here, as in many other cases, the personal courage and prestige of Shibusawa prevailed. The company continued and, after years of operating losses, success was finally achieved. Even then success for a few years meant no more than a bare 5–10 percent profit rate.

The obvious questions that arise in view of these persistent low profits and the technological problems pertain to capital supply and to the motivations for investment. How was it possible that such large losses could be absorbed? From what source did the entrepreneurs gather the capital to afford these typically long waiting periods? What motivated them to keep on innovating in spite of the complex problems?

The question about capital supply for these private ventures cannot be answered easily, for the methods of securing capital were involved and by no means uniform. We shall see in Chapter Six how the most successful entrepreneurs — those who built empires of industry and finance — gathered their capital. Government subsidies played an important part, but while some received much, others got almost nothing. Direct subsidies in the form of grants, low-interest loans, and cheap sales of government enterprises were perhaps not so important as the opportunities created for the political merchants to amass fortunes as official army suppliers during military operations, and in other types of official and semiofficial trading and banking transactions. And in the frequent cases where future entrepreneurs accumulated huge gains as supply merchants or as foreign traders and merchants of fortune in the turbulent years around the Restoration, we still need an explanation for why these same men began to invest in modern industry in spite of the obvious risks involved. There must have been pressures and inducements in operation that do not become apparent in profit and loss figures, and to these I now turn.

THE QUESTION OF ECONOMIC RATIONALITY

There is risk in attempting to specify the motives for investment decisions. A man himself often does not know precisely why he makes one decision as against another; it is all the less likely that someone else should know the reason. The records that we have were not written from the viewpoint of psychological or historical accuracy; are lavish in praise of their heroes and stress lofty motivations in order to add to their stature. The patriotic angle in particular is often strongly emphasized, because these times were zealous ones. But such post-factum biographical idolizations must be discounted as sources for serious research on motivation.

I am not concerned here with the motivations of individual men, but rather with the trends and prevailing public valuations that demanded at least outward conformity. There is little doubt that the average Meiji entrepreneur was largely guided by the same motivations that prevail in other times and circumstances. But a part of his actions was determined by quite special forces, and it was this that often tipped the scale in favor of decisions that may puzzle the pure-bred profit maximizer.

The particular way in which modern technology entered Japan certainly had much to do with the kind of response offered by the pioneers of industry. The task was felt to be a challenge, not only personally but socially and nationally. Enough has been said on this point in Chapter Four in dealing with the *bummei kaika* and *fukoku kyōhei* attitudes. Cases were not few in which entrepreneurs stubbornly carried on because they hated to concede defeat — they considered themselves representatives of Japan, as do athletes in the modern Olympic Games. Or an entrepreneur could become completely absorbed in his task after he had achieved some initial success. This is of course a rather common phenomenon, found frequently among artists and scholars, but also among industrialists. Asano Sōichirō, the pioneer in cement production is an example. He used to spend all day in his factory until he finally became ill and threw up blood; yet he could not be persuaded to take a rest. Asked whether he loved money more than his life, he replied that more than money, and more than his own life, he loved his work. If his work so required, he did not mind giving everything to it.[60]

If we leave out the more common motivations that were not specific to the Meiji era, and those which of themselves cannot explain the persistence of a dynamic innovational drive in spite of high risks and low profits, we have to seek out a strong supplementary motivating force elsewhere. There is much circumstantial evidence: we know the general patterns of thought of the period; a clear picture can be gained of the ideology of Shibusawa and a few other business leaders. From this material we can form a hypothesis about prevailing motivations among entrepreneurs; the hypothesis can be made plausible, but it will be open to challenge. Although the attitudes of the entrepreneurs must be viewed in their complex entirety, we can perhaps best examine them under three headings, each throwing light on a particular facet of essentially the same phenomenon.

Optimism: Miscalculations and Time Horizons

Entrepreneurs are probably more often than not optimistic; otherwise they would not commit themselves to untried things. The early Japanese entrepreneurs were great optimists because of their unbounded faith in Western technology and because of their own ignorance of the practical difficulties involved. We can probably attribute much of their initiative to sanguine miscalculation. The steady encouragements offered by the government contributed to this state of mind.

We have seen that the rush to found national banks must be explained largely by the lack of other investment possibilities and by the strong government stress on the certainty of success. In cotton spinning, too, the same factors were operating. The enthusiasts of the first years did expect to reap high returns on their capital investments. Much of the railway boom, at least initially, was undoubtedly also the result of this kind of miscalculation.

Optimistic miscalculations also occur in advanced nations among seasoned entrepreneurs, but these entrepreneurs have the advantage of reliable standards of comparison, and are able and even forced to take a cool and rational look at the actual risks and uncertainties. In developed countries, where the innovations are carried out against a background of a known general technology and where experts are available, optimism will be kept in bounds by the facts. In Meiji Japan the harsh facts were often disclosed only after the investment decisions had been made. In Japan, however, there were frequent cases wherein optimism played a more active role. My impression is that the more important entrepreneurs were not so much victims of miscalculation as they were men who consciously viewed future returns according to a long time horizon and by applying unusually optimistic discounting factors. In order to understand this dynamic optimism, we must first examine briefly these methods of discounting.

The rational choice among various investment possibilities depends essentially on the discounting factor. Even if the Meiji entrepreneurs did not bother about the details of discounting procedures, they must have known the general rule that the present value of an income stream shrinks with a rise in the interest rate. High returns after a waiting period of five years look different if a 5 percent or a 10 percent rate prevails; the same investment may be desirable at 5 percent and may be completely irrational at 10 percent. This means simply that interest rates, which are but an expression of the relative scarcity of capital, dictate through the free play of the money market the types and gestation periods of investments. If capital is scarce, long-term investments with initially low returns will be "vetoed" by the high capital cost, no matter how important such investments may be in the long run and for the economy as a whole. The high discounting factor makes all future benefits shrink too much relative to the opportunity cost involved. The market mechanism directs funds through high interest rates toward present rather than future benefits, since the latter would require too much immediate sacrifice.

From all we have seen so far, the leading Meiji entrepreneurs did not discount rationally by the prevailing interest rates or by opportunity costs. They gave little weight to the sacrifices they imposed both on the public and on themselves. They had instead some absolute goal, some nondiscounted future value in mind. With their newly acquired faith in the modern era and all that went with it, they could not be shaken by intermediate losses; they knew that in the end they would succeed.

The conflict between the long view and the short became evident at the collapse of the Kyoto Pottery Company. This company was established in 1887 by the leading entrepreneur of Kyoto, Tanaka Gentarō, with 200,000 yen in capital from various sources. Tanaka's intention was to combine Japanese traditional skill in pottery with the latest production techniques of the West, and to manufacture pottery on a large scale for export. A delegation went abroad to study modern pottery, machines worth 200,000 yen were imported, and the total of fixed investments rose to 500,000 yen. But technical difficulties and unexpectedly strong foreign competition caused losses. The shareholders insisted on dividend payments, and when they did not receive any for five years they demanded that the enterprise be dissolved. A report on the collapse of the company blamed the failure on the "stupid" and short-sighted shareholders who wanted immediate results and would not tighten their belts; with more time the pottery factory could certainly have become a success.[61]

The leading entrepreneurs had firm faith in their final success, and they were vindicated. While those who kept investing in the traditional sectors gradually fell behind, the returns of the new enterprises began to skyrocket. The view of the top entrepreneurs was basically dynamic, not static. They believed in the rise of a new order which they themselves, by their innovations, would bring about. All that was said previously about the *bummei kaika* ideology is relevant here. It did not make sense to the entrepreneurs to discount according to opportunity costs at a time when things were changing so fast and when a flourishing business of today might be completely pushed to the wall in a few years. It was important that, in a sense, present values and present sacrifices be ignored. The abacus was of no use in measuring future trends, which could only be evaluated by men who did not nostalgically look back to the past.

It was said of Asano, by his son, that he did not make profit a necessary condition for the foundation of an enterprise. If the work was "in the interest of the public" and "economically reasonable," he would make a start no matter whether the profits earned would be 5 percent or 10 percent. In spite of this, however, he was sure of eventual success; in this respect he was a real *jitsugyōka* (entrepreneur) although he had started out to become a *shōnin* (merchant).[62]

The matter of the time horizon, of choosing the length of the investment and gestation periods, is of crucial importance in the process of economic development. Many a latecomer country of today faces this choice in determining its own perspective. Which types of investment should be given priority in view of the all-around scarcity of capital? The maximization of the present value of discounted future income may not be the best criterion for decisions. This approach does not take into account the dynamic chain reaction of large investments in key industries. The static application of the discounting principle may unduly permit scarce capital to be continuously siphoned into traditional lines of trade and manufacturing, or even into usurious moneylending, and thus forestall economic progress. Yet for the entrepreneur who intends to maximize nothing but his profit, the static approach appears as the optimum. Why should he bear the brunt of initial losses and low returns and set the economy into motion through his own sacrifice?

In today's underdeveloped countries the strategic pioneering investments are usually carried out by government planning agencies, which can impose the burden upon the whole population. Steel mills and irrigation dams will not only pay in the long run but, a very important point, they will change the structure of the economy; they will encourage a bold forward look by the people and kindle a sense of national purpose and achievement. This, ultimately, will far outweigh all the temporary hardships and losses that are unavoidable in the large new ventures of latecomer countries.

It was auspicious for Meiji Japan that, at a time when the government could not continue its initial building program, private entrepreneurs continued the task with almost the same bold perspective that is so characteristic of government planners. The long time horizon of the Meiji entrepreneurs is a fact, but it too calls for an explanation. One has been mentioned already: the entrepreneurs' faith in progress, their sense of being pioneers in a new era, and their optimism with respect to the new technology. However, I think that there were two more important, noneconomic, motives.

The Noncapitalist Mentality

Shibusawa wrote and spoke frequently about the ideal entrepreneur. He had to be, above all, a man with a keen sense of responsibility for the welfare of society. "While pursuing one's own advantage one should be also mindful of the opportunity for others. As one wishes to achieve one's own welfare and happiness, one has also the duty to exert oneself for the state and for society." [63] Shibusawa's business attitudes, while progressive in many ways, were hardly touched by the spirit of capitalism as it existed in the utilitarian and individualistic forms of the eighteenth-century philosophers and economists. Shibusawa's thinking was, of course, not identical with that of most of the other entrepreneurs. But, to a lesser degree, the whole status-conscious group of pioneering industrialists and foreign-trade merchants shared his outlook.

If we compare this keen sense of social responsibility with the spirit of capitalism in the West, we may say that the basic difference probably lies in divergent concepts of the relation between the individual and society. Capitalism in the West emerged through a gradual but fundamental shift in the value system. The individual, his worth and his welfare in worldly terms, moved into the central position so long reserved for the group, for society and the common good. This trend started as far back as Nominalism, which challenged the validity of universal concepts. The direction became clearer in the growth of the natural sciences, where men rejected all interference by the established religious authority with the individual's quest for objective truth. Humanism and the Renaissance were powerful movements forward toward this emancipation of the individual and of the establishment of a worldly value system. Protestantism sanctioned the supremacy of the individual by rejecting the mediation of a social authority — the Church — between God and the individual.

We need only translate this new concept of the individual into economic and purely secular terms, and we have "the economic man," who considers the achievement of material welfare as the ultimate rationale and reward for his work. "Man is dominated by the making of money, by acquisition as the ultimate purpose of life." [64] According to this capitalist creed, society and its welfare will be taken care of by automatic forces, by an invisible hand that will coordinate self-centered pursuits with the common good.

This evolution of the spirit of capitalism, as it appeared in much eighteenth-century thought, did not proceed in a smooth fashion. Rather, when the problem of man's relation to the world and to worldly activity was seen in a new light and given a new answer, that answer was at its best a religious one. The spirit of capitalism was for a time carried by a very strong religious movement which purposely set itself apart from the tradition of medieval

Christianity. Puritanism discovered its task in this world in terms of material pursuits and gave it a religious sanction. There is probably no contradiction between Max Weber's thesis that the spirit of capitalism owed its victory to the Puritans and the view that it had been prepared gradually by a shift toward the individual and toward secular values. Puritanism idealized what had previously been regarded as a lapse from spiritual concerns. Weber's term "worldly asceticism" pinpoints this mentality. What had been chided before as unworthy became now a calling by God: to do business, to accumulate, and to lose no time at it. This religiously conceived version of the spirit of capitalism, and not its selfish and materialistic basis, became the powerful urge that could drive men toward entrepreneurial endeavors in the face of great risk and sacrifice.

There seems to exist a parallel between this Western evolution and what happened to entrepreneurs in Meiji Japan. First there had been the well-established official contempt for business, maintained ostentatiously by the samurai and supported by Confucian ethics. Then came the breakdown of the Tokugawa political and economic system, and with it the disdain for material accumulation. But we do not find a smooth line of change toward a hedonistic and individualistic kind of capitalism. A new element appeared that resembled, in its function, the mentality of the Puritans. It was nothing religious, not a calling by God; it was rather a calling by the nation, by the emperor. The direction was that of service to the country in terms of business pursuits, and in the final analysis in terms of worldly success. But one's very success would be a sign of having fulfilled a noble duty. Iwasaki and Ōkura, in their quest for self-assertion, were singularly obsessed with the thought of fighting for an ideal and not just for private gains. Theirs was not a belief in the "invisible hand" that would take care of society — they were men for whom business was a sacred duty. There is a similarity between the Puritan drive to accumulate and that of the Meiji pioneers: the one was backed by a faith in God, the other by a faith in the Nation.[65] It is even possible to discover a certain parallel, however different the two men may be otherwise, between Benjamin Franklin, who preached thrift while quoting the Bible, and Shibusawa Eiichi, who preached business ethics while quoting the Analects of Confucius.

But a basic difference remains between the Puritan version of the capitalist and the type represented by Shibusawa and his school of thought. Western capitalism was ultimately individualistic; its religious sanction was individual perfection, a manifestation of one's own salvation, a problem of God and I. The Confucian version of Shibusawa stressed Society and I, the State and I, and thus demanded the subordination of the individual to the common good. This may account for a number of seeming contradictions in Japan's economic development. We encounter in Meiji Japan and later starvation wages, but not an anonymous employer-laborer relationship with hiring and firing according to the dictates of "economic rationality." We find that talented men were attracted to business, but only to those branches that were clearly recognized as in the service of the community; they had to be *jitsugyōka*, not *shōnin*. We find a ruthless drive for power and money, with a "survival of the fittest" as in Western capitalism, but then these same "fittest" assumed a role of service and worked for public objectives.

The community-centered thinking that was largely preserved by the union of Confucian traditions and Western influences can perhaps account in part for the extended time horizons of many Meiji entrepreneurs. When these men so obviously discounted present sacrifices in favor of the future success of their enterprises, the enterprise assumed a function similar to that of the family, the community, or for that matter, the merchant store. The individual — entrepreneur as well as worker — was but a part of and had to serve the higher unit, the enterprise, and work for *its* success. This is quite similar to the attitude displayed by the merchants with respect to their family businesses. But the remarkable difference was this: the merchants served their house traditions — with them the time horizon was stretched to the past — while the modern entrepreneurs applied the long view to the future. In any case, the element of time lent a nonindividualistic character to economic pursuits.

It is open to question whether an unrestrained bourgeois type of capitalism can work at all beneficially for economic development in any latecomer country. The task does not so much constitute a challenge for individuals as for society as a whole. It requires cooperation and sacrifices from the community, and responsible leadership in both the government and the private sector. In times of smooth and continuous development, the pursuit of each individual's welfare as the primary goal of activity may not reveal its inherent dangers. But whenever crises and extraordinary tasks appear, society cannot rely on an invisible hand, on an "automatic harmony" between social and private benefits. A conscious coordination of the two, and even subordination of private advantage to society's needs, is then called for. The swift and energetic modernization of the Meiji economy owed a great deal to the continuance of this kind of noncapitalist mentality among its best entrepreneurs; these men were characterized by a blend of Confucian ethics, patriotism, and faith in Western technology.

National Awakening

Nationalism unquestionably constitutes one of the most dynamic elements in the economic growth of many modern underdeveloped countries. Industrialization and a new sense of national purpose usually go together and thrive on patriotism as their common powerful motive. The determined leaders of a nation's elite, given the proper objectives, can mobilize immeasurable energies toward social and economic advance. A gradual process of development without these nationalist emotions may be less wasteful as far as capital resources are concerned; but it may evaporate without being able to overcome fast enough the great difficulties of the initial spurt. Nationalism is like a stallion; it may turn the cart upside down and create havoc, especially if the leaders are power-mad. But the same strong stallion, properly harnessed and controlled, may pull the cart of the economy all the way to the top of the hill, something a slow-moving plug horse may not accomplish. In the "new" countries, hostilities toward "oppressor countries" or toward their own former ruling classes are often only a means used to create passionate dedication to a national purpose which requires enormous sacrifices.

The Meiji was an era of national awakening. The cultural, social, and economic life that had been bottled up in the islands of Japan for over two centuries burst forth into a new spring of growth. Many events before and after the Meiji Restoration seem to the casual reader senseless and contradictory. But here was a people rushing forth with sudden energy, aware of both a new greatness and a new challenge. The greatness was epitomized in the restoration of imperial rule, accompanied by a sense of national unity and by the equality of all citizens who were to share the blessings of education and progress.

The challenge appeared first to be of a military nature. The daimyo built their cannons and the economic reformers revamped the han economies to provide capital for armaments. After the Meiji Restoration, the military aspect lost much of its importance, and the main task became economic. Attempts were made to keep up the appearance of a military challenge, in order to draw the attention of the dissatisfied samurai from their economic misery and to give their nationalism an easy outlet. The Taiwan expedition and the plan to subjugate Korea were instigated, it is said, primarily with this intention. But the militarists could not prevail; the men of the Iwakura Mission to Europe knew that the real challenge to Japan was one of economic development and industrialization. The unequal treaties left no doubt that unless full effort was made Japan, like China, could become an economic colony of the West.

It is from this vantage point and against this background that we must view the patriotic statements of the entrepreneurs. Iwasaki and Ōkura, two of the most successful zaibatsu builders, were certainly interested in personal power and money; but at the same time they were opponents of foreign competition, and they knew the importance of their work. I need not give concrete examples here: many have been mentioned already, and others will be supplied in the next two chapters when I discuss the entrepreneurs themselves. In any event, it would be wrong to deny the existence of patriotism as a most effective motive, even where other, almost contradictory, intentions appear along with it. Not all were idealists like Shibusawa, Morimura, and Kinbara, but all joined, more or less, in the acknowledged task of building a modern economy.

The feudal rulers had previously been looked upon as responsible for national affairs. The samurai were the defenders of the country. It almost seems as if the newly established *jitsugyōka* had inherited part of the former feudal responsibility for national economic affairs. The *jitsugyōka* were, it was often stated, to do business in the samurai spirit. The daimyo of Geishu is said to have proclaimed that "it is the duty of the nobility to serve the country by establishing enterprise." He ordered the building of a paper mill, the first in Japan, and used 100,000 yen of his own money for that purpose.[66] The public expected the top businessmen to display patriotic attitudes and to follow the lead of the government in modern investments. Public recognition, honor, and influence depended upon building factories and operating shipping lines to answer the threat of foreign competition. It was of secondary importance how much profit a man earned in the process of innovating; what mattered was that the chimneys begin to smoke and the machines begin to produce. The pressure of public opinion, the need to conform to an image of leadership that was largely of feudal origin, forced even those who may not have been genuine patriots to conform at least outwardly to that ideal.

There was a circular interaction between the public image of the "entrepreneur" and his duties toward Japanese economic progress, on the one hand, and the attitudes of the leading entrepreneurs, on the other. They had created their new status concept in the first place in order to gain esteem for private business. The most striking difference between the *shōnin* and the *jitsugyōka* was the latter's "mission" to build industries for the nation. If a small group suceeded in this rehabilitation effort, the larger group of important entrepreneurs had to conform to this esprit de corps. We frequently find the same men cooperating in a vast number of modern enterprises — it was all done in the single effort to build an industrial Japan.

This creation of an acceptable status image became a

very effective force in Japanese economic development. Nationalist sentiments were not channeled into battle cries and war hero worship, but into economic construction. There is a parallel case of the conscious steering of public acclaim and the creation of a status symbol for the sake of industrialization. The Saint-Simonian socialists knew that, in the tremendous effort of building their new economic order, they needed prestige and emotional support from the people. If these men called themselves "missionaries" and their institution a "bank to a higher power," they were doing essentially the same thing as the Japanese with their *jitsugyōka* status and their insistence on building factories for the sake of Japan. Gerschenkron remarks on the importance of new social values for economic development: "In a backward country the great and sudden industrialization effort calls for a New Deal in emotions. Those carrying out the great transformation as well as those on whom it imposes burdens must feel, in the words of Matthew Arnold, that 'Clearing a stage / Scattering the past about / Comes the new age.' " [67]

The challenge presented by external conditions and the dynamic leadership of the Meiji government resulted in a magnificent national revival. This was the "New Deal in emotions" that inspired the entrepreneurial elite, the men who created modern Japanese industry.

VI

THE ZAIBATSU BUILDERS

The zaibatsu, those giant combines that controlled large sectors of Japan's banking, trading, and industry until the end of the Second World War, had their origin in the early Meiji era. At a time when both capital and entrepreneurs were scarce, the emerging zaibatsu were able to seize a large share of both resources. Japan's modern industrial development, especially her drive into world markets, was spearheaded by these few combines. Their contribution to the successful breakthrough in modern industry, especially heavy industry, was of critical importance. But the fastest growth and concentration of economic power of the zaibatsu occurred after the turn of the century and up to the outbreak of the Second World War.

One of the major factors contributing to the rapid growth of the zaibatsu was their close cooperation with the government, whether in receiving subsidies or favors or in acting as government suppliers. The degree of favoritism varied, but it was never entirely absent. Another important factor was that the zaibatsu were characterized by a strategic combination of banking and industrial capital. The four largest zaibatsu — Mitsui, Mitsubishi, Sumitomo, and Yasuda — were conspicuous for supplying the capital needed for their industrial ventures from their own banks. The zaibatsu banks had the fastest growth rates. In 1936 the largest banks of Japan in order of magnitude were: Sanwa, Sumitomo, Dai Ichi, Yasuda, Mitsui, and Mitsubishi.[1] The trust companies ranked according to the totals of funds were: Mitsui, Mitsubishi, Sumitomo, and Yasuda.[2] Those who had, received more. Success in banking made possible successful investments in industry, and the visible industrial achievements raised public confidence in the stability of the zaibatsu banks.

The fact to be noted is that these large financial resources were channeled into heavy industry and transportation. Shipping, railways, mining, chemicals, metallurgical industries, and electricity were the preferred fields of zaibatsu investment. Here they pioneered and came to occupy monopoly positions because the general capital market was still too weak for effective competition. Nonzaibatsu capital flowed largely into light and traditional industries.

From the middle of the Meiji era on, the individual zaibatsu were occupied partly in establishing their own independent industrial or transportation empires — Mitsubishi in shipping, Sumitomo in copper, and Ōkura in iron mining. More often they joined with other shareholders in particular projects in which they, however, held the control. Sometimes two zaibatsu cooperated. In one rather unusual case, the three-million-yen New Osaka Hotel, we find four zaibatsu working together: Sumitomo, Ōkura, Mitsui, and Mitsubishi.[3] Through a pyramiding of control, the zaibatsu empires expanded and absorbed ever larger amounts of industrial and finance capital. At the very beginning of their rapid growth period, around 1885, we find that, with one exception, in all firms with over

half a million yen capital the zaibatsu were the leading
investors (here I am including the Fujita Company in the
zaibatsu group, to which it belonged at that time).[4]

Over and above the favorable external conditions that
promoted the zaibatsu, one must not forget the zaibatsu
builders. These combines by no means formed a homogeneous group. They differed widely with respect to their
origins; some had old merchant traditions, others started
from scratch. They differed also with respect to government connections and investment categories. But they did
resemble each other closely in the type of entrepreneurs
and managers they had. The following case studies of the
zaibatsu builders are intended to bring out this resemblance. The account of the zaibatsu growth process in
quantitative terms is kept to a minimum, serving only
as a background for the performance of the entrepreneurs.
This approach is intended to direct emphasis away from
an overly mechanistic stress on the obviously large subsidies and favors, to the remarkable achievements of personality.

The House of Mitsui and Minomura Rizaemon

The House of Mitsui was able to accumulate tremendous
wealth throughout the Tokugawa period. Its money exchanges and stores were among the most prosperous and
successful in the cities of Edo, Kyoto, and Osaka. Toward
the end of bakufu rule, Mitsui was close to collapse, as
were so many others of the financial magnates. A forced
loan of 350,000 ryo was imposed upon Mitsui when its fortunes were at an all-time low. This might well have spelled
ruin for that merchant house, but its head clerk, Minomura
Rizaemon, succeeded through personal connections with
a bakufu official in securing a remittance of 320,000 ryo of

the loan.[5] Mitsui then threw its lot in with the Restoration party before its victory, by making a substantial contribution and accepting the offer to act as the party's financial agent. With this political decision, Mitsui set out on a road that led to many later favors and to a unique position as the official government banker. The advantages the House of Mitsui was able to derive from its position were staggering.

In 1874 alone Mitsui was holding no less than 3.8 million yen and 460,000 dollars of government money free of interest, with no ruling imposed about reserves to be held.[6] During the Satsuma Rebellion the Mitsui Trading Company was commissioned to supply about two thirds of the army provisions, and it increased its wealth within one year from 100,000 yen to 500,000 yen.[7] Mitsui Hachirōe-mon, the senior member of the Mitsui Trust, occupied no fewer than fifteen positions by government appointment in connection with enterprises that had been started either through the initiative of the government or with some special privileges granted by the government.

This tie-in with government finance and the large gains that resulted from government contracts and later from government sales can easily lead one to believe that the ascendency of Japan's top zaibatsu resulted almost automatically from a combination of Tokugawa wealth and Meiji government leadership. We must not forget, however, that Mitsui was not the only recipient of such privileges; Ono and Shimada shared them, yet they collapsed. If, out of the whole group of rich Tokugawa merchant families, only two, Mitsui and Sumitomo, became zaibatsu, we have to look for some other explanation.

One of the conditions that underlay Mitsui's rise to leadership in modern banking, trading, and industry was its organizational structure. Although the Mitsui enterprises were nominally owned by several branches of the Mitsui family, control was vested in the senior member of the family group, who always received the name Hachi-rōemon.[8] But even he could not make decisions independently. The actual management of the enterprises was put into the hands of a head clerk, who had near dictatorial power. A rule of the Mitsui family dating from the seventeenth century stresses the strict subordination of the family members to the decisions of the men in charge: "Under a great general are no weak soldiers . . . you must treat your own child like any other employee until he comes of age." [9] The potentialities inherent in the strong position of the Hachirōemon and of the head clerk were not used in the later Tokugawa period, but they became crucial in the transition into the modern era. At the time of greatest crisis, the "great general" for Mitsui was found in the person of Minomura, who almost alone was responsible for Mitsui's alignment with the new government and with the new era in general.

Minomura's first great achievement for Mitsui was the aforementioned remittance of the forced loan. In appreciation of his success he was given the post of head clerk, and from then on he steered Mitsui's destinies. It is he who is credited with the decision to side with the Restoration government, in clear recognition of the trend of the times. Minomura is said to have been the most active man outside of the government in the establishment of the exchange and trading companies, and later in the foundation of the first joint-stock banks. If in many records the name of Mitsui Hachirōemon appears as the leader of new ventures and as the president of various enterprises, the man behind the scenes was Minomura. Recognizing the need to be close to the center of administration and of modern ideas, he urged that the headquarters of the

Mitsui family move to Tokyo from its centuries-old residence in Kyoto. He encountered stubborn resistance from both the Mitsui family and the Kyoto population, but eventually he succeeded, in 1873. Knowing that Mitsui could prosper only if it moved determinedly with the new trends, as early as 1872 Minomura sent five young members of the Mitsui family and two employees to the United States to study.[10] His close friendship with Inoue Kaoru became a great blessing to Mitsui; in fact, it saved Mitsui from the kind of catastrophe that befell Ono and Shimada.[11] This friendship with one of the most progressive planners of the Meiji government was based on a similarity of views and a congeniality of economic vision. If necessary, Minomura could cut resolutely through knotty managerial problems in complete disregard of traditions and sentimental attachments. He separated the old and famous Echigoya retail store in Tokyo from the rest of the Mitsui enterprises because it had been running at a loss. This separation became beneficial to the Echigoya, now the largest department-store chain in Japan, under the name of Mitsukoshi, and for Mitsui it was beneficial too.[12]

Minomura was a new man who came "from nowhere." He influenced and in the end ruled the greatest of all merchant houses, but he was not a typical merchant of the old tradition. Little is known about his early years except that he was born in poverty, probably in 1821, and that his father, a *rōnin*, died young. At the age of fourteen the orphaned Minomura came from Kyushu to Kyoto, then traveled widely throughout the country and settled in Edo at the age of nineteen to become a merchant's apprentice. His extraordinary abilities brought him into the Mitsui combine and eventually into the position of control. It can only be surmised that his extensive travels, his experience of poverty, and his unusual talents made him understand the signs of a new era sooner and more deeply than many others who had stayed at home in secure positions. As a man without allegiance to family and without prejudice of status, he fulfilled one of the conditions necessary to the new entrepreneurs: he could readily and thoroughly adapt to the new ideas and accept change. Despite Minomura's early death in 1877, his imprint on Mitsui was lasting. He took one of the oldest merchant houses and made it Japan's most powerful pioneering enterprise.

MASUDA TAKASHI

Masuda Takashi (1848–1938), the founder of the Mitsui Trading Company (Mitsui Bussan), does not seem quite to have duplicated the strategic importance of Minomura, whom he succeeded as Mitsui's most important decision maker. On the whole, he continued the innovational policies of Minomura and furthered the modernization of Mitsui. Masuda's background differed greatly from Minomura's. Born the son of a samurai official with considerable means, he moved with his father at the age of twelve, in 1860, from the island of Sado to Edo. There he learned English at the American consulate and put his knowledge to good use after the Restoration by serving as interpreter to the foreign-trade merchants in Yokohama. During one year of employment in the Ministry of Finance, he became acquainted with Inoue Kaoru, who thought so highly of his abilities that in 1872 he made him vice-president of his own newly established Senshū Trading Company.[13] That company was dissolved after one year. Minomura then requested that the talented Masuda establish a foreign-trade company within the framework of the Mitsui combine. This man, who had gained an early acquaintance with foreign trade in Yokohama, had learned English, and had also been able to gain insight into the problems of the import surplus during his employment in the Ministry of Finance, was well prepared for his task. He was convinced that in competition with the foreign companies only a large joint-stock venture could be successful.[14]

While the large gains of the Mitsui Trading Company during the Satsuma Rebellion aided its rapid expansion, Masuda's primary concern was the promotion of active foreign trading. In order to bolster his position as an exporter in the Asian market, he decided to purchase the Miike Coal Mine. He had a secret investigation made, which convinced him that, despite the heavy losses the government had incurred, he could make the mine profitable. Actually the mine became one of the greatest assets of the entire Mitsui combine, but at the time Masuda had to fight opposition to the purchase; the Mitsui Bank refused the necessary loan of a million yen, finally granting it only after Masuda had thrown in all of his personal assets. Masuda wrote that he had to make this decision alone because the others could not understand his action.[15] Like many of the leading entrepreneurs of that period he was extremely eager to promote active foreign trade and to invest in modern industry. We find him cooperating frequently with Shibusawa, although it seems that he was more of a supporter than an original planner. Masuda claimed that in all his many ventures, inside and outside of the Mitsui combine, he "did not want money but desired to work for the progress of enterprise, and strained all [his] energies to that end." [16]

NAKAMIGAWA HIKOJIRŌ

In spite of the efforts of Masuda, the House of Mitsui's fortunes began to decline after Minomura's death. The old merchant practices asserted themselves increasingly. Around 1890 the total assets of Mitsui were at their lowest point since the Restoration and caused serious anxiety.[17] The trouble spot was the Mitsui Bank, where the old clerks who had remained from the pre-Restoration period tried to gain favor with officials and large institutions by granting loans in spite of insufficient security. This was the pattern of daimyo lending of Tokugawa days, which had reaped social rewards. When the government called in its deposits from the Mitsui Bank, the bank came close to collapse; it was saved by the good offices of the old Mitsui friend, Inoue. He negotiated a loan to the Mitsui Bank from the Bank of Japan, but he also received permission from the Mitsui family to initiate a thorough reform of the bank and of the whole Mitsui combine.[18] Inoue's man was Nakamigawa Hikojirō (1854–1901), who entered Mitsui in 1890 as its chosen reformer. For the second time, the government official Inoue supplied Mitsui with an outstanding entrepreneur; in this respect, then, Mitsui "owed" its modernization to the government.

The choice of Nakamigawa may seem somewhat odd at first sight. Here was a man who went straight from a teacher's desk to prominence in Japan's industry — yet few were more successful than he. A samurai by birth and a nephew of Fukuzawa, he studied at the Keiō college. Then he spent three years in England and had a successful career as a teacher and newspaper editor. He wrote in the same vein as Fukuzawa, in favor of progress and economic rationality, and he made a point of scorning the prevalent samurai manner of citing lineage and past glories. He was made president of the Sanyō Railway Company but soon was at loggerheads with the shareholders, who acutely disliked his zeal for reform and innovation. But if the shareholders of Sanyō considered him too progressive, Inoue thought him the right man to modernize the Mitsui Bank.

Nakamigawa applied himself to the task with almost

ruthless courage. He dared to recall within one year a loan of one million yen from the powerful Higashi Honganji Temple in Kyoto, and the abbot was forced to initiate a nationwide collection to satisfy Nakamigawa, thus making him *persona non grata* among the Buddhist faithful of all Japan.[19] Although Nakamigawa had entered Mitsui through the influence of a government official, he wanted no part in any government favoritism that would interfere with business rationality. He went so far as to refuse a loan of 500 yen to a government official who could not offer sufficient security on the spot.[20] Nakamigawa's main achievement was the extension of Mitsui's industrial interests. He purchased the Tomioka filature and built two other silk-spinning mills because he foresaw a large increase in the demand for silk cloth. He secured control of the Ōji Paper Mill for Mitsui against the powerful Shibusawa-Ōkawa combination. He modernized the Shibaura Iron Works and insisted that they be kept open in spite of continued losses.[21] The man of cold economic rationality became here "irrational" in the same way that most of the other pioneering entrepreneurs did. Continued losses caused Mitsui to sever its ties with the Shibaura Iron Works after Nakamigawa's death.

In cotton spinning Nakamigawa achieved a major success, one that was crucial for the emergence of Japanese cotton spinning onto the world market. Mitsui had taken over the Kanegafuchi Spinning Mill from a group of Tokyo merchants who had invested a million yen but kept operating it at a loss. Under Mitsui management the same mill within four years lost 123,000 yen [22] and was nicknamed the "prodigal factory of Mitsui." In 1890 Nakamigawa took charge of the mill, poured another 700,000 yen into new investments, built an additional plant, and himself studied spinning from books, technicians, and workers. He then began production of fine yarns of over thirty counts, in spite of warnings from English specialists of the Platt Company and other advisers, all of whom predicted disaster. It became a do-or-die situation; yarns piled up unsold and cotton merchants called the Kanegafuchi yarns the "starved yarns." Nakamigawa later recalled that he was fully aware of the danger to the mill, but that he decided on this course for the sake of the future of Japanese cotton spinning. He succeeded in breaking down prejudices and solving technical difficulties, and he created a wedge with which Japan could effect an entry into the world market. Kanegafuchi became one of the most efficient mills in Japan.

Alongside his streamlining of the Mitsui administration and the building of a strong industrial branch went Nakamigawa's efforts to rejuvenate the company's staff of managers and clerks. He drew heavily on Fukuzawa's graduates for key positions within Mitsui and thus rid it of the remnants of Tokugawa merchant attitudes. At least seven men who later became well-known entrepreneuers were decisively influenced in their careers by Nakamigawa.[23] Thus Nakamigawa made it clear, through his own success and his employment of Fukuzawa-trained graduates, that his way to success in modern business, through books and study, was often shorter than the way from the accounting desk of the merchant stores. Nakamigawa also proved how little, in the long run, government favors could do for Mitsui, or for any other enterprise, if it was not vigorously led in the right direction by "a great general."

Iwasaki Yatarō, the Builder of Mitsubishi

The development of Mitsubishi from its small beginnings as a trading company in Tosa han to the powerful zaibatsu rival of Mitsui rested on two pillars: political connections and the genius of Iwasaki Yatarō (1834–1885). Iwasaki was daring in the extreme, but he was also shrewd in his use of men and especially in securing privileges. To this political merchant par excellence can be applied the criticism of a contemporay, who wrote: "These merchants with government connections pile up enormous profits because of their close ties with government officials. They know the laws before they are published, they receive the favorable deals in the sale of government enterprises." [24] But the same man wrote something else that is equally applicable to Iwasaki: "For business ventures Japan needs the spirit of the samurai who are ready to sacrifice their lives for the country. In competition with the foreigners only such a spirit can be successful; that is, a man must think not only of his private good but also of the benefit to the country." [25] In Iwasaki shrewdness and the spirit of the samurai were uniquely blended, and it is difficult to assess the relative strength of his two predominant motives, his drive for power and his patriotic idealism.

Iwasaki began his trading career within the framework of the Tosa han administration. There he learned very early the power of money. Although he belonged to the country samurai, who differed little from the peasants, he came into close contact with the great Tosa reformers and himself became an official. With his accumulated practical experience in trading, he did not find it difficult to exchange the samurai swords for the abacus. When after the Restoration Iwasaki acquired the official Tosa shipping company as his private property, he called it first the Ninety-Ninth Company and later changed the name to Mitsubishi. He assembled his samurai managers and told them to don the "apron of the merchants." They would fully acknowledge the power of money.[26] On the other hand, Iwasaki had been strongly influenced by Yoshida Shōin's patriotic ideas, and he remained essentially a fighter in the samurai fashion; his ambition was to make Japanese shipping competitive with the great foreign lines.

Iwasaki's close association with government officials, notably Ōkuma, made it easy for his enterprise to get huge subsidies and privileges such as no other zaibatsu got. He was considered the champion of Japan's competitive race with the foreign shipping companies. But Iwasaki was also ruthless in building a system of monopolies. In 1880 he started a documentary-bill company with over 3 million yen in capital. The customers of this company were obliged to ship their goods in Mitsubishi bottoms, to insure them with the Mitsubishi Maritime Insurance Company, and to store the freight in Mitsubishi godowns.[27]

Iwasaki's ruthless monopoly practices and his enormous profits created enemies in the government and also among leading businessmen. Shibusawa was one of them. He cooperated with others, notably with Mitsui's Masuda, to break the Mitsubishi monopoly in shipping; their endeavors culminated in the establishment of the Kyōdō Unyu Company in 1883. Ōkuma, Iwasaki's chief protector in the government, had been ousted in 1881, and Iwasaki's enemies among the officials succeeded in granting the Kyōdō Unyu Company a government subsidy — nominally a share subscription — of 2.6 million yen, thus raising the total of this powerful rival's capital to 6 million yen. In the fierce cut-throat competition, principles, personalities, and politics clashed. During the two years of war between the two giant companies, passenger fares between Kobe and Yokohama dropped from 3.50 yen to 0.25 yen.[28] Iwasaki conducted a rather unfair smear campaign against Shibusawa, charging him with working for foreign interests, while many labeled Iwasaki an enemy of the state.

This was in the last analysis a fight between two diametrically opposed principles: Shibusawa fought for an economic
order ruled by cooperation, with joint-stock companies
and fair competition. Iwasaki believed that the strong
should rule and that monopoly was a good thing because
private profits would eventually also benefit the nation:
what was good for Mitsubishi was bound to be good for
Japan. The war between the two companies ended in 1885.
Iwasaki had secretly bought up the majority of the rival
company's stock and had secured control in the new amalgamated Nihon Yūsen Company.

Although he concentrated on shipping and connected
enterprises, Iwasaki and his associate managers branched
out into other new ventures. In 1884 Iwasaki bought the
Nagasaki shipyard from the government, which had not
been able to make it a going concern. Iwasaki applied for
the purchase by pointing out that Russia was just completing her large shipyard in Vladivostok while Nagasaki
could barely handle minor repair work. He paid 539,000
yen for the yard; within a few years he had put into it
another 6 million yen and had transformed this small repair yard into Japan's largest and most modern shipyard
of the period.[29]

Iwasaki also bought the Takashima coal mine — actually
not directly from the government — which had been operated at a continued loss, and transformed it into one of
Mitsubishi's best assets.[30] He sent his close associate, Kondō
Renpei, to Hokkaido to investigate new investment possibilities, especially in mining, and to exploit the untapped
natural resources of that northern frontier area. In order
to raise capital for this Hokkaido venture, he began his
documentary-bill company. Shipping, mining, shipbuilding, and banking were the main branches of Iwasaki's
activity, and within twenty years his entrepreneurial efforts

had made Mitsubishi the second-ranking zaibatsu in Japan and a dangerous rival to Mitsui.

At the height of Mitsubishi's power, in 1936, the central Mitsubishi Company, which was totally owned by the Isawaki family, had a capital investment of 120 million yen and a net worth of 300–350 million yen. But controlled by, or at least connected with, the company was a huge industrial and financial empire of shipping, shipbuilding, mining, heavy industry, electricity, storehouses, and trading.[31]

Iwasaki was probably the boldest of all Meiji entrepreneurs. His efforts put him into the forefront of Japanese shipping and mining. He himself was not at all modest in assessing his own achievements and his contribution to Japan's economy. On his deathbed in 1885 he claimed before his friends that he was "The Man of the Far East," [32] and he regretted his untimely death because not even a third of his great plans were realized. His quest for power and greatness, combined with samurai patriotism, are reflected in his Mitsubishi family rule: "Do not take up small projects, engage only in large enterprises. Once you begin something, see to it that it becomes a success. Do not engage in speculation. Do business with a patriotic attitude." [33]

Although Iwasaki had gathered associates, all of them samurai — his company was called the "samurai company" — they did not gain prominence as independent business leaders until his death. It was his planning and his decisions that ruled the whole Mitsubishi concern. The first two paragraphs of its "constitution" spell out the dominant position of Iwasaki within the combine:

1. Although this enterprise assumes the name of a company and establishes company structure, in reality it is entirely a family enterprise and differs therefore greatly from a company

with joint capital. Therefore, all things that concern the company, praise and blame and all, are entirely up to the president.

2. All profits return to the person of the president and the losses, too, are borne by him alone.[34]

Almost all zaibatsu men shared this dictatorial attitude, although it was most openly expressed by Iwasaki and Yasuda Zenjirō. This trait contrasts strongly with Fuku-zawa's democratic principles, although Fukuzawa was close to Iwasaki and supplied Mitsubishi with a number of its most talented men. Shōda Heigorō, one of his closest asso-ciates, had been a teacher at Keiō; so had Kondō Renpei, Toyokawa Ryōhei, and Asabuki Eiji. Iwasaki himself built a school to promote business education along Fukuzawa's lines, and his preference for Fukuzawa-trained clerks and managers was proverbial. But he himself retained the men-tality of a strong-willed official, and his entrepreneurial talent, ambition, and competitive spirit made of him an un-bending and stormy leader.

HIROSE SAIHEI, THE MODERNIZER OF SUMITOMO

Sumitomo, the third-ranking zaibatsu, had many features in common with Mitsui. They traced their lines back for a few centuries and were both wealthy merchant houses. Each owed its critical transition into modern enterprise to a great leader who, with a few farsighted and fundamen-tal decisions and with political connections, turned the tide for his house. The strategic part played by Minomura in Mitsui was in many respects similar to that of Hirose Saihei (1828–1914) in Sumitomo; there were also impor-tant differences.

Sumitomo's wealth had been based on copper mining, especially since the beginning of the eighteenth century, when this house had succeeded in separating out copper from mixed ore.[35] Sumitomo became the official copper supplier for the bakufu. Its wealth increased, but for a hundred and fifty years no innovations were carried out and no business leadership was displayed. Sumitomo's once very profitable Besshi Copper Mine became a liability owing to flooding, and was kept operating only with the aid of government subsidies. When the subsidies were suspended because of the imminent outbreak of the Restoration war, the Sumitomo family considered selling the mine for 100,000 ryo. It was at this juncture that Hirose's influence and determination became crucial for Sumitomo.[36] His fight to keep the mine under Sumitomo became a promise to make it profitable again. The modernization of Besshi became Hirose's outstanding entrepreneurial achievement, and it meant for Sumitomo the start of a new era.

An adopted child of the manager of Besshi, Hirose Saihei had started working at the mine at the age of eleven. Having come up from the rank and file, he not only knew the problems better than anyone else but also loved the mine. Now as its manager he had to fight for its survival. When the government stopped its rice supplies for the 5,000 workers, he almost singlehandedly quelled their riots and succeeded in negotiating an extension of rice deliveries. He soon reorganized the food supplies for the mine, produced bean paste, soy sauce, and sake on the spot, built housing projects for the workers and schools for the children.[37] After he had succeeded in settling the disputed right of ownership of the Besshi Copper Mine between the government and Sumitomo in favor of the latter, he proceeded with its modernization, supported by Kawada Koichirō and Iwakura Tomomi. In order to avoid future difficulties that might arise from sudden investment needs or other contingencies, he began to accumulate a hundred-year stabilization fund. By 1926 this fund had reached 20 million yen.[38] With the help of foreign engineers, the output of Besshi was boosted from 420.7 tons of copper in 1868 to 601 tons in 1874 and 1,202 tons in 1885.[39]

Branching out from copper, Hirose extended the rising Sumitomo empire into allied fields and built up his own supply and sales branches. Large areas of woodland were purchased for lumber supply, and a machine-manufacturing and repair shop were affiliated with the mine. A foreign-trade department in Kobe handled Sumitomo exports, mainly copper but later coal, tea, raw silk, and other products. The Sumitomo banking branch grew during Hirose's expansion program and secured for him the supply of additional capital. Within twenty years of the Restoration, a solid basis for the Sumitomo empire had been laid by Hirose.

From then on, the development was rapid, notably because of the growth of the Sumitomo Bank and the Sumitomo Trust Company. By 1932 the Sumitomo zaibatsu comprised fourteen directly owned enterprises with a total capital stock of 380 million yen. In addition there were some seventy enterprises worth 2.5 billion yen in which Sumitomo had some 1.6–1.7 billion yen invested, receiving dividends of about 100 million yen a year.[40] In the fields of banking and heavy industry, the three zaibatsu — Mitsui, Mitsubishi, and Sumitomo — were about equal by the 1930s.

The first and most obvious reason for Hirose's achievement lies undoubtedly in an early acquaintance with his field of endeavor. He was like Asano, who loved his work "more than money and more than his life." Hirose tried to remain in copper mining; even when his leadership of

Sumitomo made him extend his sphere of interest to foreign trade and banking, he remained the "copper man." Outside of Sumitomo, he held important positions in the Osaka Copper Refining Company and the Sulphuric Acid Company, both closely connected with copper mining.[41]

Hirose's restless drive to innovate was fired by his keen interest in reading and learning, and his intimate acquaintance with Western technology. Through his close association with a French engineer employed in his mine, he himself became an expert in mining technology. Hirose was a man who fully believed in progress; it is said that he hated the prevailing stagnant and conservative atmosphere in Osaka business circles. According to him, complacency and nostalgic attachment to the past were the worst enemies of progress.[42] On this point he agreed completely with all representative innovators of the Meiji era. Hirose was a leading member of the Osaka Chamber of Commerce, where he cooperated with the entrepreneurial elite to rebuild Osaka as a city of flourishing industry and commerce.

At the time of the Besshi Copper Mine's great crisis Hirose had turned the good offices of government officials to advantage, but afterward he moved rapidly toward independence from government patronage and official ties. In this respect Hirose differed basically from Mitsui's Minomura, who had moved the Mitsui headquarters to Tokyo and had tied its destiny to the Meiji government. Sumitomo's main operating base has remained Osaka to the present day; it was modernized, but it did not move to the center of progress. Perhaps this is one reason why Sumitomo retained throughout its modern development a tendency toward conservatism, more so than did Mitsui or Mitsubishi.

YASUDA ZENJIRŌ, THE BANKER

The Yasuda zaibatsu ranked fourth among the empires of finance and industry, and its development from small beginnings was no less spectacular than that of Mitsubishi. Yasuda Zenjirō (1838–1921), who had left home at the age of twenty and gone to Edo to make a living, succeeded so well that when summing up his blessings in 1908, at the age of seventy, he controlled in his empire of finance: eleven banks, with 21.2 million yen in capital; three insurance companies, with 13.3 million; one construction company, with 5.0 million; three railway companies, with 10.63 million; and one electric company, with 1.0 million.[43]

Yasuda was appointed a member of the board of trustees of the Bank of Japan in 1882 and held the post for two years; at one time he was financial agent of the Ministry of Agriculture and Trade. But these official positions were not at all typical for Yasuda. In striking contrast to Iwasaki, Yasuda remained almost entirely independent of government support.[44] His success was due to genius, favorable circumstances, and his insatiable drive to win profits.

Born the son of a poor samurai, Yasuda Zenjirō began his trading career by selling flowers in his native village. He had learned early that money was more powerful than samurai swords, so he went to Edo where, in those days, a daring and clever man could become rich in a short time. Yasuda displayed a remarkable instinct for turning a penny and multiplied his initial five ryo through lending, trading, and exchange manipulations.[45] A few years after the Restoration, he was already a wealthy banker. But even at the height of his success, he remained miserly; on his inspection rounds of factories and on his Tokyo business trips, he would take the early cheap-rate streetcar and carry his lunch.[46]

But this man, who had set out to become rich by ruthlessly exploiting any opportunity, began later to display a remarkable degree of responsibility with respect to the use of his wealth, and thus came to rank among the great Meiji entrepreneurs. He became a tireless advocate of large and modern investments. Although we have good reason to doubt whether he was always motivated by a consideration of the public benefit in his investment decisions, his own large-scale ventures, and especially his financial backing of industrial undertakings, contributed in no small measure to the economic development of Meiji Japan. When a sulphur-mining company to which he had extended large loans continued to operate in the red and could not pay him back, he made a careful study of the technical possibilities and then took over the mine. He invested heavily by installing new machinery, putting up new buildings, and constructing a railway line to the mine site; the mine became a financial success.[47]

With regard to industry and large-scale innovations, Yasuda could at times forget his caution and appear reckless in his drive to have innovations carried out. Yasuda cooperated in many schemes of industrial pioneering with Asano Sōichirō, who was another almost reckless innovator. People used to say that lending to Asano or Amamiya was equivalent to "throwing one's money into a ditch." But Yasuda said that, if it were not for men like Asano, great enterprises would not be undertaken in Japan. He considered Asano as his "general manager" working with his money.[48] Asano, who had founded the Tōyō Shipping Company, once placed an order for three large ships with the Mitsubishi Shipyard in Nagasaki at a total cost of 15 million yen, although he had almost no money in reserve. Even Shibusawa refused to extend a loan to Asano, but Yasuda lent him 7.5 million yen in spite of the great risks that this newly established shipping company faced in its competition with foreign lines and with Mitsubishi.[49]

Toward the end of his life, Yasuda's innovating plans became almost fantastic in scope. He proposed to the Ministry of Railways that he electrify the entire Tōkaidō Railroad extending from Tokyo to Osaka, at an estimated investment of 100 million yen, but his plan was refused. Yasuda became very bitter at this rejection of his great "service to the country."[50] He had mapped out a plan to modernize the entire city of Tokyo and supply through his banks the estimated capital of some 800 million yen.[51] Over this, his last plan, he was assassinated by a fanatic because he would not contribute to the building of a "workers' hotel."[52]

The banker and entrepreneur Yasuda appears to have combined two attitudes not always found together in one man. He was, on the one hand, a pitiless "profit maximizer," especially in the early part of his career, and at times he displayed miserly traits. On the other hand, he had a genuine interest in general economic progress and in the things that would benefit the nation as a whole. Among the conditions essential to the establishment of an enterprise, he demanded, first of all, that "the purpose of the enterprise be good, that is for the public benefit, contributing to the welfare of the people and the progress of society."[53] Probably it is not wrong to attribute his zeal for innovations for the sake of Japan's advancement to his close association with the group of leading entrepreneurs. If this is true, we have here a good example of how a group spirit and status consciousness can influence the actions of men who otherwise might take a very different approach. It is also true, of course, that in such large-scale projects as the modernization of the city of Tokyo, Yasuda would have reaped his fair share of the profits, together with public acclaim for his services.

Yasuda, like Iwasaki, was a dictator within his own banking empire. It was difficult for him to find congenial men to whom he could delegate powers of decision. In this respect the zaibatsu builders were almost all alike. While Iwasaki saw to it that a few of his aides were groomed for independent entrepreneurial positions, the Yasuda concern was considerably handicaped after the death of its founder by the lack of capable managers.[54]

ŌKURA KIHACHIRŌ, THE TRADER AND INDUSTRIALIST

Ōkura Kihachirō (1837–1928) came of a rich landowner-merchant family of the Niigata district.[55] Disgusted and disillusioned by the social conditions in his village, especially by the overbearing behavior of the samurai, he left for Edo and there, at the age of eighteen and with twenty ryo as his starting capital, began his career as a businessman.[56] He was just as cold-blooded a profit seeker as Yasuda, and almost as successful. His business was trading in rifles, and he had no scruples about delivering arms to the Restoration army while living in Edo under the bakufu. Called to account by the bakufu, he replied that to a merchant money was the only thing that mattered, and he did not care whom he supported.[57] In 1872 he made a trip abroad, the first merchant to do so. Ōkura must have been greatly impressed by what he saw, for he returned to Japan a different man. He had apparently come to realize that money also meant responsibility toward his country in its quest for economic progress. Ōkura Kihachirō became an entrepreneur with a tremendous zest for new ventures that would profit both himself and Japan.

To him, as to Iwasaki, responsibility toward the nation did not preclude a ruthless drive to personal power and shrewd manipulation of government connections. Ōkura remained throughout his career a political merchant who thrived on government contracts, notably in connection with wars. In all military operations, from the Taiwan expedition to the Russo-Japanese War, he managed a lucrative army-supply business. His personal courage secured him a major contract in the Taiwan expedition. Other merchants refused the contract because they were afraid to sail with the expedition, but he accepted. The important fact about the profits gained from the army commissions is that Ōkura invested them in foreign trade, and later even more in large-scale industrial ventures.

In 1873 he founded the Ōkura Company with 150,000 yen in capital, gained chiefly from his arms trading. By the following year he had already established a branch of Ōkura in London, and he moved vigorously into foreign markets, to Korea and Southeast Asia, in an effort to expand Japan's trading position and his own power. But somehow Ōkura was not satisfied with trade alone. He was by character a pioneer and he was attracted to industry, particularly to untried fields. He disliked being an imitator and doing things that others could do equally well. When someone suggested that he invest in cotton spinning, he replied that there were already plenty of businessmen who were operating mills; he insisted that his mission was to start enterprises that others did not or could not undertake.[58]

Ōkura expanded into a wide industrial field, very much as the other zaibatsu did. The four central companies of the Ōkura concern, which were holding companies for a string of others, were: Ōkura Construction, Ōkura Trading, Ōkura Mining, and Ōkura Maritime Insurance. But Ōkura was different from the other top zaibatsu in that it did not build up its own banking branch. Ōkura is said to have declined to play both the lender and the borrower, the rich and the poor.[59] Because he lacked his own bank as a capital-supply line, he fell behind the first four zaibatsu; he lost control over a number of companies that he had initiated because expansion required new share capital, and his holdings were thereby reduced to a minority. This was the case in the Dai Nippon Beer Company and two electricity companies, among others.[60]

Ōkura experienced great difficulties in his pioneering efforts, particularly in his monopoly iron mining in China, which he started after the Sino-Japanese War. Army demand again eventually bailed him out, but he was not a man to become frightened by mounting difficulties. Prince Yamagata suggested to Ōkura at a time of crisis in his iron and steel enterprise that he apply for government subsidies, but he flatly rejected this possibility. He said that he had started out with the expectation of making profits eventually, and that he could take losses for some time. Ōkura was acclaimed by the public for his independence of the government in this instance, especially in view of his earlier ties and commissions.[61]

Ōkura extended his interests and investments over a wide range that included electricity, lumber, charcoal, pulp, chemicals, and land-reclamation schemes. Repeatedly he received the initial stimulus toward a new venture from abroad and then knew no rest until the project was carried out in Japan. Ōkura claimed that he disliked ties with the government and that his main desire was to further the cause of Japanese trade and industry.[62] We may not accept the first part of that claim at face value, but his contribution to Japanese economic growth was certainly outstanding.

FURUKAWA ICHIBEI,
THE BUILDER OF A MINING EMPIRE

Quite in the same fashion as Minomura and Yasuda, Furukawa Ichibei (1832–1919) rose from lowly origins to a position of dominance in the Meiji economy. His father was a poor soybean–cheese peddler in Kyoto. The boy had received a strong impression of social inequalities, which added to his ambitions to make good. At eighteen he left home and was variously employed; he then traveled frequently between Fukushima and Tokyo as an exporter of raw silk within the framework of the House of Ono. He built the first mechanical silk filature in Japan, one year before the government set up its Tomioka Mill in 1872.[63] Entrusted with the management of several mines in the Akita area while still the chief of the silk-export branch of Ono, he was ruined by the bankruptcy of Ono in 1874. At the age of forty-three he had to make a new start.

With the help of a loan from Shibusawa, he purchased the Ashio Copper Mine, which became the basis of his new success. There he innovated on a large scale. He dismissed the old clerks and employed a score of young Keiō graduates in 1884. He contracted with an English firm to deliver 673,120 kilograms of copper per year while he was still mining only 432,720 kilograms.[64] Under this self-imposed pressure he bought new machines, built a railroad to the mine, an electric power station, and, on the whole, made the Ashio mine one of the most modern and most efficient copper mines in Japan. He bought new copper and silver mines. By 1887 Furukawa was mining 39.8 percent of Japan's total copper output, and in 1897, only twenty-two years after he had started in copper mining, he owned or controlled ten copper mines, eight silver mines, one gold mine, and several other enterprises connected with mining.[65] At one time, when he was running a 50,000-yen loss but still kept expanding, people warned him to retrench; even Shibusawa suggested that he consolidated the mines before taking on new ones. But Furukawa insisted that he had to expand, that his only task and joy was copper mining, and that the profits were nothing but a bonus to him.[66]

In terms of general type, Furukawa seems to represent a blend between the merchant and the progressive entrepreneur. He had been associated for a long time with the House of Ono and continued to live in the merchant section of the city. Until a few years before his death, he retained the traditional merchant administration: he did not establish an office but discussed and worked out everything sitting together with his men, "smoking his tobacco," as in the old days.[67] On the other hand, he received many advanced ideas through close association with his friend Shibusawa. And yet, whereas Shibusawa was the tireless champion for the joint-stock form of enterprise, Furukawa was strongly opposed to the company form, because he hated to "bow to majority decisions." [68] Only one of all his ventures, railroad, was a genuine joint-stock enterprise. The aversion to majority decisions which characterized most zaibatsu builders was probably to a large extent based on the fear that the majority would only handicap the innovational programs, which had to be carried out very rapidly and boldly. Furukawa and Ōkura declined to follow the practice of successful businessmen in writing a "family constitution," a set of business rules to be followed by their successors. Both men insisted that men with imagination and initiative would need no rules, for these might do more harm than good by hamstringing new ventures and the enterprising spirit.[69]

ASANO SŌICHIRŌ, THE COURAGEOUS INNOVATOR

The beginnings of Asano's entrepreneurial career are very similar to Yasuda's.[70] Perhaps this was one of the reasons why these two zaibatsu builders, working their way up from poverty to great economic power, frequently cooperated and planned together. But they differed in their fields of action: Yasuda was a banker and remained, on the whole, true to this line; Asano Sōichirō (1849–1930) was an industrial innovator, a restless jack of all trades. He displayed his versatility from early youth. As the son of a rural physician, he received a classical samurai education; he ran away from home at the age of fourteen. At fifteen he was already the "employer" of a few girls in a rural manufacturing enterprise. Repeatedly he failed, but he always started something else. In 1871, at the age of twenty-four, he came to Tokyo almost penniless. He began his career there by selling ice water in the streets, switched to firewood trading, and used many other opportunities to make money. He even built toilets and collected night soil to sell it to peasants as fertilizer.

One day Asano discovered that unused coke was piling up at the gas works in Yokohama. He bought the whole pile and sold it to the Fukagawa Cement Works, where he had been told by an engineer that coke could be used for the furnaces. Asano's interest in cement production here received its first stimulus, and this marked the turning point in his life. He began to study cement production; when he later came to take over the Fukagawa Cement

Works he knew almost as much about the production techniques as an engineer working at the factory.[71] He is said to have been interested in cement above all because he considered it important "for the progress of civilization."

The Fukagawa Cement Works, established by the government in 1871, had stopped operations in 1879 because of technical difficulties. Asano rented the factory first and then purchased it for 125,000 yen in 1883. In these works the government had lost 86,801 yen in deficit operations from 1871 to 1879.[72] It felt that the losses would stop under private management and, according to Shibusawa, the government at any rate wanted to sell out the official enterprises in order to stimulate private initiative. Asano was able to make the purchase with the help of Shibusawa, who gave him a loan and induced his nephew Ōkawa, a trained engineer, to join the company.[73] From 1884 to 1889 the output of the Asano Cement Works increased fivefold. Asano installed new machinery, sent fourteen of his staff engineers and employees to Germany for further research and experience in cement manufacturing, introduced strict supervision, and streamlined the management.[74] The government subsidized Asano indirectly by placing large orders for cement. Owing to Asano's entrepreneurial talent and these government contracts, the Asano Cement Works, in contrast to other cement mills, operated very profitably, although precise figures are not available.

After the achievement of this decisive breakthrough, Asano knew no limits: he ventured into shipping, shipbuilding, and coal mining, built iron works, invested in electric power generation, and various other fields. As I have mentioned, his ambitious plans were largely supported by Yasuda. When Asano proposed to Yasuda reclamation of part of the sea between Tokyo and Yokohama,

Yasuda inspected the area and came to the conclusion that the plan was important "for the national economy" and that it should not be postponed. In that scheme Asano invested 1.5 million yen, Yasuda 0.8 million yen, Shibusawa 0.4 million yen, and a group of Tokyo nobles another 0.8 million yen.[75]

The remarkable enterpreneurial career of Asano reads like an American success story, "from newspaper boy to millionaire." The chief factor in this was Asano's entrepreneurial genius; the role of the government was of minor importance. Although there was no initial capital, Asano built a zaibatsu of his own. Initial large capital and favors received by the government were not common to all zaibatsu builders. What was common to all was their approach to the task: daring, talent, endurance, and a long time horizon. Asano was also, like Yasuda or any of the others, decisively a man of the new era, cut off by choice from adherence to established traditions, and a man who believed firmly in the modern way of doing things.

With Asano we may conveniently leave our examination of the zaibatsu builders. A few sketches more could be added, since there exists no commonly accepted line of demarkation between zaibatsu and nonzaibatsu, but this would not change the general picture that has emerged. There is a certain pattern that holds for all of the successful entrepreneurs of the period, despite incidental differences in their beginnings and in external circumstances.

Conclusions on the Zaibatsu Builders

It should have become clear by now that the zaibatsu of modern Japan did not result from bourgeois wealth in combination with government guidance and subsidies. The process was by no means as straight and simple as this.

The two zaibatsu that were built up on the basis of Tokugawa merchant capital made a sharp break with tradition, and it was because of this break that they survived and flourished. Where leadership in this direction was missing, as in the cases of the Ono and Shimada houses — both of which shared many favors with Mitsui immediately after the Restoration — initial capital accumulation and government favors profited little in the long run.

The role of the government as a supporter of modern ventures was very important indeed. But it was the indirect subsidies that were of first consequence: the government trading contracts, the depositing of official funds without interest, the low-interest long-term loans, monopolies, tax incentives, and the like. These took the place of the tariff protection which is usually necessary to shield young industries in latecomer countries. But while tariff protection across the board helps all firms in an industry, whether they are efficient or not, the Meiji government could pick its favorites on the basis of ability, which means on the basis of success. Those which received more and grew into giants were run by seasoned entrepreneurs who worked with a passion for money, for personal power, and for the country. Indirect subsidies of this kind, avoiding the inefficiencies of both tariff protection and government operation, promoted a concentration of capital that had far-reaching effects on the entire course of Japanese economic development.

The sale of the government's own model factories to the zaibatsu is sometimes said to have had an exaggerated effect upon the rise of these empires of finance and industry. But in the general framework of the zaibatsu these sales were of minor importance and did not constitute nearly so big a help as the other indirect subsidies. Those government sales that did eventually become top profit-

bearing assets did so only after further large-scale investments and innovations had been made by the zaibatsu men
themselves. The Nagasaki Shipyard and the Fukagawa
Cement Works were deficit propositions at the time of
their sale and owed their success to Iwasaki's and Asano's
talent and relentless energy.

The subordinate role of government sales to the zaibatsu
can be seen from the following table, which indicates the
purchasers and the years of the sales. Of the seven zaibatsu
discussed above, only Mitsui, Mitsubishi, Furukawa, and
Asano appear among the purchasers, not Sumitomo,
Ōkura, and Yasuda. Besides the Nagasaki Shipyard, Mitsubishi bought two mines directly and one indirectly (at
second hand) from the government. Only the Takashima
Coal Mine, purchased at second hand from Iwasaki's old
friend Gotō Shōjirō for twice the price he had paid to the
government, became of great importance to Mitsubishi;
and Gotō sold it because he kept losing money on it. Mitsui's purchase of the Miike Coal Mine was of strategic
importance, but again it was a secondhand purchase mas-
terminded by Masuda Takashi against strong opposition
within the Mitsui ranks. The other two Mitsui purchases,
Tomioka and Shinmachi, were not too important in terms
of the Mitsui operation. Actually Mitsui's strategic turn to
industry came under Nakamigawa quite independently of
government sales. Furukawa bought the Innai and Ani
mines from the government, but his main achievement
and real source of profits was the Ashio mine.

On the whole, then, the government created the enabling conditions for these entrepreneurs by generally encouraging modern enterprise and by opening possibilities
to accumulate or find capital, directly or indirectly. But the
choice of project, the investment decisions, the energy and
skill to carry them through to success, must be credited to

SALES OF GOVERNMENT ENTERPRISES
(*zaibatsu italicized*)

Enterprise	Year built or acquired	Sold by government to	Finally acquired by
Mines			
Sado (gold)	1869	1896, *Mitsubishi*	
Ikuno (silver)	1868	1896, *Mitsubishi*	
Kosaka (silver)	1869	1886, Fujita	
Innai (silver)	1875	1884, *Furukawa*	
Ani (copper)	1875	1885, *Furukawa*	
Miike (coal)	1873	1888, Sakaki	1890, *Mitsui*
Takashima (coal)	1873	1874, Gotō	1881, *Mitsubishi*
Horonai (coal)	1879	1889, Hokkaidō Tankō	
Kamaishi (iron)	1874	1883, Tanaka Chōbei	
Shipyards			
Yokosuka	1868	1872, Naval Ministry	
Nagasaki	1868	1884, lent to *Mitsubishi*	1887, *Mitsubishi*
Hyōgo	1871	1886, Kawasaki Shōzō	
Akabane Construction	1871	1883, Naval Armament Office	
Fukagawa Cement	1874	1883, lent to *Asano*	1884, *Asano*
Fukagawa Brick	1878	1884, *Asano*	
Shinagawa Glass	1876	1885, Nishimura Katsuzō	
Tomioka Silk Filature	1872	1893, *Mitsui*	
Shinmachi Spinning	1877	1887, *Mitsui*	
Senju Woolen Mill	1876	1888, army management	
Mechanical Thread	1873	1874, lent to Ueda Spinning Mill	
Aichi Spinning Mill	1878	1886, Shinoda Naokata	
Hiroshima Spinning Mill	1878	1882, Hiroshima prefecture	
Printing Office	1872	remained government-operated	

Source: Takahashi Kamekichi and Aoyama Jirō, *Nihon zaibatsu ron* (A treatise on the Japanese zaibatsu; Tokyo, 1938), pp. 54-55.

the zaibatsu builders. This sounds like common sense, yet it is often forgotten and the whole outcome viewed as a result of impersonal forces. The very differences in the start of these men, Mitsui and Sumitomo with considerable wealth, Yasuda, Ōkura, and Asano starting with nothing, Iwasaki building up an inherited han enterprise, indicate further that initial capital was not a necessary condition for becoming a zaibatsu builder or even a successful entrepreneur in Meiji Japan.

All the great Meiji entrepreneurs shared basic attitudes toward the new era: they believed in it; they worked for its implementation; they themselves were new men who had experienced at one point or another a final break with traditions, either leaving home and starting a new life, making a deliberate political decision to side with the new forces, or absorbing strong Western influences through travel and association with foreigners. The change from rugged moneymaking for the love of profit and power to more responsible entrepreneurial planning coincided with a newly perceived realization of their role in the national economy. After the uprooting of Asano, Yasuda, Ōkura, and to a lesser degree of the others — that is, after the rupture with "the past" — came the vision of a new order and a new ideal. This was strong enough to moderate, if not change, the initial profit maximizers into industrial pioneers with a sense of mission for the country and its economy. Their mutual association and cooperation, their esprit de corps, and the public and official acclaim that they won contributed in no small measure to make these zaibatsu builders great benefactors of modern Japan.

VII

FIFTY LEADING ENTREPRENEURS

The detailed presentation of the zaibatsu builders enabled us to assess, among other things, the relative role of government subsidies and of private initiative and personality in the entrepreneurial process. But it would be misleading to take the few giants of industry and banking as a basis for sweeping generalizations on all aspects of Meiji entrepreneurship. How did the less successful but still important innovators approach their task? This chapter contains an examination of fifty leading businessmen — all entrepreneurs in the broad sense; from this sampling we may be able to draw valid conclusions about Meiji entrepreneurs in general.

I have selected fifty men whose innovating activities achieved some prominence before the Sino-Japanese War of 1894–95, since these years are usually taken to mark the end of the pioneering industrial period. All of these men were active in banking, trading, or industrial enterprise along modern lines, although quite a few had started in other pursuits. My sole standard of selection was the degree of success of each entrepreneur, and in the table that appears here their names are arranged roughly in order of the relative success and importance of each man. This approach is less than ideal; it is quite conceivable that some entrepreneur who failed was a most daring and progressive man, and that his failure was fortuitous or due to the fact that he was too far ahead of his time. Cases of this kind would enrich our insight into the difficulties that the pioneers of Meiji industry had to face. But, rightly or wrongly, the published biographies make little of those who failed, and we have to take what data we can get.

The number fifty has no magic significance; it was chosen because it is large enough to permit some generalization but not too large to allow a meaningful glimpse into the life of each man. The process of selection was laborious. The top twenty or thirty were easily found; they could almost be enumerated offhand, since they are the well-known figures whose achievements stand out and have found their way into Japanese economic-history books. There was no scarcity of biographical material on these men. The task of sifting out the others was more exacting. Some collections of short biographies of Meiji businessmen were helpful in indicating all those who could qualify. The *Dai Nihon jimmei jisho* (Biographical dictionary of greater Japan) presented the bare facts in brief and reliable summaries. Imposition of my two conditions — modern enterprise and 1895 as the upper time limit for at least initial success — caused the number gradually to dwindle to about fifty. In spite of careful weighing there is, of course, nothing absolute about the selection; a few could always be exchanged with other men without in any way changing the results that emerge from this analysis.

At no point in the preparation of this book have I felt my limitations so severely as in this chapter. The vast amount of material to be handled created unusual diffi-

culties for both analysis and presentation. In the published biographies and sketches of these men, each emerges
as an individual, as an arresting personality stubbornly re-
sisting any attempt to fit him into a statistical array or
to present him by figures. The same basic characteristics
appear in most, but with differing colors and slants. The
problem was to determine how many of these differences
could be omitted without distorting reality and oversim-
plifying complex phenomena. Attitudes, motivations, and
approaches to enterprise are something so personal that
they can become all but meaningless when expressed in
true but overly broad generalizations. It is necessary to
preserve at least a part of each man's uniqueness. This
chapter thus became something of a hybrid between a
statistical analysis and biographical notes. But perhaps the
shortcomings of one approach will be partly offset by the
other, and in the end the reader may acquire a fairly comprehensive idea of what the entrepreneurs of the early
Meiji era were really like.

The arrangement of the accompanying table needs no
comment at this point; it will become clear as I proceed
with the explanation of each column. The content of the
table, and correspondingly of this chapter, falls into two
parts. The first part gives background information for
each of the fifty men; the second part presents data on
their entrepreneurial activities.

FORMATIVE INFLUENCES

The Older and the Younger Group

The year of birth is given in column 2 simply to show
the relative ages of the men. But by the same token this
column enables us to time the major political and social
events occurring during the early life of each entrepre-

SURVEY OF FIFTY LEADING ENTREPRENEURS IN THE EARLY MEIJI ERA

| Name (listed in order of success) (1) | Birth | | Formative influences (before age 20) | | Entrepreneurial type (6) | Main fields of activity (7) |
	Year (2)	Class (3)	Practical training (4)	City (5)		
Shibusawa Eiichi	1840	P	M, P	Tokyo	R	Banking, general industrial pioneering
Iwasaki Yatarō	1834	S	Official, M	Nagasaki, Tok.	R	Shipping, shipbuilding, mining, banking
Ōkura Kihachirō	1835	P	M	Tokyo	R	Trade, mining, heavy industries
Yasuda Zenjirō	1838	S	M	Tokyo	(R)	Banking, promotion of industry
Hirose Saihei	1828	S	Mining	Osaka	Cl	Mining, allied fields (Sumitomo)
Asano Sōichirō	1848	S	M	Tokyo	R	Cement, general industrial pioneering
Furukawa Ichibei	1832	M	M	Tokyo, Yok.	Cl	Mining
Godai Tomoatsu	1834	S	Official	Nagasaki, Tok.	Cl	Mining, indigo, general industrial pioneering
Kawasaki Shōzō	1837	M	M	Nagasaki	Cl	Shipbuilding, heavy industry
Tanaka Gentarō	1853	P	M	–	R	Banking, pottery, electricity ("Shibusawa of Kyoto")
Matsumoto Jūtarō	1844	P	M	Osaka	R	Banking, railways, promotion of industry in Osaka
Minomura Rizaemon	1821	S	M	Tokyo	(R)	Banking, modernization of Mitsui
Nakamigawa Hikojirō	1854	S	Student, teacher	Tokyo	R	Banking, Mitsui industries, spinning
Ōkawa Heizaburō	1860	P	M	Tokyo	Cl	Paper manufacturing, advising in other enterprises
Hara Rokurō	1844	P	Army, student	–	(R)	Banking, general promotion of industry
Kondō Renpei	1848	S	Student	Tokyo	(R)	Shipping, mining (Mitsubishi)
Masuda Takashi	1847	S	M	Tokyo, Yok.	(R)	Trade, mining, general industrial pioneering
Fujita Denzaburō	1842	M	M	–	R	Shipping, railways, general industrial pioneering
Kawasaki Hachiuemon	1837	M	M, official	–	Cl	Banking
Yamabe Takeo	1851	S	Student	Tokyo	Cl	Cotton spinning
Katakura Kentarō	1849	P	Student, P	Tokyo	Cl	Silk spinning
Kinbara Meizen	1832	P	P	–	Cl	Land improvements, banking, social-welfare schemes
Sakuma Sadaichi	1846	S	Army	Tokyo	Cl	Printing, libraries
Okuda Masaka	1847	S	M	–	R	Spinning, banking, railways ("Shibusawa of Nagoya")
Morimura Ichizaemon	1839	M	M	Tokyo	Cl	Trade
Ōtani Kahei	1844	P	M	Yokohama	(R)	Trade, banking

Name	Birth	Class	Training	City	Type	Industries
Toyokawa Ryōhei	1851	S	Student	Osaka, Tok.	Cl	Banking (Mitsubishi)
Shōda Heigorō	1847	S	Student, teacher	Tokyo	(R)	Shipping, shipbuilding, other (in Mitsubishi)
Suzuki Tōzaburō	1855	M (?)	M	—	Cl	Sugar refining
Kawada Koichirō	1836	S	Official, M	—	(R)	Shipping, banking (Mitsubishi)
Takashima Kazaemon	1832	M		Tokyo	R	Railways, gas, land reclamation
Amamiya Keijirō	1846	P		Yokohama	R	Trade, mining, railways
Nakano Buei	1838	S	Official	—	R	Railways, general industrial pioneering
Hirano Tomiji	1846	S	Shipbuilding	Tokyo	Cl	Shipbuilding
Tanaka Chōbei	1858	M	M	Tokyo	R	Mining, iron casting, gas
Hirose Sukesaburō	1844	M	M		R	Banking, railways, newspaper, education
Motoki Shōzō	1824	S	Interpreter	Nagasaki	Cl	Type printing
Tanaka Heihachi	1834	?	M	—	(R)	Trade, banking
Magoshi Kyōhei	1844	S	M	Osaka	(R)	Beer brewing, cooperation with industrial pioneers
Nishimura Katsuzō	1836	S	Teacher, M	Nagasaki, Tok.	(R)	Leather, bricks
Kashima Manpei	1822	M	M	Tokyo	Cl	Cotton spinning
Abe Taizō	1849	S	Student	Tokyo	Cl	Insurance
Doi Michio	1837	S	Student	—	R	Textiles, banking, railways
Tanaka Ichibei	1838	M	M	Osaka	R	Trade, banking, railways, shipping
Hiranuma Senzō	1836	?	M	Tokyo	(R)	Trade, banking
Nakano Goichi	1842	S	Official	Tokyo	(R)	Sulphur production, participation in Osaka industries
Yonekura Ippei	1831	P	P	—	Cl	Internal trade and rice trade
Wakao Ippei	1820	M	P	Tokyo	(R)	Internal trade, electricity
Imamura Seinosuke	1849	P	M	Yokohama	(R)	Railways, banking, participation in industrial projects
Asabuki Eiji	1849	P	Student	Osaka	(R)	Trade, cotton spinning, general promotion (Mitsui)

[249]

Totals

S: 23	M: 30	Tokyo: 27	R: 18
P: 13	Other: 9	Osaka: 6	(R): 16
M: 12	None: 11	Yokohama: 5	Cl: 16
Unknown: 2	50	Nagasaki: 5	50
50		None: 13	
		56 (doubling counting)	

Notations. Class and training: S, samurai (including physicians); M, merchant; P, peasant. Entrepreneurial type: R, romantic; (R), semiromantic; Cl, classic. These types are defined in text.

neur. It is believed that most basic attitudes and concepts are fixed during the "formative years" of adolescence and early years of manhood. Not only his parents and the kind of education but also the political events that stir up public emotions may exert a lasting impact on a man's view of life and society. Because of the selected time limits we do not, of course, get much differentiation with respect to age groupings. Roughly, the men all lived through the same turbulent years of the pre-Restoration period, with its uprisings, the controversy over the opening of the ports, and the rallying resistance against the bakufu. They were all influenced by patriotic attitudes; if we try to find differences in this respect, we have to content ourselves with something other than black and white contrasts.

If we call the men born before 1840 the "older group" and those born in 1840 or later the "younger group," we meet a few rather surprising facts. Among the twenty-one entrepreneurs of the older group, we find all the founders of the zaibatsu except one, Asano. By "founders of the zaibatsu" I do not mean precisely the same men mentioned in the previous chapter; here I shall leave out Masuda and Nakamigawa, who entered Mitsui only after it had already taken its turn toward modern enterprise. Included are two who were not treated in Chapter Six: Kawasaki Hachiuemon and Kawasaki Shōzō, who founded zaibatsu of their own, although of somewhat smaller size than those discussed before. Another characteristic of the older men is their tendency to "go it alone," to maintain private ownership, in contrast to the company form so frequently and strongly urged by Shibusawa. A third feature of the older men is their semiofficial approach, characterized by ties with the government and the receipt of privileges and commissions from the government.

These three characteristics can probably be explained

by the way in which these men entered their entrepreneurial careers. They belonged predominantly to two
classes, officials and adventurer-merchants. The officials
like Godai, Hara, Motoki, Kawada, and, of course, Iwasaki were naturally inclined to continue the familiar approach, to maintain close political ties to the government
and to promote enterprise in the spirit of the *fukoku
kyōhei* (wealthy nation, strong army) in which they had
grown up in the han administrations. Even in the private
wing of the economy, these men remained half officials.

Doi Michio,[1] who abandoned his samurai status prior
to the Restoration and moved to Osaka to engage in trade,
occupied an official post under Godai which started him
off on his business career. Doi retained the official approach
all through his life. He became a promoter of modern
establishments, cooperated with others, and staged exhibitions to stimulate industrial advance. Examples of this
kind are numerous.

Those who made their start as adventurer-merchants
usually began in a very rough way, not caring about the
government or about anything except money. Men of this
type were Ōkura, Yasuda, Tanaka Heihachi, Takashima,
Morimura, Hiranuma, Nishimura, and Wakao. But in their
dealings these same men began to realize the weakness of
Japan's trading position. They then came under the influence of nationalism, which was particularly strong in
Tokyo, and so eventually combined their private moneymaking with public service by carrying out government
commissions. Increasingly they turned toward projects that
were in the public interest. Almost anyone who had participated in the fears, hopes, and enthusiasms of the Restoration became a patriot in those days, whatever social
group he belonged to.

Kashima Manpei [2] was a cotton merchant of Tokyo who

established the first private cotton-spinning mill because he thought that this was the only way to drive down the price of calicoes. In the face of a host of difficulties and much resistance, he carried his plan through. He later had machines constructed according to his own designs; they cost him far more than imported ones would have, but he insisted on making Japanese cotton spinning independent of imported machines. Kashima was not only a successful spinner whose mill never had losses, but he was also a bold and politically minded man. He advocated the opening of the ports and carried on business dealings with foreigners at a time when such actions could very well inspire assassination by fanatics.

Whether merchants or samurai, these men became involved in the political matrix and behaved like officials, and they felt that their own work was almost as important as that of the government leaders. Iwasaki's dictum, "I am the Man of the Far East," and Takashima's remark, "Even if Prince Itō should die, as long as Takashima lives there is no need to worry about the affairs of the country," [3] characterize the strong and prideful political make-up of the men of the older group.

The former adventurer-merchants had amassed their starting capital through boldness and shrewdness in foreign trade or from government commissions. Therefore they needed no joining of capital and remained lone-wolf entrepreneurs who built their own empires of trade and industry. The officials, too, could dispense with the cooperation of shareholders, and to them especially the idea of bowing to majority decisions must have been hard to accept. This probably explains why the older men favored private ownership and why some of them built such large empires for themselves.

The younger group, in contrast, tended more toward the

joint-stock form of enterprise, with less reliance on government help. This tendency cannot be pinned down with figures because the same man sometimes had one or two enterprises under his personal control and ownership, while he cooperated as a shareholder in a string of others. The same holds true with regard to government favors. Government subsidies and favoritism tapered off gradually. Nakamigawa best indicates this emerging trend, with his clear-cut economic rationality and exclusive reliance on other people's money — he could accumulate no capital in his position as a teacher. To what extent a genuine turn toward democratic ideas, majority rule, and cooperation were involved is difficult to say. The government became less generous in meting out favors, and the younger men had had little occasion to build up their own capital; so they were forced to depend on the capital of shareholders and on the cooperation of men like Shibusawa, Yasuda, Hara, and Masuda. The Chamber of Commerce and the leadership of Shibusawa welded the men together more firmly as an entrepreneurial group; cooperation in joining capital for large well-planned ventures thus became easier.

Class Origins

Of the fifty men in the table, twenty-three were of samurai origin, thirteen were peasants' sons, twelve were born as merchants; the class origins of the remaining two could not be ascertained. Some qualifications must be introduced here. A few of these attributions could be disputed and changed: for example, one might call Ōkura the son of a peasant or of a merchant, since his father was both, and the same could be said of two or three others; two or three country samurai could also be called peasants, since they differed in almost nothing but name from rich peasants who were commoners. Finally, the physicians, who were usually commoners, are here included in the samurai group because of the samurai-like education, occupation, and social privileges, which made them too unlike merchants and peasants to be grouped among them. Excluding country samurai and physicians, then, we would have seventeen or eighteen clear-cut samurai.

Even so, my sample seems to indicate that the samurai were best represented and that the merchants supplied relatively few leading entrepreneurs; perhaps this is what one would have expected from the start. But we must be careful not to draw the wrong conclusions from this. It by no means proves that the samurai as a class supplied more entrepreneurs than either the rich peasants or the merchants, relative to their total number. In fact, the sample points if anything in the opposite direction and indicates that, considering the total numbers of the three groups, the samurai were more poorly represented than the other two groups. Poor peasants and artisans, who hardly had a chance to become entrepreneurs, made up about 85 percent of Japan's population in the early Meiji era. Of the remaining 15 percent, about 7 percent of the population were samurai (according to the broad definition), some 5 percent merchants, and 3 percent rich peasants. Again, I emphasize that these percentages are approximations because the definitions and demarcations, especially between the merchants and rich peasants, and between ordinary peasants and rich peasants, cannot be clearly established. If we pay no attention to the relative size of the three groups, we can easily come to the conclusion that the samurai as a class were the innovators, and then build on this a theory like the one sketched at the beginning of Chapter Two. In order to make the case stronger in one direction or another, one has only to impose certain conditions on the sample. For instance, if we exclude the trading sector, we get a still stronger preponderance of samurai as against merchants, who in turn were better represented in the trading sector and in cotton spinning. All sectors were included in the sample, provided that the enterprises established by the entrepreneur were modern and that he joined in the efforts at pioneering so common to the modern business elite of the early Meiji years.

Some students of Meiji business maintain that industrial leadership and innovations were a near monopoly of the samurai class; they cite examples of the innovators within the Mitsui and Mitsubishi zaibatsu and a few others where samurai concentration was most pronounced. Then again we find assertions that merchants predominated as business leaders throughout the Meiji; these statements are based on a survey of those who held prominent positions in the largest businesses, including domestic trading and manufacturing of the traditional type. In the second approach the crucial distinction between innovating (entrepreneurship in the sense used here) and routine business is completely dropped. If such a point conveys anything at all it is that, by the middle of the Meiji, merchants and their capital were still dominant in the traditional sectors of business. This in turn strengthens my conclusions that merchants as a class were the least progressive group of all.

It was mentioned in Chapter Three that the entrepreneurs of peasant origin did not as a rule stay in their villages; they went to the city — usually Tokyo — early in their lives. Only two of the peasants here became entrepreneurs in their villages, Katakura and Kinbara. Katakura used his large landholdings as the financial basis for a silk filature, and Kinbara devoted his energies to land improvements and rural welfare projects. The others, such as Ōkura, Hara, Amamiya, Asabuki, and Shibusawa, left home, resolutely breaking the fetters of village traditions and limitations.

The merchants' sons in the sample similarly broke with family rules and guild restrictions and usually left their fathers' businesses to gain freedom of action. Whether peasants or merchants, they were restless young men, dissatisfied with society and with conditions at home. Of the merchants' sons, Hirose Sukesaburō and Suzuki had traveled and tried various new things before achieving entrepreneurial success; Fujita had been a political adventurer more interested in fighting battles than in his father's lucrative business and sake brewery.[4] Morimura was a poor man but he was disgruntled with the merchants' ways, and in his later career he never tired of scoring the low business morale and ethics of merchants in general.[5] Tanaka Ichibei had rejected the idea of continuing his inherited business as a wholesaler in Osaka and decided to become an entrepreneur of the modern type.[6] Most of the men with merchant backgrounds, then, were anything but the typical shōnin described in Chapter One.

My conclusion is that class origin was not of decisive importance in molding entrepreneurs. All three groups of samurai, peasant, and merchant descendants in the sample had cut the ties to their previous economic life — the samurai by force of events, the others usually by free choice. Economically, the men had to start all over again, at least insofar as their approaches and places of activity were concerned, although some entered existing enterprises which they either reorganized themselves or which had been modernized by a predecessor.

The surprisingly equal representation of the classes according to numerical strength — the rich peasants as a class being no exception — confirms the conclusion that the

socioeconomic forces peculiar to one class were of secondary importance in influencing entrepreneurial careers. The
voluntary cutting of ties to the past, which resulted in economic uprootedness, the migration to the centers of foreign influence, indicate that the political and ideological
forces at work in Tokugawa society before the Restoration
constituted the single most important factor in the making
of entrepreneurs. These forces were not confined to any
one class; any man who was able to follow the course of
events intelligently could be affected. Thus the economic
uprootedness and the new start in a new place are only indicators of the dynamics of political and social pressures.
The men were not uprooted ideologically, but belonged
to the first wave of a general trend. The entrepreneurs
were genuine children of the same national ferment that
brought forth the Meiji Restoration itself.

Book Learning and Practical Training

The subject of book learning as against practical experience was touched upon when I dealt with the introduction of new technologies at the plant level. It was
indicated there that the modern entrepreneurs displayed
a tendency toward a theoretical, bookish approach, in the
tradition of those who had built cannons and even blast
furnaces according to descriptions found in foreign books.
The samurai companies often foundered because of inexperience in business matters. It is interesting to see the
degrees of both book learning and practical experience that
prevailed among our fifty men. Column 4 of the table
indicates how many had received some business experience
before starting their independent entrepreneurial activities. At least thirty out of the fifty had worked in a merchant store, been peddlers, or done business of some sort
before the age of twenty.[7] If we count the officials and those

who had been employed in mining and shipbuilding before starting as entrepreneurs, we get thirty-nine out of fifty with practical training. These men must have been able to avoid the blunders of the usual samurai business methods.

It would be valuable to have similar figures on the formal educational backgrounds of the men, but unfortunately the available biographical material is not precise enough to permit this. How many years of study are required to make a man "educated" in our sense? And even if the years of study were known, we would not know how many interruptions and side jobs had helped to fill that time. From my endeavor to gain information on this subject, however, the general notion was confirmed that the large majority of the fifty men, say 70 percent, did receive an above-average education, one comparable with that of the samurai.[8] Chief among these, of course, are the ten listed as students and teachers, of whom seven were Fukuzawa men. The sample therefore confirms the previously established evidence that book learning was of great importance and almost a necessary condition to becoming an entrepreneur in the early Meiji years.

The ten student-entrepreneurs throw light upon another interesting trend that emerged in these years. Of the ten, only one, Abe, built up his own enterprise; the others rose to power and achieved their pioneering success within the framework of existing enterprises, mainly the Mitsui, Mitsubishi, and Shibusawa combines. The reason is rather obvious, of course; they were "drafted" from the classroom into their jobs and rose to top positions because of their knowledge, attitudes, and talents, as well as their friendly connections with Fukuzawa, Iwasaki, Shibusawa, and Inoue. These men started a tradition of close connections with certain colleges and enterprises whereby graduates of these colleges had the best chance of entering the big concerns and rising to high positions in them. Thus the well-known preferential treatment and support existing between the *gakubatsu* (school clique) and the zaibatsu (used here in the rather broad sense of leading enterprises) really started in these years when the Keiō and shortly afterwards the Waseda universities supplied the zaibatsu with talented and progressive managers.

Places of Early Influence:
Tokyo, Yokohama, Nagasaki, Osaka

Places of origin, like class origins, seem to have had no significance as a source of entrepreneurs. In the sample the largest single contingent, seven in all, were born in Edo. Considering that of the city's population about half were samurai and half merchants, the number indicates nothing significant. Actually the fifty men represent all parts of Japan with only a slight preponderance from the south-western han, notably Tosa, where Iwasaki and his associates originated. Dismissing place of birth as of no consequence in determining entrepreneurial careers, let us see whether the places of early influence had any significance.

A glance at the table shows the following: twenty-seven out of fifty had moved to Tokyo — or at least had spent some time there — before the age of twenty; six had some Osaka experience; five were in Nagasaki and five in Yoko-hama; thirteen had no experience in these cities before reaching the age of twenty.

Nagasaki decisively stimulated five of the men to turn to modern enterprise. All were born before 1838 and therefore belong to the older group. During their adolescence Nagasaki was the only place where firsthand experience of Western technology was available. The contact with foreigners and the shocking realization of Western economic and military superiority became for all five the decisive factor that set them on the path toward entrepreneurship.

Kawasaki Shōzō [9] conceived his great interest in ship-building there; when he saw the disparity between the large foreign steamers and the small Japanese boats, he decided then and there to spend his energies to improve the Japanese situation and to work in shipbuilding instead of trade. He eventually became a great shipbuilder and the founder of the Kawasaki zaibatsu. Motoki Shōzō learned Dutch and eventually became so inspired by books and the art of printing that he made his own type and printed a Dutch-Japanese dictionary. This was the start of his career as a pioneer in printing.[10] For Iwasaki as well as for Godai the sojourn in Nagasaki contributed much to the formation of their progressive ideas. The case of Nishimura is not quite so clear: he had studied chemistry in Nagasaki and started brick manufacturing; then he ventured into other things, and only later did he turn again to brick manufacturing, but not as his main field of enterprise.[11]

Osaka as the background for six of our men has an altogether different meaning. To begin with, it is surprising that the major city of commerce and capital is not better represented. We saw how little Hirose Saihei, the modernizer of the Sumitomo zaibatsu, owed to Osaka's influence. Asabuki had taught English in Osaka; Toyokawa had been there working for Iwasaki; but both Asabuki and Toyokawa became entrepreneurs in Tokyo, after absorbing Fukuzawa's ideas in the Keiō college.

Magoshi Kyōhei left his native village for Osaka and joined Kōnoike as a merchant apprentice. Dissatisfied with this position, he became an innkeeper and then met Masuda who had come from Tokyo. Masuda recognized Magoshi's talents and spent a few evenings telling him about the "new spirit of enterprise" that prevailed in

Tokyo. After reading the *Saikoku risshi hen* (Success story of Western countries), Magoshi decided to leave Osaka in 1872 and go to Tokyo to "breathe the new air." There he had his hair cut short, ate beef — "so far nothing unclean had ever entered his mouth" — and thus became a man of the new era.[12]

Matsumoto Jūtarō had come to Osaka at thirteen as a merchant apprentice, but he and Tanaka Ichibei became part of a team of Osaka modernizers who were acutely conscious of their alienation from the established traditions of that city. It would be wrong to deny that Osaka, too, received direct foreign influence, especially within the first few years after the opening of the port in 1868; but compared with Nagasaki, Yokohama, and especially Tokyo, Osaka remained in the backwaters of the new era and did not exercise a particularly strong stimulus upon entrepreneurship.

Tokyo and Yokohama were of course by far the most important cities for their effects on entrepreneurs. The two cities are close together and shared several important aspects in those years. There was first the golden opportunity for adventurers, the "free-for-all" after the opening of the ports and around the time of the Restoration. The cases of Ōkura, Yasuda, and Asano were often repeated. Youngsters who were dissatisfied with their social position or work at home left for Yokohama or Edo. Two further cases may be taken as illustrations.

Wakao Ippei, a peddler in raw silk and tobacco, came to Edo to "become a samurai"; when he failed he went home but later returned to try to become a scholar; again he could make no headway. Off and on he tried various types of trading, moving into the import-export business in Yokohama, dealing in raw silk, sugar, and cotton. Like Yasuda, he made a killing in paper-money exchange and

secured handsome profits from government contracts during the Satsuma Rebellion. Then he moved up to respectable entrepreneurial tasks, built a silk-spinning mill for
which he had the machines constructed according to his
own designs, and finally became a member of the entrepreneurial elite in Tokyo, cooperating in a large variety of
modern enterprises.[13]

Imamura Seinosuke, a poor peasant's son, left his home
to start a new life in Yokohama before he was sixteen. He
returned home, but three years later came back to Yokohama to make another start. He tried money exchanging
and other businesses, but got nowhere; he moved to Tokyo
and made some profit on the stock exchange. In 1884 he
went to the United States and Europe, and the trip made
a different man of this adventurer-merchant. He opened
a small banking business in his house, but then went into
railway building, founding, or at least cooperating in,
twelve railway companies, occupied an important position
in the Chamber of Commerce, and joined in many large-
scale modern ventures.[14]

The rampant opportunities were but one advantage of
coming to these cities; almost inevitably these men came
into contact there with the new era and often also with
foreigners. It was in Tokyo that Morimura Ichizaemon
conceived the idea of becoming a "merchant of the *bummei kaika*," and he sent his younger brother to Fukuzawa
who was to make of him a "soldier in the field of foreign
trade." [15]

Sakuma Sadaichi, who had traveled far and wide within
Japan, was struck in Tokyo by the new spirit of progress
and distinguished himself by working to establish popular
rural libraries, in order to spread civilization among the
people. He was a quixotic man — first a samurai to the
bone, who would choose a sword over a rifle, then doing an

about-face to distinguish himself in enterprise. He kept Mill's *Principles of Political Economy* by his bed and read it every evening. When he was once asked what his faith was, he answered, "My faith is Mill." [16] But Sakuma was a typical patriot and samurai for whom Mill probably meant no more than belief in modern enterprise, not a liberal and laissez-faire ideology; therefore he did not differ from Shibusawa whose "bible" was the Analects of Confucius.

The very closeness of the government seat gave Tokyo, and to a lesser extent Yokohama, a unique advantage. At a time when newspapers were still a rarity and unknown outside the cities, the inspiring leadership of the dynamic Meiji leaders could not have the same stimulating impact in other cities. The programs and slogans originated in Tokyo and were discussed on the streets by everyone. The political and progressive climate of this city gave a strongly political cast to the Tokyo group of entrepreneurs; here the men could also gain easiest access to funds both from the government and through cooperation among themselves.

Summing up all the formative influences to which the fifty entrepreneurs were exposed, we notice a clear pattern. Neither class origin nor initial capital resources was of decisive importance; what mattered most was the new ideology, the new system of values, that each man had to absorb. If the entrepreneurs were to be innovators and pioneers, they had to be men of the new era, men who believed in the future of the Meiji Restoration. Capital was supplied from various sources, as has been shown in the case of the zaibatsu men. Certain key factors stand out which facilitated the necessary change in ideology or values: original dissatisfaction with conditions at home, which led these men to leave and become economically uprooted; learning, which became a vehicle for the new

ideas and an aid in grasping the complexities of the enterprise system; finally, a "center" from which the new ideas
radiated and attracted the dissatisfied and the dissenters.
The closeness between entrepreneurs and government officials stemmed from their sharing of a common task and a
common viewpoint. This made these entrepreneurs sometimes act like officials, and in spite of their "faith in Mill"
they were hardly touched by laissez faire and the spirit
of capitalism.

The Entrepreneurial Performance: Biographical Notes

What did the fifty entrepreneurs do, in which lines did
they innovate? How did they approach their problems,
and what were the main difficulties they encountered?
There are many questions of this kind that we should like
to have answered. But generalizations are even more difficult here than in relation to the formative elements. It
seems best to let the variations as well as the similarities
among our men come out in brief notes on each of those
who have not yet been given particular attention. In order
to give to the whole a semblance of logic and to make possible short summaries of certain features, a grouping is used
as indicated by columns 6 and 7 of the table. Although
both columns pertain to all of the men, the biographical
note on each will appear only once, either under his "entrepreneurial type" or under his "main field of activity."

Romantic Type and Classical Type

A distinction according to range of innovating activity
is indicated by the terms *romantic type* and *classical type*.
The romantic type [17] is characterized by founding one company after another in rapid succession, moving from one

field of enterprise to another, leaving the details and continuation to others. The classical type is the opposite, the man who remains throughout his life within the field in which he is an expert. He may build subsidiary enterprises, even a whole industrial empire, but all of them will be essentially in the original line of his entrepreneurial success. In reality we find many mixed cases which will not fit entirely into either of these categories; in my table these are designated the *semiromantic type,* to show that they lean more toward the romantic type.

The classical entrepreneurs were not numerous during the early Meiji era. In the table only sixteen are thus labeled, and even they crossed the line on occasion. Those who remained in one field were the foreign-trade merchants Yonekura and Morimura, and the bankers Kawasaki Hachiuemon, Abe, and Toyokawa of Mitsubishi. In industry the classical entrepreneurs were the strongheaded pioneers who were fascinated by their one great task and carried it through. They acquired so much technical knowledge in the course of time that they broke the path for many followers. In cotton spinning there was the Tokyo merchant Kashima and the college graduate Yamabe, and in silk spinning Katakura. Furukawa and Hirose Saihei in mining, Ōkawa in paper manufacturing, and Kawasaki Shōzō in shipbuilding also came close to the one-line entrepreneurs.

Sakuma Sadaichi and Motoki Shōzō,[18] both mentioned earlier, were pioneers in printing. They both realized that civilization was inevitably connected with education, and education with printing. Each was absolutely dedicated to his task. Motoki was forty-five years old when he first succeeded in type printing, after innumerable trials. He resigned an official position and began a printing enterprise in Nagasaki with 4,000 yen; he moved to Tokyo in 1873 and later established branch offices in Osaka and Yokohama. Nor could Sakuma's determination be broken by difficulties and losses. He once replied to a friend who cautioned him to stop investing and save for his children: "I was born naked and I intend therefore to die naked; if I should die somebody else will take care of the education and upbringing of my children. But I have to continue to work as long as my life lasts and to serve the interest of others." [19]

Hirano Tomiji [20] lived for shipbuilding. In Nagasaki he had become interested in this work; later he bought the Ishikawajima Shipyard, which the government had abandoned and partly dimantled, and began to construct sailing ships and even steamers. In spite of his enthusiasm, he was in constant trouble, and it was Shibusawa who kept him afloat. The total of Hirano's debt to Shibusawa amounted to 100,000 yen. Hirano was supposed to pay 8 percent and to add "in the case of profits" half of the profits. In about ten years of continued lending Shibusawa only once received the interest payment. Yet he kept extending loans although, he reflected, as a commercial banker he was really not supposed to do so. Both Hirano and Shibusawa believed firmly in eventual success, and, equally important for them, they felt the necessity to build Japanese ships. The determination to stem the reliance on imports was characteristic of Hirano. When there was a debate about whether pipes for Tokyo's water mains should be imported or produced in Japan, Hirano was lying ill in bed; he got up and gave speeches against importation of the pipes, and during one of these speeches he died.

Suzuki Tōzaburō [21] achieved his fame in sugar refining. An uneducated sugar and candy retailer, he started to manufacture sugar. His struggle was a very long one; he first succeeded in producing crystal sugar after some seven or eight years of trials, but could find almost no buyers. He then decided to produce refined sugar because of his concern that all refined sugar was imported. Although some people encouraged him, he had to wait two years, until 1886, for financial cooperation. In 1890 he produced his first refined sugar; in 1895 he founded a refining company. He had worked alone; none of the great promoters and business leaders gave him any support until he achieved success. Only later, when he was already famous, did he cooperate with men like Inoue and Masuda. Suzuki and Hirano were very similar in approach; their natural strong interest in one kind of enterprise was enforced by the desire to compete with imports and to make Japan independent.

The romantic entrepreneurs were influenced in their approach to business by a strong sense of urgency: much had to be done, and few were ready to do it. The founders went from one task to another; often we find them involved in a string of uncoordinated ventures. They were not much concerned with details. Shibusawa once discussed his engagement in so many diverse projects. He agreed that "according to the principle of division of labor" one ought to engage thoroughly in only one kind of business. But, he added apologetically, "the conditions of the time left no other choice." [22] Magoshi had also been involved in a large variety of industrial ventures; but during a trip abroad he realized that there businessmen usually stuck to one line and therefore achieved great success. As a result of this new insight, he severed his ties with many establishments and concentrated almost exclusively on brewing beer. He became Japan's leading brewer. [23]

Amamiya Keijirō, [24] like so many others, began his business career in Yokohama with making money by any means that came to hand. After a trip abroad, he changed his approach and decided to become an entrepreneur. He imported machines and set up a flour mill, but had great difficulty in selling the flour because the Japanese were not used to eating bread. Amamiya had to sell part of his flour to Russia; then he imported high-grade wheat and distributed it free to peasants in an all-out drive to break down their prejudice. He also began making experiments in electric-power generation. Amamiya was the first and last man to open an iron mine entirely with private capital, investing over half a million yen in it, and he operated at a loss for years. Although he was president of a railway company, he urged nationalization of the railroads, apparently because the varying freight rates hurt industry and especially mining, in which he had invested heavily. Amamiya put his hand to a large variety of enterprises, founding, cooperating, consulting, and occupying honorary positions.

Tanaka Gentarō,[25] who was called "the Shibusawa of Kyoto," had supposedly conceived the idea of a career as an entrepreneur while studying English in Kobe, at the age of twenty-one. Tanaka did not experience a break with the past; his father had already opened a bank in Kyoto, and the son entered this business. In 1884 he founded the Kyoto Stock Exchange with his father. Because of his integrity and proverbial economic foresight (people used to say that Tanaka Gentarō would "light his lamp at noon already and turn it off at midnight"), he was able to achieve a position of influence and leadership in Kyoto. His chief concern was to innovate and to work for the modernization of Kyoto. He founded a string of enterprises, ranging from a previously mentioned pottery company to weaving and electricity. He is said to have founded the Kyoto Savings Bank mainly for the purpose of gathering capital for new enterprises. Anticipating prolonged difficulties with his electrical company, he insisted that the burden be shared by the whole population and so made a collection drive for capital contributions. For the twenty-odd enterprises that he founded he received no support from the government, but he cooperated closely with other industrial leaders, notably Shibusawa. As soon as an enterprise had been firmly established, Tanaka seems to have lost interest in it and gone on to new projects.

Takashima Kazaemon [26] was a man with a passion for promoting new things. The son of a village headman, he had left his home for Edo to make his fortune. He became a pioneer in a wide range of projects, sometimes under government auspices, sometimes in cooperation with others, sometimes on his own. He was active in railways, land reclamation, mining, utilities, and school building. Because of his deep interest in the railway program, the government appointed him to reclaim part of the sea between Tokyo and Yokohama to permit a straight connection for the Tokyo-Yokohama line. He employed about 3,000 workers on this project. In Hokkaido he reclaimed a large area of wasteland. In 1871 Takashima built a foreign-language school for 700 students with 30,000 yen of his own capital and urged Fukuzawa to teach in it. This man who had served a five-year sentence under the bakufu for establishing illicit trading relations with foreigners became a romantic entrepreneur with such a high degree of public responsibility that he would later compare his own importance to the country with that of Prince Itō.

Okuda Masaka [27] played a role in Nagoya similar to that of Tanaka Gentarō in Kyoto and was called "the Shibusawa of Nagoya." A dissatisfied official and a man with experience in trading operations, Okuda started his career as an industrialist with the foundation of the Owari Cotton Spinning-Mill in 1888. When the mill began to show

losses, he was advised to make good by speculative purchases and sales policies based on the rather violent price
fluctuations of raw cotton and yarns. He rejected such a
suggestion, maintaining that "an industrialist . . . has to
continue steadily with production, and his profits must
come from the progress of industry itself; profits from
speculation are despicable." [28] His disdain for salesman-
ship and pride in being an industrialist and a pioneer are
clearly expressed in these words. Okuda founded the
Nagoya Stock Exchange, became president of the Chamber of Commerce, spearheaded many new establishments
in banking, electricity, and gas, and founded a freight-car
construction company with 600,000 yen in capital.

Kinbara Meizen [29] was not an industrialist in the proper
sense, but he certainly was an innovator and a reformer.
As the son of a rich peasant, he decided to invest in agriculture on a large scale. His great projects included river
regulation, bridge building, and drainage systems. He
established a water-regulation school, pioneered in cattle
breeding, and built roads in rural areas; he also managed
a bank. Kinbara became well known for organizing an
institution for the care and rehabilitation of prisoners.
All his efforts seem to have been motivated principally
by a genuine and selfless patriotism and a desire to raise
the level of social well-being. Shibusawa, Morimura, Sakuma, and Kinbara are usually considered the most idealistic of the Meiji entrepreneurs. Whereas Shibusawa was
guided by Confucian ethics, Kinbara became a Christian,
and probably a good deal of his idealism was stimulated by
his new faith. He not only dedicated himself entirely to
his welfare schemes and rural innovations, but he asked
and received cooperation from the government, from
bankers and industrialists, and from the public through
collection drives.

These are only a few examples of entrepreneurs of the romantic type. The leading ones — Shibusawa, Godai, Asano, and Ōkura — have already been sufficiently discussed; others will receive attention in a different connection. But the general trend to bold innovations in many lines, to an almost headlong rushing from one task to another, is characteristic of the large majority of our fifty representative entrepreneurs.

The Bankers

Classification of these business leaders according to their field of activity presents a real difficulty because of the prevalence of the romantic type. With very few exceptions, we should call them all industrialists. Bankers and foreign-trade merchants usually ended up by establishing several industrial plants or founding railway companies or public-work projects. The subdivision here, then, should be taken loosely and not in any exclusive sense.

The bankers enjoyed high prestige in Meiji Japan owing to the success of the national banks. Banks were regarded as instruments for the building of modern industry. The foremost bankers extended long-term loans or invested directly in large projects with a long gestation period. Shibusawa, Yasuda, Nakamigawa, and others were not only great bankers; they were equally great as industrialists. Minomura, who should also be called a banker, was born too early to turn to industry. In addition to Shibusawa, Yasuda, Minomura, and Nakamigawa, we may classify seven others as primarily bankers: Hara, Toyokawa, Matsumoto, Kawasaki Hachiuemon, Hirose Sukesaburō, Kawada, and Abe.

Hara Rokurō, the son of a village headman, has been called one of the "big five" in the business world, together with Shibusawa, Yasuda, Ōkura, and Furukawa. Hara had been a fierce *sonnō jōi* partisan in his native Choshu han and had engaged in many battles. He decided to leave his military career in 1871 while studying in the United States, following the advice of a friend who stressed that the foundation of a strong country lies not in its army but in its trade and manufacturing.[30] He studied at Yale University for three years and in London for three more years. Hara started his entrepreneurial career after his return to Japan in 1877, with the foundation of the country's hundredth bank; then he became co-founder of Japan's first savings bank. From then on he moved out into an unbelievably broad range of activities. We find him engaged in such fields as electricity, railways, spinning, shipping, mining and paper manufacturing. He now fought for the competitive strength of his country with the same determination with which he had previously battled rioting peasants and bakufu forces.

Toyokawa Ryōhei [31] and Kawada Koichirō [32] were both Mitsubishi men whose independent achievements are somewhat overshadowed by the genius of Iwasaki. Toyokawa worked mainly in public relations for Mitsubishi. He had valuable connections with Fukuzawa's college. As president of the Mitsubishi Bank and vice-president of the Bankers' Association, he wielded great influence in the promotion of the Keiō spirit. He insisted that the new age needed new men. Kawada gained prominence as president of the Bank of Japan, in which position he is credited with the reversal of official policy from promotion of agriculture to stress on trade and industry.

Hirose Sukesaburō [33] and Abe Taizō [34] were mainly insurance men who championed this new line of business in Japan. Hirose had been an accomplished and successful merchant at the age of seventeen. He helped impoverished fellow merchants in various ways and had a school built to promote business education. He established a few banks, promoted railway construction, and in 1890 founded a newspaper; but his primary interest shifted to insurance. Abe was teaching English at Keiō at the age of twenty-one; at twenty-three he became an employee of the Ministry of Education. Later he went back to teaching and again returned to the ministry, which sent him on a trip to the United States. There he conceived the idea of introducing insurance into Japan, and after his return in 1881 he founded Japan's first insurance company, in cooperation with Mitsubishi's influential Shōda. Today Abe's Meiji Life Insurance Company is one of the largest in Japan. He traveled extensively, crisscrossing the country to spread the insurance idea and to establish branch offices.

Matsumoto Jūtarō [35] displayed from early boyhood an insatiable thirst for advancement in business. Dissatisfied with his slow progress in Kyoto, he went to Osaka at thirteen; there he could not become independent as quickly as he had hoped because of the strict guild rules, so he started anew on his own as a peddler. Next he turned to trading with imported goods and eventually became very successful as a manufacturer of woolen cloth. When he had amassed a handsome fortune, "he began to think of the public good." [36] After 1878 he applied himself to the reorganization of the Osaka money market. Through establishing and amalgamating banks, he rose to a dominant position, became president of the Osaka Bankers' Association, and used his financial strength and influence to promote modern industry in that city. After banking, Matsumoto's main fields of activity were railway building (he founded four railway companies and invested in others), cotton spinning, beer brewing, sugar refining, and education. He founded an "education insurance company" and opened the first nursery school in Japan. By 1898 his total yearly income was surpassed only in Osaka by that of Sumitomo.[37]

Kawasaki Hachiuemon [38] was a cautious banker with little direct interest in trading or industry. He was also one of the very few men who did not experience a major shift away from past activities. As a merchant in Mito han, he had been able to accumulate considerable capital through the operation of the bakufu mint. After the Restoration he continued in almost the same line as a prefectural money exchanger. Gradually he turned to modern banking, achieved great success, and rose to the stature of a zaibatsu builder. But he remained a fully conservative banker, quite in contrast to the others in the sample. His principles were honesty, diligence, thrift, and accumulation, which could have been taken straight from any of the Tokugawa merchant house rules. They compare unfavorably with the dicta of men like Iwasaki, Asano, Yasuda, and Ōkura insofar as daring and entrepreneurial vigor are concerned.

All the great bankers except Kawasaki Hachiuemon came to a turning point, after which they became not only interested in but completely absorbed by the task of national promotion. They sponsored modern banking, industry, and even education, more or less because they "began to think of the public good," realizing that their acquired wealth also meant a new responsibility for the progress of the economy.

The Men in Foreign Trade

The efforts of the government to establish trade companies soon after the Restoration ended in failure; no further attempts were made to organize the foreign-trade sector centrally, and the initiative was more or less left to individuals. But contemporary opinion attached great importance to competition with foreign countries, and the endeavors of a small group of pioneers must be understood against the background of that urgency — this helps to explain the unusual self-assurance and bold planning of these foreign-trade merchants. Ōkura and Masuda have already received sufficient attention in other connections. They were among the top men in foreign trade, though they both moved from trade increasingly into industry.

Morimura Ichizaemon [39] is probably the most interesting among these trade merchants because of his extraordinary idealism. At the age of thirteen he had vowed before a shrine never to deviate from the path of honesty, and he not only kept his promise faithfully but became a fighter for high business ethics. He started in great poverty, running a night stall in Tokyo. Gradually Morimura gained some ground, tried his luck in mining operations, then in fishing and salt production, and profited from government trade commissions. But, surprisingly, he severed his ties as an official merchant because of the corruption that prevailed in these commission deals. He then turned to foreign trade; he had his younger brother learn English and sent him to New York for further study; this brother opened a branch office of Morimura in New York. Morimura was extremely conscious of being different from most of the other merchants in his stress on absolute honesty. He eventually extended his activities to banking and cotton spinning; he also built several schools.

Ōtani Kahei [40] gained sufficient experience and money during his employment with the Smith Baker Company in Yokohama to start an independent tea-export business. He became very successful and, like Morimura, felt a responsibility toward Japan's trade position. He organized the Tea Traders' Association, staged and promoted exhibitions on foreign trade, and spoke frequently in various parts of the country on his two favorite subjects, the necessity of foreign trade and honesty in business. Ōtani argued that to the Westerners honesty was more valuable than life, and he held that a man should atone with his life for cheating because of the damage done to society.[41] Ōtani maintained a lively interest in civic affairs and actively promoted general welfare and education. For nine years he was a member of the Upper House.

Hiranuma Senzō and Yonekura Ippei displayed similar characteristics, and their careers can be sketched rather briefly. Hiranuma [42] was a merchant of fortune in the earlier part of his business life. Like Wakao, mentioned as a foreign-trade merchant in an earlier context, he made money by speculating in grain, stocks, and real estate in Yokohama, thus amassing over 10 million yen in capital. He was severely criticized for his usurious moneylending. In foreign trade he was very successful and eventually turned also to industrial investments in cotton spinning, railways, and electric companies. He, too, built a school and became known as a promoter of and contributor to public-welfare projects.

Yonekura Ippei [43] was born a merchant but participated in the *sonnō jōi* movement and was imprisoned. Later he became a prefectural official, resigned, and went to China to survey the market for Japanese products. He began with tea and lumber exports. In 1871 we find him in Tokyo establishing a bank, with a partner, with 500,000 yen in capital; then he built a paper mill. After 1872 he concentrated solely on the domestic and foreign rice trade; he organized and then controlled the Tokyo rice market.

There are a few common characteristics of these prominent foreign-trade merchants of the early Meiji era. These men usually had entered the port cities as penniless upstarts, who were not too particular about their methods of making money; and they made money, thanks to their talent and boldness and to the turbulent conditions of the time and their machinations with government officials. Then came a decisive turning point, their "conversion" from profit maximization by any method to a realization of responsibility to the country; they subsequently became merchants of the *bummei kaika*. In this capacity they insisted on honesty, reliability, and the honor of trade.

This same turn toward a new sense of responsibility as soon as a certain level of wealth and economic prominence had been acquired was seen among other men of the sample: Yasuda, Matsumoto, and Asano are typical. The newly acquired wealth, often gained by questionable methods, gave these men a real power over others; whether they wanted to or not, they became public figures. But it was almost impossible in Meiji Japan to be a public figure and to disregard the pressure of public opinion. Public opinion, in turn, acclaimed only those who combined wealth with progressive and responsible action, as indicated by the policies of the government itself. Public opinion and the new standards set by a few leaders like Shibusawa were, I believe, very real and effective factors in changing many men with talent and boldness into responsible entrepreneurs. For these men the problem of initial capital accumulation had been solved before their pioneering began; they could surmount initial difficulties in the new ventures and even sustain large losses for some time, compensated now by their sense of greatness and their firm belief in final success.

Also common to this group is the tendency to turn to industrial investments and to move gradually away from trade, to leave it to other men and to start, in the words of Ōkura, "enterprises that others do not or cannot undertake." It almost seems as if the foreign-trade merchants, in spite of their insistence on their honesty and patriotic motivations, could not otherwise establish a sufficiently striking contrast between themselves and men who were only interested in quick profits, as they in fact had been themselves. The real honor and entrepreneurial prestige were to be gained in modern industry and it was here that the cream of the Meiji business world tended to concentrate.

The Political Merchants

It does not seem necessary at this stage to marshal a set of representative men in order to illustrate the outstanding features of the Meiji industrial pioneers. The chapter on the zaibatsu builders showed the prevailing attitudes among the top industrialists; further examples were presented in the discussion of the classical and romantic types. The few remaining men in my sample who have not yet received any detailed attention will help to throw additional light on two aspects, or rather approaches, of the Meiji entrepreneurs. We saw in an earlier context that government connections and subsidies were particularly prevalent among the older group of men, while the younger group shifted gradually toward independence and the corporate form of enterprise. Thus official enterprise and the semiofficial entrepreneurs mark the beginning of the Meiji entrepreneurial development. The group of college graduates who moved to top managerial positions without substantial capital of their own signal a new stage.

The term "political merchant" (*seishō*) was new in the Meiji vocabulary, just as the word *jitsugyōka* was. But unlike the latter it carried a derogatory meaning; it branded the lobbyists who relied on their friends among officials to receive the coveted government contracts. The Satsuma Rebellion became a great boon to political merchants who obtained army delivery contracts or shipping monopolies. The outstanding examples here are Iwasaki, Ōkura, Masuda, and Matsumoto. Godai, too, remained very close to his former co-officials after he left office, and his half-million-yen loan from the government for an indigo plant was not the only favor he received. Even Yasuda and Shibusawa, who were extremely independent men, did not go entirely empty-handed when indirect subsidies were being offered. Yet Shibusawa was at no point criticized or called a political merchant; rather, he was praised for his independence from government help. The criticism of the political merchants was mainly directed either at those who were out only to make a "killing" under government cover, those who swarmed around the officials like bees around honey in order to gain favors, or, as in the case of Iwasaki, at ruthless monopoly power that thrived under the wing of a powerful faction within the government.

There was a system in the privileges that were handed out so liberally. It was thought that samurai and other newcomers with talent but no capital should be helped to build a basis, in terms of capital, for their entrepreneurial activity. These indirect subsidies were given as a matter of policy after the abolition of government enterprises, and one of the principal champions of the policy was Inoue Kaoru. He not only knew how to pick able men for Mitsui; other political merchants also relied on his good offices to secure privileges. Himself a man with keen insight into the economic problems that the entrepreneurs faced, Inoue usually knew whom to subsidize.

The policy of indirect subsidies to would-be entrepreneurs naturally raised a thorny ethical problem. How much favoritism and how much corruption were involved in this type of indirect stimulation to entrepreneurship? Old loyalties and the *hanbatsu* (han cliques) played an important role in determining the recipients of contracts. But when all is said and done, we must be careful not to apply the same standards to the early Meiji situation as we would to the present day. Not only was the need for indirect subsidy much greater at that time, but the Meiji government inherited a long-standing tradition from the Tokugawa rulers and the han. All had their *goyō shōnin* (official merchants) who made tremendous gains but at the same time had to be ready to be taxed heavily or to lend large sums on request. Thus the favors were coupled with a special duty; carrying on this tradition, the political merchants of the early Meiji were supposed to support the government and to be "taxed" by using their wealth, even at prolonged losses, for the building of modern industry.

Fujita Denzaburō is a good example of a political merchant both with respect to initial accumulation and the use of capital gained through government contracts. During the stage of accumulation, he does not seem to have been scrupulous in his methods; he was even accused of counterfeiting money.[44] This rich sake brewer's son, who knew a few top government officials from the time when he fought battles under their leadership, displayed unusual courage as well as shrewdness. He wanted and won huge profits from trade in army supplies and rice, and then was equally eager to reinvest these gains in industrial enterprises in Osaka. He built a large shoe factory, a sulphuric-acid plant, and spread out to many diverse investment activities in cooperation with his friend Nakano Goichi, and with Godai, Matsumoto, and a few others. Although he was the owner of some silver mines, he advocated the change to the gold standard as a necessity for the Japanese economy; he was acclaimed for this objectivity by contemporaries and thus proved that he was a political merchant who could think in terms of the national good.

Nakano Goichi [45] cooperated closely with Fujita. A samurai prodigy who became an official at fifteen, he had an adventurous career in military and administrative service and in trading under lucrative government commissions. He accumulated considerable wealth in army deliveries and then turned his interest to industry. He became one of the Osaka pioneers of modern enterprise and vice-president of the chamber of commerce. His vigorous entrepreneurial start came to a sudden end when he committed suicide in 1880, when only thirty-eight years old.

Kawasaki Shōzō [46] could have been included among the zaibatsu men of the previous chapter, since his shipyard was the nucleus of his empire of heavy industry. He had become interested in shipbuilding during his stay in Nagasaki, but for a considerable time had no opportunity to put his plans into action. He became friendly with Matsukata, who appointed him to make a survey of the Ryukyu Islands. From that position he was chosen to be vice-president of the Yūbin Jōkisen Company, which was the first of three attempts to break the shipping monopoly of Mitsubishi. Although Yūbin Jōkisen collapsed very shortly, Kawasaki's name was remembered among officials. With a government loan of 30,000 yen, he began in 1878 to rebuild the deserted Tsukiji Shipyard in Tokyo. He encountered innumerable difficulties of a technical nature, and few people believed he would ever succeed. When he had finally finished his first steamship, the *Hokkai Maru*, he had to make a vigorous effort to advertise. He invited over a thousand officials and businessmen to a party that actually cost him more than the *Hokkai Maru* itself.[47] It would lead us too far afield to follow the course of Kawasaki's rivalry with Mitsubishi, his purchase and extension of the Hyōgo Shipyard with government help, and the rise of his enterprises to zaibatsu dimensions. Connections with government officials and subsidies were of strategic importance to Kawasaki's success, but the basic reason was that, in his friend Baron Maejima's words, "he lived and died for shipbuilding." At the end of his life, in 1912, his yards had orders for large ships not only from Japan but also from China, Russia, and France.

Nakano Buei [48] remained a politician even after he had left his government post to become a businessman. He was a highly cultured and public-minded samurai who knew how to put his previous experience as a han administrator to good use in private business. The establishment of a horse-drawn railway in Tokyo led to his first major success. We find him later promoting and investing in railways, insurance, and even iron production. He was not so much an original innovator as a cooperator within the top group of Tokyo industrialists. As president of the chamber of commerce and the stock exchange, he exercised a moral leadership in the business community, and at the same time he kept his hand in politics, as an active member of the Liberal Party.

These few sketches of political merchants may suffice as illustrations of the way in which many entrepreneurs, and many lesser men who also tried, were able to use government connections and subsidies as stepping stones to business success. It was mentioned previously that in a certain sense all Meiji entrepreneurs were political merchants. The strict separation of the central and the private wing of the economy was slow to evolve in the politically emotional climate of the period.

The Graduates

The last group to be mentioned in this analysis of leading entrepreneurs is the managers who rose to prominence because of a college education. They constitute a separate group by virtue of their youth and because of their different approach. Among our fifty men these students-turned-entrepreneurs moved farthest away from officialdom and favoritism and also from the lone-wolf approach and the romantic approach. The heat of political emotions subsided gradually; the feeling of urgency that inspired many hasty ventures gave way to rational planning within the framework of a firmly established industrial nucleus. These newcomers from the classrooms of Fukuzawa's college were nonfeudal, nonpolitical, and eminently sensible and liberal-minded. Their emphasis was on technical knowledge and long-term planning.

We have already seen how in cotton spinning two of the Fukuzawa men achieved decisive breakthroughs: Yamabe in the Osaka Mill and Nakamigawa in his Kanegafuchi Mill. Another Fukuzawa man who is not in my sample, Okada Reikō, shared with Yamabe the leadership in cotton spinning; they both fought for rational tariff policies to make Japanese spinning competitive on the world market.[49]

Except for Abe, who applied himself to the promotion and foundation of insurance companies, the graduates in the sample were drafted into existing large companies because of their talents and educational achievements. They had no capital of their own, nor were they interested in gaining any through government favors. They relied on joint stock for their new companies, which they controlled not so much by the number of shares they held as by their entrepreneurial and technical know-how. The large zaibatsu were there to stay, but it became increasingly difficult to establish new ones; the time of tycoons in the style of Iwasaki, Yasuda, Ōkura, and Asano had come to a close. The new entrepreneurial talents were now absorbed into the existing industrial empires.

Asabuki Eiji [50] had first met his teacher Fukuzawa in Osaka. At that time he was still a fierce *jōi* man who was ready to kill Fukuzawa because the latter ate beef and advocated a complete opening of the country to Western influence. After reading Fukuzawa's books, Asabuki did an about-face: he sold his sword, went to Tokyo, and became Fukuzawa's student. From there he was invited to join Mitsubishi, and later he went to Mitsui. Apart from his managerial success, he became very valuable because of his progressive attitudes and his scouting of other graduates for these two zaibatsu.

Shōda Heigorō [51] had been a teacher at Keiō before joining Mitsubishi. He cooperated closely with Iwasaki in many ventures, but his outstanding achievements are undoubtedly the modernization of the Nagasaki Shipyard and the building of the famous Marunouchi Office Center in Tokyo. He had conceived the plan for such a center while abroad and, with the green light from Iwasaki, made his project a resounding success economically while at the same time contributing a good deal to the development of modern Tokyo.

Kondō Renpei,[52] like Shōda, had been a teacher before coming to Iwasaki. He took charge of the Mitsubishi Shipping Company in its fierce competitive battle with the government-sponsored Kyōdō Unyu Company; with Mitsubishi's victory, Kondō became president of the amalgamated Nippon Yūsen Company over which Iwasaki had gained control. Kondō was rated by his contemporaries among the top businessmen, and his advice was highly valued. It is maintained that he is primarily responsible for the fact that Japanese shipping became competitive with the great foreign lines at a comparatively early date. Although Kondō ventured into some other fields, notably mining, he remained chiefly a champion of shipping.

Ōkawa Heizaburō,[53] like Yamabe, was a Shibusawa pro-
tégé and occupied in paper manufacturing a leading position similar to that of Yamabe in cotton spinning. He
worked for a while with Asano in his cement factory and
then, as a paper-manufacturing expert, went into the Ōji
Paper Mill established by Shibusawa. He had acquired his
technical knowledge abroad and remained eager to keep
abreast of the latest foreign manufacturing methods. When
control of Ōji Paper went over to Mitsui, he left the mill
and started out on his own. He was so successful that some
writers call his "paper kingdom" a zaibatsu. Ōkawa occupied important positions in some eighty enterprises, by
virtue not so much of his capital investments as of his
expert knowledge and managerial talent.

With the trend of college graduates moving into key
positions in Japanese industry, we arrive at a new stage.
This is the postpioneering stage, which was marked by a
close cooperation betwen the *gakubatsu* and the zaibatsu,
by rational calculation based on large joint-stock capital
and technical knowledge. The change was, of course, not
abrupt. But different conditions and different problems
called for a new type of businessman.

Along with the change in entrepreneurial types went a
changing pattern of capital supply. The government subsidies tapered off, and the opportunities to profit from
economic confusion in the port cities and from military
actions disappeared. Cotton spinning was first to give indications of the new trend. After 1885, with the success of
the Osaka Mill, we find a marked difference in the type
of men who were founding the mills and supplying the
capital. When the breakthrough had been achieved, the
merchants staged their comeback and Osaka flourished
once more.

It would be interesting to follow up these indicated

trends, to show how far the changes went and how they affected the growth of the young Meiji industries. But my study here comes to a close. I was concerned with the pioneering entrepreneurs, the men who established the foundations of industry, who built their factories in the face of formidable economic and technological difficulties. That Meiji industry succeeded and kept up its vigorous growth was to the credit of these bold innovators.

CONCLUSION

We have been walking through a forest of political and economic changes, of personalities and policies, of government initiative and private endeavor, of class movements, of productivity statistics. The Meiji industrialization was indeed a complex process. We have looked only at the beginning years. These pages can lead to no final conclusions concerning the decades of the most vigorous growth, after the turn of the century, but they do show that by the time of the Sino-Japanese War private modern industry had achieved a solid basis for rapid expansion.

In the course of this study I have tried to single out the trees from the undergrowth and to indicate a few major factors that accounted for the dynamics of the Meiji economy. There is no need to summarize them all. Instead, a few facts will be put into perspective, facts that relate to the process of the formation of entrepreneurs in the private economic sector and to the general spirit of enterprise in Japan.

Throughout the early period, capital was in critically short supply; the government coffers were chronically depleted, and the private sector initially offered only a trickle of funds for industrial investment. The bourgeoisie remained conservative almost until the turn of the century.

It had been deprived of its wealth by taxation and by the operations of the merchants of fortune, and as a group it thus grew ever more timid and cautious. The samurai were dispossessed of their sustenance and told to invest and work if they wanted to eat. The peasants, too, had to keep carrying a heavy burden after the monetization of the land tax. These were all elements in a radical and painful operation that was a prerequisite for the vigorous forward march of the entrepreneurs inside and outside of the government. The fact of the matter is that capital was neither sufficient nor, by and large, in the proper hands when that march started. It was requisitioned by the government and also seized by a ruthless group of successful businessmen of a new type. Potential capital was activated through the very process of change, violently and at times with little heed to ethical considerations. National resources that had been dormant or had existed in disguised forms, such as samurai stipends, were thrown into the determined effort of the government to compensate for two centuries of stagnation and to catch up with the West. The greatest resource of all was the totality of the physical and mental energies of a rejuvenated nation.

If there is any major lesson that Meiji Japan provides for today's backward countries, it may be this: they should not require their capital to be neatly arranged in usable form. The most important resource for development is the will to succeed. If it is possible to mobilize that resource, capital can often be requisitioned from many hidden sources, and it will be newly created by the increased efforts of planning entrepreneurs and a toiling population.

Two of the Meiji Japan's great assets in mobilizing resources were undoubtedly the stability and organization of her social system and, even more, the character of her people. These variables were not the product of short-term external influences; they were gifts of nature that developed over a long period of time. The Japanese inherited from their feudal period a strong sense of discipline, loyalty, public-mindedness, and national unity. These social characteristics, paired with a high degree of diligence and intelligence, were, and are, their national treasure.

But these qualities in themselves cannot explain the dynamic advances of the Meiji era. Intoxication with the idea of progress and the determination to bring Japan, in the shortest possible time, on an even keel with the Western world was in the last analysis based on a special emotional characteristic of the Japanese. Why did other nations not respond in a similar fashion — why not India, why not China? The Japanese are known for their relentless ambition, be it in science or industry or sports. They cannot easily swallow defeat. Foreigners often note that the Japanese can never quite rid themselves of a deep-seated inferiority complex. But that inferiority complex itself stems from the ambition to be first.

After the opening of the ports, the Japanese people were shocked into a realization of their own backwardness, which had been concealed from them by the closed-door policy and by the official contempt for the Western barbarians. At this point the national capital that consisted in loyalty to the leaders, discipline, intelligence, and capacity for hard work was harnessed for the one great effort: to catch up, and fast. The "New Deal in emotions" had indeed taken hold of the nation, and it is the major explanation for the irrational, noncapitalist, dynamic, and romantic approach of the pioneering entrepreneurs. The zaibatsu builders and the political merchants found ample justification for building their private empires with whatever kind of capital they could get. The samurai Ishikawa who founded a spinning mill with a view to making cannons, Kashima the cotton merchant who built his own spinning machines to be independent of the foreigners, tycoons like Iwasaki and Ōkura: all were carried away by a combination of personal ambition and nationalism, and public acclaim was one of their most coveted rewards.

The creation of a few centers of progress made possible a snowballing effect. Forces that otherwise might have dissipated themselves in rural areas were strengthened and coordinated in Tokyo, the headquarters of the avant-garde. It is sometimes suggested that, for the sake of economizing scarce capital, one should build small-scale factories in rural areas, where underemployed labor is close to its food supply and where no cost for city buildings and no leakage for food transport is involved.[1] Japanese factories, to some extent, were built in rural districts, but the entrepreneurial elite needed a center, and it was there that the industrial push gained momentum. It was not possible for the innovators to remain in their old traditional world; they needed and wanted a new place, a new atmosphere, new conditions. A man cannot be compartmentalized — he cannot easily be a changed man economically and remain socially and otherwise tradition-bound. This is the lesson we learn from the bourgeoisie of Osaka, and from the "uprooted" men who left their homes and who had their hair cut short and ate beef as sign of their drastic break with the past.

Just as individuals could not neatly separate their economic from their social and political lives, so it was with social groups and even with the nation as a whole. A single class could not monopolize entrepreneurship, which was but an offshoot of the nation's forward thrust. Initial differences with respect to experience and to capital accumulation were like minor hurdles easily scaled by those who had started to race. Class groupings and prior distributions of capital resources were thrown into confusion, and out of that confusion emerged the bold entrepreneurs who knew how to activate and even create new capital. And the strong-willed pioneers of industry themselves, like the political leaders, were only the standard-bearers of a nation on the march.

NOTES

BIBLIOGRAPHY

GLOSSARY

INDEX

NOTES

INTRODUCTION

1. The overthrow of the Tokugawa rule and the reinstatement of the emperor as *de facto* ruler of Japan was accomplished in 1867. In January 1868 the Meiji era began, lasting until the death of Emperor Meiji in 1912. It was followed by the Taishō era (1912–1926) and the present Shōwa era (1926–).

2. G. Myrdal, *Economic Theory and Underdeveloped Regions* (London, 1958), p. 100.

3. Albert O. Hirschman, *The Strategy of Economic Development* (New Haven, 1959), *passim.*

4. Joseph A. Schumpeter, *The Theory of Economic Development* (Cambridge, Mass., 1934), pp. 128–156.

5. Joseph A. Schumpeter, *Capitalism, Socialism and Democracy*, 3rd ed. (New York, 1950), pp. 131–134.

I. THE MERCHANT CLASS

1. Oda Nobunaga (1534–1582) began to build castles as places of safety and as a means to control the rebellious warlords. His retainer and successor, Toyotomi Hideyoshi (1536–1598), continued his building program. Samurai and also merchants and artisans were settled in the new castle towns and received many privileges as a stimulus to trade and craftsmanship; for example, no tax was levied on the merchants.

The word *chōnin* (townsman) refers to both craftsmen and merchants but is often used synonymously with *shōnin* (merchant).

2. The guild system was established by the Tokugawa in the seventeenth century; but an organization similar to the guild, the *za* (seat), had existed from the Kamakura period (1192–1332) onward.

The za were associations of merchants and artisans who lived on the large manors (shōen) and enjoyed the protection of the manorial lords.

3. Tokugawa Ieyasu won his decisive victory over the forces of Hideyoshi in the battle of Sekigahara in 1600. He was appointed shogun in 1603; Oda Nobunaga and Toyotomi Hideyoshi had never been shogun although they had unified the country and had actually ruled as such. The shogun was appointed by the emperor; his full title was sei-i-tai-shōgun (barbarian-subduing great general), which indicated the original purpose of his position. The idea that the shogun's government had a military and emergency character was kept up by calling it bakufu (tent government). Although the shogun had to be appointed by the emperor, the latter had no real political power during the bakufu rule.

The Tokugawa shogun established their government in Edo, hence the name Edo period for the time of the Tokugawa bakufu rule. It was preceded by the Kamakura (1192–1332) and the Muromachi (1338–1573) periods. The last decades of the Muromachi period are also known under the name of sengoku jidai (country at war); they were terminated by the rise of Oda Nobunaga.

4. Miyamoto Mataji, Nihon girudo no kaihō (The abolition of the Japanese guilds; Osaka, 1957), p. 8.

5. Yamaguchi Kazuo, Bakumatsu bōeki shi (History of foreign trade during the last years of the Tokugawa period; Tokyo, 1943), p. 291.

6. Ibid., pp. 281–298.

7. See note 20.

8. Charles David Sheldon, The Rise of the Merchant Class in Tokugawa Japan, 1600–1868: An Introductory Survey (New York, 1958), p. 69. The passage is a translation from the Seji kenbun roku (Tales of worldly affairs).

9. When the Tokugawa moved the bakufu to Edo at the beginning of the seventeenth century, Edo was but a small hamlet; thanks to the large administration and the numerous samurai who now had to reside in Edo, it rapidly became the largest city in Japan. But it became the capital only after the emperor moved there in 1867, when it was renamed Tokyo (eastern capital), as distinguished from Kyoto (capital city).

10. The daimyo were the leaders and administrators of the feudal territories (han). This feudal administrative system was introduced by the Tokugawa. The 260-odd han varied in size and political importance and also in producing revenue for the daimyo. While the smallest yielded an equivalent of something over 10,000 koku of rice (1 koku equals 4.96 bushels), the large ones yielded between 200,000 and 1 million koku.

The Tokugawa shogun were extremely anxious to keep the daimyo under constant control. A daimyo could be transferred to another territory (unless his han was his inherited property or unless he was too powerful for such a drastic measure). Each daimyo had also to spend every second year in residence in Edo. This *sankin kōtai* system of alternate residence at the seat of the bakufu contributed greatly to the prosperity of the *chōnin* class while seriously weakening the han economies.

11. Miyamoto Mataji, *Ōsaka* (Tokyo, 1957), p. 9.

12. Kajinishi Mitsuhaya, *Shōgyō shihon oyobi kōrigashi shihon* (Trading capital and usury capital; Tokyo, 1949), p. 28.

13. For a very good description of the Tokugawa currency system, see John Whitney Hall, *Tanuma Okitsugu, 1719–1788, Forerunner of Modern Japan* (Cambridge, Mass., 1955), pp. 68–74.

14. Kanno Watarō, *Ōsaka keizai shi kenkyū* (Studies in the economic history of Osaka; Osaka 1935), pp. 171–173.

15. *Ibid.*, p. 134; also Kajinishi, *Shōgyō shihon*, pp. 29–30.

16. Kanno, *Ōsaka keizai*, p. 173.

17. Miyamoto Mataji, *Ōsaka chōnin* (The Osaka townsmen; Tokyo, 1957), p. 181.

18. Thomas C. Smith, *The Agrarian Origins of Modern Japan* (Stanford, 1959), p. 125.

19. Miyamoto, *Ōsaka chōnin*, p. 185.

20. The division into four classes had been preceded by the separation of the warrior class from the farming population under Hideyoshi, by the so-called *hei-nō-bunri* (separation of warriors and farmers) law. *Shi-nō-kō-shō* was but a popular expression for the rigid definition of status, of which these four were the main groupings. The Shinto and Buddhist ministers were a special group, and within the samurai class, too, there were subclasses.

21. Miyamoto, *Ōsaka*, p. 90.

22. The *myōji taitō* were the various privileges of the samurai class. The right to assume a family name was more easily granted; physicians usually used a family name and seem on the whole to have been rather close to the samurai class. Village headmen, too, were permitted family names. The right to carry a sword was less frequently given to commoners and was then often restricted with respect to the type of sword and the occasions when it could be carried.

23. Miyamoto Mataji, "Daimyō kashi no rishiritsu ni tsuite" (On the interest rates in daimyo lending), *Ōsaka daigaku keizaigaku* (Osaka University economics), 10.2:115–116 (November 25, 1960).

24. *Ibid.*, pp. 119–138.

25. Takegoshi Yosaburō, *Nihon keizai shi* (Japanese economic history; Tokyo, 1929), VI, 88.

26. E. S. Crawcour, "Some Observations on Merchants: A Translation of Mitsui Takafusa's *Chōnin kōken roku*, with an Introduction and Notes," *Transactions of the Asiatic Society of Japan*, 3rd series (Tokyo, 1962), 8:9–139 (December 1961). Mitsui Takafusa warned in these "observations" against daimyo lending, pointing out that once a merchant starts on this road he finds that there is no end to it: he has to lend further in order to receive interest on previous loans. But it is also evident from this document that if the daimyo did repay there was scarcely a better investment opportunity for merchant capital. The merchant house of Yoyoda had 100 million ryo in outstanding loans with daimyo before its property was confiscated by the bakufu at the beginning of the eighteenth century (*ibid.*, p. 23).

27. Miyamoto, *Ōsaka chōnin*, p. 207.

28. Honjō Eijirō, *The Social and Economic History of Japan* (Kyoto, 1935), p. 197.

29. *Ibid.*, p. 206. The rank of a samurai depended on the size of his fief, expressed in terms of koku of rice. The nominal amounts, however, were often much greater than what the daimyo would or could actually pay.

30. The expression is somewhat incorrect. Prior to the Restoration the movement was known mainly under the names *sonnō jōi* (revere the emperor, expel the barbarians) and *tōbaku* (overthrow the bakufu). Initially the Restoration itself was called *go isshin* (the new era), which then was changed to *ishin* (restoration).

31. See W. W. Rostow, *The Stages of Economic Growth* (Cambridge, Mass., 1960), *passim*; Pitirim Sorokin, *Social and Cultural Dynamics* (Boston, 1957), pp. 523–532.

32. Robert N. Bellah, *Tokugawa Religion* (Glencoe, Ill., 1957), p. 115.

33. The *oyakata-kogata* relationships existed also in the villages between the peasants' *oyakata-uchi* and *kogata-uchi* (parent-house and child-house); the peasant of the child-house had the marriages of his children arranged by the peasant of the parent-house, and a child-house peasant was careful not to outdo the peasant of the parent-house in any manifest way.

It is interesting that the same notions of *oyabun* and *kobun*, with similar almost feudal relationships between employers and underlings, persist even in present-day Japan. The extraordinary deference to the boss, to authority of any type, often puzzles foreigners. The boss is right because of his position; his views are not questioned although the same opinion or approach from a man in a lesser position may not stir a leaf. In the field of scholarship, quotations from authorities bear tremendous weight; current imported theories are often applied uncritically to conditions for which the theories

were never meant. It may perhaps be possible to trace these attitudes back to the deeply ingrained Confucian ideology of Tokugawa days.

34. Kanno Watarō, *Nihon kaisha kigyō hassei shi no kenkyū*
(Studies in the development of the company form of enterprise in
Japan; Tokyo, 1931), p. 648.

35. Miyamoto, *Ōsaka shōnin* (The Osaka merchants; Tokyo, 1958),
p. 123.

36. The *kanban* is the wooden nameplate on a store, often artistically designed with calligraphy. The *noren* is a blue cloth hanging over the entrance, still used today for restaurants and kimono
shops.

37. Miyamoto, *Ōsaka shōnin*, p. 108.

38. Miyamoto, *Ōsaka*, p. 109.

39. Miyamoto, *Ōsaka shōnin*, p. 123.

40. Tsuchiya Takao, *Nihon ni okeru keieisha seishin no hattatsu*
(The development of managerial mentalities in Japan: Tokyo,
1957), p. 34.

41. Miyamoto, *Ōsaka shōnin*, p. 131.

42. Shibusawa Eiichi, ed., *Meiji shōkō shi* (History of Meiji trade
and industry; Tokyo, 1911), p. 19.

43. Miyamoto, *Ōsaka*, p. 162.

44. The Genroku period was the classic period of culture and art
and of economic prosperity as a result of the national unification and
the long peace. The samurai turned to literature and philosophy;
the merchants prospered and spread luxury consumption.

45. See Bellah, p. 159.

46. *Ibid.*, p. 160.

47. *Ibid.*, p. 174.

48. For a brief and very clear account of the Meiji Restoration
itself, see Edwin O. Reischauer, *Japan, Past and Present* (New York,
1946), pp. 108–141.

49. Nomura Kentarō, *Ishin zengo* (Before and after the Restoration; Tokyo, 1941), pp. 106–113.

50. Inoue Kaoru (1835–1915) belonged to the Choshu group in
the Meiji government and became known particularly for his role
in economic planning and the encouragement of industry. He occupied leading positions in the Ministry of Finance, became foreign
minister in 1885, and held other ministerial positions off and on until
his death. He was the Mitsui zaibatsu's stanchest friend and saved
it from disaster several times. For an account of Minomura, see
Chapter Six.

51. Ōsaka shiyakusho (Osaka City Office), ed., *Meiji Taishō Ōsaka
shi shi* (History of Osaka City during the Meiji and Taishō eras;
Tokyo, 1935), III, 359–360.

52. Terao Kōji, *Meiji shoki Kyōto keizai shi* (Economic history of Kyoto during the early Meiji era; Kyoto, 1943), pp. 557–562.

53. Kanno, *Nihon kaisha*, p. 325.

54. *Ibid.*, pp. 367–368.

55. Shibusawa Eiichi, ed., *Meiji shōkō shi*, pp. 212–213.

56. Takahashi Kamekichi, *Meiji Taishō sangyō hattatsu shi* (The history of manufacturing during the Meiji and Taishō eras; Tokyo, 1929), pp. 105–106.

57. *Ibid.*, p. 236.

58. Takegoshi, *Nihon keizai shi*, VI, 110.

59. *Commercial Reports of Her Majesty's Consuls in Japan, 1868* (London, 1869), p. 22.

60. Ōkubo Toshimichi (1830–1878) was one of the Satsuma clique and a chief organizer of the Restoration itself, together with Iwakura, Saigō, and Kido. In 1871 he went with the Iwakura group to Europe as minister of finance. The famous encouragement of industry (*shokusan kōgyō*) policy as well as the land-tax reform were mainly his work. He was assassinated in 1878 because of his dictatorial methods.

61. Honjō Eijirō, *Nihon no keizai to shisō* (Japanese economy and thought; Kyoto, 1943), pp. 336–350.

62. Kanno Watarō, "Tsūshō kaisha, kawase kaisha" (The trade and finance companies), in Honjō Eijirō, ed., *Meiji ishin keizai shi kenkyū* (Studies in the economic history of the Meiji Restoration; Tokyo, 1930), pp. 105–300.

63. Kanno, *Nihon kaisha*, pp. 606–607.

64. *Ibid.*, p. 49.

65. *Commercial Reports, 1869–1870*, pp. 12–13.

66. Katō Toshihiko, "Development of the Monetary System," in Shibusawa Keizō, ed., *Japanese Society of the Meiji Era*, tr. S. H. Culbertson and Kimura Michiko (Tokyo, 1958), p. 196.

67. Kanno Watarō, "Kokuritsu ginkō" (The national banks), in Honjō, *Meiji ishin keizai*, p. 337.

68. *Meiji zaisei shi* (The Meiji financial history), ed. Meiji zaisei shi hensan kai (The Meiji Financial History Editorial Board; Toyko, 1905), XIII, 245.

69. Tsuchiya Takao, *Nihon no seishō* (Japan's political merchants; Tokyo, 1956), pp. 155–156.

70. *Ibid.*, pp. 160–161.

71. Honjō, *Nihon no keizai*, pp. 383ff.

72. *Ibid.*, p. 384.

73. *Ibid.*, p. 387.

74. Ōsaka shiyakusho, ed., II, 842.

75. *Ibid.*, II, 624–625.

76. *Ibid.*, III, 363.

77. *Ibid.*, II, 478–479, 576–579, 516–517.

78. *Ibid.*, II, 527–530.
79. *Ibid.*, II, 631.
80. *Ōsaka fu shi* (History of Osaka prefecture), ed. Ōsaka fu (Osaka, 1903), II, 8–10.
81. *Ibid.*, II, 9–10.
82. Samuel P. Hayes, Jr., "Personality and Culture Problems," in Bert F. Hoselitz, ed., *The Progress of Underdeveloped Areas* (Chicago, 1952), p. 207.

II. THE SAMURAI CLASS

1. Herbert Norman, *Japan's Emergence as a Modern State*, 3rd ed. (New York, 1948), p. 82.
2. G. B. Sansom, *The Western World and Japan* (New York, 1951), pp. 110–111.
3. The samurai had existed since the ninth century as a distinct class of men of arms who combined warfare and farming. They farmed in times of peace and followed their manorial lords to battle. But Nobunaga and especially Hideyoshi drew these men together in the new castle towns and severed them from the farms. This division of society into the commoners who farmed and the samurai who were given stipends for the protection of peace marked the beginning of the feudal system, which reached its height under the Tokugawa bakufu.
4. See Nitobe Inazō, *Bushido, The Soul of Japan*, 17th ed. (Tokyo, 1911), *passim*.
5. Sakada Yoshio, *Hōken jidai kōki no chōnin seikatsu* (The life of the townsmen during the later part of the feudal era; Tokyo, 1950), pp. 6–7.
6. Fukuzawa Yukichi, *The Autobiography of Fukuzawa Yukichi*, tr. Kiyooka Eiichi (Tokyo, 1948), p. 11.
7. *Ibid.*, p. 3.
8. Honjō Eijirō, *Social and Economic History*, p. 216.
9. This system was introduced in 1635 and was kept in force until 1862. The daimyo traveled with large retinues of samurai; they also had to maintain expensive mansions in Edo for their families and for those samurai who had to remain there during the daimyo's year of absence.
10. Honjō, *Social and Economic History*, p. 217.
11. The use of the terms "lower samurai" and "higher samurai" is very common but leads to a great deal of ambiguity. It is usually asserted that the lower samurai were the carriers of the *sonnō jōi* movement and the Meiji Restoration. But Albert Craig has shown convincingly that the identification of the *sonnō jōi* movement with the lower samurai is meaningless, if not positively wrong. It is mean-

ingless if a classification is adopted that designates some 85–90 percent of all samurai as lower-class members, and it is historically wrong if the division is drawn between the groups of *shi* and *sotsu*, each constituting roughly half of the total. The term "lower samurai" in my context simply means those who were so poor that they had to resort to some economic activity for a living. Nothing is asserted about their numbers, yet they apparently comprised a majority of the samurai class. It will be shown, however, that this economic condition of itself did not make these lower samurai economic innovators. They had no monopoly on the political, ideological, or economic reconstruction of Meiji Japan. See Albert Craig, "The Restoration Movement in Chōshū," *The Journal of Asian Studies* 18.2:187–197 (February 1959).

12. Fukuzawa Yukichi, "Kyūhanjō" (The conditions in the old han), in *Fukuzawa Yukichi zenshū* (The Fukuzawa Yukichi collection, Tokyo, Jiji shinpōsha [The Jiji Newspaper Publishing Co.], 1926), VI, 677–680.

13. The peasant wives and daughters spun cotton and the samurai women silk; thus even here a distinction was maintained. The Yonezawa silk cloth, a samurai home-employment product, attained national fame.

14. Yamaguchi, "Opening of Japan," p. 37.

15. Yanagida Kunio, *Japanese Manners and Customs in the Meiji Era*, tr. Charles S. Terry (Tokyo, 1957), p. 95.

16. Cf. Craig, p. 188, esp. n. 4.

17. The samurai were told in official documents that in Western countries like England and France all people were equal and had to work for their sustenance and that in Japan, too, everyone should work to make Japan prosperous. Marius B. Jansen, *Sakamoto Ryōma and the Meiji Restoration* (Princeton, 1961), pp. 361–368, has a good description of the process of abolishing samurai privileges in Tosa han.

18. Takahashi Kamekichi, *Meiji Taishō sangyō hattatsu shi*, p. 101.

19. Kabushiki kaisha 77 ginkō (The 77th Bank, Ltd.), ed., *77 nen shi* (History of 77 years; Tokyo, 1954), pp. 11–13.

20. Takahashi, *Meiji Taishō sangyō hattatsu shi*, pp. 101–102.

21. Kikkawa Hidezō, *Shizoku jusan no kenkyū* (Studies in samurai employment; Tokyo, 1935), p. 49.

22. *Ibid.*, pp. 62–63.

23. Yanagida, p. 95.

24. Tsuchiya Takao, ed., *Meiji zenki keizai shi kenkyū* (Studies in the economic history of the first part of the Meiji era; Tokyo, 1944), p. 212.

25. A militarist group in the government under the leadership of Saigō Takamori tried to use the persisting tensions between Korea

and Japan to instigate war; they wanted to solve internal difficulties by the time-honored method of turning the attention of the dissatisfied toward an external enemy. The debate over Korea came to a head in 1873: Iwakura Tomomi and the men who had toured the Western countries with him were dead set against any military adventure; Saigō and a few of his followers resigned and returned to Satsuma. Saigō then became the leader of the dissatisfied elements in the Satsuma Rebellion.

26. The conscription law had been promulgated in 1873; the Satsuma Rebellion was thus the first opportunity to test the new army of peasant draftees who had been trained according to Prussian discipline. Their victory over Japan's best samurai was seen as a victory of the new era over all reactionary elements.

27. Akashi Teruo and Suzuki Norihisa, *Nihon kinyū shi, Meiji hen* (History of Japanese banking, Meiji volume; Tokyo, 1957), p. 49.

28. *Ibid.*

29. *Ibid.*, pp. 52–53.

30. *Ibid.*, p. 58.

31. The very word "national" (*kokuritsu*) helped to convey the idea of a public function and lent distinction. In the Japanese mind a *kokuritsu* institution is almost automatically superior to a *shiritsu* (private) one. The great prize for a student is his admission to a *kokuritsu* school, and it is not only because of its lower tuition and high academic standards.

32. Akashi and Suzuki, p. 52.

33. Kanno, *Nihon kaisha*, p. 352.

34. Takahashi Kamekichi, *Waga kuni kigyō no shiteki hatten* (The historical development of our country's enterprises; Tokyo, 1956), pp. 177–178.

35. Kabushiki kaisha 77 ginkō, ed., pp. 54–55.

36. *Meiji zaisei shi*, XIII, 256–257.

37. *Ginkō kyoku dai niji hōkoku* (The second report of the Banking Bureau), ed. Ōkura shō (Tokyo, 1879–80), p. 129. The nobility (*kazoku*) included after 1869 the former *kuge,* blood relations of the imperial family, and the former feudal lords (*kō*). According to the Nobility Law of 1884, the following ranking was established: *kō* (prince), *kō* (marquis), *haku* (count), *shi* (viscount), and *dan* (baron). Noble titles of lower rank were given to prominent persons in the government and other men of merit.

38. *Meiji zaisei shi*, XIII, 603–614.

39. *Ginkō benran* (Bank handbook), ed. Ōkura shō (Ministry of Finance; Tokyo, 1911), pp. 496–497.

40. *Meiji zaisei shi*, XIII, 10–11.

41. *Shibusawa Eiichi denki shiryō* (Biographical material on Shi-

busawa Eiichi), ed. Shibusawa Seien kinen zaidan ryūmonsha (The Shibusawa Seien Dragon Door Memorial Foundation; Tokyo, 1957–1958), IV, 293, 295–312; V, 313.

42. Kanno, *Nihon kaisha*, p. 670.

43. Iwakura (1825–1883) was a *kuge* and the main organizer of the overthrow of the bakufu; it was he who directed the coup d'état of 1867. He was opposed to the liberal democratic wing and stressed the prerogatives of the emperor.

44. Kikkawa, *Shizoku jusan*, p. 99.

45. Azuma Tōsaku, *Shizoku jusan shi* (History of samurai employment; Tokyo, 1942), p. 191.

46. Kikkawa, *Shizoku jusan*, p. 99.

47. *Ibid.*, pp. 373–387.

48. Azuma, pp. 694–696.

49. *Ibid.*, pp. 191–229.

50. Shizuoka had been the domain of the Tokugawa family before its victory over the Hideyoshi forces and so differed from the daimyo trusteeships of the han. After his victory of 1600, Ieyasu took over direct control of Osaka, Nagasaki, and many other important places, harbors, and mines. The Tokugawa family thus owned a territory of one million koku. The direct political control of the bakufu extended over one fourth of Japan, via the collateral families (*shinpan*) of Owari, Kii, and Mito.

51. Azuma, pp. 6–7.

52. *Ibid.*, pp. 5–60.

53. *Ibid.*, p. 19.

54. *Ibid.*, pp. 386–387.

55. *Ibid.*, p. 382.

56. Kikkawa, *Shizoku jusan*, p. 68.

57. Azuma, pp. 351–352.

58. Ragnar Nurkse, *Problems of Capital Formation in Underdeveloped Countries*, 4th ed. (Oxford, 1955), pp. 37–38.

III. RURAL ENTREPRENEURSHIP

1. For an extensive and excellent treatment of Tokugawa agriculture, see Smith, *Agrarian Origins*.

2. Tsuchiya Takao and Ono Michio, *Kinsei Nihon nōson keizai shiron* (A historical treatise on the Modern Japanese rural economy; Tokyo, 1933), pp. 62–63.

3. Sekiyama Naotarō, *Nihon no jinkō* (The population of Japan; Tokyo, 1959), p. 70.

4. Cf. Takahashi Shinichi, *Yōgakuron* (On Western studies; Tokyo, 1939), pp. 90–92.

5. Kobayashi Yoshimasa, *Nihon shihonshugi no seisei to sono kiban* (The emergence of Japanese capitalism and its foundation; Tokyo, 1949), p. 43.

6. In the last decades of the Tokugawa period scholars frequently wrote against land reclamations, insisting that because of them yields on the old lands declined. Deforestation caused floods; old fields were either neglected or even deserted, because of the easier rent terms on the new land and because new land did not fall under the bakufu restrictions with respect to division and sale. *Nihon keizai shi jiten* (Dictionary of Japanese economic history), ed. Keizai shi kenkyūkai (Tokyo, 1954), I, 869.

7. See W. G. Beasley, "Feudal Revenue in Japan at the Time of the Restoration," *Journal of Asian Studies*, 19.3:255–272 (May 1960). The reports of the han are not uniform, but vary with respect to what is or what is not included in the total value product of the han; some apparently included cash crops while others enumerated them separately. The very terse reports which have no comments attached are therefore not easy to interpret. Japanese economic historians do not seem to rely much on the evidence from these sources.

8. Kobata Jun, "Kinsei keizai no hattatsu" (The development of the modern economy), in Kobata Jun, ed., *Kinsei shakai* (Modern society; Tokyo, 1952), IV, 216.

9. Land reclamations and improvements on a large scale were first undertaken by the bakufu under the shogun Yoshimune in the first half of the eighteenth century. Though later shogun imitated Yoshimune's policies, it was merchant capital that came to dominate land reclamations. See Hall, pp. 63–65; also Miyamoto Mataji, "Tokugawa ki Ōsaka kinkō no nōgyō keisei" (Management of agriculture in the vicinity of Osaka during the Tokugawa period), in Miyamoto Mataji, ed., *Shōgyōteki nōgyō no tenkai* (The spread of the commercialization of agriculture; Osaka, 1954), p. 12.

10. Miyamoto, *ibid.*, 14–15.

11. *Ibid.*, pp. 15–16.

12. Miyamoto, *Ōsaka chōnin*, p. 168.

13. Miyamoto, *Ōsaka shōnin*, p. 98.

14. *Jinushi sei no keisei* (The formation of the landlord system), ed. Meiji shiryō kenkyū renrakukai (Meiji Historic Material Research Association; Tokyo, 1957), pp. 150–151.

15. Egashira Tsuneharu, *Ōmi shōnin* (The Omi merchants; Tokyo 1959), pp. 110–127; also Kanno, *Ōsaka keizai*, pp. 104–120.

16. Smith, *Agrarian Origins*, p. 83.

17. Egashira, pp. 105–108.

18. Fujita Gorō, *Nihon kindai sangyō no seisei* (The creation of Japan's modern industry; Tokyo, 1948), pp. 247–248.

19. Horie Eiichi, *Meiji ishin no shakai kōzō* (Structure of society at the time of the Restoration; Tokyo, 1954), p. 110.

20. *Ibid.*, p. 107.

21. Yasuoka Shigeaki, "Shōgyōteki hatten to nōson kōzō" (The process of commercialization and village structure), in Miyamoto, ed., *Shōgyōteki nōgyō*, p. 112.

22. Yamaguchi Kazuo, *Meiji zenki keizai no bunseki* (Analysis of the economy of the early Meiji era; Tokyo, 1956), p. 34.

23. Smith, *Agrarian Origins*, p. 69.

24. Horie, p. 105.

25. Tsuchiya Takao, ed., *Hōken shakai hōkai katei no kenkyū* (Studies in the disintegration process of feudal society; Kyoto, 1927), pp. 391–483.

26. Horie, pp. 108–109.

27. *Ibid.*, p. 151.

28. Yasuoka, p. 71.

29. Horie, p. 155.

30. Smith, *Agrarian Origins*, p. 73.

31. Fujita, p. 241.

32. Smith, *Agrarian Origins*, p. 174.

33. Fujita, p. 101.

34. Horie, p. 164.

35. Smith, *Agrarian Origins*, pp. 121–122.

36. *Ibid.*, p. 147.

37. Shōji Kichinosuke, *Henkaku ni okeru nōmin shisō no mondai* (The problem of peasant thought during the period of change; Tokyo, 1952), p. 27.

38. Nishinoiri Aiichi, *Asano, Shibusawa, Ōkawa, Furukawa Concern tokuhon* (The Asano, Shibusawa, Ōkawa, Furukawa Concern reader; Tokyo, 1937), pp. 97–100.

39. Hara Kunizō, ed., *Hara Rokurō ō den* (Biography of the Honorable Hara Rokurō; Tokyo, 1923), I, 8–13.

40. *Dai Nihon gaikoku bōeki* (The foreign trade of great Japan), ed. Nōshōmushō shōmukyoku (Ministry of Agriculture and Trade, Department of Trade; Tokyo, 1911), p. 6.

41. Thomas C. Smith, *Political Change and Industrial Development in Japan: Government Enterprise, 1868–1880* (Stanford, 1955), p. 57. Smith gives here a very good account of the first phase of Japanese mechanical silk reeling.

42. The House of Ono, as a partner of the First National Bank, borrowed from it 1.3 million yen as additional capital for its silk-reeling investments. When, on government order, the reserves had to be replenished, Ono was found insolvent and went into bankruptcy in 1875. *Nihon keizai shi jiten*, I, 181.

43. Shōji Kichinosuke, *Meiji ishin no keizai kōzō* (The structure

of the economy of the time of the Meiji Restoration; Tokyo, 1958), pp. 306–308.

44. *Zaikai bukko ketsubutsu den* (Biographies of outstanding men in the business world), ed. Jitsugyō no shakaisha (The Business World Co.; Tokyo, 1936), I, 342–348.

45. *Nihon sangyō shi taikei, sōron hen* (An outline history of Japanese industry, summary volume), ed. Chihō shi kenkyū kyōgikai (Regional History Research Association; Tokyo, 1961), p. 243.

46. Azuma, pp. 191–229.

47. *Ibid.*, p. 639.

48. Ōkubo Shigetarō, ed., *Gumma ken sangyōka meikan* (Biographical directory of silk industrialists of Gumma prefecture; Maebashi, 1910), *passim*.

49. Sata Kaiseki, a Buddhist monk and scholar, made himself the spokesman of the dissatisfied elements; he wrote in favor of shutting out foreign goods completely, and he organized rallies and formed associations to fight against imports of Western goods. Honjō Eijirō, ed., *Meiji ishin keizai shi kenkyū* (Studies in the economic history of the Meiji Restoration; Tokyo, 1930), pp. 761–765.

50. Hattori Shisō and Shinobu Seizaburō, *Meiji senshoku keizai shi* (Economic History of Meiji dyeing and weaving; Tokyo, 1937), pp. 104–120.

51. Kinugawa Taiichi, *Honpō menshi bōseki shi* (History of Japanese cotton spinning; Osaka, 1937), III, 49–85.

52. *Ibid.*, II, 215–216.

53. *Ibid.*, IV, 237–239.

54. *Ibid.*, IV, 205.

55. *Ibid.*, V, 31.

56. *Ibid.*, IV, 78–85.

57. *Ibid.*, IV, 362.

58. Yamaguchi, *Meiji zenki keizai*, p. 14. The figures are surprising, at least to me. Professor William Lockwood first pointed out to me the importance of the traditional manufacturing sector.

59. Egashira, *Ōmi shōnin*, p. 105.

60. Yamaguchi, *Meiji zenki keizai*, p. 108.

61. As an illustration of this gradual decline of vegetable-oil production, Furushima traces the records of a rich farmer and oil producer in the Kinki area. From 1868 to 1893 the amount of vegetable oil produced kept declining from 68 koku to 21 koku, and oil extraction was finally stopped completely in 1897. Furushima Toshio, *Kisei jinushi sei no seisei to tenkai* (The emergence and spread of the parasitic landlord system; Tokyo, 1952), p. 109.

62. Takahashi Kamekichi, *Meiji Taishō sangyō*, p. 254.

63. Tōbata Seiichi and Ohkawa Kazushi, eds., *Nihon no keizai to nōgyō* (Japanese economy and agriculture; Tokyo, 1956), I, 65.

308 NOTES TO CHAPTER III

64. Tsuchiya Takao and Okazaki Saburō, *Nihon shihonshugi hattatsu shi gaisetsu* (An outline history of the development of Japanese capitalism; Tokyo, 1937), p. 205.

65. Tōbata and Ohkawa, p. 375.

66. *Nihon keizai shi jiten*, I, 556.

67. Ohkawa Kazushi et al., *The Growth Rate of the Japanese Economy since 1878* (Tokyo, 1957), p. 51.

68. *Ibid.*, p. 58.

69. *Jinushi sei no keisei*, p. 101.

70. Furushima, p. 92.

71. *Ibid.*, p. 103.

72. *Ibid.*, p. 104.

73. See R. P. Dore, "The Meiji Landlord: Good or Bad?" *Journal of Asian Studies*, 18.3 (May 1959). Dore gives a survey of the research and the variations in the evaluation of the landlords by Japanese economic historians. The bone of contention is whether the "parasitic landlords" were forerunners of capitalism or whether they strengthened feudal control over the land. The Marxist school labels them a feudalistic element; according to the Marxists, the Meiji Restoration itself was a feudal and not a bourgeois revolution. For a more comprehensive treatment of the development of tenancy during the Meiji period, see R. P. Dore, *Land Reform in Japan* (Oxford, 1959), pp. 57–68.

74. Furushima, pp. 99–108.

75. Henry Rosovsky and Kazushi Ohkawa, "The Role of Agriculture in Modern Japanese Economic Development," *Economic Development and Cultural Change*, Research Center in Economic Development and Cultural Change, University of Chicago, 9.1:2.51 (October 1960).

76. *Ibid.*, p. 45.

77. *Ibid.*, p. 46.

78. The same conclusion is reached by Lockwood, although he maintains that agricultural productivity was not promoted, but rather hindered, by the landlords. Certainly many disadvantages, social and economic, have to be attributed to the landlord system. William W. Lockwood, *The Economic Development of Japan: Growth and Structural Change, 1868–1938* (Princeton, 1954), pp. 194–196.

IV. THE INITIATIVE FROM THE CENTER

1. Conveniently summarized in Henry Rosovsky, *Capital Formation in Japan, 1868–1940* (Glencoe, Ill., 1961), pp. 57–58.

2. Sansom, *The Western World and Japan*, is one of the best references.

3. Francis Xavier had the highest praise for the Japanese, calling

them by far the most intelligent and ethically most noble of all the newly discovered peoples. He was most impressed by their aristocratic demeanor, their sense of honor and their honesty, the purity of their family life, and the relatively high standards of popular education. Elisabeth Graefin Vitzthum, ed., *Die Briefe des Francisco de Xavier, 1542–1552* (Munich, 1950), pp. 154–155.

4. In the Nagasaki area some 40,000–50,000 had secretly remained Christian and some of them were discovered by a French missionary in 1865. Subsequently, however, the government once more applied the old persecution decrees and banished over 3,000 from Nagasaki to Honshu. But the Iwakura mission of 1871 met hostile demonstrations in several places in Europe and the United States, which denounced them as persecutors of Christians. Consequently, Iwakura cabled to his government demanding immediate repeal of the banishment. In 1873, finally, the old laws were repealed and the public signs denouncing the "wicked religion" were removed. See *Katorikku daijiten* (The Catholic cyclopedia), ed. Jōchi daigaku (Sophia University), 2nd ed. (Tokyo, 1952), I, 716–718.

5. The Bansho shirabesho (place to study barbarian books) changed its name several times after the Restoration, and finally became in 1877 Tokyo University.

6. Two examples will illustrate the nervous attitude of the bakufu toward Western studies. During the great famines of the 1830s the bakufu had sought the advice of students of Western learning and implemented some of their suggestions. But when a few of these men dared to caution against driving British ships from Japanese shores, and advocated at least a partial scrapping of the closed-door policy, they were imprisoned and ended their lives as suicides. When in 1848 an enthusiast presented the German physician in Nagasaki, Philipp Franz von Siebold, with a map of Japan, he was beheaded as a traitor and 37 of his companions were imprisoned.

But such individual examples cannot prove that the bakufu was in general opposed to Western learning. While initially favoring it, with some reservations, it reversed its stand drastically in 1843, banning all Western studies except medicine; this measure resulted from an increased awareness of a foreign menace, notably pressures from Russia in the north. After the opening of the ports the bakufu supported Western studies again. Confucian scholars were divided in their appraisal of Western studies: many were unconditionally opposed, sensing in them a threat to the fundamental values of Confucianism and Japanese tradition. But those who took a positive attitude, according to the "Western science, Japanese ethics" principle, had a decisive influence on Meiji ideology.

For a thorough discussion of the relation between Western studies and Confucian philosophy in the late Tokugawa, see Warren W.

Smith, Jr., *Confucianism in Modern Japan: A Study of Conservatism
in Japanese Intellectual History* (Tokyo, 1959), pp. 20–40; Albert M.
Craig, *Chōshū in the Meiji Restoration* (Cambridge, Mass., 1961),
pp. 128–137; Kosaka Masaaki, *Japanese Thought in the Meiji Era*, tr.
David Abosh (Tokyo, 1958), pp. 9–13.

7. In principle there was no difference between Sakuma and
Yoshida. Sakuma clearly recognized the technical and even scientific
superiority of the West but considered Westerners ethical barbarians.
See Sansom, *The Western World*, pp. 253–256. To stress ethical or
cultural superiority in the face of technical or military inferiority
is nothing new; it happened in Europe repeatedly, notably between
the Germans and the English.

8. Yoshida Shōin was beheaded in 1859 because of his antibakufu
agitation. One item in the text of his death sentence reads: "He
planned to give his opinion regarding foreigners to the Bakufu"
(Sansom, *The Western World*, p. 274). On Yoshida Shōin, see also
H. van Straelen, *Yoshida Shōin, Forerunner of the Meiji Restoration* (Leiden, 1952).

9. Itō Hirobumi (1841–1909) had taken part in the Iwakura
mission to the West, and after the assassination of Ōkubo became
minister of the interior. He established the cabinet system in 1885 and
became the first prime minister of Japan.

10. Yamagata Aritomo (1838–1922) became, under Itō in 1885,
minister of the interior; then he almost took turns with Itō as prime
minister. But Itō and Yamagata represented two opposite factions.
Itō stood for strong government under civilian control, while Yamagata was a thorough militarist who originated the Japanese militarist
tradition that continued until the Second World War.

11. Shinagawa Yajirō (1843–1900) was active in the Ministry of
Agriculture and Trade after 1881, and co-organizer of the Kyōdō
Unyu Kaisha against Iwasaki's Mitsubishi Company. He was envoy
to Germany and finally minister of the interior under Matsukata.

12. Fujii Jintarō, *Outline of Japanese History in the Meiji Era*,
tr. H. K. Colton, and K. E. Colton (Tokyo, 1958), p. 24. The Charter
Oath was the result of thorough discussions by the Meiji leaders; it
outlined briefly the political course to be followed by the government. The oath was read by the emperor in the presence of all
daimyo and the members of the new government.

13. The years between 1868 and 1872 were characterized by the
strong efforts of the Meiji government to establish Shinto as an
official state religion, directed primarily against Buddhism; but these
efforts foundered because of the revival and strong resistance of
Buddhism, and partly also because of foreign pressure to repeal the
ban on Christianity. In 1872 freedom of religion was declared, but
the strong official support of Shintoism remained and was closely

linked with Japanese nationalism. See Delmer M. Brown, *Nationalism in Japan: An Introductory Historical Analysis* (Berkeley, 1955), pp. 101–103.

14. Ōkuma Shigenobu (1838–1922) was a Saga samurai and opposed to the *han batsu* (han clique of Satsuma, Choshu, and Tosa) in the Meiji government. He was one of the economic planners, a most outspoken exponent of the railway-building program, and a friend and protector of Iwasaki. In 1889 he lost his right leg in an attack by antiforeign fanatics. He became, after his resignation from the Ministry of Finance in 1881, the main benefactor of Waseda University and acted for a while as its president.

15. Ishii Mitsuru, *Nihon tetsudō sōsetsu shi wa* (Historic narrative on the building of the Japanese railways; Tokyo, 1952), pp. 147–148.

16. These efforts at times took almost ridiculous forms. At the height of the Westernization fever, dance parties were held to promote Western civilization. On April 20, 1887, Prime Minister Itō gave a grand masquerade dance in his official residence in which some 400 distinguished Japanese and foreign guests took part, among them cabinet members like Yamagata, Inoue, and businessmen like Shibusawa and Ōkura. Fujii, p. 313.

17. This fact has probably induced Hattori to argue that the *bummei kaika* was a kind of enlightenment similar to that under Frederick the Great in Prussia, manipulated from above. Hattori Shisō, *Meiji no shisō* (The thought of the Meiji era), Vol. 6 of his *Chosaku shū* (Collected writings; Tokyo, 1955), pp. 166–185.

18. Sansom, *The Western World*, p. 383.

19. Ishii Ryōichi, *Population Pressure and Economic Life in Japan* (Chicago, 1937), pp. 31–37. On the widespread practice of infanticide during the Tokugawa period, see G. B. Sansom, *Japan, A Short Cultural History*, rev. ed. (New York, 1943), pp. 516–517.

20. Tanaka Toyojirō, *Meiji no senkakusha kindai no ijin kō Godai Tomoatsu den* (Biography of the Meiji pioneer and great man of the modern age, Lord Godai Tomoatsu; Osaka, 1921), pp. 347–355.

21. It was the time of the bombardment of Kagoshima in 1863 and of the battle of Shimonoseki in 1864; these events marked a climax of antiforeign sentiment. Satsuma and Choshu han brought the country to the brink of war. But after the lesson learned during these two engagements with foreign superior warships, these two han eventually became the most pro-Western of all.

22. Fujii, p. 43. The disregard of status in this program is noteworthy because up to this point the samurai had been considered the only social group qualified for leadership. And foreign studies were aimed at training an intellectual elite.

23. Tuge Hideomi, *Historical Development of Science and Technology in Japan* (Tokyo, 1961), p. 100.

24. Tsuchiya, ed., *Meiji zenki keizai*, p. 7.

25. Tsuchiya, *Nihon no seishō*, p. 76.

26. Ishii Mitsuru, *Nihon tetsudō sōsetsu*, pp. 139–140.

27. Karazawa Tomitarō, *Nihon kyōiku shi* (History of Japanese education; Tokyo, 1953), pp. 207–208; also Sansom, *The Western World*, p. 460.

28. Egashira Tsuneharu, "Saga-han ni okeru yōshiki kōgyō" (Western-style industry in Saga han), in Honjō Eijirō, ed., *Bakumatsu keizai shi kenkyū* (Studies in the economic history of the late Tokugawa period; Tokyo, 1935), pp. 76–78.

29. Tuge, p. 97. Tuge's total of technicians according to nationalities is 519, while the total according to fields of activity is 560. Apparently there is some double counting in the latter division.

30. *Ibid.*, p. 97.

31. *Meiji zenki zaisei keizai shiryō shūsei* (Collection of material on the finance and economy of the first part of the Meiji era), ed. Ōuchi Hyōe and Tsuchiya Takao (Tokyo, 1931), XVII, 347.

32. The technicians' salaries must be considered in relation to the comparable salaries of Japanese officials. Tuge, p. 97, quotes $500 as the monthly salary of a minister in the departments of the Ministry of Industry, and the salary of the chief of foreign employees in the Department of Railways was about $2,000 per month; he goes on to say that there were some 200 foreign engineers whose salaries were about as high. This would amount to a total of $2.4 million, or about 3.5 million yen per year, at a time when the total budget of the Ministry of Industry was only half a million yen. Actually, 500–600 yen per month is probably closer to the average salary of a foreigner in Japan in the 1880s. In 1876 a French engineer employed at the Tokyo and Yokohama Gas Works received 600 yen per month (*Shibusawa Eiichi denki shiryō*, XII, 409). The monthly income of a carpenter or smith was about 20–25 yen per month, and presidents of local banks earned some 50 yen per month. According to Rathgen, there were in the late 1880s in the whole of Japan only 63 people with annual incomes of 30,000 yen or higher. Karl Rathgen, *Japans Volkswirtschaft und Staatshaushalt* (Leipzig, 1891), pp. 426–429.

33. *Sangyō kyōiku 70 nen shi* (Seventy years of industrial education), ed. Monbushō (Ministry of Education; Tokyo, 1956), pp. 12–13. A few more agricultural schools were opened in the following years in Niigata, Gifu, and Hiroshima prefectures.

34. For a good survey of the government's efforts in the field of agriculture, see R. P. Dore, "Agricultural Improvements in Japan: 1870–1900," *Economic Development and Cultural Change*, vol. 9, no. 1, pt. 2, pp. 93–107.

35. *Sangyō kyōiku 70 nen,* pp. 22–26.

36. *Ibid.,* p. 17.

37. *Ibid.,* pp. 18–19.

38. Tuge, p. 98.

39. *Meiji unyu shi* (History of Meiji transportation), ed. Unyu nippōsha (The Japan Transport Publication Co.; Tokyo, 1913), Chap. 3, p. 73. Each chapter is paginated separately.

40. Inoue Masaru, Viscount, "Japanese Communications, Railroads," in Ōkuma Shigenobu, ed., *Fifty Years of New Japan,* tr. and ed. Marcus B. Huish, 2nd ed. (London, 1910), I, 435–436.

41. Nakayama Yasumasa, ed., *Shinbun shūsei Meiji hennen shi* (Chronological history of the Meiji era compiled from newspapers; Tokyo, 1936), IV, 126–127.

42. Kinugawa, Vols. I–III, *passim.*

43. *Ibid.,* II, 369–428.

44. Takegoshi Yosaburō, ed., *Ōkawa Heizaburō kun den* (Biography of Mr. Ōkawa Heizaburō; Tokyo, 1936), pp. 98–100.

45. *Shibusawa Eiichi denki shiryō,* XII, 150–189.

46. Hara, ed., III, 333.

47. Ōnishi Rihei, *Asabuki Eiji kun den* (Biography of Mr. Asabuki Eiji; Tokyo, 1928), pp. 86–87.

48. The problems of traveling in Japan during the Tokugawa period are aptly and imaginatively described in Oliver Statler, *Japanese Inn,* Pyramid paperback ed. (New York, 1962).

49. Ishii Mitsuru, p. 154.

50. *Meiji unyu shi,* Chap. 1, p. 50.

51. *Nihon tetsudō shi* (History of the Japanese railways), ed. Tetsudō shō (Ministry of Railways; Tokyo, 1935), I, 92–93.

52. *Ibid.,* p. 113.

53. Computed from Rosovsky, *Capital Formation,* p. 25.

54. Takahashi Kamekichi and Aoyama Jirō, *Nihon zaibatsu ron* (A treatise on the Japanese zaibatsu; Tokyo, 1938), p. 43.

55. *Nihon tetsudō shi,* I, 972–973.

56. Computed from Rosovsky, *Capital Formation,* pp. 25–26.

57. The close connection between the economic reforms and military objectives has been made very clear by Egashira Tsuneharu in the following three chapters in Honjō, *Bakumatsu keizai*: "Kōchihan ni okeru bakumatsu no shinseisaku" (The new policies in Kōchi han in the last years of the Tokugawa period), "Saga-han ni okeru yōshiki kōgyō" (Western-style industry in Saga han), "Takashima tankō ni okeru nichiei kyōdō kigyō" (The joint Anglo-Japanese enterprise at the Takashima coal mine).

58. Egashira Tsuneharu, "Kōchi-han," pp. 119–120.

59. *Meiji unyu shi,* Chap. 3, p. 9.

60. Rosovsky, *Capital Formation,* pp. 165, 198–199.

61. *Ibid.,* p. 25.

62. This is an overstatement; actually the militarists stressed very strongly in the railway debates the need to build railways for the sake of army transportation. But railways were a long-range project while ships could be bought quickly.

63. *Ibid.*, pp. 199–200.

64. Takahashi and Aoyama, pp. 52–53.

65. *Meiji unyu shi*, Chap. 3, pp. 19–22.

66. *Ibid.*, Chap. 3, pp. 68–69, 183.

67. Matsukata Masayoshi (1835–1924) was one of the Satsuma men in the government and became known for his work on the land-tax reform under Ōkubo. During 1878 and 1879, while in Europe, he became well acquainted with financial matters. After his return he moved into the Ministry of Finance and took over from Ōkuma in 1881. In 1896 he served as prime minister.

68. Thomas Smith, *Political Change, passim.*

69. *Meiji zenki zaisei keizai*, XVII, 133–137.

70. Thomas Smith, *Political Change*, p. 48.

71. The Senju Woolen Mill was not sold out but was transferred to army management in 1888. It was one of the most important government enterprises and supplied the army with uniforms. Also retained were the Yokosuka Shipyard and the Akabane Construction Plant, both under the minister of the navy. The government did not want to depend for its military supplies on private industry.

72. Arizawa Hiromi, ed., *Gendai Nihon sangyō kōza* (A compendium of present-day Japanese industry; Tokyo, 1959), I, 59.

73. Takahashi and Aoyama, p. 56.

74. Ohkawa et al., p. 245.

75. Wada Hisajirō, *Asano Cement enkaku shi* (The history of Asano Cement; Tokyo, 1940), pp. 74–75.

76. Takahashi and Aoyama, p. 59.

77. Tsuchiya, ed., *Meiji zenki keizai*, p. 78.

78. *Ibid.*, p. 92.

79. Ohkawa et al., p. 79.

80. *Ibid.*, p. 79.

81. Kajinishi Mitsuhaya, *Nihon ni okeru sangyō shihon no keisei* (The formation of industrial capital in Japan; Tokyo, 1949), I, 37.

82. Yamaguchi, *Meiji zenki keizai*, pp. 93–94.

83. *Ibid.*, p. 100.

V. THE SPIRIT OF ENTERPRISE IN THE PRIVATE SECTOR

1. Mori Arinori (1847–1889) had been sent to England by his daimyo, Shimazu, prior to the Restoration; after 1868 he was employed in various embassies and became one of the most liberal-

minded men in the Meiji government. Under Itō he was Japan's first education minister and started a thorough educational reform. He was assassinated on the day of the promulgation of the constitution, in 1889, apparently because some fanatics feared he might introduce Christianity as a state religion.

2. This, of course, does not mean that the English universities educated their students primarily for business; it is a matter of emphasis on values, and in England where economics was first developed as a field of study, business pursuits tended to be valued more highly and to receive more attention than in the Prussian-oriented academic world. On the "Prussian" type of education in Japan, see Chitoshi Yanaga, *Japan since Perry*, consulting ed. Ralph E. Turner (New York, 1949), pp. 102–103.

3. Kosaka Masaaki, *Japanese Thought in the Meiji Era* (Tokyo, 1958), p. 83.

4. Shibusawa Eiichi, *Jitsugyō kōen* (Lectures on enterprise; Tokyo, 1913), II, 36–38.

5. Fukuzawa, *Autobiography*, p. 224.

6. *Fukuzawa Yukichi zenshū*, IX, 165–182.

7. Kurihara Shinichi, *Meiji kaika shiron* (An historical essay on Meiji civilization; Tokyo, 1944), pp. 11–12.

8. Tanaka Sōgorō, *Iwasaki Yatarō den* (Biography of Iwasaki Yatarō; Tokyo, 1955), pp. 205–209.

9. Kyugoro Obata, *An Interpretation of the Life of Viscount Shibusawa* (Tokyo, 1937), pp. 43–59.

10. Suzuki Gorō, *Suzuki Tōsaburō den* (Biography of Suzuki Tōsaburō; Tokyo, 1956), pp. 104–107.

11. Shibusawa spoke on many occasions, often extemporaneously, and most of these speeches and casual remarks were preserved for posterity by his admiring followers. His biographical material is now being edited; 42 volumes were printed in 1962, and more are to follow. This collection, *Shibusawa Eiichi denki shiryō*, contains over 4,000 speeches and talks of various descriptions by Shibusawa. For a good selection of speeches, see Shibusawa Eiichi, *Shōgyō dōtoku kōwa* (Discourses on business ethics) and *Jitsugyō kōen*.

12. Minamoto Yoshiie (1041–1106) was a general of the House of Genji in its long struggle against the Heike. He was called by his people the greatest samurai of Japan.

13. *Ryūmon zasshi* (Ryūmon periodical), ed. Ryūmonsha (The Dragon Door Company; Tokyo, May 1889), pp. 45–46.

14. Godai Ryūsaku, *Godai Tomoatsu den* (Biography of Godai Tomoatsu; Tokyo, 1933), p. 486.

15. Usaki Kumakichi, *Toyokawa Ryōhei* (Tokyo, 1922), p. 130.

16. Godai, p. 471.

17. Shibusawa Eiichi, *Jitsugyō kōen*, I, 227.

316 NOTES TO CHAPTER V

18. *Ibid.*, p. 199.

19. Shibusawa Eiichi, *Shōgyō dōtoku*, p. 16.

20. Tsuchiya Takao, *Nihon no keieisha seishin* (Managerial attitudes in Japan; Tokyo, 1959), p. 82.

21. *Ibid.*, p. 76.

22. Alexander Gerschenkron, "Economic Backwardness in Historical Perspective," in Bert F. Hoselitz, ed., *The Progress of Underdeveloped Areas* (Chicago, 1952), pp. 59–61.

23. *Ginkō tsūshinroku* (Bank correspondence records), ed. Ginkō shūkaijo (The Banking Center; Tokyo, January 20, 1886), pp. 514–515.

24. *Ginkō benran*, pp. 208–210.

25. *Nihon keizai tōkei sōkan* (Survey of Japanese economic statistics), ed. Asahi shinbunsha (Asahi Newspaper Co.; Tokyo, 1930), p. 457.

26. *Meiji 16 nen Tōkyō fu tōkeisho* (Statistics of Tokyo prefecture for Meiji 16 [1883]), ed. Tokyo fu; Tokyo, 1883), pp. 171–172.

27. *Meiji 14 nen tōkeihyō* (Statistical table of Meiji 14 [1881]), ed. Tokyo fu; Tokyo, 1881), pp. 155–157.

28. *Meiji 16 nen*, pp. 155–157.

29. *Meiji 14 nen*, pp. 129–139.

30. Tachikawa Tokuji, ed., *Meiji kōgyō shi, tetsudō hen* (History of Meiji industry, railway volume; Tokyo, 1932), p. 278.

31. *Meiji unyu shi*, p. 126.

32. *Meiji bunka zenshū, keizai hen* (The Meiji culture collection, economy volume), ed. Meiji bunka kenkyūkai (Research Council on Meiji Culture; Tokyo, 1957), p. 492.

33. Takahashi Kamekichi, *Meiji Taishō sangyō*, pp. 152–153.

34. Tsuchiya and Okazaki, pp. 248–249.

35. Kikkawa Hidezō, *Meiji ishin shakai keizai shi kenkyū* (Studies in the social and economic history of the Meiji Restoration; Tokyo, 1943), pp. 309–317.

36. Kinugawa, III, 207–209.

37. Arizawa, I, 66.

38. Kinugawa, II, 369–428.

39. *Ibid.*, IV, *passim*.

40. *Shigyōkai 50 nen* (Fifty years of the Paper Manufacturers' Association), ed. Hakushinsha (The Progress Co.; Tokyo, 1937), pp. 309–317.

41. *Ibid.*, p. 12.

42. Shibusawa Eiichi, *Jijoden* (Autobiography; Tokyo, 1938), p. 845.

43. Takegoshi, *Ōkawa*, pp. 98–100.

44. *Shigyōkai 50 nen*, pp. 27–28.

45. *Nihon Cement kabushiki kaisha 70 nen shi, hon hen* (Seventy-year history of Nihon Cement, Ltd., main volume), ed. Nihon Cement kabushiki kaisha shashi hensan iinkai (Editorial Committee for the History of Nihon Cement, Ltd.; Tokyo, 1955), p. 7.

46. Utsunomiya Saburō, as a leading expert on physics and chemistry, went with the Iwakura mission to Europe, and in 1875 visited the Philadelphia exhibition to study the latest cement production techniques. He had been entrusted with the technical direction of the Fukagawa Cement Factory. Wada Hisajirō, *Asano Cement*, pp. 25–32.

47. Nishida Hirotarō, *Meiji kōgyō shi, kagaku kōgyō* (History of Meiji industry, chemical industries volume; Tokyo, 1925), p. 461.

48. *Ibid.*, pp. 471–472.

49. Onoda Cement seizō kabushiki kaisha (Onoda Cement Manufacturing Company), ed., *Sōgyō 50 nen shi* (Fifty years after the founding; Tokyo, 1931), p. 108.

50. *Shibusawa Eiichi denki shiryō*, XI, 443–445.

51. German technicians who were called to demonstrate the use of imported machines were able to blow 350 bottles per hour while the Japanese workers made only 80. *Ibid.*, p. 451.

52. *Ibid.*, pp. 440–441.

53. *Meiji zenki zaisei keizai*, XVII, 133–137.

54. *Nihon tekkō shi, Meiji hen* (History of Japanese iron and steel, Meiji volume), ed. Nihon tekkō shi hensan iinkai (Editorial Committee for the History of Japanese Iron and Steel; Tokyo, 1945), p. 118.

55. *Ibid.*, p. 117.

56. *Ibid.*, pp. 117–118.

57. *Shibusawa Eiichi denki shiryō*, X, 668.

58. *Ibid.*, pp. 608–621.

59. Shibusawa Eiichi, *Jijoden*, pp. 551–553.

60. Asano Taijirō, *Asano Sōichirō* (Tokyo, 1939), appendix, pp. 5–6.

61. *Shibusawa Eiichi denki shiryō*, XI, 412–414.

62. *Nihon Cement*, pp. 6–7.

63. Shibusawa Eiichi, *Shōgyō dōtoku*, p. 3.

64. Max Weber, *The Protestant Ethic and the Spirit of Capitalism* (New York, 1956), p. 53.

65. I am indebted to Professor Reinhard Bendix for pointing out to me this functional equivalence between the Puritan spirit of capitalism and the mentality of the Meiji entrepreneurs.

66. *Shigyōkai 50 nen*, p. 9.

67. Gerschenkron, "Economic Backwardness in Historical Perspective," p. 24.

VI. THE ZAIBATSU BUILDERS

1. Katsuda Teiji, *Ōkura, Nezu Concern tokuhon* (The Ōkura and Nezu Concern reader; Tokyo, 1937), pp. 112–113.
2. *Ibid.*, p. 125.
3. *Ibid.*, p. 64.
4. Takahashi and Aoyama, p. 43.
5. Tsuchiya, *Nihon no seishō*, p. 67.
6. Takahashi and Aoyama, pp. 50–51.
7. *Ibid.*, p. 58.
8. The Mitsui constitution provided that the six-member families would be under the leadership of the oldest, Hachirōemon. When he retired, the next in line, Hachirōbei, would become Hachirōemon and the third move into second place. The individual member of the large family concern was assigned only a fixed sum that he could spend. If anyone refused to obey these regulations, he was forced into retirement and his name was taken off the family list. Honjo, *Social and Economic History*, p. 306.
9. Wada Hidekichi, *Mitsui Concern tokuhon* (The Mitsui Concern reader; Tokyo, 1937), p. 39.
10. Tsuchiya, *Nihon no seishō*, p. 76.
11. All three houses of Mitsui, Ono, and Shimada held large deposits of government funds with no rulings on reserves. In 1874 the government suddenly introduced a one-third reserve requirement, and at the same time started to call in deposits from Ono, which had overinvested and could not meet its obligations; Ono went into bankruptcy, and Shimada closed spontaneously. Mitsui, however, had been warned beforehand by Inoue, and Mitsui had thus gained time to prepare the needed reserves. Takahashi and Aoyama, p. 49; also Shibusawa Eiichi. *Jijoden*, pp. 396–401.
12. Wada Hidekichi, pp. 86–87.
13. Tsuchiya, *Nihon no seishō*, pp. 115–116.
14. Masuda Takashi, *Jijo Masuda Takashi ō den* (Autobiography of Masuda Takashi; Tokyo, 1939), p. 175.
15. *Ibid.*, p. 292.
16. *Ibid.*, p. 176.
17. Shiroyanagi Hidemitsu, *Nakamigawa Hikojirō den* (Biography of Nakamigawa Hikojirō; Tokyo, 1950), p. 211.
18. Tsuchiya Takao, *Zaibasu o kizuita hitobito* (The zaibatsu builders; Tokyo, 1955), p. 43.
19. Shiroyanagi, *Nakamigawa*, pp. 212–213.
20. *Ibid.*, p. 238.
21. *Ibid.*, p. 288.
22. *Ibid.*, p. 259.
23. Tsuchiya, *Zaibatsu*, p. 50.

24. Quoted in Kada Tetsuji, *Meiji shoki shakai keizai shisō shi* (History of social and economic thought during the early Meiji era; Tokyo, 1937), p. 713.

25. *Ibid.*, pp. 715–716.

26. Tanaka Sōgorō, *Iwasaki*, p. 130.

27. Iwai Ryōtarō, *Mitsubishi Concern tokuhon* (The Mitsubishi Concern reader; Tokyo, 1937), pp. 102–103.

28. Tsuchiya, *Nihon no seishō*, p. 106.

29. Kajinishi Mitsuhaya, *Nihon shihonshugi hattatsu shi* (History of the development of Japanese capitalism; Tokyo, 1957), p. 141.

30. Iwasaki's protector and former han official, Gotō Shōjirō, had bought the mine from the government for 500,000 yen but lost heavily. Iwasaki was eventually persuaded by Fukuzawa to purchase the mine for 900,000 yen, thus bailing Gotō out of his heavy debts. Shiroyanagi Hidemitsu, *Zaikai taiheiki* (Documents of prosperity in the financial world; Tokyo, 1948), pp. 169–189.

31. Iwai, pp. 201–204.

32. Tanaka Sōgorō, p. 301.

33. Iwai, p. 238.

34. Mitsubishi honsha hensan kyoku (Editorial Section of the Mitsubishi Head Office), ed., *Shashi* (The company history; Tokyo, 1917), No. 14, p. 1135.

35. Tsuchiya, *Zaibatsu*, pp. 126–127.

36. *Ibid.*, p. 144.

37. *Ibid.*, p. 145.

38. Tsuchiya, *Nihon no seishō*, pp. 176–177.

39. Tsuchiya, *Zaibatsu*, p. 146.

40. Nishino Kiyo, *Sumitomo Concern tokuhon* (The Sumitomo Concern reader; Tokyo, 1937), p. 40.

41. Hirose Mitsumasa, *Saihei iseki* (The glorious achievements of Saihei; Kyoto, 1926), pp. 170–171.

42. *Ibid.*, p. 76.

43. Tsuchiya, *Zaibatsu*, p. 175.

44. A notable exception occurred after the downfall of Ono and Shimada, when the government kept part of its money free of interest with the Yasuda Bank; in 1875 the Yasuda Bank held 180,000 yen of government money. Takahashi and Aoyama, p. 50.

45. In 1869 the inconvertible government bills had stood at 38:100 against specie money. Parity was then restored by government decree. Yasuda received news of the government move beforehand and bought up large amounts of bills at the low market rate, selling them a few days later at an almost 300 percent profit. Tsuchiya, *Zaibatsu*, p. 160.

46. Obama Toshie, *Yasuda Concern tokuhon* (The Yasuda Concern reader; Tokyo, 1937), p. 227.

47. Oda Shigeo, *Ningen Yasuda Zenjirō* (The man Yasuda Zenjirō; Tokyo, 1953), pp. 108–109.

48. *Ibid.*, p. 220.

49. Obama, pp. 235–237.

50. Oda, p. 214.

51. Yasuda wanted to collect the 800 million yen as deposits in his many branch banks throughout the country, paying 6.2 percent and receiving 8.5 percent on the loan for the project, thus gaining a 2.3 percent difference for his expenses and for profit. *Ibid.*, pp. 212–213.

52. *Ibid.*, p. 208.

53. *Ibid.*, pp. 139–140.

54. Obama, pp. 223–224.

55. Yokoyama Sadao, *Ningen Ōkura Kihachirō* (The man Ōkura Kihachirō; Tokyo, 1929); and Kadono Shigekurō, *Ōkura Tsuruhiko ō* (The Honorable Ōkura Tsuruhiko; Tokyo, 1924).

56. Tsuchiya, *Zaibatsu*, p. 183.

57. Hattori Shisō, *Kindai Nihon jinbutsu keizai shi* (A biographic economic history of modern Japan; Tokyo, 1955), I, 110.

58. Kadono, p. 450.

59. Katsuda, pp. 29–30.

60. *Ibid.*, p. 54.

61. Yokoyama, pp. 234–236.

62. *Ibid.*, pp. 168–170.

63. Tsuchiya, *Zaibatsu*, p. 200.

64. Konda Bunjirō, ed., *Furukawa Ichibei ō den* (Biography of the Honorable Furukawa Ichibei; Tokyo, 1926), p. 185.

65. Tsuchiya, *Zaibatsu*, pp. 204–206.

66. Konda, appendix, pp. 8–9.

67. Tsuchiya, *Zaibatsu*, p. 207.

68. Konda, p. 207.

69. *Ibid.*, letter appendix, p. 3; and Yokoyama, pp. 237–238.

70. Asano, *passim.*

71. Tsuchiya, *Zaibatsu*, p. 213.

72. Wada Hisajirō, pp. 86–87.

73. Shibusawa Eiichi, *Jijoden*, pp. 622–623.

74. Wada Hisajirō, pp. 104–106.

75. Asano, pp. 526–532.

VII. FIFTY LEADING ENTREPRENEURS

1. *Zaikai bukko ketsubutsu den*, II, 130–133.

2. Hattori and Shinobu, pp. 104–120; and Kinugawa I, 271–332.

3. *Dai Nihon jinmei jisho* (The great Japan biographical diction-

ary), ed. Dai Nihon jinmei jisho kankōkai (The Great Japan Biographical Dictionary Editorial Board; Tokyo, 1926), p. 1481.

4. Tsuchiya, *Nihon no seishō*, pp. 191–205.

5. *Zaikai bukko katsubutsu den*, II, 522–527.

6. *Ibid.*, pp. 2–6.

7. The age of twenty is not to be taken with mathematical exactness. In some cases the man may have actually been twenty-one or twenty-two when he moved to a new place or started a new career.

8. The difference between Western and Confucian studies does not matter too much at this late stage. Many Confucian scholars advocated the opening of the country as ardently as any Western scholar could have done; more often than not Western and Confucian studies were pursued by the same man.

9. Yamamoto Mitsuhiko, *Kawasaki Shōzō* (Tokyo, 1918), pp. 49–50.

10. *Zaikai bukko ketsubutsu den*, II, 506–511.

11. Ōsawa Shōzō, ed., *Nishimura Katsuzō ō den* (Biography of the Honorable Nishimura Katsuzō; Tokyo, 1921).

12. Ōtsuka Eizō, *Magoshi Kyōhei ō den* (Biography of the Honorable Magoshi Kyōhei; Tokyo, 1935), pp. 38–43.

13. Naitō Fumijirō, *Wakao Ippei* (Tokyo, 1914).

14. *Zaikai bukko ketsubutsu den*, I, 133–138.

15. Tsuchiya, *Nihon no keieisha seishin*, p. 178.

16. Toyohara Matao, *Sakuma Sadaichi shōden* (Short biography of Sakuma Sadaichi; Tokyo, 1904), pp. 166–167.

17. See Fritz Redlich, *History of American Business Leaders* (Ann Arbor, 1940), I, 19.

18. *Zaikai bukko ketsubutsu den*, II, 506–511; and *Dai Nihon jinmei jisho*, p. 2672.

19. Toyohara, p. 221.

20. *Shibusawa Eiichi denki shiryō*, XI, 599–665.

21. Suzuki, *passim*.

22. Shibusawa Eiichi, *Jijoden*, pp. 841–843.

23. Ōtsuka Eizō, p. 154.

24. Amamiya Keijirō, "Amamiya Keijirō shi kokkai jigyō keireki dan" (A narrative of the patriotic enterprises of Mr. Amamiya Keijirō), and "Amamiya Keijirō shi kiroku" (Records on Mr. Amamiya Keijirō), MSS (Tokyo University Library, n.d.).

25. Miura Toyoji, *Tanaka Gentarō ō den* (Biography of the Honorable Tanaka Gentarō; Kyoto, 1934).

26. Uemura Chōsaburō, *Donshō Takashima Kazaemon ō den* (Biography of the Honorable Donshō Takashima Kazaemon; Tokyo, 1914).

27. *Zaikai bukko ketsubutsu den*, I, 247–249; and Kinugawa, IV, 309–326.

28. Kinugawa, IV, 322.

29. Tsuchiya, *Nihon no keieisha seishin*, pp. 194–231; and Tsuboya Zenjirō, *Jitsugyōka hyakuketsu den* (Biographies of 100 outstanding entrepreneurs; Tokyo, 1893), VI, 177–186.

30. Hara, ed., I, 109.

31. Usaki, *passim*; and Tsuchiya, *Zaibatsu*, pp. 96–104.

32. Tsuchiya, *Zaibatsu*, pp. 77–85.

33. *Zaikai bukko ketsubutsu den*, II, 306–309.

34. *Ibid.*, pp. 5–10; and *Dai Nihon jinmei jisho*, pp. 92–93.

35. Matsumoto ō dōzō kensetsu kai (Association for the Erection of a Bronze Statue of Matsumoto), ed., *Sōgon Matsumoto Jūtarō ō den* (Biography of the magnificent Matsumoto Jūtarō; Tokyo, 1922).

36. *Ibid.*, p. 18.

37. Miyamoto Mataji, "Matsumoto Jūtarō," *Ōsaka kōgyōkai geppō* (Monthly bulletin of the Osaka Industrial Association), No. 14 (May 15, 1960), p. 16.

38. *Zaikai bukko ketsubutsu den*, I, 378–382.

39. Tsuchiya, *Nihon no keieisha seishin*, pp. 168–193.

40. Modeki Gentarō, *Ōtani Kahei ō den* (Biography of the Honorable Ōtani Kahei; Tokyo, 1931).

41. *Ibid.*, p. 517.

42. *Zaikai bukko ketsubutsu den*, II, 288–291.

43. *Ibid.*, pp. 624–626.

44. Iwashita Seishū, *Fujita ō genkōroku* (Records of the words and deeds of the Honorable Fujita; Tokyo, 1913); Shiroyanagi Hidemitsu, *Nihon fugō hassei gaku* (A study of the emergence of the Japanese rich; Tokyo, 1920), pp. 18–103.

45. *Dai Nihon jinmei jisho*, p. 1892.

46. Yamamoto, *passim*.

47. *Ibid.*, pp. 101–102.

48. Usuda Sadakei, *Nakano Buei ō* (The Honorable Nakano Buei; Tokyo, 1934).

49. Kinugawa, II, 99–109.

50. Ōnishi, *passim*.

51. Tsuchiya, *Zaibatsu*, pp. 104–114.

52. *Ibid.*, pp. 85–95.

53. Takegoshi, *Ōkawa, passim*.

CONCLUSION

1. Nurkse, *Problems of Capital Formation in Underdeveloped Countries*, pp. 38–39.

BIBLIOGRAPHY

Akashi Teruo 明石照男 and Suzuki Norihisa 鈴木憲久.
Nihon kinyū shi, Meiji hen 日本金融史, 明治編
(History of Japanese banking, Meiji volume). Tokyo, 1957.

Amamiya Keijirō 雨宮敬治郎. "Amamiya Keijirō shi kokka
jigyō keireki dan" 雨宮敬次郎氏国家事業経
歴談 (A narrative of the patriotic enterprises of Mr.
Amamiya Keijirō. MS, apparently autobiographical; Tokyo
University Library, n. d.

------"Amamiya Keijirō shi kiroku" 雨宮敬治郎氏記録
(Records on Mr. Amamiya Keijirō). MS; Tokyo University
Library, n. d.

Arizawa Hiromi 有沢広已 , ed. Gendai Nihon sangyō kōza
現代日本産業講座 (A compendium of present-day
Japanese industry), vol. 1. Tokyo, 1959.

Asano Taijirō 浅野泰治郎 Asano Sōichirō 浅野総一郎.
Tokyo, 1939.

Azuma Tōsaku 我妻東策. Shizoku jusan shi 士族授産史
(History of samurai employment). Tokyo, 1942.

Beasley, W. G. "Feudal Revenue in Japan at the Time of the Meiji
Restoration," Journal of Asian Studies, 19. 3:255-272
(May 1960).

Bellah, Robert. Tokugawa Religion. Glencoe, Ill. , 1957.

Brown, Delmer M.   Nationalism in Japan: An Introductory
   Historical Analysis.   Berkeley, 1955.

Commercial Reports of Her Majesty's Consuls in Japan, 1868 and
   1869-1870.   London, 1869 and 1871.

Craig, Albert M.   "The Restoration Movement in Chōshū," The
   Journal of Asian Studies, 18.2:187-197 (Feb. 1959).

------Chōshū in the Meiji Restoration.   Cambridge, Mass., 1961.

Crawcour, E.S.   "Some Observations on Merchants: A Translation
   of Mitsui Takafusa's Chōnin kōken roku, with an Introduction
   and Notes,"   Transactions of the Asiatic Society of Japan,
   3rd ser., 8:1-139 (Dec. 1961).   Tokyo, 1962.

Dai Nihon gaikoku bōeki 大日本外国貿易 (The foreign trade
   of great Japan), ed.   Nōshōmushō shōmukyoku 農商務省
   商務局 (Ministry of Agriculture and Trade, Department
   of Trade).   Tokyo, 1911.

Dai Nihon jinmei jisho 大日本人名辞書 (The great Japan
   biographical dictionary), ed. Dai Nihon jinmei jisho kankōkai
   大日本人名辞書刊行会 (Great Japan Biographical
   Dictionary Editorial Board).   Tokyo, 1926.

Dore, R.P.   Land Reform in Japan.   Oxford, 1959.

------"The Meiji Landlord: Good or Bad?" Journal of Asian Studies,
   18.3:343-355 (May 1959).

------"Agricultural Improvements in Japan: 1870-1900," Economic
   Development and Cultural Change, vol. 9, no. 1, pt. 2,
   pp. 69-91 (Oct. 1960).   Research Center in Economic Development and Cultural Change, University of Chicago.

Egashira Tsuneharu 江頭恒治 "Kōchi-han ni okeru bakumatsu no shinseisaku" 高知藩における幕末の新政策 (The new policies in Kochi han in the last years of the Tokugawa period); in Honjō Eijirō, ed., Bakumatsu keizai shi kenkyū, pp. 101-131.

------"Saga-han ni okeru yōshiki kōgyō" 佐賀藩における洋式工業 (Western-style industry in Saga han); in Honjō Eijirō, ed., Bakumatsu keizai shi kenkyū, pp. 59-100.

------"Takashima tankō ni okeru nichiei kyōdō kigyō" 高嶋炭鉱における日英共同企業 (The joint Anglo-Japanese enterprise at the Takashima coal mine); in Honjō Eijirō, ed., Bakumatsu keizai shi kenkyū, pp. 23-58.

------Ōmi shōnin 近江商人 (The Omi merchants). Tokyo, 1959.

Fujii Jintarō. Outline of Japanese History in the Meiji Era, tr. H. K. Colton and K. E. Colton. Tokyo, 1958.

Fujita Gorō 藤田五郎. Nihon kindai sangyō no seisei 日本近代産業の生成` (The creation of Japan's modern industry). Tokyo, 1948.

Fukuzawa Yukichi 福沢諭吉. Fukuzawa Yukichi zenshū 福沢諭吉全集 (The Fukuzawa Yukichi collection), vols. 6, 9, 10. Tokyo: Jiji shinpōsha 時事新報社 (Jiji Newspaper Publishing Co.), 1926.

------"Kyūhanjō" 旧藩状` (The conditions in the old han); in Fukuzawa Yukichi zenshū, VI, 677-696.

------The Autobiography of Fukuzawa Yukichi, tr. Kiyooka Eiichi. Tokyo, 1948.

Furushima Toshio 古島敏雄. Kisei jinushi sei no seisei to tenkai 近世地主制の生成と展開 (The emergence and spread of the parasitic landlord system). Tokyo, 1952.

Gerschenkron, Alexander. "Economic Backwardness in Historical Perspective," in Bert F. Hoselitz, ed., The Progress of Underdeveloped Areas, pp. 3-29.

Ginkō benran 銀行便覧 (Bank handbook), ed. Ōkura shō 大藏省 (Ministry of Finance). Tokyo, 1911.

Ginkō kyoku dai ni ji hōkoku 銀行局第二次報告 (The second report of the Banking Office), ed. Ōkura shō. Tokyo, 1879-1880.

Ginkō tsūshinroku 銀行通信録 (Bank correspondence records), ed. Ginkō shūkaijo 銀行集会所 (The Banking Center). Tokyo, Jan. 20, 1886.

Godai Ryūsaku 五代龍作. Godai Tomoatsu den 五代友厚伝 (Biography of Godai Tomoatsu). Tokyo, 1933.

Hall, John Whitney. Tanuma Okitsugu, 1719-1788, Forerunner of Modern Japan. Cambridge, Mass., 1955.

Hara Kunizō 原邦造, ed. Hara Rokurō ō den 原六郎翁伝 (Biography of the Honorable Hara Rokurō. 3 vols.; Tokyo, 1923.

Hattori Shisō 服部之総, ed. Kindai Nihon jinbutsu keizai shi 近代日本人物経済史 (A biographic economic history of modern Japan), vol. 1. Tokyo, 1955.

------Meiji no shisō 明治の思想 (The thought of the Meiji era); Chosaku shū 著作集 (Collected writings), vol. 6. Tokyo, 1955.

Hattori Shisō and Shinobu Seizaburō 服部之総・信夫清三郎 Meiji senshoku keizai shi 明治染色経済史 (Economic history of Meiji dyeing and weaving). Tokyo, 1937.

Hayes, Samuel P. Jr. "Personality and Culture Problems," in
Bert F. Hoselitz, ed., The Progress of Underdeveloped
Areas, pp. 203-229.

Hirose Mitsumasa 広瀬満正 . Saihei iseki 宰平遺蹟 (The
glorious achievements of Saihei). Kyoto, 1926.

Hirschman, Albert O. The Strategy of Economic Development.
New Haven, 1959.

Honjo Eijiro 本庄榮治郎 . The Social and Economic History
of Japan. Kyoto, 1935.

------ Nihon no keizai to shiso 日本の経済と思想
(Japanese economy and thought). Kyoto, 1943.

------, ed. Meiji ishin keizai shi kenkyu 明治維新経済史
研究 (Studies in the economic history of the Meiji
Restoration). Tokyo, 1935.

------, ed. Bakumatsu keizai shi kenkyu 幕末経済史研究
(Studies in the economic history of the late Tokugawa period).
Tokyo, 1935.

Horie Eiichi 堀江英一. Meiji ishin no shakai kozo 明治維
新の社会構造 (Structure of society at the time of
the Restoration). Tokyo, 1954.

Hoselitz, Bert F., ed. The Progress of Underdeveloped Areas.
Chicago, 1952.

Inoue Masaru, Viscount. "Japanese Communications, Railroads,"
in Okuma Shigenobu, Fifty Years of New Japan, I, 424-446.

Ishii Mitsuru 石井満. Nihon tetsudo sosetsu shi wa 日本鉄
道創設史話 (Historic narrative on the building of
the Japanese railways). Tokyo, 1952.

327

Ishii Ryoichi.   Population Pressure and Economic Life in Japan.
  Chicago, 1937.

Iwai Ryotaro 岩井官太郎 .   Mitsubishi Concern tokuhon
  三菱コンツェルン 讀本 (The Mitsubishi Concern reader).
  Tokyo, 1937.

Iwashita Seishu 岩下清周 .   Fujita o genkoroku 藤田翁言
  行録 (Records of the words and deeds of the Honorable
  Fujita).   Tokyo, 1913.

Jansen, Marius B.   Sakamoto Ryoma and the Meiji Restoration.
  Princeton, 1961.

Jinushi sei no keisei 地主制の形成 (The formation of the
  landlord system), ed.   Meiji shiryo kenkyu renrakukai
  明治史料研究連絡会 (Meiji Historic Material
  Research Association).   Tokyo, 1957.

Kabushiki kaisha 77 ginko 株式会社七十七銀行 (The 77th
  Bank Ltd.), ed.   77 nen shi 七十七年史 (History of seventy-
  seven years).   Tokyo, 1954.

Kada Tetsuji 加田哲二 .   Meiji shoki shakai keizai shiso shi·
  明治初期社会経済思想史 (History of social
  and economic thought during the early Meiji era).   Tokyo,
  1937.

Kadono Shigekuro 門野重九郎 .   Okura Tsuruhiko o 大倉
  鶴彦翁 (The Honorable Okura Tsuruhiko).   Tokyo, 1924.

Kajinishi Mitsuhaya 楫西光速 .   Nihon ni okeru sangyo shihon
  no keisei 日本における産業資本の形成 (The
  formation of industrial capital in Japan), vol. 1.   Tokyo,
  1949.

328

------Shōgyō shihon oyobi kōrigashi shihon 商業資本及び
高利貸資本 (Trading capital and usury capital). Tokyo,
1949.

------Nihon shihonshugi hattatsu shi 日本資本主義発達史
(History of the development of Japanese capitalism). Tokyo,
1957.

Kajinishi Mitsuhaya et al. Nihon ni okeru shihonshugi no hattatsu,
nenpyō hen 日本における資本主義の発達, 年
表編 (The development of capitalism in Japan, chronology
volume). Tokyo, 1953.

Kanno Watarō 管野和太郎. Nihon kaisha kigyō hassei shi no
kenkyū 日本会社企業発生史の研究 (Studies
in the development of the company form of enterprise in
Japan). Tokyo, 1931.

------"Kokuritsu ginkō" 国立銀行 (The national banks); in
Honjō Eijirō, ed., Meiji ishin keizai shi kenkyū, pp. 301-357.

------"Tsushō kaisha, kawase kaisha" 通商会社, 為替会社
(The trade and finance companies); in Honjō Eijirō, ed., Meiji
ishin keizai shi kenkyū, pp. 105-300.

------Ōsaka keizai shi kenkyū 大阪経済史研究 (Studies in
the economic history of Osaka). Osaka, 1935.

Karasawa Tomitarō 唐沢富太郎. Nihon kyōiku shi 日本教
育史 (History of Japanese education). Tokyo, 1953.

Katō Toshihiko. "Development of the Monetary System," in Shibusawa
Keizō, ed., Japanese Society of the Meiji Era, pp. 181-235.

Katorikku daijiten カトリック大辞典 (The Catholic cyclopedia), ed.
Jōchi daigaku 上智大学 (Sophia University), vol. 1. 2nd
ed.; Tokyo, 1952.

Katsuda Teiji 勝田貞次 . Ōkura, Nezu Concern tokuhon
大倉.根津コンツェルン讀本 (The Ōkura and Nezu Concern
reader). Tokyo, 1937.

Kinugawa Taiichi 絹川太一 . Honpō menshi bōseki shi
本邦綿糸紡績史 (History of Japanese cotton spinning).
7 vols.; Osaka, 1937.

Kikkawa Hidezō 吉川秀造 . Shizoku jusan no kenkyū 士族授
産の研究 (Studies in samurai employment). Tokyo, 1935.

------Meiji ishin shakai keizai shi kenkyū 明治維新社会
経済史研究 (Studies in the social and economic history
of the Meiji Restoration). Tokyo, 1943.

Kobata Jun 小葉田淳 . "Kinsei keizai no hattatsu" 近世経済
の発達 (The development of the modern economy); in
Kobata Jun, ed., Kinsei shakai 近世社会 (Modern society),
vol. 4. Tokyo, 1952.

Kobayashi Yoshimasa 小林良正 . Nihon shihonshugi no seisei to
sono kiban 日本資本主義の生成とその基盤
(The emergence of Japanese capitalism and its foundation).
Tokyo, 1949.

Konda Bunjirō 昆田文次郎 , ed. Furukawa Ichibei ō den 古
河市兵衛翁伝 (Biography of Furukawa Ichibei).
Tokyo, 1926.

Kosaka Masaaki. Japanese Thought in the Meiji Era, tr. David Abosh.
Tokyo, 1958.

Kurihara Shinichi 栗原信一 . Meiji kaika shiron 明治開化史
論 (An historical essay on Meiji civilization). Tokyo,
1944.

Kyugoro Obata. An Interpretation of the Life of Viscount Shibusawa.
Tokyo, 1937.

330

Lockwood, William W.   The Economic Development of Japan:
   Growth and Structural Change, 1868-1938.   Princeton, 1954.

Masuda Takashi 益田孝. Jijo Masuda Takashi ō den 自叙益田
   孝翁伝   (Autobiography of Masuda Takashi).   Tokyo,
   1939.

Matsumoto ō dozō kensetsu kai   松本翁銅像建設会
   (Association for the Erection of a Bronze Statue of Matsumoto),
   ed.   Sōgen Matsumoto Jutarō ō den   雙軒松本重太
   郎翁伝   (Biography of the magnificent Matsumoto Jutarō).
   Tokyo, 1922.

Meiji 14 nen tōkeihyō 明治十四年統計表 (Statistical table
   of Meiji 14 [1881]), ed. Tokyo fu.   Tokyo, 1881.

Meiji 16 nen Tōkyō fu tōkeisho 明治十六年東京府統計書
   (Statistics of Tokyo prefecture for Meiji 16 [1883]), ed.
   Tokyo fu.   Tokyo, 1883.

Meiji bunka zenshū, keizai hen   明治文化全集 経済編
   (The Meiji culture collection, economy volume), ed. Meiji
   bunka kenkyūkai 明治文化研究会 (Research Council
   on Meiji Culture).   Tokyo, 1957.

Meiji unyu shi 明治運輸史 (History of Meiji transportation),
   ed. Unyu Nippōsha   運輸日報社   (Japan Transport
   Publication Co.).   Tokyo, 1913.

Meiji zaisei shi 明治財政史 (The Meiji financial history),
   ed. Meiji zaisei shi hensan kai 明治財政史編纂会
   (Meiji Financial History Editorial Board), vol. 13.
   Tokyo, 1905.

Meiji zenki zaisei keizai shiryō shūsei   明治前期財政史料
   集成 (Collection of material on the finance and economy

of the first part of the Meiji era), ed. Ōuchi Hyōe 大内
兵衛 and Tsuchiya Takao 土屋喬雄 , vol. 17.
Tokyo, 1931.

Mitsubishi honsha hensan kyoku 三菱本社編纂局 (Editorial
Section of the Mitsubishi Head Office), ed. Shashi 社史
(The company history), no. 14. Tokyo, 1917.

Miura Toyoji 三浦豊二 . Tanaka Gentarō ō den 田中源太
郎翁伝 (Biography of the Honorable Tanaka Gentarō).
Kyoto, 1934.

Miyamoto Mataji 宮本又二 . "Tokugawa ki Ōsaka kinkō no
nōgyō keiei" 徳川期大阪近郊の農業経営
(Management of agriculture in the vicinity of Osaka during
the Tokugawa period); in Miyamoto Mataji, ed., Shōgyōteki
nōgyō no tenkai. 商業的農業の展開

------Nihon girudo no kaihō 日本ギルドの解放 (The abolition
of the Japanese guilds). Osaka, 1957.

------Ōsaka 大阪 . Tokyo, 1957.

------Ōsaka chōnin 大阪町人 (The Osaka townsmen). Tokyo,
1957.

------Ōsaka shōnin 大阪商人 (The Osaka merchants). Tokyo,
1958.

------"Matsumoto Jūtarō" 松本重太郎 ; in Ōsaka kōgyōkai
geppō 大阪工業会月報 (Monthly bulletin of the Osaka
Industrial Association), no. 14 (May 16, 1960).

------"Daimyō kashi no rishiritsu ni tsuite" 大名貸の利子
率について (On the interest rates in daimyo lending);
in Ōsaka daigaku keizaigaku 大阪大學經済學
(Osaka University economics), vol. 10, no. 2 (Nov. 25, 1960).

------, ed. Shōgyōteki nōgyō no tenkai 商業的農業の展開 (The spread of the commercialization of agriculture). Osaka, 1954.

Modeki Gentarō 茂出木源太郎. Ōtani Kahei ō den 大谷 嘉兵衛翁伝 (Biography of the Honorable Ōtani Kahei). Tokyo, 1931.

Myrdal, G. Economic Theory and Underdeveloped Regions. London, 1958.

Naitō Fumijirō 内藤文治郎. Wakao Ippei 若尾逸平. Tokyo, 1914.

Nakayama Yasumasa 中山泰昌, ed. Shinbun shūsei Meiji hennen shi 新聞集成明治編年史 (Chronological history of the Meiji era compiled from newspapers), vol. 4. Tokyo, 1936.

Nihon Cement kabushiki kaisha 70 nen shi, hon hen 日本セメント 株式会社七十年史 本編 (Seventy-year history of Nihon Cement Ltd., main volume), ed. Nihon Cement kabushiki kaisha shashi hensan iinkai 日本セメント 株式 会社 社史編纂委員会 (Editorial Committee for the History of Nihon Cement Ltd.). Tokyo, 1955.

Nihon keizai shi jiten 日本経済史辞典 (Dictionary of Japanese economic history), ed. Keizai shi kenkyūkai 経済史研究会. 2 vols.; Tokyo, 1954.

Nihon keizai tōkei sōkan 日本経済統計総鑑 (Survey of Japanese economic statistics), ed. Asahi shinbunsha 朝 日新聞社 (Asahi Newspaper Co.). Tokyo, 1930.

Nihon sangyōshi taikei, sōron hen 日本産業史大系, 総論編 (An outline of Japanese industry, summary volume), ed. Chihō shi kenkyū kyōgikai 地方史研究協議会 (Regional History Research Association). Tokyo, 1961.

Nihon tekkō shi, Meiji hen 日本鉄工史 明治編 (History of Japanese iron and steel, Meiji volume), ed. Nihon tekkō shi hensan iinkai 日本鉄工史 編纂委員会 (Editorial Committee for the History of Japanese Iron and Steel). Tokyo, 1945.

Nihon tetsudō shi 日本鉄道史 (History of the Japanese railways), ed. Tetsudō shō 鉄道省 (Ministry of Railways), vol. 1. Tokyo, 1935.

Nishida Hirotarō 西田広太郎. Meiji kōgyō shi, kagaku kōgyō 明治工業史 化學工業 (History of Meiji industry, chemical industries volume). Tokyo, 1925.

Nishijima Tōshū 西嶋東州. Nihon shigyō hattatsu shi 日本紙業發達史 (History of the development of Japanese paper manufacturing). Tokyo, 1942.

Nishino Kiyo 西野喜與. Sumitomo Concern tokuhon 住友コンツエルン讀本 (The Sumitomo Concern reader). Tokyo, 1937.

Nishinoiri Aiichi 西野入愛一. Asano, Shibusawa, Ōkawa, Furukawa Concern tokuhon 浅野,渋沢,大川,古河,コンツエルン讀本 (The Asano, Shibusawa, Ōkawa, Furukawa Concern reader). Tokyo, 1937.

Nitobe Inazo. Bushido, The Soul of Japan. 17th ed.; Tokyo, 1911.

Nomura Kentarō 野村兼太郎. Ishin zengo 維新前後 (Before and after the Restoration). Tokyo, 1941.

Norman, Herbert. Japan's Emergence as a Modern State. 3rd ed.; New York, 1948.

334

Nurkse, Ragnar. Problems of Capital Formation in Underdeveloped
Countries. 4th ed.; Oxford, 1955.

Obama Toshio 小汀利得. Yasuda Concern tokuhon 安田コンツェ
ルン讀本 (The Yasuda Concern reader). Tokyo, 1937.

Obata Kyugoro. An Interpretation of the Life of Viscount Shibusawa.
Tokyo, 1937.

Oda Shigeo 織田誠夫. Ningen Yasuda Zenjirō 人間安
田善次郎 (The man Yasuda Zenjirō). Tokyo, 1953.

Ohkawa Kazushi et al. The Growth Rate of the Japanese Economy
since 1878. Tokyo, 1957.

Ohkawa Kazushi and Henry Rosovsky. "The Role of Agriculture
in Modern Japanese Economic Development," Economic
Development and Cultural Change, vol. 9, no. 1., pt. 2,
pp. 43-67 (Oct. 1960). Research Center in Economic Development and Cultural Change, University of Chicago.

Ōkubo Shigetarō 大久保茂太郎, ed. Gumma ken sangyōka
meikan 群馬県蠶業家名鑑 (Biographical directory
of silk industrialists of Gumma prefecture). Maebashi, 1910.

Ōkuma Shigenobu, Count, ed. Fifty Years of New Japan, tr. and
ed. Marcus B. Huish, vol. 1. 2nd ed.; London, 1910.

Ōnishi Rihei 大西理平. Asabuki Eiji kun den 朝吹英二君
伝 (Biography of Mr. Asabuki Eiji). Tokyo, 1928.

Onoda Cement seizō kabushiki kaisha 小野田セメント製造
株式会社 (Onoda Cement Manufacturing Company),
ed. Sōgyō 50 nen shi 創業五十年史 (Fifty years after
the founding). Tokyo, 1931.

Ōsaka fu shi 大阪府史 (History of Osaka prefecture), ed.
Ōsaka fu, vol. 2. Osaka, 1903.

Ōsaka shiyakusho 大阪市役所 (Osaka City Office), ed.   Meiji
    Taishō Ōsaka shi shi 明治,大正,大阪市史   (History
    of Osaka City during the Meiji and Taishō eras), vols. 2, 3.
    Tokyo, 1935.

Ōsawa Shōzō 大沢省三 , ed.   Nishimura Katsuzō ō den 西村
    勝三翁伝 (Biography of the Honorable Nishimura Katsuzō).
    Tokyo, 1921.

Ōtsuka Eizō 大塚榮三 . Magoshi Kyōhei ō den 馬越恭平
    翁伝 (Biography of the Honorable Magoshi Kyōhei).
    Tokyo, 1935.

Ōtsuka Takematsu 大塚武松 , ed.   Hansei ichiran 藩制一覧
    (Summary of han governments).   2 vols.; Tokyo, 1928-1929.

Rathgen, Karl.   Japans Volkswirtschaft und Staatshaushalt.
    Leipzig, 1891.

Redlich, Fritz.   History of American Business Leaders, vol. 1.
    Ann Arbor, 1940.

Reischauer, Edwin O.   Japan, Past and Present. New York, 1946.

Rosovsky, Henry.   Capital Formation in Japan, 1868-1940.
    Glencoe, Ill. , 1961.

Rostow, W.W.   The Stages of Economic Growth. Cambridge, Mass.,
    1960.

Ryūmon zasshi 龍門雑誌 (Ryūmon periodical), ed. Ryūmonsha
    龍門社 (The Dragon Door Company). Tokyo, May 1889.

Sakada Yoshio 坂田吉雄 . Hōken jidai kōki no chōnin seikatsu
    封建時代後期の町人生活   (The life of the towns-
    men during the later part of the feudal era). Tokyo, 1950.

Sangyō kyōiku 70 nen shi 産業教育七十年史 (Seventy years of
　　industrial education), ed. Monbushō 文部省 (Ministry of
　　Education). Tokyo, 1956.

Sansom, G. B.　Japan, A Short Cultural History.　Rev. ed.; New
　　York, 1943.

------The Western World and Japan.　New York, 1951.

Schumpeter, Joseph A.　Capitalism, Socialism and Democracy.
　　3rd ed.; New York, 1950.

------The Theory of Economic Development.　Cambridge, Mass.,
　　1934.

Sekiyama Naotarō 関山直太郎.　Nihon no jinkō 日本の人
　　口 (The population of Japan).　Tokyo, 1959.

Sheldon, Charles David.　The Rise of the Merchant Class in
　　Tokugawa Japan, 1600-1868: An Introductory Survey.
　　New York, 1958.

Shibusawa Eiichi 渋沢栄一.　Jitsugyō kōen 実業講演
　　(Lectures on enterprise).　2 vols.; Tokyo, 1913.

------Jijoden 自叙伝 (Autobiography).　Tokyo, 1938.

------Shōgyō dōtoku kōwa 商業道徳講話 (Discourses on
　　business ethics).　Tokyo, n. d.

------, ed.　Meiji shōkō shi 明治商工史 (History of Meiji
　　trade and industry).　Tokyo, 1911.

Shibusawa Eiichi denki shiryō 渋沢栄一伝記史料
　　(Biographical material on Shibusawa Eiichi), ed. Shibusawa
　　Seien kinen zaidan ryūmonsha 渋沢青淵記念財団
　　龍門社 (Shibusawa Seien Dragon Door Memorial Foundation),
　　vols. 10-12.　Tokyo, 1957-1958.

Shibusawa Keizō, ed.　Japanese Society of the Meiji Era, tr. S. H.
　　Culbertson and Kimura Michiko.　Tokyo, 1958.

337

Shigyōkai 50 nen 紙業界五十年 (Fifty years of the Paper Manufacturers' Association), ed. Hakushinsha 博進社 (The Progress Co.). Tokyo, 1937.

Shiroyanagi Hidemitsu 白柳秀湖 . Nihon fugō hassei gaku 日本富豪発生學 (A study of the emergence of the Japanese rich). Tokyo, 1920.

------Zaikai taiheiki 財界大平記 (Documents of prosperity in the financial world). Tokyo, 1948.

------Nakamigawa Hikojirō den 中上川彦次郎伝 (Biography of Nakamigawa Hikojirō). Tokyo, 1950.

Shōji Kichinosuke 庄司吉之助 . Henkaku ni okeru nōmin shisō no mondai 変革における農民思想の門題 (The problem of peasant thought during the period of change). Tokyo, 1952.

------Meiji ishin keizai no kōzō 明治維新経済の構造 (The structure of the economy of the time of the Meiji Restoration). Tokyo, 1958.

Smith, Thomas C. Political Change and Industrial Development in Japan: Government Enterprise, 1868-1880. Stanford, 1955.

------The Agrarian Origins of Modern Japan. Stanford, 1959.

Smith, Warren W. Jr. Confucianism in Modern Japan: A Study of Conservatism in Japanese Intellectual History. Tokyo, 1959.

Sorokin, Pitirim. Social and Cultural Dynamics. Boston, 1957.

Statler, Oliver. Japanese Inn. Pyramid paperback ed.; New York, 1962.

Straelen, Henry van. Yoshida Shōin, Forerunner of the Meiji Restoration. Leiden, 1952.

Suzuki Gorō 鈴木五郎. Suzuki Tōsaburō den 鈴木藤三郎伝 (Biography of Suzuki Tōsaburō). Tokyo, 1956.

Tachikawa Tokuji 立川得治, ed. Meiji kōgyō shi, tetsudō hen 明治工業史. 鉄道編. (History of Meiji industry, railway volume). Tokyo, 1932.

Takahashi Kamekichi 高橋亀吉. Meiji Taishō sangyō hattatsu shi 明治.大正産業発達史 (The history of manufacturing during the Meiji and Taishō eras). Tokyo, 1929.

------Waga kuni kigyō no shiteki hatten 我国企業の史的発展 (The historical development of our country's enterprises). Tokyo, 1956.

Takahashi Kamekichi and Aoyama Jirō 青山二郎. Nihon zaibatsu ron 日本財閥論 (A treatise on the Japanese zaibatsu). Tokyo, 1938.

Takahashi Shinichi 高橋慎一. Yōgakuron 洋学論 (On Western studies). Tokyo, 1939.

Takegoshi Yosaburō 竹越与三郎. Nihon keizai shi 日本経済史 (Japanese economic history), vol. 6. Tokyo, 1929.

------, ed. Ōkawa Heizaburō kun den 大川平三郎君伝 (Biography of Mr. Ōkawa Heizaburō). Tokyo, 1936.

Tanaka Sōgorō 田中惣五郎. Iwasaki Yatarō den 岩崎弥太郎伝 (Biography of Iwasaki Yatarō). Tokyo, 1955.

Tanaka Toyojirō 田中豊次郎. Meiji no senkakusha kindai no ijin kō Godai Tomoatsu den 明治の先覚者近代の偉人侯五代友厚伝 (Biography of the Meiji pioneer and great man of the modern age, Lord Godai Tomoatsu). Osaka, 1921.

Terao Kōji 寺尾宏二 . Meiji shoki Kyōto keizai shi 明治
初期京都経済史 (Economic history of Kyoto
during the early Meiji era). Kyoto, 1943.

Tōbata Seiichi and Ohkawa Kazushi 東畑精一, 大川一司,
eds. Nihon no keizai to nōgyō 日本の経済と農業
(Japanese economy and agriculture), vol. 1. Tokyo, 1956.

Toyohara Matao 豊原又男 . Sakuma Sadaichi shōden 佐久
間貞一小伝 (Short biography of Sakuma Sadaichi).
Tokyo, 1904.

Tsuboya Zenjirō 坪谷善二郎 . Jitsugyōka hyakuketsu den
実業家百傑伝 (Biographies of 100 outstanding
entrepreneurs). 6 vols.; Tokyo, 1893.

Tsuchiya Takao 土屋喬雄 . Zaibatsu o kizuita hitobito 財閥
を築いた人々 (The zaibatsu builders). Tokyo, 1955.

------Nihon no seishō 日本の政商 (Japan's political merchants).
Tokyo, 1956.

------Nihon ni okeru keieisha seishin no hattatsu 日本における
経営者精神の発達 (The development of
managerial mentalities in Japan). Tokyo, 1957.

------Nihon no keieisha seishin 日本の経営者精神
(Managerial attitudes in Japan). Tokyo, 1959.

------, ed. Hōken shakai hōkai katei no kenkyū 封建社会
崩壊過程の研究 (Studies in the disintegration process
of feudal society). Tokyo, 1927.

------, ed. Meiji zenki keizai shi kenkyū 明治前期経
済史研究 (Studies in the economic history of the first
part of the Meiji era). Tokyo, 1944.

Tsuchiya Takao and Ono Michio 小野道夫 . Kinsei Nihon nōson keizai shiron 近世日本農村経済史論 (An historical treatise on the modern Japanese rural economy). Tokyo, 1933.

Tsuchiya Takao and Okazaki Saburō 岡崎三郎 . Nihon shihonshugi hattatsu shi gaisetsu 日本資本主義発達史概設 (An outline history of the development of Japanese capitalism). Tokyo, 1937.

Tuge Hideomi. Historical Development of Science and Technology in Japan. Tokyo, 1961.

Uemura Chōsaburō 植村澄三郎 . Donshō Takashima Kazaemon ō den 呑象髙嶋嘉左衛門翁伝 (Biography of the Honorable Donshō Takashima Kazaemon). Tokyo, 1914.

Usaki Kumakichi 鵜崎熊吉 . Toyokawa Ryōhei 豊川良平 . Tokyo, 1922.

Usuda Sadakei 薄田貞敬 . Nakano Buei ō 中野武栄翁 (The Honorable Nakano Buei). Tokyo, 1934.

Uyehara, S. The Trade and Industry of Japan. Rev. ed.; London, 1936.

Vitzthum, Elisabeth Graefin, ed. Die Briefe des Francisco de Xavier, 1542-1552. Munich, 1950.

Wada Hidekichi 和田日出吉 . Mitsui Concern tokuhon 三井コンツェルン讀本 (The Mitsui Concern reader). Tokyo, 1937.

Wada Hisajirō 和田寿次郎 . Asano Cement enkaku shi 浅野セメント沿革史 (The history of Asano Cement). Tokyo, 1940.

Weber, Max.   The Protestant Ethic and the Spirit of Capitalism.
New York, 1956.

Yamaguchi Kazuo 山口和雄. Bakumatsu bōeki shi 幕末貿
易史 (History of foreign trade during the last years of the
Tokugawa period). Tokyo, 1943.

------Meiji zenki keizai no bunseki 明治前期経済の分析
(Analysis of the economy of the early Meiji era). Tokyo,
1956.

------"The Opening of Japan at the End of the Shōgunate and Its
Effects," in Shibusawa Keizō, ed., Japanese Society of the
Meiji Era, pp. 1-46.

Yamamoto Mitsuhiko 山本実彦. Kawasaki Shōzō 川崎正
蔵. Tokyo, 1918.

Yanaga Chitoshi.   Japan since Perry, consulting ed. Ralph E.
Turner. New York, 1949.

Yanagida Kunio.   Japanese Manners and Customs in the Meiji Era,
tr. Charles S. Terry. Tokyo, 1957.

Yasuoka Shigeaki 安岡重明 · "Shōgyōteki hatten to nōson kōzō"
商業的発展と農村構造 (The process of com-
mercialization and village structure); in Miyamoto Mataji,
ed., Shōgyōteki nōgyō no tenkai. 商業的農業の展開

Yokoyama Sadao 横山貞雄 . Ningen Ōkura Kihachirō 人間
大倉喜八郎 (The man Ōkura Kihachirō).
Tokyo, 1929.

Zaikai bukko ketsubutsu den 財界物故傑物伝 (Biographies
of outstanding men in the business world), ed. Jitsugyō no
shakaisha 実業の社会社. (The Business World Co.).
2 vols.; Tokyo, 1936.

GLOSSARY

Abe Taizō 阿部泰蔵

Akabane 赤羽

Akebono shinbun 曙新聞

Akizuki 秋月

Ani 阿仁

Arita 有田

Asahi Maru 旭丸

Ashio 足尾

bakufu 幕府

Bansho shirabesho 藩書調所

Besshi 別子

bummei kaika 文明開化

bushi wa kuwanedo takayōji 武士は喰わねど高楊子

chō 町

chōnin 町人

Chōshū 長州

daimyō 大名

dan (shaku) 男 (爵)

Dejima 出島

Dewa 出羽

dō 堂

Doi Michio 土居道夫

Echigoya 越後屋

Fujita Denzaburō 藤田伝三郎

Fukagawa 深川

fukoku kyōhei 富国強兵

gaku batsu 學閥

Gakumon no susume 學問の勤め

geisha 芸者

Geishū 芸州

Genji 源氏

genkan 玄関

geta 下駄

go isshin 御一新

gonin gumi 五人組

gōnō 豪農

Gotō Shōjirō 後藤象二郎

goyō shōnin 御用商人

goyōkin 御用金

Hachirōbei 八郎兵衛

Hachirōemon 八郎衛門

haku (shaku) 伯 (爵)

han 藩

han batsu	藩閥		kaikoku	開国
hanchi	半知		Kaisei kan	開成館
hei-no bunri	兵農分離		kaisha	会社
hibachi	火鉢		Kaitoku dō	懐徳堂
Hokkai Maru	北海丸		Kakeda	掛田
Hokkaidō tankō	北海道炭鉱		kakeya	掛屋
Hōrai	蓬莱		Kamaishi	釜石
Horonai	幌内		Kanakin	金巾
			kanban	看板
Ichikawa	市川			
Ikuno	生野		Kaneda Ichihei	金田市兵衛
Imamura Seinosuke	今村清之助		Kanegafuchi	鐘ヶ淵
Innai	院内		Kankōryō	勧工寮
Inoue Kaoru	井上馨		kanson minpi	官尊民卑
Inoue Masaru	井上勝		Kashima Manpei	鹿島万平
Ishida Baigan	石田梅巌		Kashimaya	加島屋
Ishikawa	石川		Katakura Kentarō	片倉兼太郎
Ishikawa Masaryū	石河正龍		Katō Yukichi	加藤勇吉
ishin	維新		Kawada Koichirō	川田小一郎
Itō Hirobumi	伊藤博文		Kawasaki Hachiuemon	
Iwaki	磐城		川崎八右衛門	
Iwakura Tomomi	岩倉具視		kazoku	華族
Iyo	伊予		Keiō gijuku	慶応義塾
			Kido Takayoshi	木戸孝允
Jitsugyō no Nihonsha	実業之日本社		Kii	紀伊
jitsugyōka	実業家		kimono	着物
jōkamachi	城下町		Kinai	畿内
			Kinbara Meizen	金原明善
Kaga	加賀		Kinki	近畿
Kagaya	加賀屋			

344

kisei jinushi	寄生地主		Maruya	丸屋
Kitsu	木津		Maruzen	丸善
kō (shaku)	公 (爵)		Masuya	枡屋
kō (shaku)	侯 (爵)		Matsukata Masayoshi	松方正義
Kōbu daigakkō	工部大學校		Matsumae	松前
kobun	子分		Meiji	明治
Kōgaku ryō	工學寮		Meirokusha	明六社
kogata	子方		Meiwa	明和
kogata uchi	子方家		Miike	三池
koku	石		Minamoto Yoshiie	源義家
kokuritsu	国立		Minomura Rizaemon	

kisei jinushi 寄生地主
Kitsu 木津
kō (shaku) 公 (爵)
kō (shaku) 侯 (爵)
Kōbu daigakkō 工部大學校
kobun 子分
Kōgaku ryō 工學寮
kogata 子方
kogata uchi 子方家
koku 石
kokuritsu 国立
Kondō Renpei 近藤廉平
Kōnoike 鴻池
Kosaka 小坂
Kōseikan 弘成館
kotatsu 炬燵
Kuga 久我
kuge 公卿
kumiai 組合
kuramoto 蔵元
kurayashiki 蔵屋敷
Kurihara Nobuchika 栗原信近
Kuroda Kiyotaka 黒田清隆
Kuwahara 桑原
Kyōdō unyu kaisha 共同運輸会社
kyōsō 競走

Maejima 前島
Marunouchi 丸ノ内

Maruya 丸屋
Maruzen 丸善
Masuya 枡屋
Matsukata Masayoshi 松方正義
Matsumae 松前
Meiji 明治
Meirokusha 明六社
Meiwa 明和
Miike 三池
Minamoto Yoshiie 源義家
Minomura Rizaemon
三野村利左衛門
miso 味噌
Mito 水戸
Mitsui bussan 三井物産
Mitsukoshi 三越
Miyake Sekian 三宅石庵
Mori Arinori 森有礼
Morimura Ichizaemon
森村市左衛門
Motoki Shōzō 本木昌造

myōgakin 冥加金
myōji taitō 苗字帯刀

Nakano Goichi 中野梧一
Nakatsu 中津
Nippon yūsen kaisha
日本郵船会社

noren	暖簾	Sakaki	榊
		sake	酒
o-chōnin san	御町人さん	Sakuma Shōzan	佐久間象山
Oda Nobunaga	織田信長	samurai	侍
Ōji seishi	王子製紙	sankin kōtai	参勤交代
Okada Reikō	岡田令髙	Sanwa	三和
Ōki Tamihira	大木民平	sanyō	幇用
Ōkubo Toshimichi	大久保利通	Sata Keiseki	佐用介石
Okuda Masaka	奥田正香	Satō Gentabei	佐藤源太兵衛
Ōkuma Shigenobu	大隈重信	Satsuma	薩摩
Ōmi	近江	Satsumaya Hanbei	薩摩屋半兵衛
Ono	小野	sei-i-tai shōgun	征夷大將軍
Ōsaka kappan seizōsho		seishō	政商
	大阪活版製造所	Seiyō jijo	西洋事情
Owari	尾張	Sekigahara	関ヶ原
oyabun	親分	sengoku jidai	戰国時代
oyakata	親方	Senjū	千住
oyakata uchi	親方家	Senshū kaisha	先收会社
		Settsu	攝津
rangakusha	蘭學者	shi	子
rōnin	浪人	shi (shaku)	子 (爵)
ryō	両	shi-nō-kō-shō	士農工商
ryōgaeya	両替屋	Shiba	芝
ryōshu	領主	Shibaura	芝浦
		Shimada	島田
Saga	佐賀	shimatsu	始末
Saigō Takamori	西郷隆盛	Shimazu Nariakira	島津斉彬
saikaku	才覺	Shimonoseki	下関
Saikoku risshi hen	西國立志編		

346

Shinagawa	品川	tōfu	豆腐
Shinagawa Yajirō	品川弥二郎	Tokugawa Ieyasu	德川家康
shingaku	心學		
Shinmachi	新町	Tomioka	富岡
Shinoda Naotaka	篠田直方	tonya	問家
shinpan	親藩	Tosa	土佐
Shinshū	信州	Tōyō	東洋
Shintō	神道	Toyotomi Hideyoshi	豊臣秀吉
Shirakawa	白河	Tsukiji	築地
shiritsu	私立	Tsūshōshi	通商司
Shōda Heigorō	正田平五郎		
shōgun	將軍	Uchiike	内池
Shokkō gakkō	職工學校	Ueda	上田
shokusan kōgyō	殖産興業	Utsunomiya Saburō	宇都宮三郎
Shōnai	庄内		
shōnin	商人	Waseda	早稲田
sonnō jōi	尊王攘夷	ya	屋
sotsu	卒	Yamabe Takeo	山辺丈夫
		Yamagata Aritomo	山県有朋
Takashima	高嶋	Yamato	大和
Tanaka Chōbei	田中長兵衛	yen	円
Tanaka Heihachi	田中平八	Yokoyama Hisatarō	横山久太郎
Tanaka Ichibei	田中市兵衛	Yonekura Ippei	米倉一平
tatami	畳	Yūbin jōkisen kaisha	郵便蒸気船会社
Tenpo	天保	za	座
terakoya	寺小屋	zaibatsu	財閥
tōbaku	討幕		

INDEX

Abacus, 25
Abe Taizō, 272–273
Adoption of merchants by samurai, 21
Agriculture: cultivated area, 73–74; labor force, 109–110; productivity, Meiji, 109–110, 157; productivity, Tokugawa, 73–75; technology, 109, 110, 127–128
Aichi Cement Mill, 190–191
Akabane Construction, 150–151
Akita han, 64, 80
Amamiya Keijirō, 11, 267–268
Ancestors, authority of, 23
Ani Copper Mine, 152
Asabuki Eiji, 136, 226, 260, 284
Asano Cement Works, 153–154, 190, 238–239
Asano Sōichirō, 153, 192, 231–232, 238–240; attitudes, 197, 200–201
Ashio Copper Mine, 236

Bakufu: status quo policies, 7–8, 9, 17; Western learning, 115–116, 117
Balance of payments, 186. See also Imports
Bank of Japan, 149
Bankers' Association, 170
Banks: capital, 57; private banks, 57, 59; promotion of, 57–58; national (1872), 36, 56; national (1876), 56–57; zaibatsu banks, 212, 218, 219, 228, 230–232, 272
Bansho shirabesho, 116
Besshi Copper Mine, 227–228
Book learning. See Education
Bummei kaika: as new era, 114, 120, 164, 173; impact on entrepreneurs, 260–261, 262–263

Capital supply: for economic development, 3, 288; for Meiji indus-

try, 195, 211–214, 280, 285. See also Government subsidies
Capitalism, spirit of, 202–204
Cash cropping, 80–82
Castle towns, 7
Charter Oath, 118–119
Chōnin, 7. See also Merchants
Cement mills. See Aichi; Asano; Fukagawa
Classical entrepreneurial type, defined, 264–267
Commercial schools, 128. See also Education
Commutation of samurai stipends, 52–53, 54, 57
Company system, merchant reaction to, 31–32. See also Joint stock
Competition, aversion of merchants to, 30–31
Confucianism: ideology, 22, 204, 205–206; scholars, 26–27, 116–117; and Shibusawa, 174, 205–206
Consumption patterns, 101–102
Copper mining, 227–229, 236–237
  Mines: Ani, 152; Ashio, 236; Besshi, 227–228
Cotton spinning: advantages of Japan, 156; capital supply, 99, 100; depression, 99, 186–187; encouragement of, 96, 155–156; entrepreneurs in, 97, 98, 188, 252; efficiency, 97, 187; location of mills, 99; technology, 132 133, 161
  Mills: Hiroshima, 186; Ichikawa, 186; Kagoshima, 132; Kanegafuchi, 220–221; Osaka, 99, 188; Owari, 269–270; Sakai, 38
Cotton weaving, 100

Dai Ichi Bank. See First National Bank; Shibusawa

Daimyo, loans to, 19–21, 30
Deflation. *See* Matsukata
Demand, lack of, 153, 194, 281
Dictatorial attitudes, 225–226, 233
Discounting, 198–199, 200–201
Doi Michio, 251
Dutch learning, 115. *See also* Education

Echigoya store, 216
Economy, mid-Meiji, 156–161
Edo, 14, 52. *See also* Tokyo
Education: agricultural, 127–128; commercial, 128–129; compulsory, 124; and entrepreneurs, 134–135, 166–167, 171, 258; industrial, 129–130; and merchants, 26–27; promoted by entrepreneurs, 169–170, 171, 269, 273, 275, 276; of samurai, 61; in Tokugawa, 75, 88; Western, 115–117
Emperor, role of, 118–119
Employment: industrial, 152, 159–160, 161; rural, 86, 87, 157
Entrepreneurs: older group, 250–252; younger group, 253
Entrepreneurship: in Japan, 12, 25; Schumpeterian, 4, 6; for underdeveloped countries, 2–4, 8, 288
Exchange companies, 34–35
Exhibitions, 155

Factory production, 159–160
Fairs, 155
Family names, 19, 34
Family rules, 23, 237–238, 274
Fertilizer, 78, 109
Filial piety, 22, 28
First National Bank, 168, 212. *See also* Shibusawa
Flury-Herald, 168
Forced loans, 16, 35, 213
Formative years, entrepreneurs, 250
Franklin, Benjamin, 205
Fujita Denzaburō, 40, 154, 256, 280
Fukagawa Cement, 190, 238–239
Fukoku kyōhei, 143, 145, 251
Fukushima area, 84–85, 88
Fukuzawa Yukichi: attitudes, 174, 226; general influence, 120, 124,

164–167; influence on entrepreneurs, 226, 284
Furukawa Ichibei, 236–238

Gakubatsu, 259, 285
Genroku era, 49
Gerschenkron model, 112–113
Godai Tomoatsu: and government, 171–172, 251, 279; Osaka industry, 38–39, 41; travel to West, 122
Gonin gumi, 23, 70, 71, 83, 86
Gotō Shōjirō, 38, 188, 242
Government: leadership, 113; mining, 150; officials, 162–163, 174; railways, 138–141, 145; shipping, 143–145; spinning, 186; subsidies, 223, 227, 241–242, 279–280; and zaibatsu, 242
Goyō shōnin, 280. *See also* Merchants, political
Goyōkin. See Forced loans
Graduates, 221, 283
Guilds, 8–9, 10, 11, 30
Gumma prefecture, 94–95

Han: abolishment, 52; debts, 19–21, 30; economic reforms, 82, 142–143; *hanbatsu*, 279–280
Hanchi system, 49
Hara Rokurō, 88, 135, 251, 271–272
Hideyoshi, Toyotomi, 47
Hino merchants, 79
Hirano: house of, 24; Tomiji, 41, 143, 266
Hiranuma Senzō, 276
Hirose Saihei, 40, 41, 226–229
Hirose Sukesaburō, 256, 272–273
Hiroshima Spinning Mill, 186
Hokkaido, 77–78, 224
Honesty: Meiji entrepreneurs, 172–173, 275, 276, 277; Tokugawa merchants, 24

Ichikawa Mill, 186
Imamura Seinosuke, 262
Imperial University, 165, 173
Imports: of cotton goods, 96, 187; effects, 101; import-competing industries, 185; opposition to, 96, 98, 136, 266

Individualism, 203, 205–206
Industry: export-competing, 91–95; import-competing, 185–196; growth, 156–161; location, 160; private sector, 152
Infanticide, 73, 121
Inflation, 149, 150
Innovations: antipathy of merchants to, 23–25; performed by entrepreneurs, 185–196, 220–221, 236–237, 239–240
Inoue Kaoru, 30, 118, 122; supporter of Mitsui, 216, 217, 219; of other entrepreneurs, 279
Inoue Masaru, 131
Insurance, 273, 283
Interest rates: Meiji, 57, 177–178, 186; Tokugawa, 16, 19–20
Investments, merchant: banking, 34, 36, 59; cotton spinning, 99–100, 188; land reclamation, 71–77; traditional sectors, 255
Iron mining: Kamaishi, 150, 192–193; Ōkura, 235
Ishida Baigan, 27
Itō Hirobumi, 118, 122
Iwakura Tomomi, 62, 122, 140
Iwasaki Yatarō: career, 222–226; and Fukuzawa, 167, 169; patriotism, 145, 204, 208; as political merchant, 145–146, 222–223, 251; and Shibusawa, 168–169, 223–224; and Tosa han, 142–143

Jitsugyō no nihonsha, 170
Jitsugyōka, 172, 173, 176, 201, 209–210
Joint stock, 237, 283; capital, totals of, 158–159; principle, government, 63; Shibusawa, 168–169, 224, 253. See also Company system

Kagaya family, 76
Kagoshima Spinning Mill, 132
Kaitoku Dō, 26
Kakeya, 18, 19
Kamaishi iron mines, 150, 192–193
Kanban, 24, 31
Kaneda Ichihei, 98

Kanegafuchi Spinning Mill, 220–221
Kanson minpi, 162, 165
Kashima Manpei, 97–98, 251–252
Kashimaya, House of, 21
Katakura Kentarō, 93, 255
Katō Yukichi, 35
Kawada Koichirō, 251, 272
Kawasaki Hachiuemon, 224
Kawasaki Shōzō, 260, 281–282
Keiō Gijuku: education of samurai, 61; influence, 260; graduates in enterprise, 236, 283, 284; spirit, 164, 165
Kinbara Meizen, 255, 270
Kōbu Daigakkō, 129
Kogakuryō, 129
Kogata. See Oyakata-kogata
Kondō Renpei, 224, 226, 284
Kōnoike, House of: attitudes, 24, 37; daimyo lending, 19–20; forced loans, 16; land reclamation, 76
Kōseikan, 38–39
Kuramoto, 18
Kurihara Nobuchika, 98
Kuroda Kiyotaka, 123
Kyōdō Unyu Company, 146, 180, 223
Kyoto, 31, 268–269
Kyoto-Otsu Railway, 131
Kyoto Pottery Company, 199–200

Laissez faire, 152–153
Land reclamations, 75–77, 269
Land tax: Meiji, 105–106, 106–110; Tokugawa, 70, 75
Landlords, 75–76, 107–110
Landownership, 70–71, 83, 107–108
Lending: to daimyo, 19–21, 30; to peasants, 78; to samurai, 62–63
Loyalty, 22–23, 28

Maejima, Baron, 282
Magoshi Kyōhei, 260–261, 267
Manufacturing: Meiji, survey of, 156–161; in Osaka, 38–42; Tokugawa, rural, 79, 84–87
Marunouchi Office Center, 284
Maruya Company, 184

Masuda Takashi, 217–218, 223, 275; cooperation with others, 191, 192, 194
Masuya, House of, 21
Matsukata, Minister of Finance, 66, 98, 149, 281; deflation, 66, 149–150, 180–181, 185–186
Matsumoto Jūtarō, 40, 261, 273–274
Meirokusha, 120
Merchants: adventurer-merchants, port cities, 10–11, 251, 261–262, 276–277; attitudes, 21–28, 32, 33, 37, 163, 255; as entrepreneurs, 256; lending, 18–21; political merchants, survey, 278–282; social standing, 17–18, 163. See also Investments, merchant
Miike Coal Mine, 150, 218
Military build-up, 144
Mill, John Stuart, 165, 263
Mills. See Cotton spinning
Minamoto Yoshiie, 170
Minomura Rizaemon, 29, 168, 213–217
Mint in Osaka, 39
Miso, 79, 102, 103
Mitsubishi, 143, 211, 212, 221–226; bank, 272; competition with Kyōdō Unyu Company, 146, 284; family rule, 225–226; and Fukuzawa, 167; subsidies received, 146, 154, 242
Mitsui, 24, 34, 211, 212, 213; alliance with Restoration movement, 29–30; bank, 218, 219; Bussan, 154, 214, 218; family rule, 215; and First National Bank, 36, 168; foreign travels, 123; government favors, 214, 219; Hachirōemon, 214, 215; industry, 138–139, 220–221; recruitment of managers, 221
Miyake Sekian, 26
Money: exchanges, 15–16; inconvertible notes, 36, 149; Tokugawa, 13, 15, 30
Monopolies, 154, 223, 234
Mori Arinori, 128, 165, 169
Morimura Ichizaemon, 256, 262, 275
Motoki Shōzō, 41, 251, 260, 265–266

Myōgakin. See Forced loans
Myōji taitō privilege, 19, 34

Nagasaki: influence on entrepreneurs, 259–260; samurai companies in, 64; Tosa trading company, 142–143
Nakamigawa Hikojirō, 219–221, 253
Nakano Buei, 282
Nakano Goichi, 40, 281
Nakatsu han, 50
Nippon Railway Company, 180
Nippon Yūsen Company, 224, 284
Nishimura Katsuzō, 191, 260
Noren, 24

Oda Nobunaga, 47
Ōji Paper Mill, 189, 220, 285
Okada Reikō, 283
Ōkawa Heizaburō, 133, 189, 239, 285
Ōki Tamihira, 119
Ōkubo Toshimichi, 33, 63, 149, 152, 172
Okuda Masaka, 269–270
Ōkuma Shigenobu: and Fukuzawa, 164; and Iwasaki, 223; government enterprises, 149; railway program, 119, 123; and Shibusawa, 168
Ōkura Kihachirō, 233–234, 253; attitudes, 204, 208, 277; entrepreneurial activity, 40, 154, 234–235
Omi merchants, 77–79, 99, 102–103
Ono, 168, 236, 237; First National Bank, 34, 36; in silk spinning, 92–93
Onoda Cement, 191
Optimistic attitudes, 198
Osaka: banks, 273; industrial and trading capital, 41–42; influence on entrepreneurs, 260–261; large companies, 41; population, 14; position in trade, 14, 33, 42, 81. See also Cotton spinning; Merchants; Industry
Osaka Spinning Mill, 99, 132, 133, 187–188
Ōtani Kahei, 173, 275–276

Oyakata-kogata (*oyabun-kobun*), 23, 71, 83

Paper manufacturing, 38, 188–190, 220, 285
Patriotism, 116–117, 174–175, 207–210
Peasants: uprisings, 10, 54, 72; rich, 87–88
Physicians, 253–254
Political merchants. *See* Merchants
Politics, influence on entrepreneurs, 257, 282. See also *Bummei kaika*; Government; Tokyo
Population: figures in Tokugawa, 72–73; growth encouraged in Meiji, 121; percentages of classes, 254
Prefectures, established, 52
Printing, 260, 265
Price index, 104, 107, 186
Protestant ethic, 22
Puritanism, 204–205

Railways: in Europe, 136–137; Kyoto-Otsu line, 139; necessity for Japan, 137–138; private lines, 138–139, 140–141, 182–183; profits, 139, 141, 183, 184; subsidies, 138–139, 140; Tokyo-Aomori line, 140, 182–183; Tokyo-Yokohama line, 139
Restoration: effects on entrepreneurs, 251–252; effects on merchants, 28–30
Rice: forced purchases, 16; price, 107; stipends to samurai, 49–50; stored in Osaka, 18. *See also* Commutation
Rents, agricultural, 75, 107
Romantic entrepreneurial type, defined, 264–265, 267–271
Rōnin, 51, 216
Ryōshu, 69
Ryūmonsha, 170
Ryūmon zasshi, 170

Saga han, 55, 126
Saikaku, 25–26
Saint Simonian socialists, 210
Sakai Spinning Mill, 38
Sake brewing, 79, 84, 102–103

Sakuma Sadaichi, 189–190, 262–263, 265–266
Sakuma Shōzan, 117
Samurai: attitudes, 44, 47–49, 62, 68, 222; class groupings, 45, 50–51; companies, 63–65, 94; entrepreneurial role, 46; entrepreneurs of samurai origin, 254–255; foundation of national banks, 57–61; government confidence in, 55, 62; impoverishment, 21, 49–54, 62, 66; revolts, 54–55, 62
Sankin kōtai travels, 49, 52
Sanwa Bank, 212
Sanyō, 25
Sanyō Railway Company, 219
Satō Gentabei, 85
Satsuma: han monopoly trade, 82; Rebellion, 55, 146, 154, 214
Schumpeter, Joseph A., 4, 176
Seclusion of Japan, 113–118. See also *Sonnō-jōi* movement
Seiyō jijō (Fukuzawa), 166
Sendai han, 21, 53, 80
Shibaura Iron Works, 220
Shibusawa Eiichi: attitudes, 165, 202, 205, 279; career, 167–168; and education, 88, 169–170; and entrepreneurial status, 167–175; industrial cooperation, 191, 237, 239, 240; and joint-stock enterprise, 223–224; lending to entrepreneurs, 236, 266; promoting national banks, 60; Oji Paper Mill, 133, 189; Osaka Spinning Mill, 99, 132, 133, 187–188; other industrial ventures, 133, 191, 192, 194–195; as romantic entrepreneurial type, 267
Shimada, House of, 34, 36
Shimatsu, 25
Shinagawa Glass Factory, 152, 191
Shinagawa Yajirō, 118
Shingaku philosophy, 26–28
Shintoism, 119
Shipbuilding: Meiji, 145, 260; Tokugawa, 142. *See also* Shipyards
Shipping: Meiji, 130–131, 281, 284; subsidies for, 145–146; Tokugawa, 141–142; tonnage, 143, 146

Shipyards: Hyogo, 281; Ishikawajima, 143, 266; Nagasaki, 146,
224; Tsukiji, 281; Yokosuka, 143–
144
Shizuoka prefecture, 65
Shōda Heigorō, 226, 284
Shōnin, 172. See also Merchants
Silk, raw, export of, 91–92
Silk reeling: encouragement by gov-
ernment, 155; in Fukushima, 84–
85; growth, 161; in Gumma pre-
fecture, 94–95; of Ono, 92, 93;
mechanical, 92–95
Silkworms, export of, 92
Sonnō jōi, 118, 136; effect on entre-
preneurs, 276, 284; movement,
117–118
Social groupings of entrepreneurs,
253–257
Soy-sauce production, 79, 102, 103
Status, conformity of entrepreneurs
to, 164, 165, 209–210, 277–278
Subsidies. See Government
Sugar refining: Satsuma, 103–104;
Suzuki, 266–267
Sumitomo: bank, 212, 228; family
rule, 26; general development,
226–229; Tokugawa, 24
Suzuki Tōsaburō, 169, 256, 266–267

Taiwan expedition, 234
Takashima Coal Mine, 150, 224, 242
Takashima Kazaemon, 269
Tanaka Chōbei, 150, 192–193
Tanaka Gentarō, 199–200, 268
Tanaka Ichibei, 256, 261
Tea, export of, 91
Technology: foreign technicians
and teachers, 126–127, 129, 130–
131, 229; lack of experts, 132,
133–134; problem of, 125, 134,
192; theoretical bias, 126, 134,
135–136; training, 127, 129–130,
135, 257–258
Tenancy, 83, 86, 107–108
Terakoya, 88, 124
Time horizons, 199–200
Tōfu, 38

Tokugawa government. See Bakufu
Tokyo: adventurer-merchants in,
10–11, 230, 233, 234; influence on
entrepreneurs, 262–263, 275, 290;
merchant companies in, 31
Tokyo Gas Company, 194–195
Tokyo University, 165, 173
Tomioka filature, 193–194, 220
Tonya, 14
Tosa han, 142–143, 222
Tōyō Shipping Company, 231
Toyokawa Ryōhei, 171, 226, 260,
272
Trade, foreign: conditions after
Restoration, 32; entrepreneurs in,
96, 274–278; trading companies,
34–35. See also Imports
Tradition, break with, by entre-
preneurs, 255–257
Travels abroad: entrepreneurs, 167,
233, 272, 275; government pro-
gram, 122–123; Mitsui, 216
Tsūshōshi, 33–34

Uchiike family, 79
Utsunomiya Saburō, 190

Vegetable-oil production, 103
Village: headmen, 70; social structure, 70–71, 83, 86–87; unsuited
for entrepreneurs, 255–256

Wakao Ippei, 261–262
Warehouses, Osaka, 18–20, 30
Weber, Max, 21–22, 204
Western civilization, 120–121
Western learning. See Education

Yamabe Takeo, 133, 188, 283
Yamagata Aritomo, 118, 235
Yasuda Zenjirō, 11, 212, 230–233,
239–240
Yokohama, 10–11, 217, 261–262, 275,
276
Yokoyama Hisatarō, 193
Yonekura Ippei, 276
Yoshida Shōin, 117, 223
Yubin Jōkisen Company, 281